INTRODUCTION TO THE THEORY
OF SPACE–CHARGE
OPTICS

Dr. GYULA ANDRÁS NAGY, C. Sc.

and

Dr. MIKLÓS SZILÁGYI, C. Sc.

FOREWORD

BY

Prof. DENNIS GABOR F.R.S.,

D. Sc., D. Eng., F. Inst. P., M.I.E.E.,

NOBEL-PRIZE WINNER

TRANSLATED

BY

GY. F. LÁSZLÓ (Chapters 1, 2 and 6) and

M. SZILÁGYI (Chapters 3, 4 and 5)

A HALSTED PRESS BOOK

JOHN WILEY & SONS
NEW YORK

PHYSICS

This book was originally published in Hungarian under the
title *Bevezetés a tértöltésoptika elméletébe* by
Akadémiai Kiadó, Budapest

First published in the United Kingdom 1974 by
The Macmillan Press Ltd

Published in the U.S.A.
by Halsted Press, a Division
of John Wiley & Sons, Inc.,
New York

Printed in Hungary

Library of Congress Cataloging in Publication Data
Nagy, Gyula András.
Introduction to the theory of space-charge optics
"A Halsted Press book".
Translation of Bevezetés a tértöltésoptika elméletébe.
Includes bibliographical references
1. Electron optics 2. Electromagnetic fields
I. Szilágyi, Miklós, joint author. II. Title
QC447. N313 537.516 76-39107

ISBN 0-471-62867-0

FOREWORD TO THE ENGLISH EDITION

by Dennis Gabor

By dedicated effort, extended over many years, the two authors of this book have produced what is so far the most comprehensive treatise on a field of great technological importance. The significance of space-charge was first understood 70 years ago, when Child and Langmuir demonstrated that it was this effect which limited the flow of electrons in high vacua and determined the characteristics of electron valves. Electron beams became of importance twenty years later, first in television tubes, later in beam devices for microwaves and more recently as technological tools for the melting, welding and drilling of refractory materials. The most recent achievement of electron beam machining is the long-playing television record, which could never have been produced by mechanical means.

The theoretical treatment of space-charge problems was hampered from the start by considerable mathematical difficulties. It led to non-linear partial differential equations which could be analytically solved only in some special, mostly trivial cases. The researchers had to use tedious series expansions, or they resorted to analogue models, some of them very ingenious. The advent of the digital computer finally solved these difficulties, though at the cost of physical insight. There is hardly a numerical electron space-charge problem that could not be set up on a computer, but the computer tells one only what it is asked; it seldom gives inspiration for new, creative improvements. But it is just as well that it still leaves room for the inventive human brain.

Vast as the work is that has been already done, it is by no means finished. Ion beams would be superior to electron beams for many purposes of micromachining, but ion beam sources are still far from perfection. Electron beams too ought to be taken to a higher level of power for purposes such as X-ray lasers and perhaps also for hydrogen fusion. Hundreds of kiloamperes have been already produced in beams for nanoseconds, but this is probably only a beginning.

In summarising their own and other people's research in this impressive volume, the authors have done admirable work. It is particularly welcome that they are giving to the West, for the first time, a comprehensive survey of the vast work which has been done in this field in the USSR. I hope that their work will receive the appreciation which it deserves.

London

D. Gabor

AUTHORS' PREFACE
TO THE ENGLISH EDITION

The effects of space-charge are of principal importance in a number of devices, therefore space-charge optics has come into prominence in research work. Development of the different branches of science does not proceed at the same rate. Research on electron and ion optics developed rapidly, but it is obvious that its development has suffered as research on solid materials has come into prominence in the recent past. However, this situation has become advantageous. Research on solid materials, as well as the problems of semi-conductor and integrated circuits' production demanded the utilisation of electron and ion technologies as well as different electron and ion beam devices for measurements and analyses. Nowadays, the development of technology and the devices for analyses and measurements is one of the important industrial and scientific research tasks.

Electron and ion beam technologies serve as bases for many branches of industry, whereas in materials science they are irreplaceable for analysis and measurement. These technological and measuring devices were already of great importance when the Hungarian edition of this book was published. Since that time they have become much more significant and may be found in all fields of technical and scientific life. The authors have, therefore, not listed all the fields of applications.

Six years have passed since the Hungarian edition of the book was published and since that time many new results have been obtained and published, e.g. Kirstein, P. T.–Kino, G. S.–Waters, W. E.: *Space-Charge Flow*, McGraw-Hill, New York, 1967; (Sushkov, A. D.–Molokovskiy, S. I.) Сушков, А. Д.–Молоковский, С. И.: Интенсивные электронные и ионные пучки *(High-density Electron and Ion Beams)*, Энергия, Ленинград, 1972. This in itself proves the importance and timeliness of this field of science.

With the above comments in mind, together with a number of other facts, it can be stated that electron and ion optics belong to the fundamental sciences.

As background information we enumerate some viewpoints that were taken into consideration when collecting materials and writing this book.

Some chapters of the English edition have been enlarged and considerably more references have been given in this edition. The very large number of papers needed very careful selection and evaluation, as well as some compression of the subject matter. An endeavour was made to select materials of permanent value when completing both this and the Hungarian version. We have also enlarged the index to a considerable extent.

Formerly—mainly in the field of technical sciences—on grounds of experience it was necessary to put the laws of nature into simpler words. Ingenious approximations were resorted to so that the necessary calculations could be carried out. Today more exact formulations are required and they can be arrived at more easily by the help of computers. We endeavoured to consider all these requirements and to determine the limits of validity in most of the fundamental cases.

Nowadays, apart from the formation of complex sciences, as technology and research become more specialised and probe more and more deeply in the selected field, such a monograph, covering a comparatively narrow field, is of increasing importance. It is felt that this monograph will be most useful if it were to become available to readers everywhere and, in our opinion, the English edition of this book is likely to be a great help in achieving this aim.

The present book includes the authors' own results as well, and as with the Hungarian edition these are not mentioned in the preface. Nonetheless they may be easily found, as these results are discussed in more than 30 paragraphs.

On the occasion of the publication of the English edition, the authors wish to commemorate the late Dr. E. Winter, Academician, who is considered as one of the initiators and originators of the research work in Hungary in the field of electron and space-charge optics.

We wish to express our gratitude to Prof. D. Gabor F. R. S., for his kind interest in our book. This is of special value for us as it is he who has solved many of the fundamental problems in the field of space-charge optics.

The authors are aware that a number of themes, e.g. thermal velocities, high-velocity flows, were not able to be included in the present work, but they hope that their research in the above-mentioned fields will be published in the future. Then possibly, the needs of those who found this introduction useful will be satisfied.

The authors

PREFACE

During recent years, employment of various branches of electron optics has increasingly gained ground in Hungary. Though Elektronoptika (*Electron Optics*) by V. M. Kelman and S. Ya. Yavor in 1965 gave the basic concepts and a thorough coverage of numerous fields of application, discussion of the problems associated with the generation and focusing of high-current-density electron beams is still required in Hungary.

The major fields employing space-charge optics embrace the solution of problems arising in the manufacture of microwave oscillator and amplifier valves, devices employing electron technology (heat treatment, welding, drilling, cutting, etc.) and vacuum metallurgy (melting, refining, alloying) and the solution of certain problems inherent in semiconductor technology, production of materials with specific properties, high frequency power transmission without transmission lines, etc. The advanced stage of development of the Hungarian industry is indicated by the fact that the majority of the foregoing fields are already routine practice in Hungary.

Development in most of the fields mentioned shows a growing trend: thus in Hungary the necessity exists for specialised books dealing with the bases of space-charge optics, enabling a study of the pertinent problems. We have endeavoured to compile a work aimed at satisfying these requirements, and as a starting point for the solution of unsolved problems.

There are very few books dealing with this topic in specialised foreign literature. In his book *Theory and Design of Electron Beams* J. R. Pierce endeavoured to summarise the field, when (1949 and 1954) the solution of many problems was still inadequate and thus the book may be considered rather as a reference book. N. S. Zinchenko in Курс лекций по электронной оптике (*Course of Electron Optics*) published in 1961, is essentially a review of the literature, without regard to uniformity. During the period while our manuscript was being prepared, some specialised books were published, in the Soviet Union including Электронные пушки (*Electron Guns*) by V. P. Taranenko (1964), Электронно-оптические системы приборов СВЧ (*Electron Optical Systems for Microwave Devices*) by S. I. Molokovskiy and A. D. Sushkov (1965) and Электронные пучки и электронные пушки (*Electron Beams and Electron Guns*) by I. V. Alyamovskiy (1966), which, as indicated by their titles, embrace the material of more clearly defined fields. From these works it is apparent that a unified treatment of the field was not aimed at. Nevertheless, the book by I. V. Alyamovskiy may be considered the most representative among those available in present-day literature.

Geometric space-charge optics deals with the optical properties of the multitude of paths of charged particles in cases when (space-charge) interaction between the particles may not be disregarded. The size of the present work does not permit treatment of the entire field of space-charge optics. The treatment is limited to the time-constant electric and magnetic field cases and to the investigation of electron motion in vacuum. Problems requiring consideration of relativistic effects are not dealt with, since such effects appear as factors of primary importance only in cases involving extremely high velocities. Reference to the effects of thermal velocities is only given in a few cases. Numerous references present a basis relative to these subject matters which are also not treated in the work.

With a view to practical application, our book—apart from the general fundamentals—aims at providing a detailed study of common cases of production and focusing of high current-density electron beams. In our treatment, we have started from the general fundamental theory and in all cases we have endeavoured to arrive at final formulae for practical design. We considered a uniform treatment founded upon basic equations as an important objective, since in this way it becomes possible to eliminate inconsistent results and thereby erroneous interpretations, and furthermore this method of treatment ensures a higher theoretical standard as well as added lucidity. This uniform method of treatment may involve certain errors. On the basis of experiences to be gained and opinions, refinement of the treatment will form one of our objectives in a possible second edition of this work. With special regard to the most frequent applications, the predominant part of the material discussed deals systematically with problems of space-charge optics to be solved by axially symmetric, plane symmetric and quadrupole fields. Cases extending beyond these serve mainly for widening the scope of applications.

The book comprises six chapters: those treating basic equations, space-charge flow and magnetic focusing (I, II and VI) are the works of Dr. Gyula András Nagy, while those dealing with electron guns, beam properties and electrostatic focusing (III, IV and V) are by Dr. Miklós Szilágyi. The book covers not only a very thorough elaboration of the literature—not to be found in such detail in any existing works—but also numerous original works (to give a detailed list of these is not considered necessary).

We express our thanks to Dr. Ernő Winter, Member of the Hungarian Academy of Sciences, who long ago recognised the importance of the field and whose constant support enabled the publication of our work.

We express our thanks to J. R. Pierce, who kindly gave his consent to the use of certain figures of his above-mentioned book.

The Authors

CONTENTS

I. BASIC RELATIONSHIPS AND METHODS

GYULA ANDRÁS NAGY

The book treats the sections of classical geometric electron optics dealing with the effects of space-charge, primarily those of basic and applied significance. The basic equations required for this discussion are compiled in the chapter. No less an important objective of the chapter is a discussion of the ideas associated with the various problem groups of the field, and treatment of the most important methods formed for dealing with these problems.

The electric-magnetic field is considered as time-constant, and therefore the simpler variant of the *Maxwell*'s equations relating to this case is discussed. The motions (paths) occurring in the electric-magnetic field are investigated only in cases where *Newton*'s equations apply, and hence *only the lower velocity motions* ($\varphi < 10^4$ V; the range of non-relativistic velocities) *are discussed* [34, 73, 157].

(A) TIME-CONSTANT ELECTRIC-MAGNETIC FIELD

1. MAXWELL'S EQUATIONS

Maxwell's equations are used for determination of the electric-magnetic field. The matter under discussion involves space-charge effects which cannot be neglected, and therefore space-charge must also appear in *Maxwell*'s equations. Our equations are as follows [78, 126, 156]

$$\text{curl } \mathbf{E} = \mathbf{0} \qquad\qquad 1.1$$

$$\text{div } \mathbf{E} = \frac{1}{\varepsilon_0}\varrho \qquad\qquad 1.2$$

$$\text{curl } \mathbf{B} = \mu_0\varrho\dot{\mathbf{r}} \qquad\qquad 1.3$$

$$\text{div } \mathbf{B} = 0 \qquad\qquad 1.4$$

By using **D** and **H** in equations 1.2 and 1.3, the physical significance is emphasised [145]. The force action, however, is expressed by **E** and **B**, hence preference is given to these field characteristics [146].

The meanings and dimensions of the notations used in the equations are as usual:

$\mathbf{E}$ = electric field strength (Vm^{-1});
$\mathbf{B}$ = magnetic induction (Vsm^{-2});
ε_0 = 8.8542×10^{-12} $\text{AsV}^{-1}\text{m}^{-1}$, dielectric constant of free space;
μ_0 = 1.2566 $\text{VsA}^{-1}\text{m}^{-1}$, permeability of free space;
ϱ = volumetric charge density or simply space-charge (Asm^{-3});
$\dot{\mathbf{r}}$ = space-charge flow velocity (ms^{-1}).

The term $\varrho\dot{\mathbf{r}}$ appearing in equation 1.3 represents *current density* and is denoted by **j**. Therefore

$$\mathbf{j} = \varrho\dot{\mathbf{r}} \qquad\qquad 1.5$$

Current density is measured in Am^{-2} units.

With knowledge of the *space-charge* ϱ appearing in the equations, the *charge q* in a finite, or infinite, space part can be calculated. The calculation represents the volume integration of the space-charge over the part of space in question

$$q = \int\limits_{V} \varrho dv \qquad\qquad 1.6$$

The meaning of q in equation 1.6 is therefore: $q =$ electric charge (As).

In the following discussion, though the electron appears as a point-like particle with charge (and mass), the material discussed is also applicable to ions. The electronic charge is

$$q = -e \qquad\qquad 1.7$$

where the value of e (positive quantity) is [164, 166, 167]

$$e = 1.6019\times10^{-19}\,\text{As} \qquad\qquad 1.8$$

Note: (i) Other equations may be used in place of 1.1, 1.2, 1.3, 1.4. Their introduction is justified by the fact that these may be used for investigations performed with approximative calculations.

Let us consider the following identity

$$\varDelta\mathbf{y} \equiv \text{grad div } \mathbf{y} - \text{curl curl} \mathbf{y} \qquad\qquad 1.9$$

Substituting equations 1.1 and 1.2 into 1.9 we obtain

$$\varDelta\mathbf{E} = \frac{1}{\varepsilon_0}\,\text{grad } \varrho \qquad\qquad 1.10$$

Now substitute equations 1.3 and 1.4 into 1.9

$$\varLambda\mathbf{B} = -\,\mu_0\,\text{curl } \varrho\dot{\mathbf{r}} \qquad\qquad 1.11$$

1.10 and 1.11 being the required equations.

(ii) From the identity of

$$\text{div curl } \mathbf{B} \equiv 0 \qquad\qquad 1.12$$

and from 1.3, it follows that

$$\text{div } (\varrho\dot{\mathbf{r}}) = 0 \qquad\qquad 1.13$$

(iii) In all space-charge optics problems discussed in this book, the electric and magnetic fields do not vary with time; consequently, electric and magnetic fields are independent of each other. With primary reference to the equation $\mathbf{j}_v = \gamma(\mathbf{E} + \mathbf{E}_b)$ inter-dependency of the fields is discussed in the literature. In his article [125], starting from energetic bases, the author proves the independency of the fields.

2. ELECTRIC-MAGNETIC POTENTIALS

Equations 1.1, 1.2, 1.3 and 1.4 are now available as axioms of the electric-magnetic field. These may be applied to actual and practical problems if we are able to produce the necessary solutions.

Potential theory deals with the solution of Maxwell's (and other partial) *equations.* Before we turn to the description of the solution, we introduce the potential functions [28, 145, 149].

Two unknown vector functions, **E** and **B** figure in *Maxwell's* equations. The functions ϱ and $\dot{\mathbf{r}}$, and constants ε_0 and μ_0 are assumed known. From the structure of the equations and from physical considerations (see note iii at the end of §1), it may be ascertained that **E** and **B** are independent. Thus, solution of **E** and **B** may be sought separately.

(a) The scalar potential

Let us first consider the determination of **E** and the introduction of the scalar potential.

Equations 1.1 and 1.2 determine the three components of **E**, their determination, however, requires the solution of a complicated system of equations. The determination of **E** may be reduced to the determination of one single unknown function instead of three. On the other hand, the newly introduced function involves the solution of a second-order differential equation while the differential equation relating to the three components of **E** are of first order.

Let us denote the scalar potential by φ. The field strength of **E** is derived from φ by

$$\mathbf{E} = -\operatorname{grad} \varphi \qquad\qquad 2.1$$

In accordance with 2.1 the three components of **E** are obtained from the introduced φ (apart from a constant eliminated during differentiation). Now the differential equation determining φ is to be derived, taking into consideration that **E** derived therefrom must satisfy equations 1.1 and 1.2.

Equation 1.1 is satisfied, in an identical way, since

$$\operatorname{curl} \mathbf{E} = \operatorname{curl}(-\operatorname{grad} \varphi) \equiv 0 \qquad\qquad 2.2$$

Equation 1.2 is satisfied by giving with its aid the differential equation referring to φ

$$\operatorname{div} \mathbf{E} = \operatorname{div}(-\operatorname{grad} \varphi) = \frac{1}{\varepsilon_0} \varrho \qquad\qquad 2.3$$

Equation 2.3 may be written in a different form

$$\Delta \varphi = -\frac{1}{\varepsilon_0} \varrho \qquad\qquad 2.4$$

Equation 2.4 is known also as *Poisson's differential equation.* The newly introduced quantity is therefore: φ potential (V).

(b) The vector potential

Secondly, we shall deal with the determination of **B**, and with the introduction of the vector potential.

Although the system of equations 1.3 and 1.4 determines the three components of **B**, the three unknown functions are to be determined in such a manner that they satisfy a system consisting of four equations. Instead of this, the determination of **B** is reduced to the determination of a vector function which satisfies only one vectorial differential equation. Again, this introduces a function involving the solution of a system of second-order differential equations, while the system of differential equations determining **B** involves only first-order equations.

Let us denote the vector potential as **A**. Field strength **B** is derived from **A** by

$$\mathbf{B} = \text{curl } \mathbf{A} \qquad\qquad 2.5$$

According to equation 2.5 the three components of **B** can be obtained from **A** if (i) one constant vector is eliminated by the differentiation, and (ii) the divergence of **A** is disregarded. This means we may choose **A** at will since the divergence of **A** plays no role in the generation of **B**. For the sake of simplicity, let

$$\text{div } \mathbf{A} = 0 \qquad\qquad 2.6$$

It remains to derive th edifferential equation determining **A** in such a way that **B** will satisfy equations 1.3 and 1.4.

Equation 1.4 is identically satisfied since

$$\text{div } \mathbf{B} = \text{div curl } \mathbf{A} \equiv 0 \qquad\qquad 2.7$$

Equation 1.3 is satisfied in such a way that using it the differential equation referring to **A** is given as

$$\text{curl } \mathbf{B} = \text{curl curl } \mathbf{A} = \mu_0 \varrho \dot{\mathbf{r}} \qquad\qquad 2.8$$

Considering the identity

$$\text{curl curl } \mathbf{A} \equiv \text{grad div } \mathbf{A} - \Delta\mathbf{A} \qquad\qquad 2.9$$

and rearranging equations 2.6, and 2.8 we get

$$\Delta\mathbf{A} = - \mu_0 \varrho \dot{\mathbf{r}} \qquad\qquad 2.10$$

This is *Poisson's vector differential equation.*

The latest introduced quantity is therefore: **A** vector potential (Vs m^{-1}).

Note: Vector **A** is undetermined not only to the extent of one constant vector, but also to that of a fairly optional function. Consider

$$\mathbf{A} = \mathbf{C} + \mathbf{A}_0 + \text{grad } \psi \qquad\qquad 2.11$$

Now, let us determine the derivatives

$$\text{curl } \mathbf{A} = \text{curl } \mathbf{A}_0 = \mathbf{B} \qquad\qquad 2.12$$

since

$$\text{curl } \mathbf{C} \equiv 0 \qquad\qquad 2.13$$

and

$$\text{curl grad } \psi \equiv 0 \qquad\qquad 2.14$$

Thus, the value and derivation of $\mathbf{B}$ remain unaltered. Furthermore

$$\text{div } \mathbf{A} = \text{div } \mathbf{A}_0 + \Delta\psi = 0 \qquad\qquad 2.15$$

since

$$\text{div } \mathbf{C} \equiv 0 \qquad\qquad 2.16$$

Therefore, $\mathbf{A}$ remains divergence-free.
As a result, the 'fairly optional function' satisfies the following equation

$$\Delta\psi = -\text{div } \mathbf{A}_0$$

3. EXACT SOLUTION OF THE POTENTIAL EQUATIONS BY THE USE OF QUADRATURES

We shall now solve equation 2.4 relating to φ and equation 2.10 relating to $\mathbf{A}$, in the case of the latter taking into consideration the supplementary condition 2.6 [28, 156].

Similarly with the ordinary differential equations, supplementary conditions are necessary for the solution of partial differential equations, if a single solution is to be chosen from the general solution. The supplementary conditions belonging to the next differential equations are called *boundary conditions*.

(a) Electric field

We will first deal with the solution of equation 2.4 referring to φ.
The boundary conditions relative to equation 2.4 are as follows

$$\varphi = \varphi_p \qquad\qquad 3.1$$

$$\text{grad } \varphi = -\mathbf{E}_p \qquad\qquad 3.2$$

The boundary conditions φ_p and $-\mathbf{E}_p$ are the values of functions φ and $\mathbf{E}$ taken on the closed surface surrounding the investigated space section.

Note: Boundary conditions 3.1 and 3.2 must contain no contradictions: they are compatible. In special cases of unique solution, either the one or the other boundary condition is necessary. The boundary problem relating to the linear combination of the two boundary conditions can also be solved [25, 26, 94, 95, 122, 123].

We are not detailing the derivation known from the literature [28, 146] and only the results are given. Solution of the differential equation relating to φ with the boundary conditions is as follows

$$\varphi(\mathbf{r}) = \frac{1}{4\pi\varepsilon_0} \int_V \frac{\varrho(\mathbf{r}_0)}{|\mathbf{r} - \mathbf{r}_0|} \, dv_0 - \frac{1}{4\pi} \int_F \frac{\varphi_p(\mathbf{r}_0)(\mathbf{r} - \mathbf{r}_0)}{|\mathbf{r} - \mathbf{r}_0|^3} \cdot d\mathbf{f}_0 -$$

$$-\frac{1}{4\pi} \int_F \frac{\mathbf{E}_p(\mathbf{r}_0)}{|\mathbf{r} - \mathbf{r}_0|} \cdot d\mathbf{f}_0 \qquad 3.3$$

In order to avoid misunderstandings we point out that the space points in which the potential values are sought are denoted by $\mathbf{r}$, varying values of the integration variable marked as $\mathbf{r}_0$ cover the definition regions of firstly ϱ, secondly φ_p and thirdly $\mathbf{E}_p$. The definition region of φ is a volume within the investigated space section or possibly a resultant of several partial sections. The definition region of φ_p is the boundary surface of the investigated space section, or possibly several surface sections. The definition region of $\mathbf{E}_p$ is similar to the definition region of φ_p.

Figure I.1 facilitates the comprehension of the symbols.

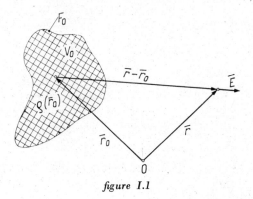

figure I.1

(b) Magnetic field

Secondly we deal with the solution of equation 2.10 relative to $\mathbf{A}$. The boundary conditions appertaining to equation 2.10 are the following

$$\mathbf{A} = \mathbf{A}_p \qquad 3.4$$

$$\text{curl } \mathbf{A} = \mathbf{B}_p \qquad 3.5$$

The boundary conditions $\mathbf{A}_p$ and $\mathbf{B}_p$ are the values of functions taken on the closed surface surrounding the investigated space section.

The derivation known from the literature [28, 146, 156] is also not given here, only the results are reported. Solution of the differential equation relative to **A** with the boundary conditions

$$\mathbf{A(r)} = \frac{\mu_0}{4\pi} \int_V \frac{\varrho(\mathbf{r}_0)\dot{\mathbf{r}}(\mathbf{r}_0)}{|\mathbf{r} - \mathbf{r}_0|} \, dv_0 - \frac{1}{4\pi} \int \frac{[\mathbf{n} \cdot \mathbf{A}_p(\mathbf{r}_0)](\mathbf{r} - \mathbf{r}_0)}{|\mathbf{r} - \mathbf{r}_0|^3} \, df_0 -$$

$$- \frac{1}{4\pi} \int_F \frac{[\mathbf{n} \times \mathbf{A}_p(\mathbf{r}_0)] \times (\mathbf{r} - \mathbf{r}_0)}{|\mathbf{r} - \mathbf{r}_0|^3} \, df_0 - \frac{1}{4\pi} \int_F \frac{\mathbf{n} \times \mathbf{B}_p(\mathbf{r}_0)}{|\mathbf{r} - \mathbf{r}_0|} \, df_0 \qquad 3.6$$

The remarks concerning the scalar potential case (also those concerning boundary conditions) are also valid here.

The symbols are of similar meanings to those used in the scalar potential formulae.

Note: The solutions of equations 1.1 and 1.2 and also 1.3 and 1.4 can be given directly, without introduction of the potentials [28].

First let us write the formula relative to **E**. The corresponding boundary condition is then

$$\mathbf{E} = \mathbf{E}_p \qquad 3.7$$

The boundary condition $\mathbf{E}_p$ is understood to be on the closed surface surrounded by the investigated space section.

The solution of the differential equation relative to **E**, as appertaining to the boundary condition is therefore

$$\mathbf{E(r)} = \frac{1}{4\pi\varepsilon_0} \int_V \frac{\varrho(\mathbf{r}_0)(\mathbf{r} - \mathbf{r}_0)}{|\mathbf{r} - \mathbf{r}_0|^3} \, dv_0 - \frac{1}{4\pi} \int_F \frac{[\mathbf{n} \cdot \mathbf{E}_p(\mathbf{r}_0)](\mathbf{r} - \mathbf{r}_0)}{|\mathbf{r} - \mathbf{r}_0|^3} \, df_0 -$$

$$- \frac{1}{4\pi} \int_F \frac{[\mathbf{n} \times \mathbf{E}_p(\mathbf{r}_0)] \times (\mathbf{r} - \mathbf{r}_0)}{|\mathbf{r} - \mathbf{r}_0|^3} \, df_0 \qquad 3.8$$

Now let us write the formula relative to **B**. The respective boundary condition is then

$$\mathbf{B} = \mathbf{B}_p \qquad 3.9$$

The boundary condition $\mathbf{B}_p$ is understood to be on the closed surface surrounded by the investigated space section.

The solution of the differential equation relative to **B**, appertaining to the boundary condition is therefore

$$\mathbf{B(r)} = \frac{\mu_0}{4\pi} \int_V \frac{\varrho(\mathbf{r}_0)\dot{\mathbf{r}}(\mathbf{r}_0) \times (\mathbf{r} - \mathbf{r}_0)}{|\mathbf{r} - \mathbf{r}_0|^3} \, dv_0 - \frac{1}{4\pi} \int_F \frac{[\mathbf{n} \cdot \mathbf{B}_p(\mathbf{r}_0)](\mathbf{r} - \mathbf{r}_0)}{|\mathbf{r} - \mathbf{r}_0|^3} \, df_0 -$$

$$- \frac{1}{4\pi} \int_F \frac{[\mathbf{n} \times \mathbf{B}_p(\mathbf{r}_0)] \times (\mathbf{r} - \mathbf{r}_0)}{|\mathbf{r} - \mathbf{r}_0|^3} \, df_0 \qquad 3.10$$

Formulae 3.8 and 3.10, and similarly 3.3 and 3.6 may be used for approximative computations.

4. EXACT SOLUTION OF THE POTENTIAL EQUATIONS
BY OTHER METHODS

The exact solution of the potential equations is possible not only by quadratures. Methods of separation of variables and the infinite series method form the most important and also the most readily accessible accurate methods of integrating the equations. These methods will be discussed later, in as much detail as possible. Further integrating methods will only be mentioned since the knowledge required for their application is not readily available. Among these, however, the method of variation must be emphasised, since the application of this method covers a wide field. The significance of the methods not mentioned is not considerable and these appear only in certain specific cases.

(a) Solution of Poisson's equation

Before describing the integration methods to be dealt with later, some brief general information with regard to solution of *Poisson*'s equation may be obtained from the following.

Poisson's partial differential equations occurring in this discussion of problems belong to the group of linear second-order inhomogeneous equations (1.10, 1.11, 2.4, 2.10, 5.11, 5.36, 6.11, 7.7, 7.28, 8.10, 8.17).

Let us denote the differential equation to be solved in the following manner

$$DU = G \qquad\qquad 4.1$$

where D denotes the differential operator, U the function sought and G the inhomogeneity (or excitation). $G = G(\mathbf{r})$, i.e. function of location.

In our case

$$U = U_p \qquad\qquad 4.2$$

is the boundary condition which appertains to equation 4.1, enabling us to find a unique solution. $U_p(\mathbf{r}_0)$ is the function given on the surface surrounding the region.

The homogeneous equation corresponding to equation 4.1 is

$$DU = 0 \qquad\qquad 4.3$$

Let the functions

$$U = U_h(\mathbf{r}), \quad h = 1, 2, \ldots \qquad\qquad 4.4$$

be the solutions of the homogeneous equation. The sum of these solutions formed with arbitrary constants C_h

$$U = \sum_h C_h U_h(\mathbf{r}) \qquad\qquad 4.5$$

is also solution of the homogeneous equation. If this is a function of one (or more) parameters, e.g. $U_h(\mathbf{r}, \lambda)$, then integral

$$U = \int_\lambda C(\lambda) U_h(\mathbf{r},\lambda) d\lambda \qquad\qquad 4.6$$

is also a solution [$C(\lambda)$ is independent of $\mathbf{r}$]. Let the function

$$U = U_i(\mathbf{r}) \qquad\qquad 4.7$$

ibe a solution of the inhomogeneous equation. The use of function 4.7 gives the general solution of the inhomogeneous equation

$$U = U_i + \sum_h C_h U_h \qquad\qquad 4.8$$

When satisfying the boundary condition 4.2 one solution pertaining to a defined C_h series of values is selected from equation 4.8. If necessary for the solution of the actual task, the second term on the right-hand side of equation 4.8 should be substituted by the right-hand side expression of equation 4.6. In the usual manner we determine the solution of the homogeneous equation which satisfies the inhomogeneous boundary condition, and that solution of the inhomogeneous equation where the boundary value equals zero. We, therefore, solve the systems of equations

$$DU_h = 0 \qquad\qquad 4.9$$
$$U_h = U_p$$

and

$$DU_i = G$$
$$U_i = 0 \qquad\qquad 4.10$$

If

$$U = U_i + U_h \qquad\qquad 4.11$$

then

$$DU = DU_i + DU_h = G \qquad\qquad 4.12$$

and on the boundary we have

$$U = U_i + U_h = U_p \qquad\qquad 4.13$$

The solution of U_i does not necessarily assume a value of zero on the boundary. However, in this case the boundary value prescribed for U_h must be modified by the boundary value of U_i.

In accordance with this, the solution of space-charge (and current-density) problems leading to *Poisson's* differential equation is performed in the following manner [40, 41, 163]:

(i) We seek an arbitrary solution of *Poisson's* (inhomogeneous) equation which satisfies arbitrary boundary conditions.

(ii) We determine the modified boundary conditions.

(iii) We determine the general solution of *Laplace*'s homogeneous equation, which satisfies the modified boundary conditions.

It will be seen that *the determination of the general solution of the inhomogeneous equation is reduced to the determination of the general solution of the homogeneous equation.* It is therefore understandable that the *determination of the general solution of Laplace's equation is of fundamental importance.*

Note: the boundary problem set forth is not the only one to occur in the solution of *Poisson*'s equation. Construction of the solution in the case of the other boundary problems takes place on the model of the method described, with appropriate alterations.

(b) Separation of the variables

The most important exact method for the solution of potential equations representing partial differential equations is the method of separation of the variables.

In this method the partial differential equation is broken up into a system of ordinary differential equations. We, then, determine the solution of the ordinary differential equations. The solution is matched to the boundary conditions by an appropriate choice of the parameter system occurring during the decomposition.

The following are further important questions which arise in pursuing this method.

1) The specific geometrical features which are the characteristics of individual cases must certainly be exploited. The method of exploitation is the employment of the coordinate system taking into account the geometric characteristics, i.e. transformation of the variables. This group of problems is well known, and is therefore omitted in our discussions [122, 123].

2) It is necessary to ascertain whether the differential equation in the coordinate system employed can be separated into a system of ordinary differential equations.

3) It is necessary to ascertain whether the function given on the boundary can be expressed with the help of the function systems obtained as solution of ordinary differential equations; in other words, whether the boundary function can be expanded in series with the solution functions. See [25, 26] for the answer to this question.

Some pages are devoted to the conditions of separability, a subject which is not given in Hungarian literature [121].

A given partial differential expression can be reduced to a system of ordinary differential expressions only in defined coordinate systems [120].

We shall investigate the separability of Laplace's differential expression in the orthogonal coordinate system. Laplace's equation with the *Lamè* coefficients $h_i (i = 1, 2, 3)$ and the orthogonal coordinates $x_i (i = 1, 2, 3)$ [122, 123] is as follows

$$\Delta\varphi = \frac{1}{h_1 h_2 h_3} \left[\frac{\partial}{\partial x_1} \left(\frac{h_2 h_3}{h_1} \frac{\partial\varphi}{\partial x_1} \right) + \frac{\partial}{\partial x_2} \left(\frac{h_3 h_1}{h_2} \frac{\partial\varphi}{\partial x_2} \right) + \right.$$

$$+ \frac{\partial}{\partial x_3} \left(\frac{h_1 h_2}{h_3} \frac{\partial \varphi}{\partial x_3} \right) \right] = 0 \qquad 4.14$$

Notation of the product-form solution

$$\varphi(x_1, x_2, x_3) = X_1(x_1) X_2(x_2) X_3(x_3) \qquad 4.15$$

Substituting 4.15 and dividing by φ

$$\frac{1}{X_1} \frac{\partial}{\partial x_1} \left(\frac{h_2 h_3}{h_1} \frac{\partial X_1}{\partial x_1} \right) + \frac{1}{X_2} \frac{\partial}{\partial x_2} \left(\frac{h_3 h_1}{h_2} \frac{\partial X_2}{\partial x_2} \right) +$$

$$+ \frac{1}{X_3} \frac{\partial}{\partial x_3} \left(\frac{h_1 h_2}{h_3} \frac{\partial X_3}{\partial x_3} \right) = 0 \qquad 4.16$$

Let

$$\frac{h_2 h_3}{h_1} = f_1(x_1) F_1(x_2, x_3) \qquad 4.17$$

$$\frac{h_3 h_1}{h_2} = f_2(x_2) F_2(x_1, x_2) \qquad 4.18$$

$$\frac{h_1 h_2}{h_3} = f_3(x_3) F_3(x_1, x_2) \qquad 4.19$$

Substituting the above into 4.16 we obtain

$$\frac{F_1}{X_1} \frac{\partial}{\partial x_1} \left(f_1 \frac{\partial X_1}{\partial x_1} \right) + \frac{F_2}{X_2} \frac{\partial}{\partial x_2} \left(f_2 \frac{\partial X_2}{\partial x_2} \right) +$$

$$+ \frac{F_3}{X_3} \frac{\partial}{\partial x_3} \left(f_3 \frac{\partial X_3}{\partial x_3} \right) = 0 \qquad 4.20$$

If the equation is separable, the solution functions X_i $(i = 1, 2, 3)$ are dependent upon two constants arising during the separation $(f_1, f_2, f_3, F_1, F_2, F_3$
are not dependent upon these constants, since these are characteristics of
the chosen coordinate system). Separating one of the variables, using notation G for the various function relations arising during separation

$$G_{1, 2}(x_1, x_2) = G_3^+(x_3) = \lambda_1 \qquad 4.21$$

whence

$$G_{1,2}(x_1, x_2) = \lambda_1 \qquad 4.22$$

$$G_3(x_3, \lambda_1) = 0 \qquad 4.23$$

The remaining two variables after separation

$$G_1^+(x_1, \lambda_1) = G_2^+(x_2, \lambda_1) = \lambda_2 \qquad 4.24$$

whence

$$G_1(x_1,\lambda_1,\lambda_2) = 0 \tag{4.25}$$

$$G_2(x_2,\lambda_1,\lambda_2) = 0 \tag{4.26}$$

Differentiating equation 4.20 with respect to λ_1 and λ_2

$$F_1 \frac{\partial}{\partial \lambda_1}\left[\frac{1}{X_1}\frac{\partial}{\partial x_1}\left(f_1 \frac{\partial X_1}{\partial x_1}\right)\right] + F_2 \frac{\partial}{\partial \lambda_1}\left[\frac{1}{X_2}\frac{\partial}{\partial x_2}\left(f_2 \frac{\partial X_2}{\partial x_2}\right)\right] +$$
$$+ F_3 \frac{\partial}{\partial \lambda_1}\left[\frac{1}{X_3}\frac{\partial}{\partial x_3}\left(f_2 \frac{\partial x_3}{\partial X_3}\right)\right] = 0 \tag{4.27}$$

$$F_1 \frac{\partial}{\partial \lambda_2}\left[\frac{1}{X_1}\frac{\partial}{\partial x_1}\left(f_1 \frac{\partial X_1}{\partial x_1}\right)\right] + F_2 \frac{\partial}{\partial \lambda_2}\left[\frac{1}{X_2}\frac{\partial}{\partial x_2}\left(f_2 \frac{\partial X_2}{\partial x_2}\right)\right] +$$
$$+ F_3 \frac{\partial}{\partial \lambda_2}\left[\frac{1}{X_3}\frac{\partial}{\partial x_3}\left(f_3 \frac{\partial X_3}{\partial x_3}\right)\right] = 0 \tag{4.28}$$

Now let us introduce the notation

$$M_{i1} = \frac{-1}{f_1}\frac{\partial}{\partial \lambda_1}\left[\frac{1}{X_i}\frac{\partial}{\partial x_i}\left(f_i \frac{\partial X_i}{\partial x_i}\right)\right], \quad i = 1,2,3 \tag{4.29}$$

$$M_{i2} = \frac{-1}{f_i}\frac{\partial}{\partial \lambda_2}\left[\frac{1}{X_i}\frac{\partial}{\partial x_i}\left(f_i \frac{\partial X_i}{\partial x_i}\right)\right], \quad i = 1,2,3 \tag{4.30}$$

Using these, equations 4.27 and 4.28 become

$$f_1 F_1 M_{11} + f_2 F_2 M_{21} + f_3 F_3 M_{31} = 0 \tag{4.31}$$

$$f_1 F_1 M_{12} + f_2 F_2 M_{22} + f_3 F_3 M_{32} = 0 \tag{4.32}$$

From equations 4.31 and 4.32 the following ratios are obtained for the expressions $f_1 F_1, f_2 F_2, f_3 F_3$

$$\frac{f_2 F_3}{f_1 F_1} = \frac{M_{31}M_{12} - M_{11}M_{32}}{M_{21}M_{32} - M_{31}M_{22}} = \frac{A_{23}}{A_{13}} \tag{4.33}$$

$$\frac{f_3 F_3}{f_1 F_1} = \frac{M_{11}M_{22} - M_{22}M_{12}}{M_{21}M_{32} - M_{31}M_{22}} = \frac{A_{33}}{A_{13}} \tag{4.34}$$

where A_{13}, A_{23}, A_{33} are cofactors of the determinant

$$S = \begin{vmatrix} M_{11} & M_{12} & 0 \\ M_{21} & M_{22} & 0 \\ M_{31} & M_{32} & 0 \end{vmatrix} \tag{4.35}$$

Comparing equations 4.17, 4.18 and 4.19 with equations 4.33 and 4.34 we obtain

$$\frac{h_1^2}{h_2^2} = \frac{A_{23}}{A_{13}} \qquad 4.36$$

$$\frac{h_1^2}{h_3^2} = \frac{A_{33}}{A_{13}} \qquad 4.37$$

$$\frac{h_2^2}{h_3^2} = \frac{A_{33}}{A_{23}} \qquad 4.38$$

Equations 4.36, 4.37 and 4.38 form the first group of the separability conditions.
From equations 4.33 and 4.34

$$f_1 \frac{F_1}{A_{13}} = f_2 \frac{F_2}{A_{23}} = f_3 \frac{F_3}{A_{33}} \qquad 4.39$$

4.39 is satisfied only when

$$\frac{F_1}{A_{13}} = f_2 f_3 \qquad 4.40$$

$$\frac{F_2}{A_{23}} = f_1 f_3 \qquad 4.41$$

and

$$\frac{F_3}{A_{33}} = f_1 f_2 \qquad 4.42$$

therefore

$$f_1 \frac{F_1}{A_{13}} = f_2 \frac{F_2}{A_{23}} = f_3 \frac{F_3}{A_{33}} = f_1 f_2 f_3 \qquad 4.43$$

Equation 4.43 forms the second group of the separability conditions.
With equations 4.17, 4.18, 4.19

$$\frac{h_2 h_3}{h_1} = f_1 f_2 f_3 A_{13} \qquad 4.44$$

$$\frac{h_3 h_1}{h_2} = f_1 f_2 f_3 A_{23} \qquad 4.45$$

$$\frac{h_1 h_2}{h_3} = f_1 f_2 f_3 A_{33} \qquad 4.46$$

Substituting equations 4.44, 4.45 and 4.46 into equation 4.16

$$\frac{f_2 f_3 A_{13}}{X_1} \frac{\partial}{\partial x_1} \left(f_1 \frac{\partial X_1}{\partial x_1} \right) + \frac{f_1 f_3 A_{23}}{X_2} \frac{\partial}{\partial x_2} \left(f_2 \frac{\partial X_2}{\partial x_2} \right) +$$

$$+ \frac{f_1 f_2 A_{33}}{X_3} \frac{\partial}{\partial x_3} \left(f_3 \frac{\partial X_3}{\partial x_3} \right) = 0 \qquad\qquad 4.47$$

and transforming with equations 4.47, 4.44, 4.45, 4.46

$$\frac{1}{h_1^2 f_1 X_1} \frac{\partial}{\partial x_1} \left(f_1 \frac{\partial X_1}{\partial x_1} \right) + \frac{1}{h_2^2 f_2 X_2} \frac{\partial}{\partial x_2} \left(f_2 \frac{\partial X_2}{\partial x_2} \right) +$$

$$+ \frac{1}{h_3^2 f_3 X_3} \frac{\partial}{\partial x_3} \left(f_3 \frac{\partial X_3}{\partial x_3} \right) = 0 \qquad\qquad 4.48$$

For the determinant 4.35

$$0 = M_{11} A_{13} + M_{21} A_{23} + M_{31} A_{33} \qquad\qquad 4.49$$

$$0 = M_{12} A_{13} + M_{22} A_{23} + M_{32} A_{33} \qquad\qquad 4.50$$

$$0 = 0 \cdot A_{13} + 0 \cdot A_{23} + 0 \cdot A_{33} \qquad\qquad 4.51$$

Dividing 4.49 by A_{13}, 4.50 by A_{23} and 4.51 by A_{33}

$$0 = M_{11} \frac{A_{13}}{A_{13}} + M_{21} \frac{A_{23}}{A_{13}} + M_{31} \frac{A_{33}}{A_{13}} \qquad\qquad 4.52$$

$$0 = M_{12} \frac{A_{13}}{A_{23}} + M_{22} \frac{A_{23}}{A_{23}} + M_{32} \frac{A_{33}}{A_{23}} \qquad\qquad 4.53$$

$$0 = 0 \cdot \frac{A_{13}}{A_{33}} + 0 \cdot \frac{A_{23}}{A_{33}} + 0 \cdot \frac{A_{33}}{A_{33}} \qquad\qquad 4.54$$

Substituting equations 4.36, 4.37 and 4.38 into equations 4.52, 4.53 and 4.54

$$0 = M_{11} \frac{h_1^2}{h_1^2} + M_{21} \frac{h_1^2}{h_2^2} + M_{31} \frac{h_1^2}{h_3^2} \qquad\qquad 4.55$$

$$0 = M_{12} \frac{h_2^2}{h_1^2} + M_{22} \frac{h_2^2}{h_2^2} + M_{32} \frac{h_2^2}{h_3^2} \qquad\qquad 4.56$$

$$0 = 0 \cdot \frac{h_3^2}{h_1^2} + 0 \cdot \frac{h_3^2}{h_2^2} + 0 \cdot \frac{h_3^2}{h_3^2} \qquad\qquad 4.57$$

Multiplying equation 4.55 by λ_1/h_1^2, 4.56 by λ_2/h_2^2 and 4.57 by λ_3/h_3^2 $(\lambda_3 = 0)$

$$0 = \lambda_1 \frac{M_{11}}{h_1^2} + \lambda_1 \frac{M_{21}}{h_2^2} + \lambda_1 \frac{M_{31}}{h_3^2} \qquad 4.58$$

$$0 = \lambda_2 \frac{M_{12}}{h_1^2} + \lambda_2 \frac{M_{22}}{h_2^2} + \lambda_2 \frac{M_{22}}{h_3^2} \qquad 4.59$$

$$0 = \lambda_3 \frac{0}{h_1^2} + \lambda_3 \frac{0}{h_2^2} + \lambda_3 \frac{0}{h_3^2} \qquad 4.60$$

Adding the sum of equations 4.58, 4.59 and 4.60 to equation 4.48 and using an abbreviated form of writing

$$\sum_{i=1}^{3} \frac{1}{h_i^2} \left[\frac{1}{f_i X_i} \frac{\partial}{\partial x_i} \left(f_i \frac{\partial X_i}{\partial x_i} \right) + \sum_{k=1}^{3} \lambda_k M_{ik} \right] = 0 \qquad 4.61$$

Identity 4.61 exists if all three terms in parentheses are equal to zero. By rearranging and using the symbol of ordinary differentiation

$$\frac{1}{f_i} \frac{d}{dx_i} \left(f_i \frac{dX_i}{dx_i} \right) + X_i \sum_{k=1}^{3} \lambda_k M_{ik} = 0, \qquad i = 1, 2, 3 \qquad 4.62$$

In the three differential equations given by 4.62 only one independent variable occurs in each equation: thus separation of the variables has been performed.

(c) The infinite series method

The solution of potential equations may be sought in the form of infinite series. The series will assume the following form

$$\varphi = \sum_{i=0}^{\infty} \sum_{j=0}^{\infty} \sum_{k=0}^{\infty} a_{ijk} F_{ijk}(\mathbf{r}) \qquad 4.63$$

The coefficients a_{ijk} in 4.63 are unknown constants, the components $F_{ijk}(\mathbf{r})$ are known functions. If the dependency upon all variables is not given, the solution of the potential equations is also unknown. In this case, unknown functions will appear in the infinite series expressing the potential function, and the result of the calculation gives only the *structure* of the series produced under the given circumstances. This case will occur frequently in later discussions, e.g. axially symmetric and other fields.

The unknown constants a_{ijk} are determined by the solution of the system of equations with an infinite number of unknowns, which are obtained by substituting equation 4.63 into the differential equation to be solved, and satisfying the boundary conditions [21].

This procedure is illustrated by the power series solution of equation 7.7. The power series is assumed in the following form

$$\varphi(y, z) = \sum_{i=0}^{\infty} \sum_{j=0}^{\infty} a_{ij} y^i z^j \qquad 4.64$$

Series expansion of the space-charge (excitation)

$$\varrho(y, z) = \sum_{i=0}^{\infty} \sum_{j=0}^{\infty} \varrho_{ij} y^i z^j \qquad 4.65$$

Equations 4.64 and 4.65 are substituted, after index transformation, into equation 7.7 and reduced to zero

$$\sum_{i=2}^{\infty} \sum_{j=2}^{\infty} \left[i(i-1)a_{i,j-2} + j(j-1) a_{i-2,j} + \frac{1}{\varepsilon_0} \varrho_{i-2,j-2} \right] y^{i-2} z^{j-2} = 0 \quad 4.66$$

Identity 4.66 exists in a region if the coefficients of all the powers of the variables y and z in the given region are equal to zero

$$i(i-1)a_{i,j-2} + j(j-1)a_{i-2,j} + \frac{1}{\varepsilon_0} \varrho_{i-2,j-2} = 0 \qquad 4.67$$

In equation 4.67 $i = 2, 3 \ldots$ and $j = 2, 3 \ldots$ Let the equation of the boundary curve be

$$y = y(z) \qquad 4.68$$

and its power series

$$y = \sum_{k=0}^{\infty} b_k z^k \qquad 4.69$$

Let the boundary potential be

$$\varphi_p = \varphi[y(z), z] = \varphi_p(z) \qquad 4.70$$

and its power series

$$\varphi_p = \sum_{k=0}^{\infty} c_k z^k \qquad 4.71$$

Substituting the series 4.69 and 4.71 into 4.64 we obtain

$$\sum_{k=0}^{\infty} c_k z^k = \sum_{i=0}^{\infty} \sum_{j=0}^{\infty} a_{ij} \left(\sum_{k=0}^{\infty} b_k z^k \right)^i z^j \qquad 4.72$$

By equalising the equal powers of z in equation 4.72 the unknowns a_{ij} appear as functions of b_k and c_k.

The unknowns a_{ij} may be determined from the system of equations 4.67 and the system of equations yielded by 4.71.

(d) Other methods

The variation method. The electric-magnetic field may also be calculated as an extreme value (stationary value) of a given functional. The functional is a definite integral of the invariant *Lagrange* function of the field as referred to a given region [40, 41, 96, 97, 113]. The *Lagrange* function of the electric-magnetic field [122, 123] is as follows

$$L = \frac{\varepsilon_0}{2} (\text{grad } \varphi)^2 - \frac{1}{2\mu_0} (\text{curl } \mathbf{A})^2 - \varrho\varphi + \varrho\dot{\mathbf{r}} \cdot \mathbf{A} \qquad\qquad 4.73$$

The electric-magnetic fields derived by the variation method with the help of the Maxwell's equations are identical, and thus the two starting bases are equivalent. In the first case the *Lagrange* function and in the second case *Maxwell's* equations are given.

The method is important from the aspect, among others, of approximative calculation processes.

Presentation of the application of the variation method would be necessary, at least in case of boundary problems pertaining to equations 2.4 and 2.10. Since, however, the supplementary knowledge would require certain space-demanding derivations, the description of this efficient procedure has been omitted. For informative purpose, however, we may state that the solution of the respective problems requires the determination of an extreme value of a functional in each case.

The method of Green functions. The solution of potential equations 2.4 and 2.10 can also be given with the help of the *Green* functions [16, 22]. The *Green* functions also satisfy *Laplace's* and *Poisson's* differential equations. In comparison to the original problem, the reduction is due to the simplified boundary conditions on the one hand and on the other to the simplified excitation as related to the original case. Solution of the original differential equations is obtained in the form of definite integrals formed by *Green* functions.

The method of integral equations. Determination of the potentials may be obtained also by the method of integral equations [36, 96, 97, 119]. The unknown function, together with other functions, also figures in the integral equation as an integrand. Well-elaborated general methods for determination of the unknown function are known and these may be used as bases for approximative procedures. The only drawback of the integral equation method necessitates into employing of a considerable amount of knowledge, which as yet has not attained widespread recognition. Nevertheless this method is worthy of attention.

The Laplace transformation and other functional transformations. We now seek the transformed equation of the differential equation to be solved. In many cases the transformed differential equation is of a simpler structure than the original. Therefore the solution is more easily accessible.

The transformed differential equation may also be reduced to an algebraic equation. In this case the transformation of the required function may be expressed by algebraic means from the algebraic equation. In both cases the transformation tables extended to very many functions are used [40, 41] for inverse transformation.

Conformal mapping. One of the methods of the determination of potential fields with planar distribution is conformal mapping [50, 98]. Both real and imaginary components of the functions of a complex variable satisfy the two-variable *Laplace* equation, and this therefore may be chosen as a potential function in a region. Since there is only one function of complex variable which assumes the values prescribed on the boundary of the region, the chosen potential function is the only function which will also satisfy the boundary conditions. The equation yielding the function of complex variable and obtaining given values along the real axis (as a boundary) which we defined on the upper half-plane, and similarly the equation yielding the function of complex variable and obtaining given values on the unit circle (as a boundary) which are defined within the unit circle, are known. The problem is therefore solved, if we find a transformation of the given boundary to either the real axis or the unit circle. The solution defined for the interior of the unit circle or for the upper half-plane may be transformed inversely.

(B) ELECTRIC-MAGNETIC FIELDS WITH
SPECIFIC STRUCTURE

In the preceding section we have dealt with eletric-magnetic fields in general, with regard to both the basic equations and their solutions. Knowledge of these characteristics has a primary use in theoretical applications.

Electric-magnetic fields with specific characteristics, however, have a wider application; we have in mind the realisation of more practical purposes.

In this section we shall introduce and describe some electric-magnetic fields with specific structures, which are employed over very large ranges [81, 133].

5. AXIALLY SYMMETRIC FIELDS

The basic property of axially symmetric fields, according to convention, is that in a suitably chosen coordinate system *the lines of force of both electric and magnetic fields in the plane through the axis of rotation of the coordinate system remain unchanged when the plane is rotated at an arbitrary angle around the axis of rotation.* It is obvious from this definition that the field-strength components in the direction of α are equal to zero and that *components which differ from zero are independent of* α (choosing the cylindrical coordinate system)

$$\mathbf{E} = E_r \mathbf{e}_r + E_\alpha \mathbf{e}_\alpha + E_z \mathbf{e}_z \qquad 5.1$$

$$E_r = E_r(r,z); \; E_\alpha \equiv 0; \; E_z = E_z(r,z) \qquad 5.2$$

$$\mathbf{B} = B_r \mathbf{e}_r + B_\alpha \mathbf{e}_\alpha + B_z \mathbf{e}_z \qquad 5.3$$

$$B_r = B_r(r,z); \; B_\alpha \equiv 0; \; B_z = B_z(r,z) \qquad 5.4$$

From the preceding equations it becomes obvious that the plane (r,z) was chosen as rotated plane.

(a) Electric field

Now let us write equations 2.1 and 2.4 in the valid form for the axially symmetric coordinate system

$$E_r = -\frac{\partial \varphi}{\partial r} \qquad 5.5$$

$$E_\alpha = -\frac{1}{r}\frac{\partial \varphi}{\partial \alpha} \equiv 0 \qquad 5.6$$

$$E_z = -\frac{\partial \varphi}{\partial z} \qquad 5.7$$

$$\frac{1}{r}\frac{\partial}{\partial r}\left(r\frac{\partial \varphi}{\partial r}\right) + \frac{1}{r^2}\frac{\partial^2 \varphi}{\partial \alpha^2} + \frac{\partial^2 \varphi}{\partial z^2} = -\frac{1}{\varepsilon_0}\varrho \qquad 5.8$$

Since the components of the electric field follow from the derivatives with respect to the variables of the potential function, the potential is necessarily a function of two variables

$$\varphi = \varphi(r,z) \qquad\qquad 5.9$$

Thus it follows from equation 2.4 and the second term of equation 5.2 that space-charge is also a function of two variables

$$\varrho = \varrho(r,z) \qquad\qquad 5.10$$

In the present case equation 5.8 takes the following form

$$\frac{\partial^2 \varphi}{\partial r^2} + \frac{1}{r}\frac{\partial \varphi}{\partial r} + \frac{\partial^2 \varphi}{\partial z^2} = -\frac{1}{\varepsilon_0}\varrho \qquad\qquad 5.11$$

The field-strength components are according to equations 5.5, 5.6 and 5.7.

(b) Magnetic field

In order to find the specific form of the vector potential and the current density vector, let us write equations 2.5, 2.8 and 2.6 in their coordinate form

$$B_r = \frac{1}{r}\frac{\partial A_z}{\partial \alpha} - \frac{\partial A_\alpha}{\partial z} \qquad\qquad 5.12$$

$$B_\alpha = \frac{\partial A_r}{\partial z} - \frac{\partial A_z}{\partial r} \qquad\qquad 5.13$$

$$B_z = \frac{1}{r}\frac{\partial}{\partial r}(rA_\alpha) - \frac{1}{r}\frac{\partial A_r}{\partial \alpha} \qquad\qquad 5.14$$

$$\frac{1}{r}\frac{\partial}{\partial \alpha}\left(\frac{1}{r}\frac{\partial}{\partial r}(rA_\alpha) - \frac{1}{r}\frac{\partial A_r}{\partial \alpha}\right) - \frac{\partial}{\partial z}\left(\frac{\partial A_r}{\partial z} - \frac{\partial A_r}{\partial z}\right) = \mu_0 j_r \qquad\qquad 5.15$$

$$\frac{\partial}{\partial z}\left(\frac{1}{r}\frac{\partial A_z}{\partial \alpha} - \frac{\partial A_\alpha}{\partial z}\right) - \frac{\partial}{\partial r}\left(\frac{1}{r}\frac{\partial}{\partial r}(rA_\alpha) - \frac{1}{r}\frac{\partial A_r}{\partial \alpha}\right) = \mu_0 j_\alpha \qquad\qquad 5.16$$

$$\frac{1}{r}\frac{\partial}{\partial r}\left(r\frac{\partial A_r}{\partial z} - r\frac{\partial A_z}{\partial r}\right) - \frac{1}{r}\frac{\partial}{\partial \alpha}\left(\frac{1}{r}\frac{\partial A_z}{\partial \alpha} - \frac{\partial A_\alpha}{\partial z}\right) = \mu_0 j_z \qquad\qquad 5.17$$

$$\frac{1}{r}\frac{\partial}{\partial r}(rA_r) + \frac{1}{r}\frac{\partial A_\alpha}{\partial \alpha} + \frac{\partial A_z}{\partial z} = 0 \qquad\qquad 5.18$$

Due to the second term of equation 5.4, and to the independency of α (first and third terms of 5.4)

$$B_\alpha = \frac{\partial A_r}{\partial z} - \frac{\partial A_z}{\partial r} \equiv 0 \qquad 5.19$$

$$0 = \mu_0 j_r \qquad 5.20$$

$$\frac{\partial}{\partial z}\left(\frac{1}{r}\frac{\partial A_z}{\partial \alpha} - \frac{\partial A_\alpha}{\partial z}\right) - \frac{\partial}{\partial r}\left(\frac{1}{r}\frac{\partial}{\partial r}(rA_z) - \frac{1}{r}\frac{\partial A_r}{\partial \alpha}\right) = \mu_0 j_\alpha \qquad 5.21$$

$$0 = \mu_0 j_z \qquad 5.22$$

$$\frac{1}{r}\frac{\partial}{\partial r}(rA_r) + \frac{1}{r}\frac{\partial A_\alpha}{\partial \alpha} + \frac{\partial A_z}{\partial z} = 0 \qquad 5.23$$

Since $B_\alpha \equiv 0$ and it is a rotational component

$$B_\alpha = (\operatorname{curl} \mathbf{A})_\alpha \equiv 0 \qquad 5.24$$

therefore A_r and A_z may be given as the gradient of (potential) function N^*

$$A_r = \frac{\partial N^*}{\partial r} \qquad 5.25$$

$$A_z = \frac{\partial N^*}{\partial z} \qquad 5.26$$

Considering equation 5.24

$$B_\alpha = (\operatorname{curl} \mathbf{A})_\alpha = (\operatorname{curl} \operatorname{grad} N^*)_\alpha \equiv 0 \qquad 5.27$$

which forms a part of an identity of the vector analysis: the first component of the vectorial identity. Equation 5.27 may be derived also on the basis of *Young's* theorem

$$B_\alpha = \frac{\partial}{\partial z}\frac{\partial N^*}{\partial r} - \frac{\partial}{\partial r}\frac{\partial N^*}{\partial z} \equiv 0 \qquad 5.28$$

since the mixed second-order partial derivatives are equal to each other.

However, according to equation 2.11, owing to the arbitrary state of ψ, function N^* may be chosen so that

$$N^* \equiv 0 \qquad 5.29$$

This requirement demands the following conditions relative to ψ

$$\frac{\partial \psi}{\partial r} = -C_r - A_{0r} \qquad 5.30$$

$$\frac{\partial \psi}{\partial z} = -C_z - A_{0z} \qquad 5.31$$

The conditions 5.30 and 5.31 are in harmony with equation 2.17. Since N^* equals zero, A_r and A_z are likewise identical with zero

$$A_r \equiv 0; \qquad A_z \equiv 0 \tag{5.32}$$

Using this the final results are

$$B_r(r,z) = -\frac{\partial A_\alpha}{\partial z}; \qquad B_\alpha \equiv 0; \qquad B_z(r,z) = \frac{\partial A_\alpha}{\partial r} + \frac{1}{r} A_\alpha \tag{5.33}$$

$$j_r \equiv 0; \qquad j_\alpha = j_\alpha(r,z); \qquad j_z \equiv 0 \tag{5.34}$$

$$A_r \equiv 0; \quad A_\alpha = A_\alpha(r,z); \quad A_z \equiv 0 \tag{5.35}$$

$$\frac{\partial^2 A_\alpha}{\partial r^2} + \frac{1}{r}\frac{\partial A_\alpha}{\partial r} - \frac{1}{r^2} A_\alpha + \frac{\partial^2 A_\alpha}{\partial z^2} = -\mu_0 j_\alpha \tag{5.36}$$

It is seen therefore that *the vector potential and the current-density vector have only one component each,* and these components are dependent only on two variables.

The characteristics discussed in the above refer to the most general case of axially symmetric fields. It will be seen later that further prescriptions are to be used for practical applications.

Finally we must draw attention to an important fact following from the results obtained: *a field of the discussed structural properties may obviously only be produced by the specific excitations derived.*

We shall present the prescriptions to be used for practical applications, and these will be justified when discussing the equations of motion. Prescriptions relative to the electric field (see equations 5.2, 5.9, 5.10)

$$\varrho(r,z) = \varrho(-r,z) \tag{5.37}$$

$$\varphi(r,z) = \varphi(-r,z) \tag{5.38}$$

$$E_r(r,z) = -E_r(-r,z); \quad E_\alpha(r,z) \equiv 0; \quad E_z(r,z) = E_z(-r,z) \tag{5.39}$$

Prescriptions relevant to the magnetic field (see equations 5.33, 5.34 and 5.35)

$$j_r(r,z) \equiv 0; j_\alpha(r,z) = -j_\alpha(-r,z); \ j_z(r,z) \equiv 0 \tag{5.40}$$

$$A_r(r,z) \equiv 0; A_\alpha(r,z) = -A_\alpha(-r,z); A_z(r,z) \equiv 0 \tag{5.41}$$

$$B_r(r,z) = -B_r(r,z); B_\alpha(r,z) \equiv 0; B_z(r,z) = B_z(-r,z) \tag{5.42}$$

The prescriptions are simple: they determine the even or odd parity of the field characteristics.

The variable r cannot assume a negative value in the cylindrical coordinate system. Thus the prescriptions given are suitable only for the determination of the forms of the series. When discussing the equations of motion, however, it will be seen that by the introduction of the concept of the meridian plane, the negative values of variable r are also introduced.

3*

(c) The series of the axially symmetric electric field

Using the method of power series expansion as described in § 4, we determine the specific structure of the solution of equation 5.11, taking into account equations 5.37 and 5.38.

The coefficients of the pertaining power series are calculated from the space-charge distribution assumed as known (or given).

The origin of the space-charge distribution under discussion may be arbitrary (but only axially symmetric). Consideration may be given to the electron beam's own space-charge, since this also excites axially symmetric field-strength distribution. The following series appears as the final result of the calculation

$$\varrho(r,z) = \varrho_0 + \varrho_2 r^2 + \varrho_4 r^4 + \ldots = \sum_{\nu=0}^{\infty} \varrho_{2\nu} r^{2\nu} \qquad 5.43$$

In equation 5.43 the coefficients are functions of z

$$\varrho_{2\nu} = \varrho_{2\nu}(z) \qquad 5.44$$

The unknown potential distribution is obtained with the help of a power series

$$\varphi(r,z) = \varPhi_0 + \varPhi_2 r^2 + \varPhi_4 r^4 + \ldots = \sum_{\nu=0}^{\infty} \varPhi_{2\nu} r^{2\nu} \qquad 5.45$$

In equation 5.45 the unknown coefficients are functions of z

$$\varPhi_{2\nu} = \varPhi_{2\nu}(z) \qquad 5.46$$

The potential values measurable in the points of axis z are called the axis potential

$$\varphi(0,z) = \varPhi_0(z) \qquad 5.47$$

Relations exist between the coefficients $\varPhi_{2\nu}$ in equation 5.46. For elucidation of these relations, we shall determine the derivatives appearing in equation 5.11, from equation 5.45

$$\frac{1}{r}\frac{\partial \varphi}{\partial r} = \sum_{\nu=1}^{\infty} 2\nu \varPhi_{2\nu} r^{2\nu-2} \qquad 5.48$$

$$\frac{\partial^2 \varphi}{\partial r^2} = \sum_{\nu=1}^{\infty} 2\nu(2\nu-1)\varPhi_{2\nu} r^{2\nu-2} \qquad 5.49$$

$$\frac{\partial^2 \varphi}{\partial r^2} = \sum_{\nu=0}^{\infty} \varPhi_{2\nu}'' r^{2\nu} \qquad 5.50$$

We substitute now equations 5.43, 5.48, 5.49 and 5.50 into equation 5.11. After rearrangement, the following is obtained

$$\sum_{\nu=1}^{\infty}\left[4\nu^2\Phi_{2\nu} + \Phi''_{2\nu-2} + \frac{1}{\varepsilon_0}\varrho_{2\nu-2}\right]r^{2\nu-2} = 0 \qquad\qquad 5.51$$

Identity 5.51 can be satisfied only if the coefficient of each power of r is chosen as zero. Hence the following recursive relation is obtained

$$\Phi_{2\nu} = -\frac{1}{4\nu^2}\left(\Phi''_{2\nu-2} + \frac{1}{\varepsilon_0}\varrho_{2\nu-2}\right) \qquad \nu = 1, 2 \ldots \qquad 5.52$$

The relations between the coefficients $\Phi_{2\nu}$ of equation 5.52 can now be determined in an indirect manner. Direct determination is possible by means of the following formula (from 5.52, by successive substitution into the same equation)

$$\Phi_{2\nu} = (-1)^{\nu}\frac{1}{2^{2\nu}(\nu!)^2}\left\{\Phi_0^{(2\nu)} + \frac{1}{\varepsilon_0}\sum_{\mu=1}^{\nu}(-1)^{\nu-\mu}\times\right.$$

$$\left.\times 2^{2(\nu-\mu)}[(\nu-\mu)!]^2\varrho_{2\nu-2\mu}^{(2\mu-2)}\right\} \qquad \nu = 1, 2 \ldots \qquad 5.53$$

According to formula 5.53 which gives the relations between the coefficients, any of the coefficients can be expressed by Φ_0. Therefore, it will be understood that a special name (axis potential) has been allotted to function Φ_0.
Using equation 5.53, the potential distribution 5.45 alters as follows

$$\varphi(r,z) = \sum_{\nu=0}^{\infty}\frac{(-1)^{\nu}}{(\nu!)^2}\left\{\Phi_0^{(2\nu)} + \frac{1}{\varepsilon_0}\sum_{\mu=1}^{\nu}(-1)^{\nu-\mu}\times\right.$$

$$\left.\times 2^{2(\nu-\mu)}[(\nu-\mu)!]^2\varrho_{2\nu-2\mu}^{(2\mu-2)}\right\}\left(\frac{r}{2}\right)^{2\nu} = \Phi_0 - \frac{1}{4}\left(\Phi_0'' + \frac{1}{\varepsilon_0}\varrho_0\right)r^2 +$$

$$+\frac{1}{64}\left[\Phi_0^{(IV)} + \frac{1}{\varepsilon_0}(\varrho_0'' - 4\varrho_2)\right]r^4 - \frac{1}{2304}\left[\Phi_0^{(VI)} +\right.$$

$$\left.+\frac{1}{\varepsilon_0}(\varrho_0^{(IV)} - 4\varrho_2'' + 64\varrho_4)\right]r^6 + \ldots \qquad\qquad 5.54$$

The convention

$$\sum_{\mu=1}^{0}a_{\mu} = 0 \qquad\qquad 5.55$$

appears in 5.54, showing that zero value is assumed for the sum without terms [40, 41, 49].

With the help of equation 5.54 the potential may be calculated at any arbitrary point if Φ_0 is known ($\varrho_{2\nu}$ and the derivatives are given).

The field-strength components in the field under discussion can be calculated from equations 5.5 and 5.7

$$E(r,z) = \sum_{\nu=1}^{\infty} \frac{(-1)^{\nu+1}}{(\nu!)^2} \left\{ \Phi_0^{(2\nu)} + \frac{1}{\varepsilon_0} \sum_{\mu=1}^{\nu} (-1)^{\nu-\mu} \times \right.$$

$$\left. \times\, 2^{2(\nu-\mu)} \left[(\nu-\mu)!\right]^2 \varrho_{2\nu-2\mu}^{(2\mu-2)} \right\} \left(\frac{r}{2} \right)^{2\nu-1} = \frac{1}{2} \left(\Phi_0'' + \frac{1}{\varepsilon_0} \varrho_0 \right) r -$$

$$- \frac{1}{16} \left[\Phi_0^{(IV)} + \frac{1}{\varepsilon_0} (\varrho_0'' - 4\varrho_2) \right] r^3 + \frac{1}{384} \left[\Phi_0^{(VI)} + \frac{1}{\varepsilon_0} (\varrho_0^{(IV)} - \right.$$

$$\left. - 4\varrho_2'' + 64\varrho_4) \right] r^5 - \ldots \tag{5.56}$$

$$E_z(r,z) = \sum_{\nu=0}^{\infty} \frac{(-1)^{\nu+1}}{(\nu!)^2} \left\{ \Phi_0^{(2\nu+1)} + \frac{1}{\varepsilon_0} \sum_{\mu=0}^{\nu} (-1)^{\nu-\mu} \times \right.$$

$$\left. \times\, 2^{2(\nu-\mu)} \left[(\nu-\mu)!\right]^2 \varrho_{2\nu-2\mu}^{(2\mu-1)} \right\} \left(\frac{r}{2} \right)^{2\nu} = -\Phi_0' + \frac{1}{4} \left(\Phi_0''' + \frac{1}{\varepsilon_0} \varrho_0' \right) r^2 -$$

$$- \frac{1}{64} \left[\Phi_0^{(V)} + \frac{1}{\varepsilon_0} (\varrho_0''' - 4\varrho_2') \right] r^4 + \ldots \tag{5.57}$$

It can be seen that equation 5.56 satisfies the first term of 5.39 and equation 5.57 satisfies the third term of 5.39.

(d) Series of the axially symmetric magnetic field

Using the method of power series expansion as described in §4, we determine the specific structure of the solution of the homogeneous equation pertaining to equation 5.36, taking into account the second term of equation 5.41.

Excited by suitable current-density distribution, or a permanent magnet, the vector potential field is considered as given. *The current-density distribution of the investigated electron beam itself cannot be taken into consideration, since this does not excite axially symmetric induction distribution.* Moreover, in the classical case this may be omitted.

The vector potential distribution is given with the help of a power series

$$A_\alpha(r,z) = \alpha_1 r + \alpha_3 r^3 + \ldots = \sum_{\nu=0}^{\infty} \alpha_{2\nu+1} r^{2\nu+1} \tag{5.58}$$

In equation 5.58 the unknown coefficients are functions of z

$$\alpha_{2v+1} = \alpha_{2v+1}(z) \qquad 5.59$$

The double amount of the function α_1 *is called the axis induction* (this notation will be verified later)

$$2\alpha_1(z) = B_0(z) \qquad 5.60$$

Relations exist between the coefficients α_{2v+1} of equation 5.58 and for elucidation, the derivatives (and other functions) appearing in equation 5.36 are determined from 5.58

$$\frac{A_\alpha}{r^2} = \sum_{v=0}^{\infty} \alpha_{2v+1} r^{2v-1} \qquad 5.61$$

$$\frac{1}{r} \frac{\partial A_\alpha}{\partial r} = \sum_{v=0}^{\infty} (2v+1)\alpha_{2v+1} r^{2v-1} \qquad 5.62$$

$$\frac{\partial^2 A_\alpha}{\partial r^2} = \sum_{v=1}^{\infty} 2v(2v+1)\alpha_{2v+1} r^{2v-1} \qquad 5.63$$

$$\frac{\partial^2 A_\alpha}{\partial z^2} = \sum_{v=0}^{\infty} \alpha''_{2v+1} r^{2v+1} \qquad 5.64$$

Equations 5.61, 5.62, 5.63 and 5.64 are now substituted into the homogeneous equation pertaining to 5.36. After arranging, we obtain

$$\frac{\alpha_1}{r} - \frac{\alpha_1}{r} + \sum_{v=1}^{\infty} [4v(v+1)\alpha_{2v+1} + \alpha''_{2v-1}]r^{2v-1} \equiv 0 \qquad 5.65$$

Identity 5.65 is satisfied when the coefficients of all powers of r are chosen as equal to zero. Thereby, the following recursion relation is obtained

$$\alpha_{2v+1} = -\frac{1}{4v(v+1)} \alpha''_{2v-1} \qquad 5.66$$

The relations existing between the coefficients α_{2v+1} can be determined in an indirect manner from equation 5.66. Direct determination is possible with the following formula (similarly to 5.53)

$$\alpha_{2v+1} = \frac{(-1)^v}{2^{2v}v!(v+1)!} \alpha_1^{(2v)}, \quad v = 1, 2, \ldots \qquad 5.67$$

Substituting equation 5.60 into equation 5.67

$$\alpha_{2v+1} = \frac{(-1)^v}{2^{2v+1}v!(v+1)!} B_0^{(2v)}, \quad v = 1, 2, \ldots \qquad 5.68$$

According to formula 5.68 for the relation between the coefficients, any coefficient can be expressed by B_0. Thus, it can be readily understood that we have given the function B_0 a special name: axis induction.

Using equation 5.68, the vector-potential distribution 5.58 is modified in the following way

$$A_\alpha(r, z) = \sum_{v=0}^{\infty} \frac{(-1)^v}{v!(v+1)!} B_0^{(2v)} \left(\frac{r}{2}\right)^{2v+1} =$$

$$= \frac{1}{2} B_0 r - \frac{1}{16} B_0'' r^3 + \frac{1}{384} B_0^{(IV)} r^5 - \dots \qquad 5.69$$

By means of equation 5.69 and knowing B_0, the vector potential can be calculated for any given point.

In the field under discussion the induction components can be calculated from the first and third equations of 5.33

$$B_r(r, z) = \sum_{v=0}^{\infty} \frac{(-1)^{v+1}}{v!(v+1)!} B_0^{(2v+1)} \left(\frac{r}{2}\right)^{2v+1} =$$

$$= -\frac{1}{2} B_0' r + \frac{1}{16} B_0''' r^3 - \frac{1}{384} B_0^{(V)} r^5 + \dots \qquad 5.70$$

$$B_z(r, z) = \sum_{v=0}^{\infty} \frac{(-1)^v}{(v!)^2} B_0^{(2v)} \left(\frac{r}{2}\right)^{2v} =$$

$$= B_0 - \frac{1}{4} B_0'' r^2 + \frac{1}{64} B_0^{(IV)} r^4 - \dots \qquad 5.71$$

If, using equation 5.71, we let

$$B_z(0, z) = B_0(z) \qquad 5.72$$

then not only the separate naming but also the choice of the name allotted to B_0 will become clear: *the axis induction contains the values of the induction distribution measurable in the points of the axis z*: namely, the component $B_r(0, z)$ equals zero in all points of the axis.

It can be seen that 5.70 satisfies the first equation of 5.42, while 5.71 satisfies the third equation of 5.42

In the following, in order to economise on the indices, some of those introduced in the foregoing will be omitted. We shall write $A(r, z)$ in place of $A_\alpha(r, z)$, $j(r, z)$ in place of $j_\alpha(r, z)$, $\Phi(z)$ in place of $\Phi_0(z)$ and $B(z)$ in place of $B_0(z)$.

Note: Equation 5.11 is valid for all points of the field in the case of an axially symmetric electric field. At the points of the axis of rotation, however, this cannot be used for approximative calculations since the second term would become meaningless. We determine a more simple form of equation 5.11, in which the previous limit value is already calculated and is suitable for approximative calculations [72].

Let us now observe equation 5.54, and produce successively the differential expressions in the first two terms of equation 5.11

$$\frac{\partial \varphi}{\partial r} = -\frac{1}{2}\left(\Phi_0'' + \frac{1}{\varepsilon_0}\varrho_0\right) r + \dots \tag{5.73}$$

$$\frac{1}{r}\frac{\partial \varphi}{\partial r} = -\frac{1}{2}\left(\Phi_0'' + \frac{1}{\varepsilon_0}\varrho_0\right) + \dots \tag{5.74}$$

$$\frac{\partial^2 \varphi}{\partial r^2} = -\frac{1}{2}\left(\Phi_0'' + \frac{1}{\varepsilon_0}\varrho_0\right) + \dots \tag{5.75}$$

Let us determine the limits of equations 5.74 and 5.75 at the points $r = 0$

$$\frac{1}{r}\frac{\partial \varphi}{\partial r}\bigg|_{r=0} = -\frac{1}{2}\left(\Phi_0'' + \frac{1}{\varepsilon_0}\varrho_0\right) \tag{5.76}$$

$$\frac{\partial^2 \varphi}{\partial r^2}\bigg|_{r=0} = -\frac{1}{2}\left(\Phi_0'' + \frac{1}{\varepsilon_0}\varrho_0\right) \tag{5.77}$$

It will be seen that on the axis

$$\frac{1}{r}\frac{\partial \varphi}{\partial r}\bigg|_{r=0} = \frac{\partial^2 \varphi}{\partial r^2}\bigg|_{r=0} \tag{5.78}$$

Thus, *Poisson's* equation in the points along the axis (in the place of $r = 0$)

$$2\frac{\partial^2 \varphi}{\partial r^2} + \frac{\partial^2 \varphi}{\partial z^2} = -\frac{1}{\varepsilon_0}\varrho \tag{5.79}$$

6. DERIVATION OF AXIALLY SYMMETRIC INDUCTION DISTRIBUTION FROM THE FLUX FUNCTION

In order to facilitate an approximative calculation of the magnetic field, the field may be derived in a manner differing from the previously known method.

The vector potential given for calculation of the induction distribution satisfies equation 5.36. The same induction distribution may be derived also from the flux function, in the following manner [28, 81].

The flux function in case of axially symmetric induction distribution

$$\Psi = \int_F \mathbf{B} \cdot d\mathbf{f} = 2\pi \int_0^r r B_z dr \tag{6.1}$$

Differentiating equation 6.1

$$\frac{\partial \Psi}{\partial r} = 2\pi r B_z \tag{6.2}$$

$$\frac{\partial \Psi}{\partial z} = 2\pi \int_0^r r \frac{\partial B_z}{\partial z} dr \tag{6.3}$$

Equation 1.4 in cylindrical coordinates in case of axially symmetric induction distribution

$$\frac{\partial B_z}{\partial z} = -\frac{1}{r}\frac{\partial}{\partial r}(rB_r) \qquad 6.4$$

Substituting equation 6.4 into 6.3

$$\frac{\partial \Psi}{\partial z} = -2\pi \int_0^r \frac{\partial}{\partial r}(rB_r)dr = -2\pi rB_r \qquad 6.5$$

Differentiating equation 6.2

$$\frac{\partial^2 \Psi}{\partial r^2} = 2\pi B_z + 2\pi r \frac{\partial B_z}{\partial r} \qquad 6.6$$

Expressing B_z from equation 6.2 and substituting into 6.6

$$\frac{\partial^2 \Psi}{\partial r^2} = \frac{1}{r}\frac{\partial \Psi}{\partial r} + 2\pi r \frac{\partial B_z}{\partial r} \qquad 6.7$$

Differentiating equation 6.5

$$\frac{\partial^2 \Psi}{\partial z^2} = -2\pi r \frac{\partial B_r}{\partial z} \qquad 6.8$$

Summing equations 6.7 and 6.8

$$\frac{\partial^2 \Psi}{\partial r^2} + \frac{\partial^2 \Psi}{\partial z^2} = \frac{1}{r}\frac{\partial \Psi}{\partial r} + 2\pi r \left(\frac{\partial B_z}{\partial r} - \frac{\partial B_r}{\partial z}\right) \qquad 6.9$$

Equation 1.3 in cylindrical coordinates, in the case of axially symmetric induction distribution

$$\frac{\partial B_r}{\partial z} - \frac{\partial B_z}{\partial r} = \mu_0 j_\alpha \qquad 6.10$$

Substituting equation 6.10 into 6.9 and rearranging

$$\frac{\partial^2 \Psi}{\partial r^2} - \frac{1}{r}\frac{\partial \Psi}{\partial r} + \frac{\partial^2 \Psi}{\partial z^2} = -2\pi\mu_0 r j_\alpha \qquad 6.11$$

Equation 6.11 is the differential equation of the flux function. It is practical to use this equation mainly for approximative calculations since it is simpler in structure than the vector-potential differential equation. The relation between the flux function and the vector potential is simple

$$\Psi = \int_F \mathbf{B}\cdot df = \int_F \operatorname{curl}\mathbf{A}\cdot df = \int_L \mathbf{A}\cdot dl = 2\pi rA_\alpha \qquad 6.12$$

It can be established from the above that

$$\Psi(0, z) = 0 \tag{6.13}$$

$$\Psi(r, z) = \Psi(-r, z) \tag{6.14}$$

7. FIELDS WITH PLANAR DISTRIBUTION

The basic property of fields with planar distribution, according to conventions, is that in a suitably chosen coordinate system the vectors of both the electric and magnetic fields can be given by two components for any plane parallel to the chosen coordinate plane. In other words: *the full pattern of the lines of force in planes parallel with the chosen basic plane remains unaltered.* It is required also that *the entire field should be independent of the variable pertaining to the axis perpendicular to the basic plane* (the force patterns of planes parallel to the basic plane are projected perpendicularly and not obliquely). Choosing the rectangular Cartesian coordinate system

$$\mathbf{E} = E_x \mathbf{e}_x + E_y \mathbf{e}_y + E_z \mathbf{e}_z \tag{7.1}$$

$$E_x \equiv 0; \ E_y = E_y(y, z); \ E_z = E_z(y, z) \tag{7.2}$$

$$\mathbf{B} = B_x \mathbf{e}_x + B_y \mathbf{e}_y + B_z \mathbf{e}_z \tag{7.3}$$

$$B_x \equiv 0; \ B_y = B(y, z); \ B_z = B_z(y, z) \tag{7.4}$$

From the foregoing it can be seen that plane (y,z) was chosen as the basic plane.

(a) Electric field

The components of the electric field follow from the derivatives with respect to the variables of the potential function; therefore the potential may be a function of two variables only

$$\varphi = \varphi(y, z) \tag{7.5}$$

From equation 2.4 and the first equation of 7.2 it follows that the space-charge is also a function of two variables

$$\varrho = \varrho(y, z) \tag{7.6}$$

In the present case equation 2.4 takes the following form

$$\frac{\partial^2 \varphi}{\partial y^2} + \frac{\partial^2 \varphi}{\partial z^2} = -\frac{1}{\varepsilon_0} \varrho \tag{7.7}$$

The components of the field strength are

$$E_y(y, z) = -\frac{\partial \varphi}{\partial y} \tag{7.8}$$

$$E_z(y, z) = -\frac{\partial \varphi}{\partial z} \tag{7.9}$$

(b) Magnetic field

In order to obtain the special form of the vector potential and the current-density vector, we write equations 2.5, 2.8 and 2.6 in their coordinate forms

$$B_x = \frac{\partial A_z}{\partial y} - \frac{\partial A_y}{\partial z} \tag{7.10}$$

$$B_y = \frac{\partial A_x}{\partial z} - \frac{\partial A_z}{\partial x} \tag{7.11}$$

$$B_z = \frac{\partial A_y}{\partial x} - \frac{\partial A_x}{\partial y} \tag{7.12}$$

$$\frac{\partial}{\partial y}\left(\frac{\partial A_y}{\partial x} - \frac{\partial A_x}{\partial y}\right) - \frac{\partial}{\partial z}\left(\frac{\partial A_x}{\partial z} - \frac{\partial A_z}{\partial x}\right) = \mu_0 j_x \tag{7.13}$$

$$\frac{\partial}{\partial z}\left(\frac{\partial A_z}{\partial y} - \frac{\partial A_y}{\partial z}\right) - \frac{\partial}{\partial x}\left(\frac{\partial A_y}{\partial x} - \frac{\partial A_x}{\partial y}\right) = \mu_0 j_y \tag{7.14}$$

$$\frac{\partial}{\partial x}\left(\frac{\partial A_x}{\partial z} - \frac{\partial A_z}{\partial x}\right) - \frac{\partial}{\partial y}\left(\frac{\partial A_z}{\partial y} - \frac{\partial A_y}{\partial z}\right) = \mu_0 j_z \tag{7.15}$$

$$\frac{\partial A_x}{\partial x} + \frac{\partial A_y}{\partial y} + \frac{\partial A_z}{\partial z} = 0 \tag{7.16}$$

Due to the first equation of 7.4 and to the independency of x (second and third equations of 7.4)

$$B_x = \frac{\partial A_z}{\partial y} - \frac{\partial A_y}{\partial z} = 0 \tag{7.17}$$

$$\frac{\partial}{\partial y}\left(\frac{\partial A_y}{\partial x} - \frac{\partial A_x}{\partial y}\right) - \frac{\partial}{\partial z}\left(\frac{\partial A_x}{\partial z} - \frac{\partial A_z}{\partial x}\right) = \mu_0 j_x \tag{7.18}$$

$$0 = \mu_0 j_y \tag{7.19}$$

$$0 = \mu_0 j_z \tag{7.20}$$

$$\frac{\partial A_x}{\partial x} + \frac{\partial A_y}{\partial y} + \frac{\partial A_z}{\partial z} = 0 \qquad\qquad 7.21$$

In accordance with the method followed in case of axially symmetric systems and with regard to the first term of equation 7.4, a potential function N is introduced for derivation of A_y and A_z. Here, too, it is true that due to equation 2.11 N may be chosen identical to zero, prescribing the following requirements for function ψ of equation 2.11

$$\frac{\partial \psi}{\partial y} = - C_y - A_{0y} \qquad\qquad 7.22$$

$$\frac{\partial \psi}{\partial z} = - C_z - A_{0z} \qquad\qquad 7.23$$

The conditions 7.22 and 7.23, as confirmed by differentiation, are in harmony with equation 2.17.

By choosing function N identical to zero, A_y and A_z are also identically zero

$$A_y \equiv 0; \quad A_z \equiv 0 \qquad\qquad 7.24$$

Using 7.24, the final results are as follows

$$B_x \equiv 0; \quad B_y(y, z) = \frac{\partial A_x}{\partial z}; \quad B(y, z) = - \frac{\partial A_x}{\partial y} \qquad 7.25$$

$$j_x = j_x(y, z); \quad j_y \equiv 0; \quad j_z \equiv 0 \qquad\qquad 7.26$$

$$A_x = A_x(y, z); \quad A_y \equiv 0; \quad A_z \equiv 0 \qquad\qquad 7.27$$

$$\frac{\partial^2 A_x}{\partial y^2} + \frac{\partial^2 A_x}{\partial z^2} = - \mu_0 j_x \qquad\qquad 7.28$$

From the final results it is clear that *both the vector potential and the current-density vector have only one component each.* These components are dependent on two variables only.

The characteristics discussed in the foregoing also refer to the most general cases of fields with planar distribution. It will be seen that further prescriptions are used for practical applications.

From these results it follows that: *the field with the discussed structural properties may be produced only by means of the specific excitations derived.*

(c) Plane-symmetric electric and magnetic fields

The plane-symmetric electric and magnetic fields belong to the fields with planar distribution. They are characterised by mirror symmetry with respect to the plane (x, z) perpendicular to the basic plane (y, z).

When discussing equations of motion, the prescriptions to be used in practical applications will be justified. The determining prescriptions referring to the electric field (see equations 7.2, 7.5 and 7.6)

$$\varrho(y, z) = \varrho(-y, z) \tag{7.29}$$

$$\varphi(y, z) = \varphi(-y, z) \tag{7.30}$$

$$E_x(y, z) \equiv 0; \quad E_y(y, z) = -E_y(-y, z); \quad E_z(y, z) = E_z(-y, z) \tag{7.31}$$

Determining prescriptions referring to the magnetic field (see equations 7.4, 7.26 and 7.27)

$$j_x(y, z) = -j_x(-y, z); \quad j_y(y, z) \equiv 0; \quad j_z(y, z) \equiv 0 \tag{7.32}$$

$$A_x(y, z) = -A_x(-y, z); \quad A_y(y, z) \equiv 0; \quad A_z(y, z) \equiv 0 \tag{7.33}$$

$$B_x(y, z) \equiv 0; \quad B_y(y, z) = -B_y(-y, z); \quad B_z(y, z) = B_z(-y, z) \tag{7.34}$$

The prescriptions give even or odd parity of the field characteristics.

(d) The series of the plane-symmetric electric field

Similarly to the case of the axially symmetric field, it is necessary to determine the series structure satisfying equation 7.7. Equations 7.29 and 7.30 must be taken into consideration.

The coefficients of the respective power series are calculated from the space-charge distribution assumed as known (given).

The origin of the space-charge distribution under discussion may be arbitrary. The space-charge of the investigated electron beam may be taken into consideration since this also excites plane-symmetric field-strength distribution. As the final result, the following series appears

$$\varrho(y, z) = \varrho_0 + \varrho_2 y^2 + \varrho_4 y^4 + \ldots = \sum_{\nu=0}^{\infty} \varrho_{2\nu} y^{2\nu} \tag{7.35}$$

In equation 7.35 the coefficients are functions of z

$$\varrho_{2\nu} = \varrho_{2\nu}(z) \tag{7.36}$$

The power series of the potential distribution

$$\varphi(y, z) = \Phi_0 + \Phi_2 y^2 + \Phi_4 y^4 + \ldots = \sum_{\nu=0}^{\infty} \Phi_{2\nu} y^{2\nu} \tag{7.37}$$

In equation 7.37 the unknown coefficients are also functions of z

$$\Phi_{2\nu} = \Phi_{2\nu}(z) \tag{7.38}$$

The potential values measurable in the points of axis z are termed the axis potential, as in the case of axial symmetry

$$\varphi(0, z) = \Phi_0(z) \qquad 7.39$$

Relations exist between the coefficients $\Phi_{2\nu}$ in equation 7.37. The relations are determined by the method used in the case of axial symmetry. Finally, the following recursion relations are obtained

$$\Phi_{2\nu} = -\frac{1}{2\nu(2\nu - 1)}\left(\Phi''_{2\nu-2} + \frac{1}{\varepsilon_0}\varrho_{2\nu-2}\right), \quad \nu = 1, 2, \ldots \qquad 7.40$$

Relations between the coefficients $\Phi_{2\nu}$ of equation 7.40 can be established indirectly. The direct determination possible by means of the following formula (see 5.53 as an example)

$$\Phi_{2\nu} = (-1)^\nu \frac{1}{(2\nu)!}\left\{\Phi_0^{(2\nu)} + \right.$$

$$\left. + \frac{1}{\varepsilon_0}\sum_{\mu=1}^\nu (-1)^{\nu-\mu}(2\nu - 2\mu)!\, \varrho_{2\nu-2\mu}^{(2\mu-2)}\right\}, \quad \nu = 1, 2, \ldots \qquad 7.41$$

Similarly to the case of axial symmetry, all coefficients may be expressed by Φ_0. The function Φ_0 is termed axis potential.

Using equation 7.41, the potential distribution 7.37 can be expressed as follows

$$\varphi(y, z) = \sum_{\nu=0}^\infty \frac{(-1)^\nu}{(2\nu)!}\left\{\Phi_0^{(2\nu)} + \frac{1}{\varepsilon_0}\sum_{\mu=1}^\nu (-1)^{\nu-\mu} \times\right.$$

$$\left. \times (2\nu - 2\mu)!\, \varrho_{2\nu-2\mu}^{(2\mu-2)}\right\} y^{2\nu} = \Phi_0 - \frac{1}{2}\left(\Phi''_0 + \frac{1}{\varepsilon_0}\varrho_0\right) y^2 +$$

$$+ \frac{1}{24}\left[\Phi_0^{(IV)} + \frac{1}{\varepsilon_0}(\varrho''_0 - 2\varrho_2)\right] y^4 - \frac{1}{720}\left[\Phi_0^{(VI)} + \right.$$

$$\left. + \frac{1}{\varepsilon_0}(\varrho_0^{(IV)} - 2\varrho''_2 + 24\varrho_4)\right] y^6 + \ldots \qquad 7.42$$

With the help of equation 7.42, the potential can be calculated at any point, provided that Φ_0 is known ($\varrho_{2\nu}$ and their derivatives are given).

The field-strength components in the plane-symmetric field discussed can be calculated from equations 7.8 and 7.9

$$E_y(y,z) = \sum_{\nu=1}^{\infty} \frac{(-1)^{\nu+1}}{(2\nu-1)!} \left\{ \Phi_0^{(2\nu)} + \frac{1}{\varepsilon_0} \sum_{\mu=1}^{\nu} (-1)^{\nu-\mu} \times \right.$$

$$\left. \times (2\nu - 2\mu)!\, \varrho_{2\nu-2\mu}^{(2\mu-2)} \right\} y^{2\nu-1} = \left(\Phi_0'' + \frac{1}{\varepsilon_0} \varrho_0 \right) y -$$

$$- \frac{1}{6} \left[\Phi_0^{(IV)} + \frac{1}{\varepsilon_0} (\varrho_0'' - 2\varrho_2) \right] y^3 + \frac{1}{120} \left[\Phi_0^{(VI)} + \right.$$

$$\left. + \frac{1}{\varepsilon_0} (\varrho_0^{(IV)} - 2\varrho_2'' + 24\varrho_4) \right] y^5 - \dots \qquad 7.43$$

$$E_z(y,z) = \sum_{\nu=0}^{\infty} \frac{(-1)^{\nu+1}}{(2\nu)!} \left\{ \Phi_0^{(2\nu+1)} + \frac{1}{\varepsilon_0} \sum_{\mu=1}^{\nu} (-1)^{\nu-\mu} \times \right.$$

$$\left. \times (2\nu - 2\mu)!\, \varrho_{2\nu-2\mu}^{(2\mu-1)} \right\} y^{2\nu} = - \Phi_0' + \frac{1}{2} \left(\Phi_0''' + \frac{1}{\varepsilon_0} \varrho_0' \right) y^2 -$$

$$- \frac{1}{24} \left[\Phi_0^{(V)} + \frac{1}{\varepsilon_0} (\varrho_0''' - 2\varrho_2') \right] y^4 + \frac{1}{720} \left[\Phi_0^{(VII)} + \right.$$

$$\left. + \frac{1}{\varepsilon_0} (\varrho_0^{(V)} - 2\varrho_2''' + 24\varrho_4') \right] y^6 - \dots \qquad 7.44$$

It can be seen that equation 7.43 satisfies the second term of 7.31, and equation 7.44 satisfies the third term of 7.31.

(e) The series of the plane-symmetric magnetic field

Taking the previously followed process as a pattern, and taking into account the first term of equation 7.33, we determine the structure necessary for the solution of the homogeneous equation pertaining to equation 7.28.

With excitation by appropriate current-density distribution, or permanent magnet, the vector potential field is considered as given. *The own current-density distribution of the investigated electron beam cannot be taken into consideration, since this does not excite plane-symmetric induction distribution.* In the classical case this, moreover, may be omitted.

The vector potential distribution is given with the help of a power series

$$A_x(y,z) = \alpha_1 y + \alpha_3 y^3 + \dots = \sum_{\nu=0}^{\infty} \alpha_{2\nu+1} y^{2\nu+1} \qquad 7.45$$

In equation 7.45 the unknown coefficients are functions of z

$$\alpha_{2\nu+1} = \alpha_{2\nu+1}(z) \qquad 7.46$$

Function α_1 multiplied by minus one is termed axis induction (this notation will be verified later)

$$- \alpha_1(z) = B_0(z) \qquad 7.47$$

The relations between the coefficients of equation 7.45 have been determined by the method used previously. We obtain the following

$$\alpha_{2\nu+1} = -\frac{1}{2\nu(2\nu+1)}\,\alpha''_{2\nu-1}, \qquad \nu = 1, 2, \ldots \qquad 7.48$$

The relations between the coefficients $\alpha_{2\nu+1}$ of equation 7.48 are determined indirectly. Formulae serving direct determination, by the standard method are as follows

$$\alpha_{2\nu+1} = (-1)^\nu \frac{1}{(2\nu+1)!}\,\alpha_1^{(2\nu)}, \qquad \nu = 1, 2, \ldots \qquad 7.49$$

$$\alpha_{2\nu+1} = (-1)^{\nu+1} \frac{1}{(2\nu+1)!}\,B_0^{(2\nu)}, \qquad \nu = 1, 2, \ldots \qquad 7.50$$

In accordance with equation 7.50 determining the relations between the coefficients, all the coefficients can be expressed by B_0. It is therefore obvious that we have given a separate name, axis induction, to function B_0.

Using equation 7.50, the form of the vector-potential distribution 7.45 is modified as follows

$$A_x(y, z) = \sum_{\nu=0}^{\infty} \frac{(-1)^{\nu+1}}{(2\nu+1)!}\,B_0^{(2\nu)}y^{2\nu+1} = -B_0 y + \frac{1}{6}\,B_0''y^3 -$$

$$-\frac{1}{120}\,B_0^{(IV)}y^5 + \ldots \qquad 7.51$$

With the help of equation 7.51 the vector potential can be calculated in any point if B_0 is known.

The induction components in the case of the plane-symmetric distribution can be calculated from the second and third terms of equation 7.25

$$B_y(y, z) = \sum_{\nu=0}^{\infty} \frac{(-1)^{\nu+1}}{(2\nu+1)!}\,B_0^{(2\nu+1)}y^{2\nu+1} = -B_0'y + \frac{1}{6}\,B_0''' y^3 -$$

$$-\frac{1}{120}\,B_0^{(V)}y^5 + \ldots \qquad 7.52$$

$$B_z(y, z) = \sum_{\nu=0}^{\infty} \frac{(-1)^\nu}{(2\nu)!}\cdot B_0^{(2\nu)}y^{2\nu} = B_0 - \frac{1}{2}\,B_0''y^2 +$$

$$+\frac{1}{24}\,B_0^{(IV)}y^4 - \ldots \qquad 7.53$$

As can be seen from 7.53

$$B_z(0, z) = B_0(z) \qquad 7.54$$

therefore not only the separate notation, but also the choice of the term will be found: *the axis induction contains the values of the induction distribution measurable in the points of the axis z*, namely, component $B_y (0, z)$ equals zero in all points of the axis z.

It can be seen that equation 7.52 satisfies the second term of equation 7.34, and equation 7.53 satisfies the third term of 7.34.

Here, as in the case of axial symmetry, index economy is used, and, therefore, we shall omit the indices x and 0.

8. DERIVATION OF PLANAR INDUCTION DISTRIBUTION FROM THE SCALAR POTENTIAL IN THE EXCITATION REGION

In order to facilitate the approximative calculation of the magnetic field with planar distribution, the field can be derived from the scalar potential [116]; this method being different from the hitherto known methods.

Let the second term of equation 7.25 be extended in the following manner

$$B_y = \frac{\partial A_x}{\partial z} = -\frac{\partial \varphi^+}{\partial y} \qquad 8.1$$

Differentiating equation 8.1 with respect to z, and taking into consideration equation 7.28

$$\frac{\partial^2 A_x}{\partial z^2} = -\mu_0 j_x - \frac{\partial^2 A_x}{\partial y^2} = -\frac{\partial^2 \varphi^+}{\partial z \partial y} \qquad 8.2$$

Integrating equation 8.2 with respect to y

$$-\int_0^y \frac{\partial^2 \varphi^+}{\partial z \partial y} \, dy = -\mu_0 \int_0^y j_x dy - \int_0^y \frac{\partial^2 A_x}{\partial y^2} \, dy \qquad 8.3$$

Accomplishing the denoted (possible) integration

$$-\frac{\partial \varphi^+}{\partial z} + \frac{\partial \varphi^+}{\partial z}\bigg|_{y=0} = -\mu_0 \int_0^y j_x dy - \frac{\partial A_x}{\partial y} + \frac{\partial A_x}{\partial y}\bigg|_{y=0} \qquad 8.4$$

We shall now take into consideration the third term of equation 7.25, and rearrange equation 8.4

$$\frac{\partial \varphi^+}{\partial z}\bigg|_{y=0} + B_z\bigg|_{y=0} = -\mu_0 \int_0^y j_x dy + \frac{\partial \varphi^+}{\partial z} + B_z \qquad 8.5$$

The following requirement is prescribed in equation 8.5 regarding the determination of φ^+

$$-\frac{\partial \varphi^+}{\partial z}\bigg|_{y=0} = B_z\bigg|_{y=0} \qquad\qquad 8.6$$

Applying equation 8.6 in equation 8.5, and after rearrangement

$$B_z = -\frac{\partial \varphi^+}{\partial z} + \mu_0 \int_0^y j_x dy \qquad\qquad 8.7$$

Differentiating equation 8.1 with respect to y

$$\frac{\partial^2 \varphi^+}{\partial y^2} = -\frac{\partial^2 A_x}{\partial y \partial z} \qquad\qquad 8.8$$

Differentiating equation 8.7 with respect to z

$$\frac{\partial^2 \varphi^+}{\partial z^2} = \mu_0 \frac{\partial}{\partial z} \int_0^y j_x dy + \frac{\partial^2 A_x}{\partial z \partial y} \qquad\qquad 8.9$$

Summing equations 8.8 and 8.9

$$\varDelta \varphi^+ = \mu_0 \frac{\partial}{\partial z} \int_0^y j_x dy \qquad\qquad 8.10$$

φ^+, therefore, satisfies *Poisson's* differential equation.

Summarising the equations derived for the determination of the induction components

$$B_y = -\frac{\partial \varphi^+}{\partial y} \qquad\qquad 8.11$$

$$B_z = -\frac{\partial \varphi^+}{\partial z} + \mu_0 \int_0^y j_x dy \qquad\qquad 8.12$$

If the induction components are calculated at the point (y, z), it can be seen that these are dependent only on the current totalled up to point y. If the current density is identically zero up to the point y, the induction components can be formally derived in the same manner as from the magnetic scalar potential V_m (see § 9, item b). *The induction components are naturally dependent on the exciting current, but this is present only in the form of boundary conditions: the induction distribution given for the boundaries is determined by the total excitation.*

4*

It follows from the aforesaid that in the current-free regions $\varphi^+ = V_m$. The boundary conditions relative to φ^+ are of the same type as those pertaining to V_m. As an example, iron-air boundary surfaces may be taken as approximatively (magnetic) equipotential surfaces [128].

$\Delta\varphi^+$ equals zero not only in the current-free regions, but in case of specific current distributions also in regions containing currents. In case of uniform current distribution, for example, it is different from zero on the boundaries (with vertical components) only.

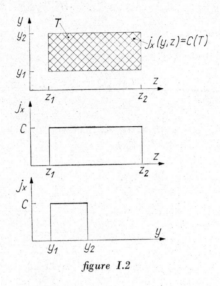

figure I.2

In the case of current distribution as shown in figure I.2

$$\int_0^y j_x dy = (y - y_1)C(T) \qquad\qquad 8.13$$

$$\Delta\varphi^+ = \mu_0(y - y_1)\frac{\partial}{\partial z}C(T) \qquad\qquad 8.14$$

In the case of specific current distributions, other equations may also be used, since the equations of the induction distribution can be derived by starting from B_z instead of B_y. In this case, the following equations are obtained

$$B_y = -\frac{\partial\varphi^+}{\partial y} - \mu_0\int_0^z j_x\,dz \qquad\qquad 8.15$$

$$B_z = -\frac{\partial\varphi^+}{\partial z} \qquad\qquad 8.16$$

$$\Delta \varphi^+ = -\mu_0 \frac{\partial}{\partial y} \int\limits_0^z j_x \, dz \qquad \text{8.17}$$

Using the equation

$$-\frac{\partial \varphi^+}{\partial y}\bigg|_{z=0} = B_y\bigg|_{z=0} \qquad \text{8.18}$$

as a complementary condition, the induction distribution can be determined by equations 8.15, 8.16, 8.17 as well as by 8.10, 8.11, 8.12. The group providing an easier calculation with the given current distribution should be chosen.

9. QUADRUPOLE FIELDS

A characteristic property of the quadrupole fields is that two preferred planes may be found in both the electric and magnetic fields. These preferred planes are invariably perpendicular to each other, and are either symmetry planes or antisymmetry planes of the field. In general, no further requirement is imposed on the quadrupole fields, and it is therefore apparent that these are more general than the fields with planar distribution and the axially symmetric fields discussed in the previous sections: *the structure of quadrupole fields can be described only with the help of three variables.*

In order to describe the quadrupole fields, a Cartesian coordinate system has been chosen, wherein two coordinate planes coincide with the symmetry or antisymmetry planes of the field. In accordance with the principle followed in the preceding sections, axis z has been chosen as axis of the system, from which it follows that the preferred planes are the x, z and the y, z coordinate planes.

In cases arising *in practical applications, arrangements of general quadrupole fields are used wherein the symmetry planes of the electric field coincide with the antisymmetry planes of the magnetic field.* Since we have already chosen the coordinate system, we may write the equations defining the even parity and odd parity requirements of the components of the electric and magnetic fields as referred to the variables x and y

$$\mathbf{E} = E_x \mathbf{e}_x + E_y \mathbf{e}_y + E_z \mathbf{e}_z \qquad \text{9.1}$$

$$E_x(x, y, z) = -E_x(-x, y, z); \quad E_y(x, y, z) = E_y(-x, y, z);$$
$$E_z(x, y, z) = E_z(-x, y, z) \qquad \text{9.2}$$

$$E_x(x, y, z) = E_x(x, -y, z); \quad E_y(x, y, z) = -E_y(x, -y, z);$$
$$E_z(x, y, z) = E_z(x, -y, z) \qquad \text{9.3}$$

$$\mathbf{B} = B_x \mathbf{e}_x + B_y \mathbf{e}_y + B_z \mathbf{e}_z \qquad \text{9.4}$$

$$B_x(x, y, z) = B_x(-x, y, z); \quad B_y(x, y, z) = -B_y(-x, y, z);$$
$$B_z(x, y, z) = -B_z(-x, y, z) \qquad \text{9.5}$$

$$B_x(x, y, z) = -B_x(x, -y, z); \quad B_y(x, y, z) = B_y(x, -y, z);$$
$$B_z(x, y, z) = -B_z(x, -y, z) \tag{9.6}$$

Both the electric and the magnetic fields may also appear separately but again in this case, the above form of writing is adhered to (see figures I.3 and I.4).

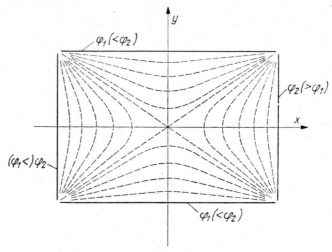

figure I.3

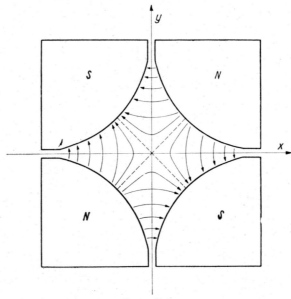

figure I.4

(a) Electric field

It follows from the previous requirements and from the relation 2.1 between the electric field and the scalar potential, not writing the simple components of the gradient in the Cartesian coordinate system, that

$$\varphi(x,y,z) = \varphi(-x,y,z); \quad \varphi(x,y,z) = \varphi(x,-y,z) \qquad 9.7$$

i.e. the scalar potential is an even function referred to the variables x and y.

In addition to the requirements already introduced which also represent the requirements of the boundary conditions, we need the conditions relating to the space-charge distribution exciting the quadrupole field. Taking the simple pattern where the lines of force of the electric field originate or end in electric charges, the following condition relating to space-charge distribution becomes clear (see figure I.5)

$$\varrho(x,y,z) = \varrho(-x,y,z); \quad \varrho(x,y,z) = \varrho(x,-y,z) \qquad 9.8$$

thus, the space-charge distribution is also expressed by an even function of the variables x and y.

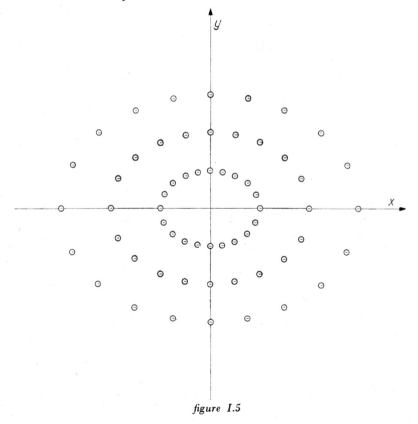

figure I.5

The electric quadrupole field is determined from the general equation 2.4, taking into consideration the even parity conditions 9.7 and 9.8 (in rare cases conditions 9.2 and 9.3 are also required). The field-strength components can be calculated from equation 2.1.

(b) Magnetic field

In fields of planar distribution and of axial symmetry, the vector potential is used for derivation of the magnetic field. In both cases considerable reduction was achieved when the specific structural properties of the fields discussed were given consideration, and the fields could be described by a single-component vector potential. This is generally not possible in the case of quadrupole fields. Our present objectives do not encompass investigation of phenomena occurring in space sections where current density is present, and therefore the magnetic field will be derived from the magnetic scalar potential. This choice results in considerable reduction in the description, and the derivations.

Equation 1.3 is homogeneous since current density is not present in the space section investigated

$$\text{curl } \mathbf{B} = 0 \qquad\qquad 9.9$$

This equation is identical in structure with equation 1.1 and therefore $\mathbf{B}$ may be derived from a scalar potential similarly to 2.1

$$\mathbf{B} = -\text{grad } V_m \qquad\qquad 9.10$$

where the scalar potential is denoted by V_m (V s m^{-1}). As a consequence of equation 1.4, the magnetic scalar potential satisfies the equation

$$\Delta V_m = 0 \qquad\qquad 9.11$$

The general solution [28, 138]

$$V_m(\mathbf{r}) = -\frac{1}{4\pi}\int_F \frac{V_{mp}(\mathbf{r}_0)(\mathbf{r}-\mathbf{r}_0)}{|\mathbf{r}-\mathbf{r}_0|^3} \cdot d\mathbf{f}_0 - \frac{1}{4\pi}\int_F \frac{\mathbf{B}_p(\mathbf{r}_0)}{|\mathbf{r}-\mathbf{r}_0|} \cdot d\mathbf{f}_0 \qquad 9.12$$

where the boundary conditions are $V_m|_p = V_{mp}$, and $-\text{grad } V_m|_p = \mathbf{B}_p$. All comments in general made with regard to the electric scalar potential, concerning boundary conditions, notations, etc. are valid in this case also.

The parity conditions relevant to the magnetic scalar potential can be established from the requirements 9.5 and 9.6 and from the relationship 9.10 between the magnetic field and the magnetic scalar potential

$$V_m(x,y,z) = -V_m(-x,y,z); \quad V_m(x,y,z) = -V_m(x,-y,z) \qquad 9.13$$

The magnetic scalar potential is an odd function with respect to the variables x and y.

Note: The general derivation and calculation of the magnetic quadrupole field is not required in this book. Nevertheless, we are giving the parity prescriptions relevant to the components of the vector potential and of the current density as a starting point for calculation of the general cases

$$A_x(x, y, z) = -A_x(-x, y, z); \; A_y(x, y, z) = A_y(-x, y, z); \quad A_z(x, y, z) = A_z(-x, y, z) \quad 9.14$$

$$A_x(x, y, z) = A_x(x, -y, z); \quad A_y(x, y, z) = -A_y(x, -y, z); \; A_z(x, y, z) = A_z(x, -y, z) \quad 9.15$$

$$j_x(x, y, z) = -j_x(-x, y, z); \; j_y(x, y, z) = j_y(-x, y, z); \quad j_z(x, y, z) = j_z(-x, y, z) \quad 9.16$$

$$j_x(x, y, z) = j_x(x, -y, z); \quad j_y(x, y, z) = -j_y(x, -y, z); \; j_z(x, y, z) = j_z(x, -y, z) \quad 9.17$$

(c) The series of the electric quadrupole field

The series structure of the electric quadrupole field is established by the procedure followed previously.

The space-charge distribution in the quadrupole field may originate from an electron beam's own space-charge, as long as the condition 9.8 is satisfied. Assuming this space-charge distribution to be known, the coefficients of the power series can be calculated by means of a series expansion. The coefficients thus obtained are functions of z

$$\varrho_{2\mu,\,2\nu} = \varrho_{2\mu,\,2\nu}(z) \qquad\qquad 9.18$$

The series itself is of the following form

$$\varrho(x, y, z) = \varrho_{00} + \varrho_{20}x^2 + \varrho_{02}y^2 + \varrho_{40}x^4 + \varrho_{22}x^2y^2 +$$

$$+ \, \varrho_{04}y^4 + \cdots = \sum_{\mu=0}^{\infty} \sum_{\nu=0}^{\infty} \varrho_{2\mu,\,2\nu}\, x^{2\mu}\, y^{2\nu} \qquad 9.19$$

The potential series

$$\varphi(x, y, z) = \Phi_{00} + \Phi_{20}x^2 + \Phi_{02}y^2 + \Phi_{40}x^4 + \Phi_{22}x^2y^2 +$$

$$\Phi_{04}y^4 + \cdots = \sum_{\mu=0}^{\infty} \sum_{\nu=0}^{\infty} \Phi_{2\mu,\,2\nu}x^{2\mu}y^{2\nu} \qquad 9.20$$

The unknown coefficients $\Phi_{2\mu,\,2\nu}$ here too are functions of z

$$\Phi_{2\mu,\,2\nu} = \Phi_{2\mu,\,2\nu}(z) \qquad\qquad 9.21$$

The electric quadrupole field is more general than either fields with planar distribution or axially symmetric fields, and can therefore no longer be characterised by one single $\Phi(z)$ function (and its derivatives), but, as will be seen later, *three functions are necessary for its description.*
Derivatives contained in equation 2.4

$$\frac{\partial^2 \varphi}{\partial x^2} = \sum_{\mu=1}^{\infty} \sum_{\nu=1}^{\infty} 2\mu(2\mu - 1)\Phi_{2\mu,\,2\nu-2}x^{2\mu-2}y^{2\nu-2} \qquad 9.22$$

$$\frac{\partial^2 \varphi}{\partial y^2} = \sum_{\mu=1}^{\infty} \sum_{\nu=1}^{\infty} 2\nu(2\nu - 1)\Phi_{2\mu-2, \, 2\nu} x^{2\mu-2} y^{2\nu-2} \tag{9.23}$$

$$\frac{\partial^2 \varphi}{\partial z^2} = \sum_{\mu=1}^{\infty} \sum_{\nu=1}^{\infty} \Phi''_{2\mu-2, 2\nu-2} \, x^{2\mu-2} y^{2\nu-2} \tag{9.24}$$

Equations 9.19, 9.22, 9.23 and 9.24 are substituted into 2.4 and ordinated

$$\sum_{\mu=1}^{\infty} \sum_{\nu=1}^{\infty} \left[2\mu(2\mu - 1) \, \Phi_{2\mu, 2\nu-2} + 2\nu(2\nu - 1) \, \Phi_{2\mu-2, 2\nu} + \right.$$
$$\left. + \Phi''_{2\mu-2, \, 2\nu-2} + \frac{1}{\varepsilon_0} \varrho_{2\mu-2, 2\nu-2} \right] x^{2\mu-2} y^{2\nu-2} \equiv 0 \tag{9.25}$$

In accordance with the usual procedure, the term in brackets in identity 9.25 is to be chosen as zero, giving rise to the following conditions

$$2\mu(2\mu - 1)\Phi_{2\mu, 2\nu-2} + 2\nu(2\nu - 1)\Phi_{2\mu-2, 2\nu} +$$
$$+ \Phi''_{2\mu-2, \, 2\nu-2} + \frac{1}{\varepsilon_0} \varrho_{2\mu-2, 2\nu-2} = 0, \quad \mu, \nu = 1, 2, 3, \ldots \tag{9.26}$$

In case of $\mu, \nu = 1$, the following equation results from 9.26

$$2\Phi_{20} + 2\Phi_{02} + \Phi''_{00} + \frac{1}{\varepsilon_0} \varrho_{00} = 0 \tag{9.27}$$

Introducing the function

$$D = D(z) = 2(\Phi_{20} - \Phi_{02}) \tag{9.28}$$

via the relations

$$\Phi_{20} = \frac{1}{2} D + \Phi_{02} \text{ and } \Phi_{02} = \Phi_{20} - \frac{1}{2} D$$

the following equations are obtained from 9.27

$$\Phi_{20} = -\frac{1}{4} \left(\Phi''_{00} - D + \frac{1}{\varepsilon_0} \varrho_{00} \right) \tag{9.29}$$

$$\Phi_{02} = -\frac{1}{4} \left(\Phi''_{00} + D + \frac{1}{\varepsilon_0} \varrho_{00} \right) \tag{9.30}$$

i.e. one function (D) is sufficient instead of two functions (Φ_{20}, Φ_{02}). For $\mu = 1, \nu = 2$, from 9.26, we obtain

$$2\Phi_{22} + 12\Phi_{04} + \Phi''_{00} + \frac{1}{\varepsilon_0} \varrho_{02} = 0 \tag{9.31}$$

and in case of $\mu = 2$, $\nu = 1$, equation

$$12\,\Phi_{40} + 2\Phi_{22} + \Phi''_{20} + \frac{1}{\varepsilon_0}\,\varrho_{20} = 0 \qquad 9.32$$

is obtained. Φ''_{02} in 9.31 is calculated from equation 9.30, and Φ''_{20} in 9.32, from 9.29. After substitution equations 9.31 and 9.32 are solved with respect to the unknown functions Φ_{04} and Φ_{40}

$$\Phi_{40} = \frac{1}{48}\left[\Phi_{00}^{(IV)} - D'' - 8\Phi_{22} + \frac{1}{\varepsilon_0}\,(\varrho''_{00} - 4\varrho_{20})\right] \qquad 9.33$$

$$\Phi_{04} = \frac{1}{48}\left[\Phi_{00}^{(IV)} + D'' - 8\Phi_{22} + \frac{1}{\varepsilon_0}\,(\varrho''_{00} - 4\varrho_{02})\right] \qquad 9.34$$

In view of the fact that in the following only first-order equations of motion will be used in our investigations, and the number of coefficients defined for the structural formula of the potential distribution is already more than necessary, we are not calculating further coefficients, neither are we introducing the formula of the general coefficient. The general formula has been discussed elsewhere [133] and with this knowledge we draw attention only to the fact that in the formulae of the coefficients obtained so far, all three functions characterising the quadrupole field have already appeared: Φ_{00}, D, Φ_{22}. *All the coefficients appearing in the potential series can be expressed by these three functions and their derivatives.*

The series of the potential distribution with the determined coefficients and the three functions introduced is as follows

$$\varphi(x, y, z,) = \Phi_{00} - \frac{1}{4}\left(\Phi''_{00} - D + \frac{1}{\varepsilon_0}\,\varrho_{00}\right)x^2 -$$

$$- \frac{1}{4}\left(\Phi''_{00} + D + \frac{1}{\varepsilon_0}\,\varrho_{00}\right)y^2 + \frac{1}{48}\left[\Phi_{00}^{(IV)} - D'' -\right.$$

$$\left. - 8\Phi_{22} + \frac{1}{\varepsilon_0}\,(\varrho''_{00} - 4\varrho_{20})\right]x^4 + \Phi_{22}\,x^2y^2 +$$

$$+ \frac{1}{48}\left[\Phi_{00}^{(IV)} + D'' - 8\Phi_{22} + \frac{1}{\varepsilon_0}\,(\varrho''_{00} - 4\varrho_{02})\right]y^4 + \cdots \quad 9.35$$

The potential value pertaining to any arbitrary point of the electric quadrupole field can be calculated from 9.35 if the axial values of the following functions are known

$$\varphi\big|_{\substack{x=0 \\ y=0}} = \Phi_{00} \text{ (axis potential)} \qquad 9.36$$

$$\frac{\partial^2\varphi}{\partial x^2}\bigg|_{\substack{x=0 \\ y=0}} - \frac{\partial^2\varphi}{\partial y^2}\bigg|_{\substack{x=0 \\ y=0}} = D \qquad 9.37$$

$$\left.\frac{\partial^4 \varphi}{\partial x^2 \partial y^2}\right|_{\substack{x=0 \\ y=0}} = 4\,\Phi_{22} \qquad\qquad 9.38$$

From 9.35, the components of the electric field strength are

$$E_x(x, y, z) = \frac{1}{2}\left(\Phi_{00}'' - D + \frac{1}{\varepsilon_0}\,\varrho_{00}\right) x - \frac{1}{12}\left[\Phi_{00}^{(IV)} - \right.$$

$$\left. - D'' - 8\,\Phi_{22} + \frac{1}{\varepsilon_0}\,(\varrho_{00}'' - 4\varrho_{20})\right] x^3 - 2\,\Phi_{22}\,xy^2 + \dots \qquad 9.39$$

$$E_y(x, y, z) = \frac{1}{2}\left(\Phi_{00}'' + D + \frac{1}{\varepsilon_0}\,\varrho_{00}\right) y - 2\,\Phi_{22}\,x^2 y -$$

$$- \frac{1}{12}\left[\Phi_{00}^{(IV)} + D'' - 8\,\Phi_{22} + \frac{1}{\varepsilon_0}\,(\varrho_{00}'' - 4\varrho_{02})\right] y^3 + \dots \qquad 9.40$$

$$E_z(x, y, z) = -\,\Phi_{00}' + \frac{1}{4}\left(\Phi_{00}''' - D' + \frac{1}{\varepsilon_0}\,\varrho_{00}'\right) x^2 +$$

$$+ \frac{1}{4}\left(\Phi_{00}''' + D' + \frac{1}{\varepsilon_0}\,\varrho_{00}'\right) y^2 + \dots \qquad 9.41$$

(d) The series of the magnetic quadrupole field

Writing the series structure for the magnetic quadrupole field will cause no difficulties using the above method, and it is in fact simpler than the series structure of the electric quadrupole field. *The current-density distribution of a beam moving in a magnetic quadrupole field cannot be taken into consideration since this current-density distribution does not excite a quadrupole field, and in the classical case it may be omitted.*

The series of the magnetic scalar potential is

$$V_m(x, y, z) = V_{11}xy + V_{31}x^3y + V_{13}xy^3 + V_{51}x^5y + V_{33}x^3y^3 +$$

$$+ V_{15}xy^5 + \dots = \sum_{\mu=0}^{\infty}\sum_{\nu=0}^{\infty} V_{2\mu+1,2\nu+1}\,x^{2\mu+1}\,y^{2\nu+1} \qquad 9.42$$

$$V_{2\mu+1,\,2\nu+1} = V_{2\mu+1,\,2\nu+1}\,(z) \qquad\qquad 9.43$$

Determination of the series structure is similar to the case of the electric field. The relations between the coefficients are calculated from the following equation

$$2\mu(2\mu + 1)V_{2\mu+1,\,2\nu-1} + 2\nu(2\nu + 1)V_{2\mu-1,\,2\nu+1} +$$

$$+ V_{2\mu-1,2\nu-1}'' = 0, \ \mu,\nu = 1, 2, 3 \dots \qquad 9.44$$

By the use of the function

$$H = H(z) = 6(V_{31} - V_{13})$$ 9.45

the coefficients $\left(V_{31} = \dfrac{1}{6} H + V_{13}; V_{13} = V_{31} - \dfrac{1}{6} H \right)$ are

$$V_{31} = -\frac{1}{12}(V''_{11} - H)$$ 9.46

$$V_{13} = -\frac{1}{12}(V''_{11} + H)$$ 9.47

$$V_{51} = \frac{1}{240}(V^{(IV)}_{11} - H'' - 72\,V_{33})$$ 9.48

$$V_{15} = \frac{1}{240}(V^{(IV)}_{11} + H'' - 72\,V_{33})$$ 9.49

Further terms and the general formula are to be found in the literature [133]. The characteristics of the magnetic quadrupole field are V_{11}, H and V_{33}, by means of which the other coefficients may be expressed. The magnetic scalar potential is

$$V_m(x, y, z) = V_{11}xy - \frac{1}{12}(V''_{11} - H)x^3y - \frac{1}{12}(V''_{11} + H)xy^3 +$$

$$+ \frac{1}{240}(V^{(IV)}_{11} - H'' - 72V_{33})x^5y + V_{33}x^3y^3 +$$ 9.50

$$+ \frac{1}{240}(V^{(IV)}_{11} + H'' - 72V_{33})xy^5 + \dots$$

Similarly to the electric quadrupole field, *the field characteristics of the magnetic quadrupole field may be calculated at all points, if the three characteristic functions are known.* As customary, the characteristic functions are brought into connection with the magnetic induction. Due to their simplicity, the derivations are not given here.

Finally, the induction components

$$B_x(x, y, z) = -V_{11}y + \frac{1}{4}(V''_{11} - H)x^2y + \frac{1}{12}(V''_{11} + H)y^3 + \dots$$ 9.51

$$B_y(x, y, z) = -V_{11}x + \frac{1}{12}(V''_{11} - H)x^3 + \frac{1}{4}(V''_{11} + H)xy^2 + \dots$$ 9.52

$$B_z(x, y, z) = -V'_{11}xy + \frac{1}{12}(V'''_{11} - H')x^3y +$$

$$+ \frac{1}{12}(V'''_{11} + H')xy^3 + \dots \qquad\qquad 9.53$$

The three induction components on the axis in the quadrupole field are equal to zero.

For summarised information on the quadrupole fields, see [101, 119, 133]

(C) APPROXIMATIVE SOLUTION OF THE POTENTIAL EQUATIONS

Numerous methods for obtaining an approximative solution of potential equations are known, since such equations are used in other applied fields of physics. Of these, the difference equation method is the most prominent and widely used, and upon this the most important method of measurement — based on analogy — is also founded. Other approximative calculation methods are more difficult and less widely used, these yield approximations based on known functions as against the method of difference equations which produces simple tabulated functional relationships.

10. METHOD OF DIFFERENCE EQUATIONS

(a) Systems of equations

The method of systems of equations is one of the procedures for the solution of potential equations. The conception is simple.

A net is stretched in the space section under investigation, and the potential values are determined only at the nodal points of the net (discreting). The differential expression in the differential equation is substituted by an approximative difference expression. The difference expression is assembled from potential values found in the nodal points of the net. The differential expression pertaining to a nodal point contains only unknown potential values, excepting those where a known potential value found in the boundary nodal points is necessary for their formation. As many differential expressions, i.e. algebraic equations, are written as the number of nodal points in the net, with unknown potential values; care must be taken, naturally, that each unknown value must figure at least once. By doing so, the solution of the differential equation is reduced to the solution of a system of algebraic equations. Since the system of equations contains also known potential values on the boundary, the boundary conditions are satisfied by the approximative solution.

A more close-meshed net corresponds to a system of more equations and a solution of greater accuracy. In the case of a net with given mesh widths, a more accurate solution pertains to higher-order approximative difference expressions of the differential expressions. The mesh may be triangular rectangular or of other form. Generally, a regular mesh is chosen: equilatera triangle, or square. They are used primarily for calculations in the inner part of the investigated region. The choice of an irregular mesh is justified by good matching to the boundary. In order to reduce the volume of calculations, all symmetries and antisymmetries available in geometric arrangements are exploited.

By using the procedure described, the error of the approximative solution can be estimated with the help of [6, 98].

(b) The relaxation method

A more practical procedure than that outlined above is now described [21, 22, 115]. The steps necessary for producing the calculation formulae are given instead of a simple description of the procedure, this not only facilitating its application in other arbitrary cases but also ensures good use of the formulae. The basic conception for the determination of the sought calculation formulae is the following:

(i) The sought function is given by a multivariable *Taylor* series in the vicinity of a selected point.

(ii) The values of the function in the net points in the vicinity of the selected point are calculated by means of the *Taylor* series.

(iii) The partial derivatives appearing in the *Taylor* series expansion are calculated from the written equations with the help of the net-point potentials.

(iv) The partial derivatives now known are substituted into the investigated differential expression, thereby establishing a relation between the potentials found in the selected point and the net points. This relationship is the formula sought.

(v) The distribution used as a starting point in determining the sought function values is a rough guess only. By repeated use of the formulae the starting distribution should be refined until the potential formula exists for all points, within *a priori* given limits of accuracy. This refinement is performed in the following manner. The calculation formula is used in the form reduced to zero, and the chosen potential values are substituted into the calculation formula. Since these potential values are not accurate, the substitution will generally yield substitution values different from zero. This value, termed as residual, must be reduced to zero or to the prescribed minute degree by suitable modification, with regard to the residual, of the chosen potential values. During the calculations a change in the sign of the residual may be observed, which, however, may be disregarded.

(c) Difference quotients

The difference quotients are required in the procedures performed with both systems of equations and relaxation calculations. For producing the difference quotients, we first write the *Taylor* series of the two-variable function $z = z(x, y)$

$$z = \sum_{\nu=0}^{\infty} \sum_{\lambda=0}^{\infty} \left[\frac{\partial^{\nu+\lambda} z}{\partial x^\nu \partial y^\lambda} \right]_{\substack{x=x_n \\ y=y_m}} \frac{(x-x_n)^\nu (y-y_m)^\lambda}{\nu! \, \lambda!} = z(x_n, y_m) +$$

$$+ z_x'(x_n, y_m)(x-x_n) + z_y'(x_n, y_m)(y-y_m) +$$

$$+ \frac{1}{2} z_{xx}''(x_n, y_m)(x-x_n)^2 + z_{xy}''(x_n, y_m)(x-x_n)(y-y_m) +$$

$$+ \frac{1}{2} z_{yy}''(x_n, y_m)(y-y_m)^2 + \cdots \qquad\qquad 10.1$$

A rectangular general net with non-uniform mesh-widths is chosen, from which, as a special case, the square net can be formed. The nodal points in the vicinity of the selected (x_n, y_m) point, and the notations used are shown in figure I.6.

The function values in the net points are denoted as shown in Table I.1.

TABLE I.1

$$
\begin{aligned}
z_0 &= z_{0,0} &&= z(x_n, y_m) \\
z_1 &= z_{1,0} &&= z(x_n + s_1 a, y_m) \\
z_2 &= z_{0,1} &&= z(x_n, y_m + r_1 a) \\
z_3 &= z_{-1,0} &&= z(x_n - s_{-1} a, y_m) \\
z_4 &= z_{0,-1} &&= z(x_n, y_m - r_{-1} a) \\
z_5 &= z_{2,0} &&= z[x_n + (s_1 + s_2)a, y_m] \\
z_6 &= z_{1,1} &&= z(x_n + s_1 a, y_m + r_1 a) \\
z_7 &= z_{0,2} &&= z[x_n, y_m + (r_1 + r_2)a] \\
z_8 &= z_{-1,1} &&= z(x_n - s_{-1} a, y_m + r_1 a) \\
z_9 &= z_{-2,0} &&= z[x_n - (s_{-1} + s_{-2})a, y_m] \\
z_{10} &= z_{-1,-1} &&= z(x_n - s_{-1} a, y_m - r_{-1} a) \\
z_{11} &= z_{0,-2} &&= z[x_n, y_m - (r_{-1} + r_{-2})a] \\
z_{12} &= z_{1,-1} &&= z(x_n + s_1 a, y_m - r_{-1} a)
\end{aligned}
$$

The function values pertaining to the net points are calculated by means of the *Taylor* series expansion. As an example, the function value z_6 is given as follows

$$z_6 = z(x_n + s_1 a, y_m + r_1 a) = \sum_{\nu=0}^{\infty} \sum_{\lambda=0}^{\infty} \left[\frac{\partial^{\nu+\lambda} z}{\partial x^\nu \partial y^\lambda} \right]_{\substack{x=x_n \\ y=y_m}} \frac{(s_1 a)^\nu (r_1 a)^\lambda}{\nu! \, \lambda!} =$$

$$= z(x_n, y_m) + z_x'(x_n, y_m)s_1 a + z_y'(x_n, y_m)r_1 a +$$

$$+ \frac{1}{2} z_{xx}''(x_n, y_m)s_1^2 a^2 + z_{xy}''(x_n, y_m)s_1 r_1 a^2 +$$

$$+ \frac{1}{2} z_{yy}''(x_n, y_m)r_1^2 a^2 + \cdots \qquad\qquad 10.2$$

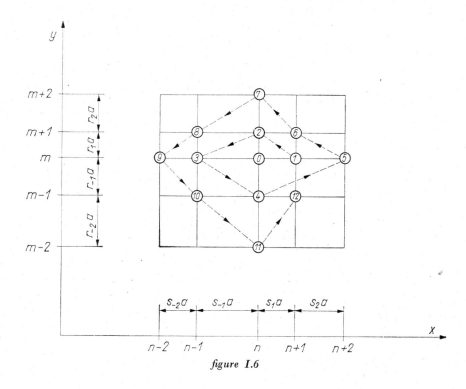

figure I.6

In the equations thus obtained the partial derivatives are considered as the unknowns to be determined. During the calculations the terms containing derivatives of higher order than that to be determined, are disregarded. It follows from z_1 and z_3 that

$$az'_x = \frac{1}{s_{-1} + s_1}(z_1 - z_3)$$ 10.3

From z_2 and z_4

$$az'_y = \frac{1}{r_{-1} + r_1}(z_2 - z_4)$$ 10.4

From z_1 and z_3

$$a^2 z''_{xx} = \frac{2}{s_{-1} s_1 (s_{-1} + s_1)}[s_{-1} z_1 - (s_{-1} + s_1)z_0 + s_1 z_3]$$ 10.5

From z_1, z_2, z_3, z_4, z_6 and z_{10}

$$a^2 z''_{xy} = \frac{1}{s_1 r_1 s_{-1} r_{-1}}(z_{10} + z_6 - z_4 - z_3 - z_2 - z_1 + 2z_0)$$ 10.6

5 Gy. Nagy—M. Szilágyi: Introduction

From z_1, z_2, z_3, z_4, z_8 and z_{12}

$$a^2 z''_{xy} = - \frac{1}{s_1 s_{-1} + s_{-1} r_1} (z_{12} + z_8 - z_4 - z_3 - z_2 - z_1 + 2z_0) \qquad 10.7$$

From z_2 and z_4

$$a^2 z''_{yy} = \frac{2}{r_{-1} r_1 (r_{-1} + r_1)} [r_{-1} z_2 - (r_{-1} + r_1) z_0 + r_1 z_4] \qquad 10.8$$

The difference quotients 10.3–10.8 are now suitable for substitution into the differential expressions occurring, for approximative calculations. Before examining the differential equation types to be solved, let us write the difference quotients pertaining to the square-mesh net. These can be calculated from equations 10.3–10.8 with the substitution of $s_{-1} = r_{-1} = s_1 = r_1 = 1$

$$a z'_x = \frac{1}{2} (z_1 - z_3) \qquad 10.9$$

$$a z'_y = \frac{1}{2} (z_2 - z_4) \qquad 10.10$$

$$a^2 z''_{xx} = z_1 - 2z_0 + z_3 \qquad 10.11$$

$$a^2 z''_{xy} = \frac{1}{2} (z_{10} + z_6 - z_4 - z_3 - z_2 - z_1 + 2z_0) \qquad 10.12$$

$$a^2 z''_{xy} = - \frac{1}{2} (z_{12} + z_8 - z_4 - z_3 - z_2 - z_1 + 2z_0) \qquad 10.13$$

$$a^2 z''_{yy} = z_2 - 2z_0 + z_4 \qquad 10.14$$

The simplicity of the formulae 10.9, 10.10, 10.11, 10.12, 10.13, 10.14 render them suitable for use inside the regions, while equations 10.3, 10.4, 10.5, 10.6, 10.7, 10.8 facilitate matching to the boundary conditions.

In the following sections we shall take in succession the differential equation types important for us, and shall introduce the formulae necessary for their solution.

11. APPROXIMATIVE CALCULATION FORMULAE
FOR ELECTRIC-MAGNETIC FIELDS OF SPECIFIC STRUCTURE

(a) Approximative calculation of fields with planar distribution

In the preceding paragraphs we used equation 7.7 for determination of the electric field and equations 7.28, 8.10 and 8.17 for determination of the magnetic field.

We shall derive the approximative calculation formula of equation 7.7, but not the others, since these can be obtained in the same manner.

The differential expression in equation 7.7 is substituted by the approximative difference expression

$$\left[\Delta\varphi\right]_{\substack{z=z_0 \\ y=y_0}} \cong \frac{2}{a^2} \frac{1}{s_{-1}s_1(s_{-1}+s_1)} \left[s_{-1}\varphi_1 - (s_{-1}+s_1)\varphi_0 + s_1\varphi_3\right] +$$

$$+ \frac{2}{a^2} \frac{1}{r_{-1}r_1(r_{-1}+r_1)} \left[r_{-1}\varphi_2 - (r_{-1}+r_1)\varphi_0 + r_1\varphi_4\right] \qquad 11.1$$

and solved for φ_0

$$\varphi_0 = \frac{s_{-1}s_1 r_{-1}r_1}{s_{-1}s_1 + r_{-1}r_1} \left[\frac{1}{s_1(s_{-1}+s_1)} \varphi_1 + \frac{1}{s_{-1}(s_{-1}+s_1)} \varphi_3 + \right.$$

$$\left. + \frac{1}{r_1(r_{-1}+r_1)} \varphi_2 + \frac{1}{r_{-1}(r_{-1}+r_1)} \varphi_4 + \frac{a^2}{2\varepsilon_0} \varrho_0 \right] \qquad 11.2$$

In equation 11.2 $\varrho_0 = \varrho(y_0, z_0)$. In case of a square-mesh net

$$\varphi_0 = \frac{1}{4} \left(\varphi_1 + \varphi_3 + \varphi_2 + \varphi_4 + \frac{a^2}{\varepsilon_0} \varrho_0 \right) \qquad 11.3$$

Approximative calculation formula of equation 7.28

$$A_{x0} = \frac{s_{-1}s_1 r_{-1}r_1}{s_{-1}s_1 + r_{-1}r_1} \left[\frac{1}{s_1(s_{-1}+s_1)} A_{x1} + \frac{1}{s_{-1}(s_{-1}+s_1)} A_{x3} + \right.$$

$$\left. + \frac{1}{r_1(r_{-1}+r_1)} A_{x2} + \frac{1}{r_{-1}(r_{-1}+r_1)} A_{x4} + \frac{\mu_0 a^2}{2} j_{x0} \right] \qquad 11.4$$

The meaning of j_{x0} in equation 11.4: $j_{x0} = j_x(y_0, z_0)$. In case of a square-mesh net

$$A_{x0} = \frac{1}{4} (A_{x1} + A_{x3} + A_{x2} + A_{x4} + \mu_0 a^2 j_{x0}) \qquad 11.5$$

Approximative calculation formula of equation 8.1

$$\varphi_0^+ = \frac{s_{-1}s_1 r_{-1}r_1}{s_{-1}s_1 + r_{-1}r_1} \left\{ \frac{1}{s_1(s_{-1}+s_1)} \varphi_1^+ + \frac{1}{s_{-1}(s_{-1}+s_1)} \varphi_3^+ + \right.$$

$$\left. + \frac{1}{r_1(r_{-1}+r_1)} \varphi_2^+ + \frac{1}{r_{-1}(r_{-1}+r_1)} \varphi_4^+ - \frac{\mu_0 a^2}{2} \left[\frac{\partial}{\partial z} \int_0^y j_x \, dy \right]_{\substack{z=z_0 \\ y=y_0}} \right\} \qquad 11.6$$

5*

In the square-mesh net case

$$\varphi_0^+ = \frac{1}{4} \left\{ \varphi_1^+ + \varphi_3^+ + \varphi_2^+ + \varphi_4^+ + \mu_0 a^2 \left[\frac{\partial}{\partial z} \int\limits_0^y j_x dy \right]_{\substack{z=z_0 \\ y=y_0}} \right\} \qquad 11.7$$

Approximative calculation formula of equation 8.17

$$\varphi_0^+ = \frac{s_{-1}s_1 r_{-1}r_1}{s_{-1}s_1 + r_{-1}r_1} \left\{ \frac{1}{s_1(s_{-1}+s_1)}\, \varphi_1^+ + \frac{1}{s_{-1}(s_{-1}+s_1)}\, \varphi_3^+ + \right.$$

$$\left. + \frac{1}{r_1(r_{-1}+r_1)}\, \varphi_2^+ + \frac{1}{r_{-1}(r_{-1}+r_1)}\, \varphi_4^+ + \frac{\mu_0 a^2}{2} \left[\frac{\partial}{\partial y} \int\limits_0^z j_x\, dz \right]_{\substack{z=z_0 \\ y=y_0}} \right\} \quad 11.8$$

In the square-mesh net case

$$\varphi_0^+ = \frac{1}{4} \left\{ \varphi_1^+ + \varphi_3^+ + \varphi_2^+ + \varphi_4^+ + \mu_0 a^2 \left[\frac{\partial}{\partial y} \int\limits_0^z j_x\, dz \right]_{\substack{z=z_0 \\ y=y_0}} \right\} \qquad . \quad 11.9$$

(b) Approximative calculation of axially symmetric fields

In the preceding paragraphs equations 5.11 and 5.79 were used for determination of the electric field, and equations 5.36 and 6.11 for determination of the magnetic field.

The formulae may be obtained similarly to derivation of formula 11.2 pertaining to equation 7.7.

The approximative calculation formula of equation 5.11 [arbitrary point (R_0, z_0)]

$$\varphi_0 = \frac{s_{-1}s_1 r_{-1}r_1}{s_{-1}s_1 + r_{-1}r_1} \left[\frac{1}{s_1(s_{-1}+s_1)}\, \varphi_1 + \frac{2R_0 + ar_1}{2R_0 r_1(r_{-1}+r_1)}\, \varphi_2 + \right.$$

$$\left. + \frac{1}{s_{-1}(s_{-1}+s_1)}\, \varphi_3 + \frac{2R_0 - ar_{-1}}{2R_0 r_{-1}(r_{-1}+r_1)}\, \varphi_4 + \frac{a^2}{2\varepsilon_0}\, \varrho_0 \right] \qquad 11.10$$

In the equation $\varrho_0 = \varrho(R_0, z_0)$. In the square-mesh net case

$$\varphi_0 = \frac{1}{4} \left(\varphi_1 + \frac{2R_0 + a}{2R_0}\, \varphi_2 + \varphi_3 + \frac{2R_0 - a}{2R_0}\, \varphi_4 + \frac{a^2}{\varepsilon_0}\, \varrho_0 \right) \qquad 11.11$$

Approximative calculation formula of equation 5.79 [axis point $(0, z_0)$]

$$\varphi_0 = \frac{s_{-1}s_1r_{-1}r_1}{2s_{-1}\,s_1 + r_{-1}r_1}\left[\frac{1}{s_1(s_{-1}+s_1)}\,\varphi_1 + \frac{2}{r_1(r_{-1}+r_1)}\,\varphi_2 + \right.$$

$$\left. + \frac{1}{s_{-1}(s_{-1}+s_1)}\,\varphi_3 + \frac{2}{r_{-1}(r_{-1}+r_1)}\,\varphi_4 + \frac{a^2}{2\varepsilon_0}\,\varrho_0\right]\qquad 11.12$$

Here $\varrho_0 = \varrho(0, z_0)$. In the square-mesh net case

$$\varphi_0 = \frac{1}{6}\left(\varphi_1 + 2\varphi_2 + \varphi_3 + 2\varphi_4 + \frac{a^2}{\varepsilon_0}\,\varrho_0\right)\qquad 11.13$$

Approximative calculation formula of equation 5.36

$$A_{z0} = \frac{2R_0^2\,s_{-1}s_1r_{-1}r_1}{2R_0^2(s_{-1}\,s_1 + r_{-1}\,r_1) + a^2s_{-1}s_1r_{-1}r_1}\left[\frac{1}{s_1(s_{-1}+s_1)}\,A_{\alpha1} + \right.$$

$$+ \frac{2R_0 + ar_1}{2R_0r_1(r_{-1}+r_1)}\,A_{\alpha2} + \frac{1}{s_{-1}(s_{-1}+s_1)}\,A_{\alpha3} + $$

$$\left. + \frac{2R_0 - ar_1}{2R_0r_{-1}(r_{-1}+r_1)}\,A_{\alpha4} + \frac{\mu_0a^2}{2}\,j_{\alpha0}\right]\qquad 11.14$$

Here $j_{z0} = j_z(R_0, z_0)$. In the square-mesh net case

$$A_{z0} = \frac{R_0^2}{4R_0^2 + a^2}\left(A_{\alpha1} + \frac{2R_0 + a}{2R_0}\cdot A_{\alpha2} + A_{\alpha3} + \frac{2R_0 - a}{2R_0}\,A_{\alpha4} + \mu_0a^2j_{\alpha0}\right)\quad 11.15$$

Approximative calculation formula of equation 6.11

$$\Psi_0 = \frac{s_{-1}s_1r_{-1}r_1}{s_{-1}s_1 + r_{-1}r_1}\left[\frac{1}{s_1(s_{-1}+s_1)}\,\Psi_1 + \frac{2R_0 - ar_1}{2R_0r_1(r_{-1}+r_1)}\,\Psi_2 + \right.$$

$$\left. + \frac{1}{s_{-1}(s_{-1}+s_1)}\,\Psi_3 + \frac{2R_0 + ar_{-1}}{2R_0r_{-1}(r_{-1}+r_1)}\,\Psi_4 + \pi\mu_0R_0a^2j_{z0}\right]\qquad 11.16$$

Here $j_0 = j(R_0, z_0)$. In the square-mesh net case

$$\Psi_0 = \frac{1}{4}\left(\Psi_1 + \frac{2R_0 - a}{2R_0}\,\Psi_2 + \Psi_3 + \frac{2R_0 + a}{2R_0}\,\Psi_4 + 2\pi\mu_0R_0a^2j_{\alpha0}\right)\quad 11.17$$

12. OTHER METHODS OF APPROXIMATIVE SOLUTION

(a) Separation of the variables

An accurate solution by separation of potential equations is obtained if we can determine the limit of the infinite series obtained. This, however, rarely occurs. Thus the only way is to approach the limit with some partial sum of the series (taking into consideration a finite number of terms of the series only). On the one hand, the partial sums of series of this type rapidly converge to the limit (it is sufficient to calculate a partial sum with a small number of terms), while on the other hand the sequence of partial sums tends towards the limit (approach with the partial sum is therefore permissible). Relations exist [49, 79] for estimation of the error of approximation by partial sums, but in practice it is profitable to follow the method which takes into account as many terms of the series as necessary so that the correction due to the terms following in sequence will be negligible.

The series expansion of the function given on the boundary takes place according to an orthogonal system of functions. The boundary function may also be expanded with the help of a series according to a non-orthogonal system of functions. In this case it is naturally a precondition that the elements of the system of functions satisfy the differential equations of the potentials, and that they be linearly independent of each other. And finally, the system of functions must be complete, or closed [37, 38, 94, 95, 122, 123]. If the above conditions are fulfilled, the boundary function is given by the following series

$$\varphi_p(x) = \sum_{\nu=0}^{\infty} b_\nu \, F_\nu \qquad\qquad 12.1$$

In equation 12.1 $F_\nu(x)$ ($\nu = 0, 1, 2, \ldots$) is the non-orthogonal system of functions, and constants b_ν are the coefficients of the series expansion. Let us now choose an arbitrary complete system of functions X_i ($i = 0, 1, 2, \ldots$) and multiply both sides of equation 12.1 by this system

$$\varphi_p X_i = \sum_{\nu=0}^{\infty} b_\nu \, F_\nu \, X_i \qquad\qquad 12.2$$

Now we shall integrate by terms over the interval (a,b)

$$\int_a^b \varphi_p \, X_i \, dx = \sum_{\nu=0}^{\infty} b_\nu \int_a^b F_\nu \, X_i \, dx \qquad\qquad 12.3$$

In equation 12.3 integrals different from zero appear now even in case of $\nu \neq i$

$$\int_a^b \varphi_p \, X_i \, dx = a_i \qquad\qquad 12.4$$

$$b_\nu \int_a^b F_\nu \, X_i \, dx = b_\nu \, c_{\nu i} \qquad\qquad 12.5$$

Substituting equations 12.4 and 12.5 into equation 12.2 we obtain

$$a_i = \sum_{\nu=0}^{\infty} b_\nu c_{\nu i}, \quad i = 0, 1, 2, \ldots \qquad 12.6$$

The unknown coefficients b_ν can now be determined from the system fn equations 12.6. Instructions for the solution of the system of equations cao be found in [98].

(b) The Ritz method

The most important method for approximative determination of the extreme values of functionals appearing in the variation method, is the *Ritz* method [22].

Let us choose a multi-parameter function which satisfies the boundary conditions at any value of the parameters of the function.

Let us denote this function by

$$y = y(x_s, c_i), \quad s = 1, 2, \ldots, m, \quad i = 1, 2, \ldots, q \qquad 12.7$$

If we form a functional with this function [105–107], the functional F will be a function of the constants c_i

$$F(c_i) = \int_V L(x_s, y, y_s) dv \qquad 12.8$$

i.e. a q-variable function. L denotes that the *Lagrange* function of the given problem is concerned. In the present case the *Lagrange* function of the electric and magnetic fields is to be used (see equation 4.73, where in case of a pure electric field $y \equiv \varphi$). The extreme value of the multi-variable functions can be found where

$$\frac{\partial F}{\partial c_i} = 0, \quad i = 1, 2, \ldots, q \qquad 12.9$$

The system of q equations 12.9 determines the q unknowns c_i. An accurate solution is approached by $y(x_s, c_i)$, with these constants c_i.

(c) The method of infinite series

It is unusual for the unknown coefficients to be determined using a generally valid formula when the solution is sought in the form of an infinite series. This difficulty is obviously caused by the system of infinite number of equations. In some cases it is sufficient to determine the coefficients necessary for the first few terms of the series, which requires solution of the system of equations resulting from omission of the coefficients with higher indices.

(d) Reduction to ordinary differential equation

The dependency of the sought function upon one or more variables, matched to the nature of the problem, may be given *a priori*. In this way the number of partial derivatives in the partial differential equation has been reduced. If the dependency upon a sufficient number of variables is given—in the most frequent two-variable cases, the dependency upon one variable—the partial differential equation is reduced to an ordinary differential equation. In the resultant ordinary differential equation all the variables may occur in the coefficients and excitations, but only the one remaining is considered as variable, while the others figure as parameters.

(e) The Galerkin method

Let us suppose that the arbitrary n-parameter function approximating the $U(\mathbf{r})$ solution function (see § 4, item a) has the following form

$$U^+(\mathbf{r}) = U_0^+(\mathbf{r}) + \sum_{\sigma=1}^{n} c_\sigma U_\sigma^+(\mathbf{r}) \qquad 12.10$$

The arbitrary function $U_0^+(\mathbf{r})$ satisfies the inhomogeneous boundary condition 4.2, and the arbitrary functions $U_\sigma^+(\mathbf{r})$ are chosen so that they satisfy the homogeneous boundary condition given in equation 4.10 (in cases of $\sigma = 1, 2, \ldots, n$) and represent the first n terms of a full system of functions. In this case, with arbitrary selection of the c_σ system (system of constants), the second term in the right-hand side of equation 12.10 also satisfies the homogeneous boundary conditions.

Let us substitute equation 12.10 into equation 4.1 reduced to zero

$$DU - G = 0 \qquad 12.11$$

Since $U^+(\mathbf{r})$ is not the exact solution, the substitution does not yield a function identical with zero, but the following function

$$\Delta(\mathbf{r}, c_\sigma) = DU^+ - G \qquad 12.12$$

which may be termed as the error function. Equation 12.12 written in detailed form is

$$\Delta(\mathbf{r}, c_\sigma) = DU_0^+(\mathbf{r}) + \sum_{\sigma=1}^{n} c_\sigma DU_\sigma^+(\mathbf{r}) - G(\mathbf{r}) \qquad 12.13$$

Let us now multiply equation 12.13 by the function $U_\nu^+(\mathbf{r})$ $(\nu = 1, 2, \ldots, n)$ and integrate over the region defined by the boundary

$$\int_V \Delta(\mathbf{r}, c_\sigma) U_\nu^+(\mathbf{r}) dv = \int_V DU_0^+(\mathbf{r}) U_\nu^+(\mathbf{r}) dv +$$

$$+ \sum_{\sigma=1}^{n} c_\sigma \int_V DU_\sigma^+(\mathbf{r}) U_\nu^+(\mathbf{r}) dv - \int_V G(\mathbf{r}) U_\nu^+(\mathbf{r}) dv \qquad 12.14$$

It is desirable that the error function is orthogonal with respect to the $U_\nu^+(\mathbf{r})$ system [7, 8, 21, 98]

$$\int_V \Delta(\mathbf{r}, c_\sigma) U_\nu^+(\mathbf{r}) dv = 0, \qquad \nu = 1, 2, \ldots, n \qquad 12.15$$

Introducing the constants

$$a_\nu = \int_V D U_0^+(\mathbf{r}) U_\nu^+(\mathbf{r}) dv, \qquad \nu = 1, 2, \ldots, n \qquad 12.16$$

$$b_\nu = \int_V G(\mathbf{r}) U_\nu^+(\mathbf{r}) dv, \qquad \nu = 1, 2, \ldots, n \qquad 12.17$$

$$d_{\sigma\nu} = \int_V D U_\sigma^+(\mathbf{r}) U_\nu^+(\mathbf{r}) dv, \quad \sigma, \nu = 1, 2, \ldots, n \qquad 12.18$$

the following system of equations is given

$$\sum_{\sigma=1}^n d_{\sigma\nu} c_\sigma = b_\nu - a_\nu, \qquad \nu = 1, 2, \ldots, n \qquad 12.19$$

The n unknown c_σ can be determined from the system of equations 12.19. The method introduced is known as the *Galerkin* method.

If such functions are chosen in equation 12.10 (which satisfy the differential equation 4.1 instead of the boundary conditions) then the constants c have to be determined by means of the *Trefftz* method [40, 41, 105, 106, 107].

(f) Approximation of the integral expressions by finite sums

All the formulae containing integral expressions (e.g. 3.3, 3.6, 3.8, 3.10, 12.8) can be approximated with finite sums by suitable partition of the region; this is a simple but laborious method.

SOME COMPLEMENTARY NOTES CONCERNING FIELD CALCULATIONS AND RELATED LITERATURE

The starting point of all results obtained in electron optics or space-charge optics consists of space calculations. Within the scope of field theory we are only dealing with electrostatics and magnetostatics, i.e. the static electric field and the static magnetic field. For determination of the field distribution the same chapter treats analysis of the electric field in appropriate detail, and also the analysis of magnetic fields, on the basis of which we were able to determine the electric field distribution and the magnetic field distribution, and even the spurious field distribution. Data required for determination of electric and magnetic field lines are not treated in the present work, but will be presented in a later review.

In the analysis of electric-magnetic fields the axially symmetric field is naturally the most important. In addition to the axially symmetric electric field or the axially symmetric electric-magnetic field, fields having plane symmetry and other special structural properties are in widespread use.

Numerous field-calculation methods are known, e.g. conformal representation, *Fourier* analysis, or variational analysis, the majority of which have been mentioned in this work. To aid the calculations, all mathematical means may be employed, e.g. complex formulation of field equations etc. Each of these calculation methods solves a boundary value problem and among these the mixed boundary problem is in practice the most complex. The mixed boundary condition is actually produced by the linear combination of the primary and secondary boundary conditions. Fortunately, the mixed condition is infrequent. When performing quadratures, it is worthwhile to choose coordinate systems which take into account the geometric characteristics of the problem, while the function- or *Jacobi* determinants appear successively when transforming. A salutary property worthy of note: the potential is practically always a single-value function of the position (apart from singular positions) and therefore the multi-valued functions may be neglected.

Knowledge of the field is necessary in order to realise a path system of suitable properties from the electron-optical aspect. The different electron-optical elements are obtained as a result of the field design, e.g. the slot-type electron lens and hole-type electron lens, which form the most important varieties of the aperture-type electron lens. The lenses include accelerating lenses, bipotential lenses, strong and weak lenses, electric circular lenses, electric cylinder lenses, etc. Mention is made of the thickness of the lens and we introduce e.g. thin and thick electric lenses, thin and thick circular lenses, or to give one of the numerous varieties its detailed definition: thick electric cylinder lens. The characteristic data of all lens types have to be determined (or taken down), e.g. focal plane, focal line, object point or object distance, magnification, etc. Similarly, for light optics, in this connection we speak of virtual image or even virtual cathode; the lenses may have errors, e.g. apertural error, or cylinder lenses may incur deflection aberrations. Optical systems built up from these elements may be of the telescopic system and so on.

The field-calculation methods mentioned are mathematical and rigorous methods operating with continuous variables. The continuous variable method is an analytical method suitable for determination of analytical solutions, however, an analytical solution may also be a continuous approximation.

Other methods are the analog methods, which have also been discussed. This method consists of analog simulation, with which certain fields, e.g., the field excited by axially symmetric electrodes, or fields of arbitrary specific electrode system can be determined. Almost all tasks can be solved with the aid of analog computation with virtually only one limitation: accuracy cannot be arbitrarily intensified. As stated in this chapter, this computation can be readily and simply used with respect to scalar fields, and hence for purposes of potential computation and magnetic flux computation. In the more simple cases, computation of the electric-magnetic field is obtained by means of flux computation. Numerical analysis based on the mathematical model has gained prominence due to the increased use of high-speed computers. Numerical computation based upon the

numerical methods is now practically absolute with respect to field computation.

These numerical methods employ discrete approximations with discrete
variables. The method of discrete variables is a finite difference method,
which, for example, also uses divided differences. With the aid of these the
arithmetical solution of field equations is obtained. The arithmetical solution of differential equations is generally determined by iterative methods.
In our case the matrix iterative analysis represents the main principled
framework. The digital simulation or the digital method comply with
computer programming possibilities, and *vice versa*, and the digital analysis
performs the necessary digital computation. The computation result may,
for example, be the computation of electric fields. The boundary-value
function or the boundary-value distribution are also necessary for these
computations, but as functions of the discrete variables. Numerous programming systems are used for these computations, with differing advantages and disadvantages. An appropriate unit system has to be chosen
for any of these computations: SI units are increasingly being used. After
selection of the unit system norming is performed, and conversion
to dimension-free (relative) variables is made. These methods are known
collectively as relaxation methods, which operate with the relaxation factor
and by different means lead to an increase in the convergence rate. The
accelerating factor is of great importance with respect to the final results
obtained from the numerous computations, and therefore determination
of the optimum relaxation factor demands careful attention. Assuming
that the stability of computation is not jeopardized, a choice may be made
from the methods and supplements corresponding to the given data: SOR
(Successive Overrelaxation), SLOR *(Successive Line Overrelaxation)*, ADI
(Alternating Direct Implicit Method), *Correction Term Method*, *Deferred
Approach to the Limit*, *Difference Correction*, and so on. Design of the mesh
pertaining to curvilinear forms is enabled by symmetromorphic equivalence; with the knowledge of the literature, the treatment of singularity
and the stagnation points can also be solved. Unequal mesh, subdivided
mesh or irregular star may be chosen for the disposition employed. The
large molecule may be used for the computation. The most important error
types are the truncation error, rounding error, and the residual error.
Propagation of error must be carefully investigated and limited.

The computations may be employed for all purposes, e.g. for calculation
of nonuniform magnetic field distribution, field perturbation due to technological causes, peak voltage in a given space section, not containing electrodes, the most favourable grid potential value, maximum and minimum
potential which can be fed to a given electrode, determination of the validity
limits of an empirical formula, auxiliary calculations for approximative
solution of potential equations by given functions, field distribution forming
in the proximity of a grid aperture, etc.

Continuing our general review, we will now cite available literature which
is more detailed.

The importance of field calculation and the demand for force-line presentation appeared a long time ago as a technically justified requirement. One

demonstration of this was given as an example in a paper many years ago [246]. The equation of equipotential lines and the equation of field lines are generally accessible [237].

Over a long period, an obstacle to field calculation was the problem of open regions. The *Green* theorem based on the *Gauss* theorem (*Stokes* theorem in planar relations) refers to closed regions, and consequently, a different procedure is used with respect to open regions. This problem has been dealt with [201] precisely and on a technical level (the first paper discussing over-relaxation). Later the paper [179] draws attention to the fact that the *Cauchy* boundary problem arising in electrode design is instable. The book [209] treats the *Cauchy* problem in detail and demonstrates that in the case of analytical boundary surface and analytical boundary condition, with open boundary, a unique solution can be obtained only in the proximity of the boundary. In other cases the solution is not stable, since, when moving away from the boundary, the errors increase exponentially. The position has become more complicated since calculations performed on open boundaries when compared with measurements made in electrolytic tanks have shown similarity [224]. Refinement of the mesh used for the calculation has not helped [254], since instability has remained: as a result, numerous calculations have been made [221], from which it appears that instability is apparent in the sixth-order approximation, or after carrying out the calculations [192] with a tenfold finer mesh, instability will also appear [185]. This law has gradually become general knowledge [206, 249, 272]. The solution was found by transforming the *Laplace* equation into a hyperbolic equation by means of transformations, thereby obtaining a stabile calculation [205, 273]. Numerous researchers have dealt with this equation and with other suitable methods [248]. Meanwhile results were produced which gave non-realisable electrodes [214] as the final result of the calculation. Finally, however, after elimination of the difficulties [215, 217], it became possible to perform the calculations with respect to involved space-charge cases also [227, 268].

With regard to varied methods of field computation, the following account is also of interest. The calculation of potentials may be performed in the case of open boundaries also, with the aid of the *Green* functions, by means of a rapidly converging numerical method [271], also in the case of a field of optional structure. A book [218] relating to the moment method is also available. The space-charge and the potential formed by its image can be determined by numerical integration [255]. Numerous articles deal with approximative potential determination by means of superimposing accurately calculable potential fields [194], introducing the flat ring coordinate system [267], and ultimately reaching trajectory computations [266]. The field of space-charge flow is determined by the method of separation of variables [236], *Poisson*'s equation is solved by means of a *Fourier* analysis [225]; the field calculations can be performed with the numerical method about complicated boundaries [189]. Although not directly connected with the subject matter of the present book, calculations (potential and trajectory) made with vector potential correction, can be performed in relativistic cases also [184].

In concord with the above, the calculation of potential fields is performed ultimately for determination of the trajectory system, and consequently, field calculations are in close connection with trajectory calculations. Paper [260] deals with potential calculations external of the beam, in a coordinate system wherein the beam edge concurs with a coordinate line; calculations of the potential and trajectory are performed with consideration of the space-charge [210, 213], paper [203] performs the calculations with regard to high perveances and high compressions, the article [278] takes into consideration thermal velocities also, while the communications [187, 240] employ a method considered highly refined among the computer methods. The integration intervals are automatically varied [187], and the equipotential and field lines, lens parameters and aberrations, etc. are calculated.

Apertures have to be formed for outlet of the beam, in the various electron guns and focusing equipment. These apertures disturb the fields and have a lens effect. In order to assess the effects, knowledge of the lens characteristics is necessary. This is dealt with in the articles [190, 191] which are widely known, and which have been further developed in numerous directions. For example, a field formed by a slot placed between parallel planes has been determined by conformal representation [238], necessary for exact trajectory calculations (the result of the calculation was qualitatively checked in an electrolytic tank). Subsequently, the effects of the anode hole of the high-perveance gun were investigated and assessed [222, 250]. A further conceptual advance was represented in giving the focal length of the aperture with consideration of the space-charge, first with primary [182], then with secondary [258] approximation. The improved *Davisson–Calbick* formula, with consideration of space-charge and magnetic field is presented in the paper [181]. Numerous further papers investigate effects of the anode hole: e.g. in the case of hole and slit apertures with high compression triode-type guns [219], investigation of the anode-hole effects of the *Pierce* gun required for conical flow [177, 251], while article [178] supplies information relative to fabrication tolerances.

In numerous cases and in given regions a field of prescribed structure has to be produced. The electrode design as required for gun design forms a notable example [256, 257]. Details of gun design comprise the material of Chapter III, and here we only deal briefly with this aspect of field computation. Arrangements which approximate electrodes representing potential surfaces are naturally considered [220], since the potential fields are continuous functions of the boundary conditions and slight variations or deviations in them cause similarly small deviations in the field to be realized.

Naturally, the more important methods are those which lead to the exact electrode shape. The paper [243] deals with electrode calculations for the strip beam relative to the circular electron trajectory, with which in the first instance *Meltzer* dealt. With a similar method the article [231] designs the necessary electrodes for the two-dimensional flow. Articles [252, 281] transform the magnetic field by means of a shielding fitting in such manner that the magnetic field lines become congruent with the flow lines. The electrode design for strip beams figures in further papers [229, 245]. Conditions relevant to changing positions of the electrodes are also investigated

[244], and experimental design is not neglected [274]. From the latter it has become apparent that the space-charge limited current resulting from the calculation can produce only a quotient below unity from the system. The numbers of computer investigations are unlimited, including the paper [193], the first large-scale and also of the digital method. Among the design methods [230], the method for non-linear flows is also of interest [198]. Full details of the computation methods are available [195].

Today, the most frequently applied field calculation method is the relaxation method which is substantiated from the most varied directions.

The origin of this method derives from *Boltzmann* [241]. The paper quoted includes a statement to the effect that the simple formula 11.3, without space-charge member, originated in 1892. The first publication of this formula was in 1908 [265], but lacking verification. Not far later the method of *deferred approach to the limit* was published [262, 263], calculating values of greater accuracy, by extrapolation of results given by coarser and finer meshes. These papers introduce the method of arithmetical solution of field equations. In further papers by these author [264], more data relative to the arithmetical solution of differential equations are presented, i.e. the effect of the finite mesh size upon the potential resultant from the nodal point are investigated. The theoretical investigations are further continued by evaluation of the truncation error [207]. Subsequently, formulae [270] serving the solution of *Laplace* and other equations appeared, including those based upon mesh divisions of non-equal distance [269]. Application of the backward, central and forward differences achieved increasing importance and form the *method of difference correction*, since in the boundary proximity the application of central differences presents difficulties [200]. An important advance appeared in 1950 due to two independently produced results [202,279]: the *over-relaxation method* (SOS method) was introduced in the field of iterative solution methods. Other publications [199] and summaries are published which deal with the auxiliary theses necessary for the iteration procedure for wider circles. One author of *successive over-relaxation* presents his results in a more accessible manner [280]. Later, an article [275] points out the limitations of the *method of deferred approach to the limit*, which cause difficulties on the borders and corners of the region. Meanwhile, the examples of applications with respect to elliptic and parabolic equations continue to grow [253], including convergence investigations. The relaxation factor related to small mesh size is estimated [204], a formula is reported [196] of calculations with nine mesh points and the iterative methods are further propagated [228]. The space-charge is taken into consideration [242], however the convergence of the given procedure remains slow. A new method appears [197], and the over-relaxation factor is again determined [186], among these, proposals are made [247] relevant to optimum and also practical determinations [239]. The ADI *(Alternating Direction Implicit Method)* method is introduced [183], and programming of this is difficult, a long calculation time is required per cycle, while on the other hand, its convergence is rapid. An example of its utilization for practical calculations is presented in communication [234] in which *Poisson*'s equation is solved by the relaxation method and trajectory computation is performed when calculating the curvilinear space-charge flow. The articles [180, 259] use differing mesh divisions in directions r and z. The logical scheme of the calculations is given in article [276]. The *Cauchy* problem is discussed in the paper [216], albeit using a method involving greatly differing means (electrolytic tank measurement is also used). The work [226] gives a program for performing the calculations, while another paper, mentioned only as an example, demonstrates that this method has achieved significant success in the field of guided waves [188]. The article [277] presents a correlation between the mesh point potentials, in which the logarithm function appears. Under-relaxation and applications are dealt with in article [235], in which formation of the rotationally symmetric and strip beams is discussed, with calculation of the many various aberrations. The number and accessibility of computer programs have become widespread [223], with further refinement and widening applications of the investigation of the methods [232, 233]. The paper [211] shows again that in the calculations of field and trajectory, accuracy is dependent — in addition to appropriate choice of the relaxation factor — upon the length of the elementary diodes chosen for the calculation. Using the ADI method, the magnetic field can be calculated from the previously measured boundary data [208], and the truncation error is investigated in the function of the network mesh size [212]. In the paper [261] the magnetic field is calculated by computer even in the most general case, in the case where permanent magnetic material, exciting current, air, and iron armature are present.

(D) DETERMINATION OF THE ELECTRIC-MAGNETIC
FIELD BY MEASUREMENT

Potential equations may be solved by computer, with the use of two basic methods One of the methods is by digital computer, while the other is based on analogy (analogue computers).

The digital computer produces the solution function in a tabulation of functions. Although the analogue computer is also able to produce a function tabulation, essentially only a series of function values based on measuring results is obtained. The calculation accuracy of digital computers is unlimited, while the accuracy of the analogue computer attains moderate, slightly better than 1%, limits, dependent on the given problem.

Analogue computers are of simple design and are easily constructed, the computing results obtained are in many cases of sufficient accuracy, and these computers can therefore be used in practice.

Digital computers are far more complicated in design and their description (the operation principle only) would occupy considerable book space. We are content with merely drawing attention to the digital computers, for reasons both of lack of space, and also since this field falls beyond the scope of our work.

More and more calculations of electron-optical interest are being performed on digital computers. Some special cases are recorded in the References [193, 585]. A study of selected papers will show the range of applicability of the digital computers.

In the following, some simple cases of the analogue computers will be dealt with.

13. ANALOGY BETWEEN ELECTRON FLOW IN A VACUUM AND CONDUCTORS

Two physical phenomena are termed analogous if the structures of the relevant equations are coincident. The field of stationary flow occurring in conductors and the field of space-charge flow in vacuum are analogous in this sense. In the following, the conditions of substitution are established. (Since the following subject slightly deviates from the field of this book, we shall deal in greater detail with the principles of the matter.)

Charge flow in mediums having conductivity is induced not only by electric forces, but may also be the effect of other forces. These forces are discussed formally as electric forces, too, although their origin is to be sought in the most different forms of interactions, between physical fields. To illustrate these forces, they may be considered as charge-separating forces, inducing flow in such a way as to cause space-charge distribution to differ from the neutral state in a certain volume. This space-charge distribution may be substituted macroscopically by a potential difference or field-strength distribution. In general cases the charge-separating force varies from place to place and is customarily substituted by field-strength distribution [145, 146]. Now, the conduction current figuring in *Maxwell's* equations, according to the generalized *Ohm's* law, is given in the following form [145, 146]

$$\mathbf{j}_v = \gamma(\mathbf{E} + \mathbf{E}_b), \quad [\text{A m}^{-2}] \tag{13.1}$$

i.e. it is considered that the current is induced jointly by the electric and the other forces. The $\mathbf{E}_b(\text{V m}^{-1})$ is termed *non-conservative* (or *external*) field strength. The value of the conductivity γ varies with the material, and according to our present purposes, it is a function of the position

$$\gamma = \gamma(\mathbf{r}), \qquad [\text{AV}^{-1}\text{m}^{-1}] \tag{13.2}$$

It has become customary to call certain excitation terms occurring in *Maxwell's* equations *space-charge density* (or *current density*). If the conductivity of a conductive material is a function of its position, an excitation term of space-charge character appears, which is customarily denoted as ϱ_2 (A s m^{-3}) and is termed conduction space charge. It will be seen that the field strength $\mathbf{E}_b$ also figures in the expression for ϱ_2 [126].

In view of this, the stationary flow in the conductor is expressed by the following *Maxwell's* equations [126]

$$\text{curl } \mathbf{E} = 0 \tag{13.3}$$

$$\text{div } \mathbf{E} = \frac{1}{\varepsilon_0} \varrho_2 \tag{13.4}$$

$$\mathbf{j}_v = \gamma(\mathbf{E} + \mathbf{E}_b) \tag{13.5}$$

$$\text{div } \mathbf{j}_v = 0 \tag{13.6}$$

First, it is necessary to determine the expression of ϱ_2. Substituting equation 13.5 into equation 13.6 and differentiating we obtain

$$\gamma \operatorname{div} \mathbf{E} + \gamma \operatorname{div} \mathbf{E}_b + (\mathbf{E} + \mathbf{E}_b) \cdot \operatorname{grad} \gamma = 0 \qquad 13.7$$

Now express div $\mathbf{E}$ from 13.7

$$\operatorname{div} \mathbf{E} = -\operatorname{div} \mathbf{E}_b - \frac{1}{\gamma} (\mathbf{E} + \mathbf{E}_b) \cdot \operatorname{grad} \gamma \qquad 13.8$$

Comparing the right-hand sides of equations 13.8 and 13.4 and expressing as ϱ_2

$$\varrho_2 = -\frac{\varepsilon_0}{\gamma} (\mathbf{E} + \mathbf{E}_b) \cdot \operatorname{grad} \gamma - \varepsilon_0 \operatorname{div} \mathbf{E}_b \qquad 13.9$$

Substituting 13.9 into 13.4

$$\operatorname{div} \mathbf{E} + \frac{1}{\gamma} \operatorname{grad} \gamma \cdot \mathbf{E} = -\frac{1}{\gamma} \operatorname{grad} \gamma \cdot \mathbf{E}_b - \operatorname{div} \mathbf{E}_b \qquad 13.10$$

Equations 13.3 and 13.10 are the basic equations of the flow-field arising in conductive media.

For identical satisfying of equation 13.3, field strength $\mathbf{E}$ is derived in the following manner from potential function φ

$$E = -\operatorname{grad} \varphi \qquad 13.11$$

Substituting 13.11 into 13.10

$$\varDelta\varphi = \frac{1}{\gamma} \operatorname{grad} \gamma \cdot \mathbf{E}_b + \operatorname{div} \mathbf{E}_b - \frac{1}{\gamma} \operatorname{grad} \gamma \cdot \operatorname{grad} \varphi \qquad 13.12$$

The conditions of substitution can now easily be established. By comparison of equations 13.12 and 30.6 we obtain

$$-\frac{\sqrt{\mathbf{j}^2}}{\varepsilon_0(2\eta)^{1/2}} \frac{1}{\sqrt{\varphi}} = \frac{1}{\gamma} \operatorname{grad} \gamma \cdot \mathbf{E}_b + \operatorname{div} \mathbf{E}_b - \frac{1}{\gamma} \operatorname{grad} \gamma \cdot \operatorname{grad} \varphi \qquad 13.13$$

Formula 13.13 yielded by comparison of the two equations shows that if conductivity of the material and the external field strength are chosen in the foregoing manner, the space-charge effect can be realised by suitable selection of these.

The boundary conditions necessary for unique solution of the equations are identical in flow problems of both types: the values of the potential must be of prescribed magnitude on the given surfaces.

14. ANALOGY IN PLANE AND AXIALLY SYMMETRIC FIELDS

The conductivity or the external field strength can be expressed either as a continuous function of the position or as a net of concentrated conductivities, i.e. as external potentials measurable at given points. Realisation of the first case is the electrolytic tank and its special cases, while realisation of the second case comprises different forms of resistance networks.

(a) Continuous dependency

Let us first view the cases of continuous dependency.

(i) When measuring planar field-strength distributions, the variation of the conductivity is performed by varying the depth of the tank

$$\gamma(x, y) = ah(x, y) \qquad\qquad 14.1$$

External field strengths are not used in this case. Thus, equation 13.13 becomes

$$\frac{\sqrt{\mathbf{j}^2}}{\varepsilon_0(2\eta)^{1/2}} \frac{1}{\sqrt{\varphi}} = \frac{1}{h} \operatorname{grad} h \cdot \operatorname{grad} \varphi \qquad\qquad 14.2$$

Equation 14.2 is solved by the step-by-step method for the surface $h(x, y)$.

(ii) In case of axially symmetric field-strength distributions the conductivity is not varied, but external field strengths are used

$$\mathbf{E}_b = \mathbf{E}_b(r, z) \qquad\qquad 14.3$$

Then equation 13.13 becomes

$$\frac{\sqrt{\mathbf{j}^2}}{\varepsilon_0(2\eta)^{1/2}} \frac{1}{\sqrt{\varphi}} = -\operatorname{div} \mathbf{E}_b \qquad\qquad 14.4$$

Equation 14.14 can be solved (directly) for the unknown div $\mathbf{E}_b$. For practical realisation, probes and external current sources are applied in the points of the potential field in order to produce given potentials which also represent the external field strengths as current flows through the probes.

By using equation 13.13, further field types can be simulated, however, we shall not deal with them.

(b) Concentrated elements

We shall now treat the cases of concentrated dependency. According to the first *Kirchhoff* law resulting from equation 13.6, with regard to any nodal point of the resistance network shown in figure I.7 it is true for the zero-index nodal point that

$$I_1 + I_2 + I_3 + I_4 = 0 \qquad\qquad 14.5$$

Using *Ohm*'s law

$$\frac{\varphi_1 - \varphi_0}{R_1} + \frac{\varphi_2 - \varphi_0}{R_2} + \frac{\varphi_3 - \varphi_0}{R_3} + \frac{\varphi_4 - \varphi_0}{R_4} = 0 \qquad 14.6$$

Solving equation 14.6 for φ_0

$$\varphi_0 = \frac{R_2 R_3 R_4}{R_2 R_3 R_4 + R_1 R_3 R_4 + R_1 R_2 R_4 + R_1 R_2 R_3} \varphi_1 +$$

$$+ \frac{R_1 R_3 R_4}{R_2 R_3 R_4 + R_1 R_3 R_4 + R_1 R_2 R_4 + R_1 R_2 R_3} \varphi_2 +$$

$$+ \frac{R_1 R_2 R_4}{R_2 R_3 R_4 + R_1 R_3 R_4 + R_1 R_2 R_4 + R_1 R_2 R_3} \varphi_3 +$$

$$+ \frac{R_1 R_2 R_3}{R_2 R_3 R_4 + R_1 R_3 R_4 + R_1 R_2 R_4 + R_1 R_2 R_3} \varphi_4 \qquad 14.7$$

Now we wish to solve equations 11.3, 11.5, 11.11, 11.13, 11.17 with the help of the resistance network. We have already stated that the effect of space-charge and of current density is realised by external field strengths introduced in the resistance networks. Therefore, it is necessary first to determine the magnitude of the elements of the resistance network (solution of the homogeneous equations pertaining to equations 7.7, 7.28, 5.11, 5.79, 6.11).

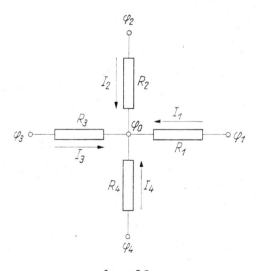

figure I.7

6*

The term containing ϱ_0 is, therefore, omitted from equation 11.3. The thereby resulting equation and 14.7 are identical if

$$\frac{1}{4} = \frac{R_2 R_3 R_4}{R_2 R_3 R_4 + R_1 R_3 R_4 + R_1 R_2 R_4 + R_1 R_2 R_3} \qquad 14.8$$

$$\frac{1}{4} = \frac{R_1 R_3 R_4}{R_2 R_3 R_4 + R_1 R_3 R_4 + R_1 R_2 R_4 + R_1 R_2 R_3} \qquad 14.9$$

$$\frac{1}{4} = \frac{R_1 R_2 R_4}{R_2 R_3 R_4 + R_1 R_3 R_4 + R_1 R_2 R_4 + R_1 R_2 R_3} \qquad 14.10$$

$$\frac{1}{4} = \frac{R_1 R_2 R_3}{R_2 R_3 R_4 + R_1 R_3 R_4 + R_1 R_2 R_4 + R_1 R_2 R_3} \qquad 14.11$$

We have a system of four equations 14.8, 14.9, 14.10, 14.11 for the four unknowns: R_1, R_2, R_3, R_4. Their solution is

$$R_1 = R_2 = R_3 = R_4 = R \qquad 14.12$$

where R is an arbitrary value. Therefore, the resistance network for the determination of the planar field-strength distribution must consist of uniform (identical value) resistances.

The term containing j_{x0} is omitted from equation 11.5. Equation 14.12 is the solution of the equation thus formed.

The term containing ϱ_0 is omitted from equation 11.11. From the equation thus formed and from 14.7 we have

$$R_1 = \frac{aR}{2R_0} \; ; \quad R_2 = \frac{aR}{2R_0 + a} \; ; \quad R_3 = \frac{aR}{2R_0} \; ; \quad R_4 = \frac{aR}{2R_0 - a} \qquad 14.13$$

Here also, R is an arbitrary value. It is worthy of note that the elements of the network are dependent on the mesh width a and on the distance R_0.

Since the field is axially symmetric, equation 11.13 may be transformed with the help of the relationship

$$\varphi_2 = \varphi_4 \qquad 14.14$$

Therefore

$$\varphi_0 = \frac{1}{6} \left(\varphi_1 + 4\varphi_2 + \varphi_3 + \frac{a^2}{\varepsilon_0} \varrho_0 \right) \qquad 14.15$$

The resistance network shown in figure I.8 is used for the solution of equation 14.15 (therefore, one half of the complete network is to be built up).

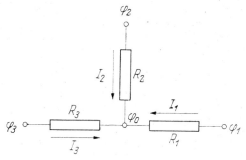

figure I.8

According to *Kirchhoff*'s law

$$I_1 + I_2 + I_3 = 0 \qquad\qquad 14.16$$

Using *Ohm*'s law we have

$$\frac{\varphi_1 - \varphi_0}{R_1} + \frac{\varphi_2 - \varphi_0}{R_2} + \frac{\varphi_3 - \varphi_0}{R_3} = 0 \qquad\qquad 14.17$$

Solving equation 14.17 for φ_0

$$\varphi_0 = \frac{R_2 R_3}{R_2 R_3 + R_1 R_3 + R_1 R_2} \varphi_1 + \frac{R_1 R_3}{R_2 R_3 + R_1 R_3 + R_1 R_2} \varphi_2 +$$

$$+ \frac{R_1 R_2}{R_2 R_3 + R_1 R_3 + R_1 R_2} \varphi_3 \qquad\qquad 14.18$$

The term containing ϱ_0 is omitted from equation 14.15. The equation thus formed is identical with equation 14.18 if

$$\frac{1}{6} = \frac{R_2 R_3}{R_2 R_3 + R_1 R_3 + R_1 R_2} \qquad\qquad 14.19$$

$$\frac{2}{3} = \frac{R_1 R_3}{R_2 R_3 + R_1 R_3 + R_1 R_2} \qquad\qquad 14.20$$

$$\frac{1}{6} = \frac{R_1 R_2}{R_2 R_3 + R_1 R_3 + R_1 R_2} \qquad\qquad 14.21$$

We have a system of three equations 14.19, 14.20, 14.21 for the three unknowns: R_1, R_2, R_3. Their solution

$$R_1 = 4R; \quad R_2 = R; \quad R_3 = 4R \qquad\qquad 14.22$$

R is an arbitrary value but of the same value as that chosen in equation 14.13. The resistances calculated from equation 14.22 can be used only as network elements connected with the axis.

The formulae yielding resistance network elements suitable for the solution of the homogeneous component of equation 11.17 may be derived from the above. Using the notations of figure I.7 we have

$$R_1 = \frac{4R_0^2 - a^2}{2aR_0}\ R; \quad R_2 = \frac{2R_0 + a}{a}\ R;$$

$$R_3 = \frac{4R_0^2 - a^2}{2aR_0}\ R; \quad R_4 = \frac{2R_0 - a}{a}\ R \qquad\qquad 14.23$$

Now there is no equivalent for the group of equations 14.22 since the values of the resistances placed on the axis are all equal to zero. It should be noted that another derivation of the resistance networks is also customary [381–384].

Since the elements of the resistance network have been determined, we now establish the values of the external field strengths introduced into the nodal points. In practice we perform the calculations for currents excited by external field strengths. The calculations will be performed with the notations given in figure I.9.

Again, in accordance with *Kirchhoff*'s law, referred to the zero-index nodal point, we have

$$I_1 + I_2 + I_3 + I_4 + I = 0 \qquad\qquad 14.24$$

According to *Ohm*'s law

$$\frac{\varphi_1 - \varphi_0}{R_1} + \frac{\varphi_2 - \varphi_0}{R_2} + \frac{\varphi_3 - \varphi_0}{R_3} + \frac{\varphi_4 - \varphi_0}{R_4} + I = 0 \qquad\qquad 14.25$$

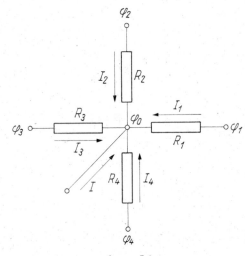

figure I.9

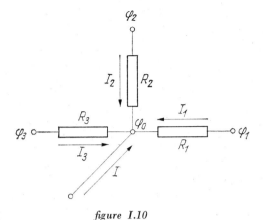

figure I.10

Since the network elements are already given by equation 14.12, the values of R_1, R_2, R_3, R_4 may be substituted into equation 14.25 and it may be solved for φ_0

$$\varphi_0 = \frac{1}{4}(\varphi_1 + \varphi_2 + \varphi_3 + \varphi_4 + RI) \qquad 14.26$$

By comparison of equations 14.26 and 11.3 we have

$$RI = \frac{a^2}{\varepsilon_0}\varrho_0 \qquad 14.27$$

Expressing I from 14.27

$$I = \frac{a^2}{\varepsilon_0 R}\varrho_0 \qquad 14.28$$

In the case of planar field-strength distribution the values of the current to be fed into the nodal points must be chosen dependent upon the value of the space-charge, i.e. according to equation 14.28.

The following formula is obtained with the help of equation 11.5

$$I = \frac{\mu_0 a^2}{R}j_{x0} \qquad 14.29$$

The formula pertaining to the axially symmetric potential field (general point, not connected with the axis)

$$I = \frac{2aR_0}{\varepsilon_0 R}\varrho_0 \qquad 14.30$$

The current to be fed to the axis points is determined with the help of figure I.10.

According to the procedure followed so far we obtain

$$I = \frac{a^2}{4\varepsilon_0 R}\, \varrho_0 \qquad\qquad 14.31$$

Finally, from equation 11.17 we have

$$I = \frac{4\pi\mu_0 a^3 R_0^2}{(4R_0^2 - a^2)R}\, j_{\alpha 0} \qquad\qquad 14.32$$

In this case it is not necessary to feed currents to the axis points. We mention that the vector potential can be calculated with the help of equation 6.12 from the flux function determined with use of the network characterised by equations 14.23 and 14.32.

Numerous publications deal with resistance networks, including consideration of space-charge and current-density effects. The reference list given at the end of this chapter gives only a summary of randomly chosen examples, but does contain the most well-known communications. Simulation of the quadrupole field and other special field types by resistance networks cause no difficulties. Moreover, simulation may be performed even in the most general cases [84].

15. ELECTROLYTIC TANK. RESISTANCE NETWORK

The best known type of equipment operating with continuous media is the electrolytic tank. The electrolytic tank theory was elaborated by *Kirchhoff* in 1845 [312]. This work by *Kirchhoff* among others was also of high significance in scientific development, since here attention is drawn to analogies existing between physical phenomena. The first electrolytic tanks to be designed on the basis of this theory were placed in operation in 1906 [311] and 1913 [296]. The continuous medium is represented by an electrolyte into which are immersed the electrodes representing the boundary condition. The electrolytic tanks are divided into two main groups according to their form of execution. There are shallow and deep tanks. The shallow tanks are used primarily for measurement of planar field strength distributions, while the deep ones are suitable for measurement of axially symmetric and general field-strength distributions [296, 305, 306].

The planar field-strength distributions are measurable also by simpler means. Let us realise a plane of γ conductivity by thin resistance paper. This resistance paper is then placed on an insulating surface and the necessary electrodes are painted on it by conducting paint [139, 302]. According to another method, a thin metal film is placed on a glass plate, and this is used in place of the resistance paper [331].

Among the electrical methods the electrolytic tank belongs to the electrical analogs, and with its aid very many problems can be solved. Examples are: electric field plotting or electric field-strength measurement. It serves also for plotting the diagram of equipotential lines or of flux lines; it is suitable for gradient plotting even as an automatic plotter. Due to its manifold applicability, it serves well as an electrical potential analyser.

The design and repair of electrolytic tank probes [348], impedance determination [289], and fabrication of two-pin probes [303] were all tasks of importance. The two-pin probe provides a means of direct field-strength measurement [338]. Square-wave excitation of the electrolytic tank is also described in the above work and in paper [323]. Field strength may also be measured with four probes [347]. The accuracy of the electrolytic tank is greatly influenced by the structural materials. Appropriate selection of these materials is aided by following papers [295, 340, 344]. The paper [313] treats prevention of capillary disturbances and the *Wagner* earthing is used according to the article [310]. Numerous old communications [305, 306, 318] and later papers [332, 339] describe tanks carried into effect. The descriptions treat electrolytic tanks of solid and also plastic dielectrics [335], which use the element known as the *Poisson* cell, and here the space-charge may also be given consideration. Numerous papers [293, 304, 342, 343] deal with the method of potential field plotting. Several equipment types are dealt with where the fields are automatically plotted [283, 300].

Types have been developed for the solution of problems involving space-charges also, where the space-charge can be taken into consideration [290, 299, 301, 325, 346]. According to paper [323], the surface space-charge density can be substituted by current density, while the space-charge can be simulated by current introduced via probes [307, 308, 316, 317, 345], or by altering the bottom of the tank [326, 327].

The magnetic field can be measured by means of the electrolytic tank. This subject is dealt with in numerous publications [286, 314, 328, 329, 330]. The solution of the measurement of large-diameter axially symmetric fields is of interest [297, 298].

A highly important application of the electrolytic tank is the determination of the electrode shape required for certain electron tube types, as treated already by *Pierce* [333]. After publication of numerous papers [336, 341], determination of the electrode form required for beams of curvilinear boundary became the order of the day [337], where the beam was simulated by current-conducting probes. Attention was paid to the effect of the anode aperture [288], and the edge of the beam was simulated by resistance plates [292]. As a generalisation of *Pierce*'s method, conducting and insulating materials are placed on the edge of the beam, for simulation of the beam edge (to the electrodes of the curvilinear flows). In this manner changes of the potential along the edge of the beam and the prescriptions respecting perpendicular field strength are satisfied [315].

A degenerate case of the electrolytic tank is also worthy of mention. The electrode system to be measured is prepared as for measurements performed with the tank. The space between the electrodes is filled out with a homogeneous, solid and conducting synthetic material, and voltage is applied to the electrodes. The voltage generates current in the synthetic material. The current generates heat in the conductive synthetic material. Due to the heat effect, the material discolours. Since the current distribution is inhomogeneous, the degree of heating and discoloration will vary from point to point in the material. On completion of the measurement, the synthetic material is sawn into plates and then the entire field can be reconstructed from the degree of discoloration [139].

The communications [319–321] present a summary of the theory and applications of the electrolytic tank.

The equipment types built up from concentrated elements can be realised in the form of resistance networks. In the foregoing we have stated that different networks are necessary for measurements of planar and axially symmetric field-strength distribution. The boundary conditions can be produced by short-circuiting the nodal points. Practical realisation of the apparatus is so simple that it can be carried out by inference from the details of the theory [350, 364, 366]. The accuracy of the equipment described is approximately 0.5–1% (including measuring accuracy).

This resistance network proposal of theoretical character dates from 1929 [358], and later (1943) this was turned into a practical proposal [364] which was first applied effectively in 1947 [354] and 1948 [380]. Subsequently, numerous realised equipments and related problems were dealt with [355, 357, 366, 368, 369, 372], and a diploma dissertation also deals with the subject [363]. A highly detailed communication [349] is available, presenting information covering practically all points. Some of the manifold subjects of the papers will be mentioned below. The article [367] points out that the resistance network is more accurate than the electrolytic tank. The temperature-dependent accuracy of the resistance network is investi-

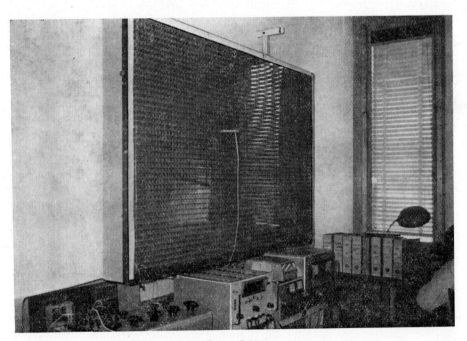

figure I.11.

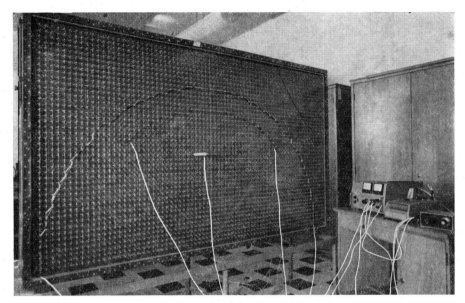

figure I.12

gated in the corresponding section of the book [385]. A small mesh size is chosen at the points of rapid potential variations, and in this respect the work [374] describes 1 : 2 and 1 : 2.5 subdivisions with diagonal resistances. In the paper [356] the resistance network is determined from a formula based on nine points. The possibility exists of employing resistances of greater value than customary in the regions more distant from the axis of rotation, in the axially symmetric systems [390]. In order to increase the measuring accuracy, recourse is made to correct the potential measured in the nodal points [353]. For determination of the potential field in the presence of space-charge, means exist in both the planar and the axially symmetric cases [352, 359–362], and current injected into the nodal point can be automatically adjusted by computer [365]. Both the resistance network and the electrolytic tank are suitable for measurement of magnetic field distribution [351, 389]. An earlier communication proved to be mathematically erroneous [370], although the final result was correct. The paper [371] points out that the resistance network is more accurate than the electrolytic tank, and takes into consideration errors of the resistances, and corrects the potential measured on the nodal point. The scalar potential network is described in papers [381, 382]. The magnetic-field-dependent permeability materials may be taken into account [373], similarly anisotropy [386–388]. A resistance network of the vector potential is described in paper [383], and in article [384] the same authors describe the resistance network of the magnetic field. The resistance network serves for investigation of numerous physical and technical problems. Paper [350] investigates radio frequency tubes; resistance errors are taken into account [379] in the iterative solution of wave equations; applied for investigation of spherical symmetry fields [375]; planar stress conditions are determined [376]; and also heat conduction or diffusion investigations are applied [377–378].

Figures I.11 and I.12 are photographs of two resistance networks (for planar and axially symmetric cases) operating in the laboratory of the Department of Theoretical Electricity, Technical University, Budapest.

The resistance networks may be considered practically more general than the electrolytic tanks. Although modelling of the spatial problems can be performed with both types, yet in case of resistance networks the 'conductivity' inhomogeneity can also be employed, since this is readily realisable in practice.

Note

(i) In most cases the shallow tanks are also suitable for measurement of axially symmetric fields. By planes intersecting the axis two sections are cut out from the axially symmetric electrode system. A field which coincides with the corresponding part of the axially symmetric field is formed by the electrode system obtained, bounded along the intersecting planes by insulators [285].

(ii) The most simple case of the determination of magnetic fields by means of electrolytic tanks is, when no currents are present in the field section to be measured. A further requirement is that the coils be shielded by a material whose permeability is high enough in comparison with that of the free space. Under these conditions the shielding material forms a magnetic equipotential surface. If this surface is realised with metal electrodes, the magnetic scalar potential field can be determined by measuring in an electrolytic tank. If currents are present, external field strengths are employed in the space section to be measured [81]. Determination of magnetic fields by means of electrolytic tanks can be performed in all known cases of practical importance [81].

In planar cases the magnetic field including the field of the coils can be determined by solution of the conjugated problem (in case of the conjugated problem, the role of the equipotential lines is interchanged with that of the lines of force). The metallic conductors correspond to the coils and the current carrying conductors of the magnetic field, while the insulator materials correspond to the materials with permeability [81, 508].

(iii) The electrolytic tank, as a simple integrator, may be used for the solution of other physical and technical problems, if these require solution of *Poisson*'s equation, or specific cases thereof. As examples we mention problems of electrical networks [322], heat conductivity problems [334], capacity determination [291], flow problems [139], pole-shape determinations [282], conform transformations [287], investigation of sheet lines [294], investigation of electron tube fields [284], designing of vacuum tubes [309], for which the electrolytic tank has been employed with success.

16. OTHER METHODS OF MEASUREMENT OF ELECTRIC-MAGNETIC FIELDS

In the preceding paragraphs we have dealt with measurements of both electric and magnetic fields, somewhat more with measurement of electric fields than with that of magnetic fields. We shall now deal with a further method of electric field measurements, i.e. measurements with the help of rubber membranes. This method is suitable for measurement of fields with planar distribution [99, 343, 402].

The equipotential electrode curves given in a plane (the given boundary conditions) are raised from the plane to a level proportional to their potentials. Raising of the curves is realised in practice in such manner that they are chosen as generating curves of straight cylindrical surfaces. The realised (and fixed) cylindrical surfaces are covered by a rubber membrane. The height of the individual points of the membranes (measured from an arbitrary base plane) satisfy *Laplace*'s equation in cases when the setting is not unduly steep. A steep setting is also permissible, with pre-stretching of the membrane [394]. *Poisson*'s equation can also be simulated if the membrane is loaded by additional vertical forces. The articles [391, 398] deal with space-charge cases. Articles [403, 404] are likewise worthy of mention since these discuss other problems of details. Some examples of the varied application possibilities of the rubber model: with the aid of a moving rubber sheet model the input region of a *Resnatron* tube was investigated [392], a stretched rubber sheet was used for vacuum tube designing [393], electron motions in the alternating field of a cathode ray tube were investigated by means of a moving rubber membrane model [396], with the aid of the rubber-membrane analogy the photoelasticity measuring method has been supplemented [400], and the membrane-analogy method has been applied for solution of heat-conduction problems [406]. Further data regarding use of the rubber sheet model are given in article [405], while at the same time paper [395] writes on the subject of rubber sheet and resistance paper serving for solution of planar tasks.

As regards further methods of electric field measurement and design, we refer to the following works [10, 32, 103, 168].

The majority of our equipments operating on electron optical principles employ magnetic field for solution of the tasks concerned. Within our present framework we are not able to treat any one or more definite equipments, and therefore we mention in general that an important constituent element of such equipments is low, medium and high current-density electron flow, produced by low, medium and high current electron guns. The low-, medium- and high-power density beams thus formed are guided through given space sectors and imaged onto given surfaces. Focusing and imaging are performed as prescribed, when the magnetic fields are according to prescription. Naturally, the arrangements producing the magnetic fields must be designed with utmost care and accuracy, and in this respect calculations offer help. Numerous methods are treated in the book, and with them, calculation of magnetic scalar and vector potential or magnetic flux can be performed. Magnetic field or flux plotting is resorted to, following the field or flux calculation, or for checking the calculation, and still more to measure complex cases. Field or flux plotting is still a part of dimensioning and designing, with which our book also deals. However, not all equipments may be directly put into use without control measurements of the magnetic field constructed, and therefore measuring implements and methods for direct measurement of the magnetic field and magnetic flux have been developed. The two main groups of the measuring equipments consist of equipments for measurement of magnetic field characteristics (e.g. magnetic flux density) in a given point or the average of that in a given region. The flux probe may be given as an example, which serves for flux measurement in axially symmetric fields. In addition, there is no end to the number of various auxiliary equipments available for the measurement, and these are mentioned briefly.

Measurement of magnetic fields has been dealt with in great detail in [424]. In addition to measurements performed with the simple coil [442, 469, 525], employment of the moving coil, and the axially oscillating coil [452, 460, 461, 468] is also customary. There are many variants of measurement by means of coil [510]. During the measurement current may flow through the coil [541]. B, B' and B" can be calculated accurately from the curve recorded with the coil [497]. The article [509] describes a hysteresis-loop plotter operating with a coil of optimum form, with noise suppressed to a low value, and a very high sensitivity, for investigation of thin magnetic films.

The rotating coil magnetometer [426, 486] is available as a factory-made product [502]. The signal supplied by the rotating coil is converted into a d.c. signal by a commutator [427]; a commutator consisting of two segments only may be used [514]. The slip-ring solutions include types where rectification, with electronic circuitry, is provided after amplification [480]. Article [550] describes a search coil connected to a rotating transformer, where a highly accurate speed stability is realised. Two coils are employed for measurements of great accuracy, one of which is placed in the reference magnetic field [470, 492, 538]. Article [421] describes a differential magnetometer where, instead of the voltage originating from the reference field, a balancing voltage from the rotating condenser is used.

An interesting variant of the rotating coil magnetometer is the 'turbo-inductor magnetometer', operated by eddy currents [411, 503].

The coils used in the magnetometers determine also the optimum shape [420, 549], even independently of the structure of the fields to be measured [449, 459, 462, 495, 496].

Numerous vibrating coil magnetometer types are in use [485]. The axial magnetic field component can be measured by longitudinal vibration [461]. In order to ensure good resolution, the vibrating coil may also oscillate in the ultrasonic region [521]. The two-coil balance method is also employed here for obtaining more accurate measurements [423]. The article [532] describes the generation of balancing voltage with the help of an in-phase vibrating condenser. Vibration is obtained by means of an a.c. fed coil, and the signals are taken from piezoquartz [551]. The gradient of the magnetic field can be measured with two vibrating coils [456].

Magnetic field measurement can also be performed with rotating equipment connected to a rotating transformer [410, 493]. In this type of equipment the inner primary winding of the rotating transformer is connected to the rotating coil performing the measurement.

A further magnetometer equipment is the 'harmonic coil' [430, 436, 466]. The articles describe the construction, investigate the approximation degree of the theoretically optimum shape, and the aberration terms [466]. Calibration with the standard magnetic field is described [436], and the manner of usage for measurement of the magnetic field gradient is demonstrated [430].

It has already been seen, but here again we repeat that the magnetic field can be measured by electrical methods also [473, 498]. The electrolytic tank may also be employed [286, 298, 314], and with two-dimensional flow even planar problems can be solved [508]. With this method, measurement of the magnetic field is performed by measuring the flow field of the conductive sheet. The poles of the magnetic field serve for the current injection [508].

Employment of the resistance network [351, 370, 389] is also general. Electron beams are deflected by the magnetic field to be measured [506, 527]; they alter the resistance of certain materials (bismuth, tellurium, antimony) [428, 530, 531] and superconductors [446]. Magnetic field measurement with the aid of magnetoresistances is very simple, and from the aspect of the necessary circuitry is also most convenient. The harmonic oscillations occurring in coils with permalloy or other non-linear cores introduced into the magnetic field also form measures of the magnetic field [416, 463, 513]. Included among the permalloy probe magnetometers [412, 491], the toroid core type is also to be found [463]. A magnetic field may be measured also by using a magnetic material displaying a rectangular hysteresis loop. The characteristics and advantages of the method known as the 'peaking strip' are discussed in the communication [484]. With employment of the biasing and the outer stray field compensating coil used in the equipment [544], a non-desirable coupling may occur, and this has to be eliminated. One method of eliminating the coupling between the sweeping and the bias coil is discussed in the article [504]; with another method [454] the test signal drops out due to the two in-series coils, and the useful signal is doubled. The peaking strip may be used for the measurement of high-value induction variation [474]. The equipment is highly stable: signal pulse stability is 0.01% after one year [520]. Applications are manifold [465], and it can be employed in both static and dynamic cases, e.g. electron synchrotron [524].

Recently the *Hall* effect [471, 512, 543] has become widely used for field measurements, and equipments using the *Hall* effect are now in the majority [478, 489, 519, 523, 547] as compared with other types of equipment. Optimum operation has been dealt with in detail [490, 526], ascertaining [488] the required setting in order to attain linearity between the magnetic field to be measured and the signal voltage. *Hall* generators are produced from the most varied materials [545]. With increase of the control current, the signal voltage may be increased by one order [528] in the pulse mode of operation, without increasing the temperature of the sheet. Accurate measurement of the signal voltage is performed with voltage-frequency conversion [501, 537]. In order to avoid temperature dependence numerous methods have been developed: maintaining the control current at a constant level [432], maintaining the sheet at a constant temperature level by using a heating element [475], incorporating a bridge circuit [479], etc. Measuring by the balance method is also customary [554], where for example the reference voltage is taken from a low-voltage source. The accuracy of this measurement is good to such a degree that the stability of permanent magnets over a long period can be measured. This type of measurement may be employed for point measurement, gradient measurement with two probes, etc. and the probe may be realised as an evaporated film [522].

The force acting on the conductor can also be used [447, 542, 555]. Numerous measurement methods are described in the works [431, 449,

481], while in the proceedings [494] the model measurement method taking into consideration the saturation phenomenon is found.

Flux meters are also suitable for measurement of the magnetic field. Article [535] provides data relative to the *Grassot* fluxmeter and the paper [477] describes a direct reading fluxmeter, with which an accuracy of 0.1% is attained. Another similar fluxmeter is the ballistic galvanometer [516], whose accuracy has been investigated in detail theoretically [455] and in practice [552]. The method of compensation is used here also [507], and compensation is achieved by means of a second coil placed in the reference field. By varying the compensating voltage [450, 453], a degree of accuracy is obtained whereby the stability of permanent magnets may be investigated [536]. A widely used variant of flux measurement with ballistic galvanometers is the 'servofluxmeter' operating with automatic compensation [425, 437, 467, 483] and which is a very old invention [448], and due to its photoelectric component is termed also the photoelectric fluxmeter.

The phenomenon of nuclear resonance [433, 445, 553] and electron resonance [533] is also suitable for measurement of the magnetic field. The proton resonance magnetometer [500] is in wide use, and provides high accuracy [517]. The measuring process employing magnetic resonance is also suitable for point measurements [440]. The greatest possible accuracy is also aimed at with this type of equipment. For example, the communication [422] presents the description of a nuclear resonance equipment, where movement of the feed cable does not perturb the measuring oscillator. It is self-evident that the frequency of the oscillator is adjustable [419, 451]. Differential magnetometers are also used here, and the two coils (with the measuring fluid) are fed by two oscillators [457]. The equipment is suitable for gradient measurement [518, 529], also with quadrupole compensating coil [435], from the compensating current of which the gradient derives directly [434]. A further article [409] treats magnetic field measurement by the parametric resonance method.

The magnetic field can be measured also with electron resonance [458], and the width of the resonance signal may correspond to $3 \times 10^{-6} \, T$ [476].

Numerous summaries of magnetic field measurement are given [81, 115, 424], and also [413, 464, 472, 487, 535, 548].

(E) CLASSICAL EQUATIONS OF MOTION

When introducing equations of motion in the literature, in most cases the start is made from the theory of point-like particles possessing mass and charge, and only later are the equations of motion of the continuous medium discussed. There is no doubt that the concept of point-like particles is the simpler. Nevertheless, our book treats the equations of motion of the continuous medium with primacy, mainly for the sake of uniformity, since when discussing the electric-magnetic field, the concept of continuous field necessarily formed the background. Secondly: the axiomatic method of discussion based on the basic equations assumes a reader's level of knowledge, where differences in abstraction play no role. By choosing this method of treatment, a closer approach to modern physics—even if only to a small degree—is achieved, whereby the equations of motion are derived from the field equations [91].

In the following discussion trajectory calculations are based on classical mechanics. We are not dealing with relativistic mechanics since this falls beyond the scope of our subject area. Since from the equations of motion relevant to continuous media the particular particle equations of motion (in our case: electron of constant value elementary mass and point-charge) are derived, and we have arrived at the dynamics of charged particles, we now impose further restrictions with regard to the material under discussion. From the field of electron optics, only one part of static electron optics is investigated, and dynamic electron optics are entirely disregarded. With the aid of the foregoing, the electric forces can be calculated, or in the more general cases, the electric-magnetic forces, and analysis of the electron trajectories can be performed. For this analysis an exact formulation of the equations of motions must be carried out, e.g. the axially symmetric case. In other fields, which now are not present, the complex formulation of trajectory equations is also customary, as for example in aberration calculations. The precise formulation of the equations of motion enable derivation of equation types necessary for the following. As most important, the paraxial formulation of the equations of motion appear, which are termed briefly first-order equations. Equations of higher order are used for aberration calculations, namely third-order equations of motion in the case of spatial motions, and second-order equations in the case of planar motions. We have made numerous references to aberration calculations, but we have not used third-order equations. Among the cases investigated were those where straight electron trajectories occurred, but in the majority of the cases curved electron trajectories were characteristic. Corresponding to the varying applications, low, medium and high current-density electron beams are required, which in most cases are of straight axis or are homocentric. According to the requirement, the beam axis may be previously chosen as a given curve. Reference is made in several places to the demands relative to the prescribed curve and the characteristics of such systems [124].

17. NEWTON'S EQUATIONS OF MOTION

Newton's equations of motion are employed for the determination of the electron trajectories. Since in *Maxwell*'s equations continuous quantities figure with respect to each space section, *we start from the equations describing the motion of continuous media also in case of Newton's equations of motion.* Therefore the *Newton*'s equations of motion [18, 132] which we require are

$$\frac{d}{dt}\,\tau\dot{\mathbf{r}} = \mathbf{f}$$

17.1

Equation 17.1 gives the motion of a continuous medium with τ mass density, moving upon the effect of force density $\mathbf{f}$. The notations represent:

τ = mass density (kg m^{-3});
$\dot{\mathbf{r}}$ = progression velocity (m s^{-1}) of the medium with τ mass density;
$\tau\dot{\mathbf{r}}$ = impulse density (kg m^{-2}s^{-1});
$\mathbf{f}$ = force density (kg m^{-2}s^{-2}).

The force density acting on the space charge flowing in the electric-magnetic field is given by the *Lorentz* expression [146]

$$\mathbf{f} = \varrho\mathbf{E} + \varrho\dot{\mathbf{r}} \times \mathbf{B}$$

17.2

in which the notations correspond to those of the preceding equation. Using equation 17.2, the *Newton*'s equations of motion determining the motion of the space-charge flow in the electric-magnetic field are

$$\frac{d}{dt}\,\tau\dot{\mathbf{r}} = \varrho\mathbf{E} + \varrho\dot{\mathbf{r}} \times \mathbf{B}$$

17.3

According to our present knowledge of physics, continuous space-charge density may be considered only as an approximation, and the concept of the point-like particle, possessing mass and charge, is also used for description of the phenomena. The possibility of employment of this approximation is illustrated in the following.

Let us view an arbitrarily chosen device operating with electrons. This device will obviously have a minimal dimension. Let us notate this distance as a. Now, after considering in sequence all electrons present in the device, let us determine the maximum distance within which two neighbouring electrons are to be found. This distance is notated as b. The continuous space-charge approximation may be employed when b is by several orders of magnitude smaller than a.

Following the pattern of the foregoing, let us establish the applicability of the concept of continuous mass distribution. In our particular case it is obvious that the mass distribution and the charge distribution constitute the same function of the position, and therefore determination of one of them is sufficient.

Since in our discussions the concept of the point-like charged particle is also used, we give the equation of motion as referred to the point-like charged particle, starting out from equation 17.3. Let us now choose a closed surface with prescribed small diameter, within which only one single point-like charged particle is present. By choosing the space section surrounded by the given surface as an integration region, the volume integral of equation 17.3 will be determined

$$\int_V \frac{d}{dt} \tau \dot{\mathbf{r}} \, dv = \int_V \varrho \, \mathbf{E} \, dv + \int_V \varrho \dot{\mathbf{r}} \times \mathbf{B} \, dv \qquad 17.4$$

We now determine the values of the integrals contained in equation 17.4. The integration and differentiation on the left-hand side of the equation may be inverted, since the variables are independent of each other. In case of a sufficiently small integration region, $\dot{\mathbf{r}}$ may be considered as constant within the region, and thus may be placed before the integral

$$\int_V \frac{d}{dt} \tau \dot{\mathbf{r}} \, dv = \frac{d}{dt} \dot{\mathbf{r}} \int_V \tau \, dv = \frac{d}{dt} m \dot{\mathbf{r}} \qquad 17.5$$

In case of a sufficiently small integration region in the first integral on the right-hand side of the equation, $\mathbf{E}$ may be considered as a constant in the region and may likewise be placed before the integral

$$\int_V \varrho \, \mathbf{E} \, dv = \mathbf{E} \int_V \varrho \, dv = q \mathbf{E} \qquad 17.6$$

In case of a sufficiently small integration region in the second integral of the right-hand side of the equation, $\dot{\mathbf{r}} \times \mathbf{B}$ may be considered as a constant in the region and may also be placed before the integral

$$\int_V \varrho \dot{\mathbf{r}} \times \mathbf{B} \, dv = \dot{\mathbf{r}} \times \mathbf{B} \int_V \varrho \, dv = q \dot{\mathbf{r}} \times \mathbf{B} \qquad 17.7$$

Substituting the calculated terms into equation 17.4 we obtain

$$\frac{d}{dt} m\dot{\mathbf{r}} = q\mathbf{E} + q\dot{\mathbf{r}} \times \mathbf{B} \tag{17.8}$$

Equation 17.8 is *Newton's* equation of motion for point-like charged particles moving in the electric-magnetic field. The expression on the right-hand side of equation 17.8 may be denoted by a single letter on the pattern of equation 17.1 [147, 153]

$$\mathbf{F} = q\mathbf{E} + q\dot{\mathbf{r}} \times \mathbf{B} \tag{17.9}$$

The newly introduced quantities are:

m = mass (kg);

$m\dot{\mathbf{r}}$ = impulse (kg m s^{-1});

$\mathbf{F}$ = force (kg m s^{-2}).

Note

(i) Exact derivation of equation 17.8, from equation 17.4 is possible only by the use of limits.

(ii) The first term on the right-hand side of equation 17.9 gives the force exerted by the electric field and acting on the charged particle. Notation $\mathbf{F}_e$ is customary.

(iii) The second term on the right-hand side of equation 17.9 gives the force exerted by the magnetic field and acting on the charged particle. Notation $\mathbf{F}_m$ is customary.

(iv) The value of mass m in case of electrons is [39, 164, 166, 167]

$$m = 9.1079 \times 10^{-31} \text{ kg} \tag{17.10}$$

The first integral of equation 17.8, i.e. the equation of energy, taking into account that $(\dot{\mathbf{r}} \times \mathbf{B}) \cdot \dot{\mathbf{r}} = 0$ is

$$\frac{1}{2} m\dot{\mathbf{r}}^2 = -q\varphi + D_0 \tag{17.11}$$

where

$$D_0 = \frac{1}{2} m\dot{\mathbf{r}}_0^2 + q\varphi_0 \tag{17.12}$$

The index 0 refers to the values at the starting point. The case when zero velocity pertains to zero potential is of considerable importance. Now $D_0 = 0$, and equation 17.11 is simplified

$$\frac{1}{2} m\dot{\mathbf{r}}^2 = -q\varphi \tag{17.13}$$

We introduce now the notation

$$\eta = \frac{e}{m} \tag{17.14}$$

7*

$e = -\oint$

which is the electronic charge to mass ratio ($A s kg^{-1}$). Using this notation, equation 17.8, in the case of constant m mass, and equation 17.13 may be written as follows

$$\ddot{\mathbf{r}} = -\eta\mathbf{E} - \eta\dot{\mathbf{r}}\times\mathbf{B} \qquad\qquad 17.15$$

$$\dot{\mathbf{r}}^2 = 2\eta\varphi \qquad\qquad 17.16$$

Equation 17.15 is the basic equation of electron motion, and equation 17.16 is its first integral.

Note

(i) In the equations m represents the rest mass of the electron, the customary notation of which is m_0.

(ii) In equation 17.14 defining η, m is the rest mass. Its numerical value is [39, 164, 166, 167]

$$\eta = 1.7588 \times 10^{11} \, A s kg^{-1} \qquad\qquad 17.17$$

18. EQUATIONS OF MOTION IN AXIALLY SYMMETRIC FIELDS

By reducing to components the vector equations 17.15 and 17.16 in cylindrical coordinate system, the following system of equations is produced [130, 153]

$$\ddot{r} - r\dot{\alpha}^2 = -\eta E_r - \eta(r\dot{\alpha}B_z - \dot{z}B_\alpha) \qquad\qquad 18.1$$

$$r\ddot{\alpha} + 2\dot{r}\dot{\alpha} = -\eta E_\alpha - \eta(\dot{z}B_r - \dot{r}B_z) \qquad\qquad 18.2$$

$$\ddot{z} = -\eta E_z - \eta(\dot{r}B_\alpha - r\dot{\alpha}B_r) \qquad\qquad 18.3$$

$$\dot{r}^2 + r^2\dot{\alpha}^2 + \dot{z}^2 = 2\eta\varphi \qquad\qquad 18.4$$

Although it is generally known, let it be mentioned that in the present case a vector assumes the form

$$\mathbf{r}(t) = r(t)\mathbf{e}_r + \alpha(t)\mathbf{e}_\alpha + z(t)\mathbf{e}_z \qquad\qquad 18.5$$

and the points represent differentiation with respect to time.

In the case of position vectors α equals zero and figures only in the unit vector expressions

$$\mathbf{e}_r = \cos\alpha\,\mathbf{i} + \sin\alpha\mathbf{j}; \quad \mathbf{e}_\alpha = -\sin\alpha\,\mathbf{i} + \cos\alpha\mathbf{j}; \quad \mathbf{e}_z = \mathbf{k}$$

The simpler equations pertaining to axially symmetric field-strength distribution are derived from the general equations 18.1, 18.2, 18.3, 18.4.

(a) Time-dependent equations

Equations 5.2 and 5.4 are used for derivation of the equations of motion relevant to this case. After simple substitutions we obtain

$$\ddot{r} - r\dot{\alpha}^2 = -\eta E_r - \eta\dot{\alpha}B_z \qquad 18.6$$

$$r\ddot{\alpha} + 2\dot{r}\dot{\alpha} = -\eta(\dot{z}B_r - \dot{r}B_z) \qquad 18.7$$

$$\ddot{z} = -\eta E_z + \eta\dot{r}\dot{\alpha}B_r \qquad 18.8$$

$$\dot{r}^2 + r^2\dot{\alpha}^2 + \dot{z}^2 = 2\eta\varphi \qquad 18.9$$

Using equations 5.5, 5.7, 5.33, we now substitute the potentials instead of the field-strength components and writing A instead of A_α

$$\ddot{r} - r\dot{\alpha}^2 = \eta\,\frac{\partial\varphi}{\partial r} - \eta\dot{\alpha}\frac{\partial}{\partial r}(rA) \qquad 18.10$$

$$r\ddot{\alpha} + 2\dot{r}\dot{\alpha} = \eta\dot{z}\frac{\partial A}{\partial z} + \eta\frac{\dot{r}}{r}\frac{\partial}{\partial r}(rA) \qquad 18.11$$

$$\ddot{z} = \eta\frac{\partial\varphi}{\partial z} - \eta r\dot{\alpha}\frac{\partial A}{\partial z} \qquad 18.12$$

where we have employed the identity

$$\frac{1}{r}\frac{\partial}{\partial r}(rA) = \frac{1}{r}A + \frac{\partial A}{\partial r} \qquad 18.13$$

A further identity is also used

$$\frac{d}{dt}(rA) = \dot{r}A + r\left(\frac{\partial A}{\partial r}\dot{r} + \frac{\partial A}{\partial z}\dot{z}\right) \qquad 18.14$$

and the left-hand side of equation 18.11 is transformed

$$\frac{1}{r}\frac{d}{dt}(r^2\dot{\alpha}) = r\ddot{\alpha} + 2\dot{r}\dot{\alpha} \qquad 18.15$$

Now the new form of equation 18.11 becomes

$$\frac{1}{r}\frac{d}{dt}(r^2\dot{\alpha}) = \eta\frac{1}{r}\frac{d}{dt}(rA) \qquad 18.16$$

Transforming equation 18.16

$$\frac{d}{dt}\left(\frac{r^2\dot{\alpha}}{\eta} - rA\right) = 0 \qquad 18.17$$

and integrating

$$\frac{r^2 \dot{\alpha}}{\eta} - rA = C \qquad\qquad 18.18$$

The value of the constant of integration C can be calculated from the initial conditions, using the customary notations of the initial value, the function values taken at the moment of time $t = t_0$ are denoted by zero index

$$r(t_0) = r_0; \quad \alpha(t_0) = \alpha_0; \quad z(t_0) = z_0 \qquad\qquad 18.19$$

$$\dot{r}(t_0) = \dot{r}_0; \quad \dot{\alpha}(t_0) = \dot{\alpha}_0; \quad \dot{z}(t_0) = \dot{z}_0 \qquad\qquad 18.20$$

$$\varphi(r_0 z_0) = \varphi_0; \quad A(r_0, z_0) = A_0 \qquad\qquad 18.21$$

Using the necessar initial conditions

$$C = \frac{1}{\eta} r_0^2 \dot{\alpha}_0 - r_0 A_0 \qquad\qquad 18.22$$

Now

$$\dot{\alpha} = \eta \frac{rA + C}{r^2} \qquad\qquad 18.23$$

is used in place of equation 18.11.

Equations 18.10 and 18.12 may be written in a simplified form, by introduction of the *generalised potential*

$$Q = \varphi - \frac{\eta}{2} \left(A + \frac{C}{r} \right)^2 \qquad\qquad 18.24$$

Using equation 18.24

$$\ddot{r} = \eta \frac{\partial Q}{\partial r} ; \quad \ddot{z} = \eta \frac{\partial Q}{\partial z} \qquad\qquad 18.25$$

The right-hand sides of equation 18.25 may be considered as *generalised field-strength components*, apart from η.

To prove the first equation of 18.25, let us differentiate equation 18.24

$$\frac{\partial Q}{\partial r} = \frac{\partial \varphi}{\partial r} - \eta \left(A + \frac{C}{r} \right) \left(\frac{\partial A}{\partial r} - \frac{C}{r^2} \right) \qquad\qquad 18.26$$

Substituting equation 18.23 into 18.26

$$\frac{\partial Q}{\partial r} = \frac{\partial \varphi}{\partial r} - r\dot{\alpha} \left(\frac{\partial A}{\partial r} - \frac{C}{r^2} \right) \qquad\qquad 18.27$$

and taking into account the identity

$$\frac{\partial A}{\partial r} = B_z - \frac{1}{r} A \qquad\qquad 18.28$$

subsequent upon the third equation of 5.33 and thereafter, using equation 18.23 we obtain

$$\frac{\partial Q}{\partial r} = \frac{\partial \varphi}{\partial r} - r\dot{\alpha}\left(B_z - \frac{1}{\eta}\dot{\alpha}\right) \qquad 18.29$$

Substituting 18.29 into 18.25 and rearranging, equation 18.6 is obtained, which is equivalent to 18.10. The second equation of 18.25 is directly proven by differentiation of 18.24, and with substitution of 18.23 (18.12 is a direct result, after performing the foregoing).

The introduced generalised potential is also used for the approximative calculation procedures and for determination of the trajectories by measurement [578, 587].

(b) Equations of the geometrical trajectory

Our equations derived so far give the geometrical trajectory of the electron and the relevant time of travel. In most cases we are not interested in the time of travel, and we seek only the trajectory. This space curve will be given in the form

$$\mathbf{r}(z) = r(z)\mathbf{e}_r + \alpha(z)\mathbf{e}_\alpha + z\mathbf{e}_z \qquad 18.30$$

The initial conditions pertaining to point $z = z_0$ are evident

$$r(z_0) = r_0; \quad \alpha(z_0) = \alpha_0 \qquad 18.31$$

$$r'(z_0) = r_0'; \quad \alpha(z_0) = \alpha_0' \qquad 18.32$$

For producing the differential equation relevant to the functions $r(z)$ and $\alpha(z)$, we start from the identities

$$\dot{\alpha} = \frac{d\alpha}{dt} = \frac{d\alpha}{dz}\frac{dz}{dt} = \alpha'\dot{z} \qquad 18.33$$

$$\dot{r} = \frac{dr}{dt} = \frac{dr}{dz}\frac{dz}{dt} = r'\dot{z} \qquad 18.34$$

$$\ddot{r} = \frac{d^2r}{dt^2} = \frac{d^2r}{dz^2}\left(\frac{dz}{dt}\right)^2 + \frac{dr}{dz}\frac{d^2z}{dt^2} = r''\dot{z}^2 + r'\ddot{z} \qquad 18.35$$

Equations 18.33 and 18.34 are substituted into 18.9 and $\dot{z}^2$ is expressed

$$\dot{z}^2 = \frac{2\eta\varphi}{1 + r'^2 + r^2\alpha'^2} \qquad 18.36$$

Equations 18.23 and 18.36 are then substituted into equation 18.33, and solved for α'

$$\alpha' - \eta\frac{1}{r^2}\frac{rA + C}{\left\{2\eta\varphi - \eta^2\left(A + \frac{C}{r}\right)^2\right\}^{1/2}}(1 + r'^2)^{1/2} = 0 \qquad 18.37$$

Substituting equations 18.6, 18.8, 18.23, 18.36, 18.37 into equation 18.35 and rearranging we have

$$r'' + \frac{1 + r'^2}{2\varphi - \eta \left(A + \dfrac{C}{r}\right)^2} \left\{ E_r - r'E_z + \eta \left(A + \frac{C}{r}\right) \left[B_z + \right. \right.$$

$$\left. \left. + r'B_r - \frac{1}{r}\left(A + \frac{C}{r}\right) \right] \right\} = 0 \qquad\qquad 18.38$$

Equations 18.37 and 18.38 are the required differential equations. Their defect, and indirectly that of α', is that the potentials and field strength occur mixed in the equations. This defect can be eliminated by writing the derivatives of the potentials.

The above differential equations can also be given in the function of the generalised potential, and its derivatives, the generalised field-strength components. The course of demonstration corresponds to that of the previous case with the difference that here equation 18.25 is used instead of 18.6 and 18.8. The final results are

$$\alpha' - \eta \frac{1}{r^2} \frac{rA + C}{(2\eta Q)^{1/2}} (1 + r'^2)^{1/2} = 0 \qquad\qquad 18.39$$

$$r'' - \frac{1 + r'^2}{2Q} \left(\frac{\partial Q}{\partial r} - r' \frac{\partial Q}{\partial z} \right) = 0 \qquad\qquad 18.40$$

No omissions have been made in the equations of motion valid for the electron, in case of axially symmetric field-strength distribution, and therefore these are of general validity and provide exact solutions.

Equations 18.38 and 18.40 may be used independently: $\alpha(z)$ and its derivatives do not figure in the equations. They are characteristic of the motion types discussed and may be considered as *basic equations*.

19. EQUATIONS OF MOTION IN FIELDS WITH
PLANAR DISTRIBUTION

By reducing vector equations 17.15 and 17.16 to their components in the Cartesian coordinate system, the following system of equations appears [129]

$$\ddot{x} = -\eta E_x - \eta(\dot{y}B_z - \dot{z}B_y) \qquad\qquad 19.1$$

$$\ddot{y} = -\eta E_y - \eta(\dot{z}B_x - \dot{x}B_z) \qquad\qquad 19.2$$

$$\ddot{z} = -\eta E_z - \eta(\dot{x}B_y - \dot{y}B_x) \qquad\qquad 19.3$$

$$\dot{x}^2 + \dot{y}^2 + \dot{z}^2 = 2\eta\varphi \qquad\qquad 19.4$$

Similarly to the axially symmetric case, we give herewith the expression of the position vector

$$\mathbf{r}(t) = x(t)\mathbf{e}_x + y(t)\mathbf{e}_y + z(t)\mathbf{e}_z \qquad 19.5$$

The differentiation with respect to time is denoted by a dot.

The simpler equations pertaining to the planar field-strength distribution are derived from the general equations 19.1, 19.2, 19.3, 19.4.

Note: It is customary to write the general equations of a charged particle moving in quadrupole field in the Cartesian coordinate system. Therefore, in the given general equations 19.1–19.4 the field-strength components and the scalar potential are to be identified with those of the quadrupole field. Due to the more general character of the quadrupole field we do not find a generalised potential (Q) valid for all cases, and therefore no simple forms, similar to those for the axially symmetric and the fields with planar distribution, exist. Consequently, we treat the equations of motion occurring in the quadrupole field in full detail only in the paraxial case.

(a) Time-dependent equations

Equations of motion relevant to the fields with planar distribution are derived from equations 7.2 and 7.4. After simple substitution we obtain

$$\ddot{x} = -\eta(\dot{y}B_z - \dot{z}B_y) \qquad 19.6$$

$$\ddot{y} = -\eta E_y + \eta\dot{x}B_z \qquad 19.7$$

$$\ddot{z} = -\eta E_z - \eta\dot{x}B_y \qquad 19.8$$

$$\dot{x}^2 + \dot{y}^2 + \dot{z}^2 = 2\eta\varphi \qquad 19.9$$

From equations 19.6, 19.7, 19.8, 19.9 we are able to establish that the electron trajectory is generally a curve in space, and only in special cases does it become a planar curve.

Now, using equations 7.8, 7.9, 7.25, let us substitute the potentials, writing A instead of A_x in consideration of the close of § 7, instead of the field-strength components employing the following identity

$$\frac{dA}{dt} = \frac{\partial A}{\partial y}\dot{y} + \frac{\partial A}{\partial z}\dot{z} \qquad 19.10$$

Equation 19.6 can be integrated then on the pattern of the axially symmetric case. The value of the constant of integration C can be calculated from the initial conditions

$$x(t_0) = x_0;\ y(t_0) = y_0;\ z(t_0) = z_0 \qquad 19.11$$

$$\dot{x}(t_0) = \dot{x}_0;\ \dot{y}(t_0) = \dot{y}_0;\ \dot{z}(t_0) = \dot{z}_0 \qquad 19.12$$

$$\varphi(y_0, z_0) = \varphi_0;\quad A(y_0, z_0) = A_0 \qquad 19.13$$

Finally, equation

$$\dot{x} = \eta(A + C) \qquad\qquad 19.14$$

is obtained. In equation 19.14

$$C = \frac{1}{\eta}\dot{x}_0 - A_0 \qquad\qquad 19.15$$

The generalised potential

$$Q = \varphi - \frac{\eta}{2}(A + C)^2 \qquad\qquad 19.16$$

may be introduced in case of fields with planar distribution, whereby the following simple equations of motion can be obtained

$$\ddot{y} = \eta\frac{\partial Q}{\partial y} ; \quad \ddot{z} = \eta\frac{\partial Q}{\partial z} \qquad\qquad 19.17$$

In order to verify the proposition 19.17, we differentiate 19.16, substitute 19.14 and multiply by η.

(b) Equations of the geometrical trajectory

The geometrical trajectory is given in the form of

$$\mathbf{r}(z) = x(z)\mathbf{e}_x + y(z)\mathbf{e}_y + z\mathbf{e}_z \qquad\qquad 19.18$$

The necessary initial conditions are

$$x(z_0) = x_0; \quad y(z_0) = y_0 \qquad\qquad 19.19$$
$$x'(z_0) = x'_0; \quad y'_0(z_0) = y'_0 \qquad\qquad 19.20$$

In order to produce differential equations relevant to functions $x(z)$ and $y(z)$, the identities

$$\dot{x} = \frac{dx}{dt} = \frac{dx}{dz}\frac{dz}{dt} = x'\dot{z} \qquad\qquad 19.21$$

$$\dot{y} = \frac{dy}{dt} = \frac{dy}{dz}\frac{dz}{dt} = y'\dot{z} \qquad\qquad 19.22$$

$$\ddot{y} = \frac{d^2y}{dt^2} = \frac{d^2y}{dz^2}\left(\frac{dz}{dt}\right)^2 + \frac{dy}{dz}\frac{d^2z}{dt^2} = y''\dot{z}^2 + y'\ddot{z} \qquad\qquad 19.23$$

are used.

The following are yielded by the known method

$$\dot{z}^2 = \frac{2\eta\varphi}{1 + x'^2 + y'^2} \qquad\qquad 19.24$$

$$x' - \eta \frac{A + C}{[2\eta\varphi - \eta^2(A + C)^2]^{1/2}} (1 + y'^2)^{1/2} = 0 \qquad\qquad 19.25$$

$$y'' + \frac{1 + y'^2}{2\varphi - \eta(A + C)^2} [E_y - y'E_z - \eta(A + C)(B_z + y'B_y)] = 0 \quad 19.26$$

The required differential equations are 19.25 and 19.26, which can also be written with the exclusive use of the potentials.

The above differential equations in the function of the generalised potential are

$$\frac{d}{dz}$$

$$x' - \eta \frac{A + C}{(2\eta Q)^{1/2}} (1 + y'^2)^{1/2} = 0 \qquad\qquad 19.27$$

$$y'' - \frac{1 + y'^2}{2Q} \left(\frac{\partial Q}{\partial y} - y' \frac{\partial Q}{\partial z} \right) = 0 \qquad\qquad 19.28$$

In the equations of motion valid for the electron in the case of planar field-strength distribution, no omissions have been made, hence they are of general validity and give exact solutions.

Equations 19.26 and 19.28 can be treated independently: $x(z)$ and its derivatives do not figure in the equations. They are characteristic of the motion type discussed and may be considered as *basic equations*.

20. PARAXIAL EQUATIONS OF MOTION

In many cases of realised electric-magnetic fields, the course of the motions is such that the field strengths occurring in the space section used for motion can be well approached by first-order expressions. Equations of motion constructed with the help of field-strength components thus obtained well determine the motion in the space section concerned; moreover, handling of the equations of simpler structure facilitates solution searching.

It has been seen that non-linear expressions of the unknown functions are contained in the equations of motion. Simplification is also resorted to in this respect, and only paraxial motion is permitted in the space section used for motion.

Paraxial motion represents such motion where the distance of the points of the trajectory is measured from a given plane, in our case from plane x, z, or from a given axis, in our case from axis z, and the angles between the tangents of the trajectory and the given plane or axis are of such value that when expanding both characteristics in series, first-order expressions are satisfactory. In other words, both the distance and the angle are small.

The equations of motion constructed in the above manner are called paraxial or first-order equations of motion.

The paraxial equations of motion will be constructed for cases of field strengths with planar distribution 7.43, 7.44 and 7.52, 7.53 derived from the potentials given by the series 7.42 and 7.51, field strengths with axially symmetric distribution 5.56, 5.57 and 5.70, 5.71 derived from the potentials

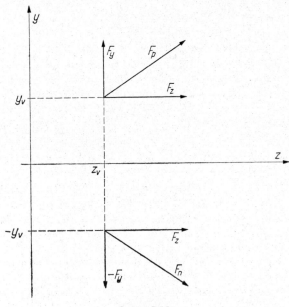

figure I.13

given by the series 5.54, 5.69 and the quadrupole fields 9.39, 9.40, 9.41 and 9.51, 9.52, 9.53 derived from the potentials given by the series 9.35, 9.50. *Motion types having symmetry properties pertain to the field-strength distributions under discussion.*

By comparison of field strengths with plane-symmetric distribution (7.43, 7.44, 7.52, 7.53) according to figure I.13, the following will be readily understood.

The paths of the electrons started with mirror-symmetric initial conditions with respect to axis z are mirror-symmetric with respect to axis z. Since there are no restrictions, apart from the initial conditions, to the conditions along the axis x, it may be stated in general that with regard to the plane x, z (mirror plane) the paths form the reflected images of each other.

Viewing the field strengths with axially symmetric distribution (5.56, 5.57, 5.70, 5.71) in the meridian plane according to figure I.14, the following will be recognised.

The paths of the electrons started with initial conditions mirror-symmetric with respect to axis z are mirror-symmetric to this axis. Since the angular displacement α retains this symmetry, it may be stated in general that the paths are rotationally symmetric with respect to axis z.

In view of the above, for the motions in quadrupole fields the mirror-symmetry of the initial conditions must be specified in the two preferred

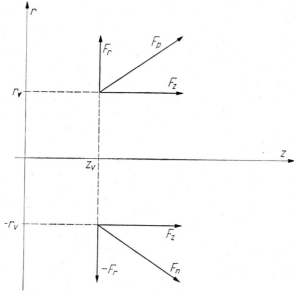

figure I.14

planes, perpendicular to each other, occurring in the quadrupole fields. In this case, the two preferred planes will be the planes of symmetry (mirror planes) for the beam produced.

21. PARAXIAL EQUATIONS OF MOTION
IN AXIALLY SYMMETRIC FIELDS

Let us substitute the first-order expressions of the series 5.56, 5.57, 5.69, 5.70, 5.71, which are

$$E_r(r, z) = \frac{1}{2}\left(\Phi'' + \frac{1}{\varepsilon_0}\varrho_0\right) r \qquad 21.1$$

$$E_z(r, z) = -\Phi' \qquad 21.2$$

$$A(r, z) = \frac{1}{2} Br \qquad 21.3$$

$$B_r(r, z) = -\frac{1}{2} B'r \qquad\qquad 21.4$$

$$B_z(r, z) = B \qquad\qquad 21.5$$

into equations 18.22, 18.6, 18.23, 18.8

$$C = \frac{1}{\eta} r_0^2 \dot{\alpha}_0 - \frac{1}{2} B_0 r_0^2 \qquad\qquad 21.6$$

$$\ddot{r} = -\eta \left[\frac{1}{2} \left(\Phi'' + \frac{1}{\varepsilon_0} \varrho_0 \right) + \frac{\eta}{4} B^2 \right] r + \eta^2 C^2 \frac{1}{r^3} \qquad\qquad 21.7$$

$$\dot{\alpha} = \eta \left(\frac{1}{2} B + C \frac{1}{r^2} \right) \qquad\qquad 21.8$$

$$\ddot{z} = \eta \Phi' \qquad\qquad 21.9$$

Equations 21.6, 21.7, 21.8, 21.9 are the time-dependent paraxial equations. Let us detail the last term of equation 21.7

$$\eta^2 C^2 \frac{1}{r^3} = \frac{r_0^4 \dot{\alpha}_0^2}{r^3} - \eta B_0 \frac{r_0^4 \dot{\alpha}_0}{r^3} + \frac{\eta^2 B_0^2}{4} \frac{r_0^4}{r^3} \qquad\qquad 21.10$$

With regard to the unknown functions and the initial values of equation 21.10, the first term of the right-hand side is of third order, the second term is of second order, and only the third term is of first order. Therefore, instead of equation 21.7

$$\ddot{r} = -\eta \left[\frac{1}{2} \left(\Phi'' + \frac{1}{\varepsilon_0} \varrho_0 \right) + \frac{\eta}{4} B^2 \right] r + \frac{\eta^2 B_0^2 r_0^4}{4} \frac{1}{r^3} \qquad\qquad 21.11$$

may be used, since in most cases the terms of higher order may be neglected. The advantage of this equation over equation 21.7 is that knowledge of $\dot{\alpha}_0$ is not necessary for determination of r. Equation 21.7 is used only in cases of high initial angular velocities.

The geometric trajectory equations may be obtained by the above substitutions from either equations 18.37, 18.38, or from 18.39, 18.40, taking into consideration also that r'^2 may be neglected in comparison with the unit. The value of C given in these equations is in accordance with equation 21.6. The first-order expression of the series 5.54 is also necessary

$$\varphi(r, z) = \Phi \qquad\qquad 21.12$$

The substitution results

$$\alpha' - \frac{\eta}{(2\eta\Phi)^{1/2}} \left[\frac{1}{2} B + C \frac{1}{r^2} \right] = 0 \qquad\qquad 21.13$$

$$\Phi r'' + \frac{1}{2}\Phi'r' + \left[\frac{1}{4}\left(\Phi'' + \frac{1}{\varepsilon_0}\varrho_0\right) + \frac{\eta}{8}B^2\right]r - \frac{\eta}{2}C^2\frac{1}{r^3} = 0 \quad 21.14$$

Equations 21.13, 21.14 are the paraxial equations of the geometrical trajectory. Equation 21.14 is also the paraxial basic equation.

The last term of equation 21.14 is exactly 1/2 η-fold of the last term of 21.7. Therefore, the remarks relating to this equation are valid here, too. Therefore, instead of equation 21.14, the equation

$$\Phi r'' + \frac{1}{2}\Phi'r' + \left[\frac{1}{4}\left(\Phi'' + \frac{1}{\varepsilon_0}\varrho_0\right) + \frac{\eta}{8}B^2\right]r - \frac{\eta B_0^2}{8}\frac{r_0^4}{r^3} = 0 \quad 21.15$$

may also be used; its advantage is that knowledge of $\dot{\alpha}_0$ is not required for the determination of r. Equation 21.14 is used in case of high initial angular velocities.

Equation 21.15 may also be considered as basic equation.

Note

(i) Equations 21.13, 21.14, 21.15 can be obtained from equations 21.6, 21.7, 21.8, 21.9, 21.11 by using the well-known method of elimination of time.

(ii) The concept of meridian plane may be introduced when calculating the distance of the electron from the axis either from equation 21.14 or from 21.15. We then say that the electron motion takes place in a plane rotating at α' 'angular velocity' (equation 21.13) around axis z. In the meridian plane r may be either positive or negative.

22. PARAXIAL EQUATIONS OF MOTION IN FIELDS
WITH PLANAR SYMMETRY

Now we substitute the first-order expressions of the series 7.43, 7.44, 7.51, 7.52, 7.53, which are

$$E_y(y, z) = \left(\Phi'' + \frac{1}{\varepsilon_0}\varrho_0\right)y \qquad\qquad 22.1$$

$$E_z(y, z) = -\Phi' \qquad\qquad 22.2$$

$$A(y, z) = -By \qquad\qquad 22.3$$

$$B_y(y, z) = -B'y \qquad\qquad 22.4$$

$$B_z(y, z) = B \qquad\qquad 22.5$$

into equations 19.15, 19.14, 19.7, 19.8

$$C = \frac{1}{\eta}\dot{x}_0 + B_0 y_0 \qquad\qquad 22.6$$

$$\dot{x} = \eta(C - By) \qquad\qquad 22.7$$

$$\ddot{y} = -\eta\left[\Phi'' + \frac{1}{\varepsilon_0}\varrho_0 + \eta B^2\right]y + \eta^2 CB \qquad 22.8$$

$$\ddot{z} = \eta\Phi' + \eta\dot{x}_0 B'y \qquad\qquad 22.9$$

Equations 22.6, 22.7, 22.8, 22.9 are the time-dependent paraxial equations. In most cases the second term of the right-hand side of equation 22.9 may be neglected.

Note: The complete term $\eta^2 CB'y$ is not contained in the right-hand side of equation 22.9 since the second term in the right-hand side of equation

$$\eta^2 CB'y = \eta\dot{x}_0 B'y + \eta^2 y_0 B_0 B'y \qquad 22.10$$

is a second-order expression of the unknown function y and of the initial value of y_0.

The equations of the geometrical trajectory are obtained from equations 19.25, 19.26 or from equations 19.27, 19.28 by the preceding substitutions, taking into account that y'^2 may be disregarded in comparison with the unit. The value of C included in these equations is in accordance with equation 22.6. The first-order expression of series 7.42 is also required

$$\varphi(y, z) = \Phi \qquad\qquad 22.11$$

The result of the substitution is

$$x' - \frac{\eta}{(2\eta\Phi)^{1/2}}(C - By) = 0 \qquad 22.12$$

$$\Phi y'' + \frac{1}{2}\Phi'y' + \frac{1}{2}\left[\Phi'' + \frac{1}{\varepsilon_0}\varrho_0 + \eta B^2\right]y - \frac{\eta}{2}CB = 0 \qquad 22.13$$

Equations 22.12, 22.13 are the paraxial equations of the geometrical trajectory. Equation 22.13 is also the paraxial basic equation.

Note

(i) Equations 22.12, 22.13 may be obtained also from equations 22.6, 22.7, 22.8, 22.9, using the method of time elimination.

(ii) Claculating the distance of the electron from the plane (x, z) according to equation 22.13, the concept of the meridian plane may be introduced. We then say that the electron motion takes place in the meridian plane perpendicular to axis x and moving at 'velocity' x' (equation 22.12) in the direction of x.

23. PARAXIAL EQUATIONS OF MOTION IN QUADRUPOLE FIELDS

On the pattern of the foregoing, the first-order forms (9.39, 9.40, 9.41, 9.51, 9.52, 9.53) of the field characteristics are

$$E_x(x, y, z) = \frac{1}{2}\left[\Phi''_{00} - D + \frac{1}{\varepsilon_0}\varrho_{00}\right]x \qquad 23.1$$

$$E_y(x, y, z) = \frac{1}{2} \left[\Phi_{00}'' + D + \frac{1}{\varepsilon_0} \varrho_{00} \right] y \qquad 23.2$$

$$E_z(x, y, z) = - \Phi_{00}' \qquad 23.3$$

$$B_x(x, y, z) = - V_{11} y \qquad 23.4$$

$$B_y(x, y, z) = - V_{11} x \qquad 23.5$$

$$B_z(x, y, z) = 0 \qquad 23.6$$

With these formulae the *time-dependent paraxial equations of motion* from equations 19.1, 19.2, 19.3 are as follows

$$\ddot{x} = - \frac{\eta}{2} \left[\Phi_{00}'' - D + \frac{1}{\varepsilon_0} \varrho_{00} \right] x - \eta \, V_{11} \, x\dot{z} \qquad 23.7$$

$$\ddot{y} = - \frac{\eta}{2} \left[\Phi_{00}'' + D + \frac{1}{\varepsilon_0} \varrho_{00} \right] y + \eta \, V_{11} \, y\dot{z} \qquad 23.8$$

$$\ddot{z} = \eta \Phi_{00}' + \eta V_{11} (x\dot{x} - y\dot{y}) \qquad 23.9$$

Note: In case of the time-dependent form of paraxial equations of motion referred to quadrupole fields, second-order expressions of the unknown functions must be allowed, otherwise the equations have no terms containing magnetic field.

Equations of the geometrical trajectory, with first-order approximation of equation 9.35

$$\varphi(x, y, z) = \Phi_{00} \qquad 23.10$$

Using the same method as in the foregoing, we obtain

$$x'' + \frac{\Phi_{00}''}{2\Phi_{00}} x' + \left[\frac{1}{4\Phi_{00}} \left(\Phi_{00}'' - D + \frac{1}{\varepsilon_0} \varrho_{00} \right) + \frac{\eta \, V_{11}}{(2\eta\Phi_{00})^{1/2}} \right] x = 0 \quad 23.11$$

$$y'' + \frac{\Phi_{00}''}{2\Phi_{00}} y' + \left[\frac{1}{4\Phi_{00}} \left(\Phi_{00}'' + D + \frac{1}{\varepsilon_0} \varrho_{00} \right) - \frac{\eta \, V_{11}}{(2\eta\Phi_{00})^{1/2}} \right] y = 0 \quad 23.12$$

Note

(i) In the first-order case of the geometrical trajectory equations, there is a function V_{11} characterising the magnetic field, therefore these are paraxial equations, according to the customary definitions.

(ii) If we disregard the space-charge term ϱ_{00}, the two equations of motion are independent of each other (either equation can be integrated without knowledge of the solution of the other).

SUPPLEMENTARY OBSERVATIONS ON THE
EQUATIONS OF MOTION

Derivation of the basic equations of motion of electron optics was the result of laborious and lengthy work. The most important result, and also the theoretical basis of electron optics are given in the paper [559] published in 1926, in which it was demonstrated that similarly to light rays, electron rays may be focused by means of electric and magnetic fields. This article was the first to derive angular momentum (*Busch* theorem), etc. soon after, in 1938, systems of curved central trajectory were dealt with [561], but at that time without success. However, a partial success, since the discussion presumed as spatial is of planar validity only, is represented by the article [607]. Parallel with this work, however, *G. A. Grinberg* achieved good results, which are published for example in his book [80]. The author of the present chapter has arrived at the final solution which cannot be further generalised [591] in the subject matter investigated. Two further articles dealing with systems of curvilinear basic trajectories are noteworthy. One is of a high standard and detailed [602], while the other deals with applications of the helical axis systems [567]. The latter article investigates the resolving power of the system in the mass-spectrometry application.

The completion as regards basic problems forms no obstacle to further work on the problems, some details of which are mentioned as examples. The basis of electron dynamics summarised with aid of the *Hamilton* formalism and explanation of the optical analogy is dealt with in the works [566, 568]. Numerous theorems are given in these works, which are suitable for general purposes (from generalised velocity restrictions on induction; generalised momentum; freedom from rotation; invariants, etc.). Determination of permissible and non-permissible motions of electrons moving in circular symmetric magnetic fields is treated in the work [564], as determinable from the curves plotted in the coordinate system of the kinetic energy and the generalised angular momentum. Article [562] treats the *Gauss* beamlet, and [560] gives information on the expansion of paraxial theory, with reference to gun design. Among the motions some with exact solutions were found, and these are dealt with in articles [593] and [605], the latter of which sets out from the *Hamilton* formalism and treats the spherical symmetric system as an axially symmetric system.

(F) APPROXIMATIVE SOLUTION OF THE EQUATIONS OF MOTION

Practice cannot wait until all possible trajectories are determined from theoretically available functions (available in tables). In all cases (even in the case of the helical axis for example) the path has to be approximated with the given accuracy. Numerical ray tracing serves for trajectory computation, with which the arithmetical solution of trajectory equations is obtained. Among the other forms of approximative solution is for example, approximation in sections by means of known functions, where the computation is performed by adoption of a linearly varying field characteristic (in the given case e.g. linearly decreasing).

Numerous methods have been evolved, the most suitable being selected for each case. Today, however, the mechanical and time-devouring trajectory computations are being performed increasingly by computers. The methods of electron-optical simulation—in a qualified sense, methods of trajectory simulation—are now fully developed and are readily available. It is perhaps unnecessary to add that these methods are available with respect to low-, medium- and high-current density beams, or low-, medium- and high-voltage electron beams.

24. STEP-BY-STEP INTEGRATION

This method employs the Taylor series expansion [578, 587] *for the integration.* The solution function in the vicinity of point x_0 is given by its *Taylor* series

$$y(z) = y(x_0) + \frac{y'(x_0)}{1!}(x - x_0) + \frac{y''(x_0)}{2!}(x - x_0)^2 + \dots \qquad 24.1$$

Differentiating equation 24.1, we obtain

$$y'(x) = y'(x_0) + \frac{y''(x_0)}{1!}(x - x_0) + \frac{y'''(x_0)}{2!}(x - x_0)^2 + \dots \qquad 24.2$$

The derivatives necessary for the series expansion are calculated by successive differentiation of the differential equation to be solved. The derivatives are naturally the functions of the initial values $y(x_0)$ and $y'(x_0)$.

Allowing a slight error, the values of the function and the values of the derivatives may be calculated for a small region in the vicinity of the point x_0 with the help of series 24.1 and 24.2

$$y(x_0 + \Delta x) = y(x_0) + \frac{y'(x_0)}{1!}\Delta x + \frac{y''(x_0)}{2!}\Delta x^2 + \dots \qquad 24.3$$

$$y'(x_0 + \Delta x) = y'(x_0) + \frac{y''(x_0)}{1!}\Delta x + \frac{y'''(x_0)}{2!}\Delta x^2 + \dots \qquad 24.4$$

Considering the values $y(x_0 + \Delta x)$ and $y'(x_0 + \Delta x)$ calculated from series 24.3 and 24.4 as new initial values, the above procedure is repeated and new initial values are obtained. This procedure is repeated until all function values of the desired region are determined. *The sequence of values thus determined, which obviously satisfies the initial conditions, is considered as an approximative solution of the differential equation* [581, 603].

(a) Plane-symmetric case

In order to eliminate y' from the differential equation 22.13, transformation of

$$y = \Phi^{-\frac{1}{4}} Y \qquad 24.5$$

is performed [the new function being $Y(x)$].

After transformation the differential equation becomes

$$Y'' + \left(\frac{\Phi''}{4\Phi} + \frac{3\Phi'^2}{16\Phi^2} \frac{\varrho_0}{2\varepsilon_0\Phi} + \frac{\eta B^2}{2\Phi}\right) Y - \frac{\eta CB}{2}\Phi^{-\frac{3}{4}} = 0 \qquad 24.6$$

8*

The derivatives contained in the *Taylor* series are calculated from equation 24.6 and the initial conditions may also be written

$$Y(z_n) = Y_n; \quad Y'(z_n) = Y'_n \tag{24.7}$$

$$Y''(z_n) = \frac{\eta CB}{2} \Phi^{-\frac{3}{4}} - \left[\frac{\Phi''}{4\Phi} + \frac{3\Phi'^2}{16\Phi^2} + \frac{\varrho_0}{2\varepsilon_0\Phi} + \frac{\eta B^2}{2\Phi} \right] Y_n \tag{24.8}$$

$$Y'''(z_n) = \left[\frac{\eta CB'}{2} \Phi^{-\frac{3}{4}} - \frac{3\eta CB\Phi'}{8} \Phi^{-\frac{7}{4}} \right] +$$

$$+ \left[\frac{3\Phi'^3}{8\Phi^3} + \frac{\eta B^2\Phi'}{2\Phi^2} - \frac{\Phi'''}{4\Phi} - \frac{\Phi'\Phi''}{8\Phi^2} - \frac{\eta BB'}{\Phi} + \right.$$

$$\left. + \frac{\varrho_0\Phi'}{2\varepsilon_0\Phi^2} - \frac{\varrho_0'}{2\varepsilon_0\Phi} \right] Y_n + \left[-\frac{\Phi''}{4\Phi} - \frac{3\Phi'^2}{16\Phi^2} - \right.$$

$$\left. - \frac{\varrho_0}{2\varepsilon_0\Phi} - \frac{\eta B^2}{2\Phi} \right] Y'_n \tag{24.9}$$

The relations 24.7, 24.8, 24.9 are substituted into the *Taylor* series 24.3, 24.4. After rearrangement

$$Y_{n+1} = \left[\frac{\eta CB}{4} \Phi^{-\frac{3}{4}} \Delta z^2 \right] + \left[1 - \frac{\Phi''}{8\Phi} \Delta z^2 - \frac{3\Phi'^2}{32\Phi^2} \Delta z^2 - \right.$$

$$\left. - \frac{\varrho_0}{4\varepsilon_0\Phi} \Delta z^2 - \frac{\eta B^2}{4\Phi} \Delta z^2 \right] Y_n + \Delta z Y'_n \tag{24.10}$$

$$Y'_{n+1} = \left[\frac{\eta CB}{2} \Phi^{-\frac{3}{4}} \Delta z + \frac{\eta CB'}{4} \Phi^{-\frac{3}{4}} \Delta z^2 - \frac{3\eta CB\Phi'}{16} \Phi^{-\frac{7}{4}} \Delta z^2 \right] +$$

$$+ \left[-\frac{\Phi''}{4\Phi} \Delta z - \frac{3\Phi'^2}{16\Phi^2} \Delta z - \frac{\varrho_0}{2\varepsilon_0\Phi} \Delta z - \frac{\eta B^2}{2\Phi} \Delta z + \right.$$

$$+ \frac{3\Phi'^3}{16\Phi^3} \Delta z^2 + \frac{\eta B^2\Phi'}{4\Phi^2} \Delta z^2 - \frac{\Phi'''}{8\Phi} \Delta z^2 - \frac{\Phi'\Phi''}{16\Phi^2} \Delta z^2 -$$

$$\left. - \frac{\eta BB'}{2\Phi} \Delta z^2 + \frac{\varrho_0\Phi'}{4\varepsilon_0\Phi^2} \Delta z^2 - \frac{\varrho_0'}{4\varepsilon_0\Phi} \Delta z^2 \right] Y_n +$$

$$+ \left[1 - \frac{\Phi''}{8\Phi} \Delta z^2 - \frac{3\Phi'^2}{32\Phi^2} \Delta z^2 - \frac{\varrho_0}{4\varepsilon_0\Phi} \Delta z^2 - \frac{\eta B^2}{4\Phi} \Delta z^2 \right] Y'_n \tag{24.11}$$

The values of the functions contained in the formulae are to be calculated in the position of the series expansion. y_n and y'_n can be calculated from equation 24.5.

The differential equation 22.12 can be solved with knowledge of the solution of 22.13. The initial conditions and the derivatives contained in the *Taylor* series are

$$x(z_n) = x_n \qquad\qquad 24.12$$

$$x'(z_n) = \frac{\eta C}{(2\eta\Phi)^{1/2}} - \frac{\eta B}{(2\eta\Phi)^{1/2}} y_n \qquad\qquad 24.13$$

$$x''(z_n) = -\frac{\eta C\Phi'}{2\Phi(2\eta\Phi)^{1/2}} + \left[\frac{\eta B\Phi'}{2\Phi(2\eta\Phi)^{1/2}} - \frac{\eta B'}{(2\eta\Phi)^{1/2}}\right] y_n - \frac{\eta B}{(2\eta\Phi)^{1/2}} y'_n \quad 24.14$$

After substitution and rearrangement

$$x_{n+1} = \left[x_n + \frac{\eta C}{(2\eta\Phi)^{1/2}}\,\varDelta z - \frac{\eta C\Phi'}{4\Phi(2\eta\Phi)^{1/2}}\,\varDelta z^2\right] +$$

$$+ \left[-\frac{\eta B}{(2\eta\Phi)^{1/2}}\,\varDelta z + \frac{\eta B\Phi'}{4\Phi(2\eta\Phi)^{1/2}}\,\varDelta z^2 - \frac{\eta B'}{2(2\eta\Phi)^{1/2}}\,\varDelta z^2\right] y_n +$$

$$+ \left[-\frac{\eta B}{2(2\eta\Phi)^{1/2}}\,\varDelta z^2\right] y'_n \qquad\qquad 24.15$$

Instead of the grouping

$$x_{n+1} = A^+ + B^+ x_n \qquad\qquad 24.16$$

grouping

$$x_{n+1} = C^+ + D^+ y_n + E^+ y'_n \qquad\qquad 24.17$$

is used in equation 24.15 thereby emphasising the character of 22.13 as the basic equation. Coefficients A^+, B^+, C^+, D^+, E^+ are introduced in order to facilitate recognition of the structure of the equations.

(b) Axially symmetric case

The transformation

$$r = \Phi^{-\frac{1}{4}} R \qquad\qquad 24.18$$

in equation 21.14 yields

$$R'' + \left(\frac{3}{16}\frac{\Phi'^2}{\Phi^2} + \frac{\varrho_0}{4\varepsilon_0\Phi} + \frac{\eta B^2}{8\Phi}\right) R - \frac{\eta C^2}{2}\frac{1}{R^3} = 0 \qquad 24.19$$

The derivatives contained in the *Taylor* series and the initial conditions are

$$R(z_n) = R_n; \ R'(z_n) = R'_n \qquad\qquad 24.20$$

$$R''(z_n) = \left(\frac{\eta C^2}{2} \frac{1}{R_n^4} - \frac{3}{16} \frac{\Phi'^2}{\Phi^2} - \frac{\varrho_0}{4\varepsilon_0\Phi} - \frac{\eta B^2}{8\Phi} \right) R_n \qquad 24.21$$

$$R'''(z_n) = \left[\frac{3}{8} \frac{\Phi'^3}{\Phi^3} - \frac{3}{8} \frac{\Phi'\Phi''}{\Phi^2} - \frac{\varrho_0'}{4\varepsilon_0\Phi} + \frac{\varrho_0\Phi'}{4\varepsilon_0\Phi^2} - \right.$$
$$\left. - \frac{\eta BB'}{4\Phi} + \frac{\eta B^2\Phi'}{8\Phi^2} \right] R_n + \left[- \frac{3}{16} \frac{\Phi'^2}{\Phi^2} - \right.$$
$$\left. - \frac{\varrho_0}{4\varepsilon_0\Phi} - \frac{\eta B^2}{8\Phi} - \frac{3\eta C^2}{2} \frac{1}{R_n^4} \right] R_n' \qquad 24.22$$

with which the final formulae become

$$R_{n+1} = \left[1 + \frac{\eta C^2}{4} \frac{1}{R_n^4} \varDelta z^2 - \frac{3}{32} \frac{\Phi'^2}{\Phi^2} \varDelta z^2 - \right.$$
$$\left. - \frac{\varrho_0}{8\varepsilon_0\Phi} \varDelta z^2 - \frac{\eta B^2}{16\Phi} \varDelta z^2 \right] R_n + \varDelta z R_n' \qquad 24.23$$

$$R_{n+1}' = \left[\frac{\eta C^2}{2} \frac{1}{R_n^4} \varDelta z - \frac{3}{16} \frac{\Phi'^2}{\Phi^2} \varDelta z - \frac{\varrho_0}{4\varepsilon_0\Phi} \varDelta z - \frac{\eta B^2}{8\Phi} \varDelta z + \right.$$
$$+ \frac{3}{16} \frac{\Phi'^3}{\Phi^3} \varDelta z^2 - \frac{3}{16} \frac{\Phi'\Phi''}{\Phi^2} \varDelta z^2 - \frac{\varrho_0'}{8\varepsilon_0\Phi} \varDelta z^2 +$$
$$+ \frac{\varrho_0\Phi'}{8\varepsilon_0\Phi^2} \varDelta z^2 - \frac{\eta BB'}{8\Phi} \varDelta z^2 + \frac{\eta B^2\Phi'}{16\Phi^2} \varDelta z^2 \right] R_n +$$
$$+ \left[1 - \frac{3}{32} \frac{\Phi'^2}{\Phi^2} \varDelta z^2 - \frac{\varrho_0}{8\varepsilon_0\Phi} \varDelta z^2 - \right.$$
$$\left. - \frac{\eta B^2}{16\Phi} \varDelta z^2 - \frac{3\eta C^2}{4} \frac{1}{R_n^4} \varDelta z^2 \right] R_n' \qquad 24.24$$

r_n and r_n' can be calculated from equation 24.18.

The differential equation 21.13 can be solved with knowledge of the solution of 21.14. The initial conditions and the derivatives contained in the *Taylor* series are

$$\alpha(z_n) = \alpha_n \qquad 24.25$$

$$\alpha'(z_n) = \frac{\eta B}{2(2\eta\Phi)^{1/2}} + \left(\frac{\eta C}{(2\eta\Phi)^{1/2}} \frac{1}{r_n^3} \right) r_n \qquad 24.26$$

$$\alpha''(z_n) = \left[\frac{\eta B'}{2(2\eta\Phi)^{1/2}} - \frac{\eta B\Phi'}{4\Phi(2\eta\Phi)^{1/2}} \right] +$$

$$+\left[-\frac{\eta C\Phi'}{2\Phi(2\eta\Phi)^{1/2}}\frac{1}{r_n^3}\right]r_n+\left[-\frac{2\eta C}{(2\eta\Phi)^{1/2}}\frac{1}{r_n^3}\right]r_n' \qquad 24.27$$

With substitution and rearrangement

$$\alpha_{n+1}=\left[\alpha_n+\frac{\eta B}{2(2\eta\Phi)^{1/2}}\Delta z+\frac{\eta B'}{4(2\eta\Phi)^{1/2}}\Delta z^2-\frac{\eta B\Phi'}{8\Phi(2\eta\Phi)^{1/2}}\Delta z^2\right]+$$

$$+\left[\frac{\eta C}{(2\eta\Phi)^{1/2}}\frac{1}{r_n^3}\Delta z-\frac{\eta C\Phi'}{4\Phi(2\eta\Phi)^{1/2}}\frac{1}{r_n^3}\Delta z^2\right]r_n+$$

$$+\left[-\frac{\eta C}{(2\eta\Phi)^{1/2}}\frac{1}{r_n^3}\Delta z^2\right]r_n' \qquad 24.28$$

(c) The case of quadrupole field

With transformations

$$x=\Phi_{00}^{-\frac{1}{4}}X;\quad y=\Phi_{00}^{-\frac{1}{4}}Y \qquad 24.99$$

equations 23.11 and 23.12 become

$$X''+\left[\frac{3}{16}\frac{\Phi_{00}'^2}{\Phi_{00}^2}+\frac{1}{4\Phi_{00}}\left(-D+\frac{1}{\varepsilon_0}\varrho_{00}\right)+\frac{\eta V_{11}}{(2\eta\Phi_{00})^{1/2}}\right]X=0 \qquad 24.30$$

$$Y''+\left[\frac{3}{16}\frac{\Phi_{00}'^2}{\Phi_{00}^2}+\frac{1}{4\Phi_{00}}\left(D+\frac{1}{\varepsilon_0}\varrho_{00}\right)-\frac{\eta V_{11}}{(2\eta\Phi_{00})^{1/2}}\right]Y=0 \qquad 24.31$$

The coefficients of the *Taylor* series are

$$X(z_n)=X_n;\quad X'(z_n)=X_n' \qquad 24.32$$

$$X''(z_n)=-\left[\frac{3}{16}\frac{\Phi_{00}'^2}{\Phi_{00}^2}+\frac{1}{4\Phi_{00}}\left(-D+\frac{1}{\varepsilon_0}\varrho_{00}\right)+\frac{\eta V_{11}}{(2\eta\Phi_{00})^{1/2}}\right]X_n \qquad 24.33$$

$$X'''(z_n)=-\left[\frac{3}{8}\frac{\Phi_{00}'\Phi_{00}''}{\Phi_{00}^2}-\frac{3}{8}\frac{\Phi_{00}'^3}{\Phi_{00}^3}+\frac{1}{4\Phi_{00}}\left(-D'+\frac{1}{\varepsilon_0}\varrho_{00}'\right)-\right.$$

$$-\frac{\Phi_{00}'}{4\Phi_{00}^2}\left(-D+\frac{1}{\varepsilon_0}\varrho_{00}\right)+\frac{\eta V_{11}'}{(2\eta\Phi_{00})^{1/2}}-\frac{\eta V_{11}\Phi_{00}'}{2(2\eta)^{1/2}\Phi_{00}^{3/2}}\bigg]X_n-$$

$$-\left[\frac{3}{16}\frac{\Phi_{00}'^2}{\Phi_{00}^2}+\frac{1}{4\Phi_{00}}\left(-D+\frac{1}{\varepsilon_0}\varrho_{00}\right)+\frac{\eta V_{11}}{(2\eta\Phi_{00})^{1/2}}\right]X_n' \qquad 24.34$$

$$Y(z_n)=Y_n;\quad Y'(z_n)=Y_n' \qquad 24.35$$

$$Y''(z_n) = -\left[\frac{3}{16}\frac{\Phi_{00}'^2}{\Phi_{00}^2} + \frac{1}{4\Phi_{00}}\left(D + \frac{1}{\varepsilon_0}\varrho_{00}\right) - \frac{\eta V_{11}}{(2\eta\Phi_{00})^{1/2}}\right]Y_n \qquad 24.36$$

$$Y'''(z_n) = -\left[\frac{3}{8}\frac{\Phi_{00}'\Phi_{00}''}{\Phi_{00}^2} - \frac{3}{8}\frac{\Phi_{00}'^3}{\Phi_{00}^3} + \frac{1}{4\Phi_{00}}\left(D' + \frac{1}{\varepsilon_0}\varrho_{00}'\right) - \right.$$
$$\left. - \frac{\Phi_{00}'}{4\Phi_{00}^2}\left(D + \frac{1}{\varepsilon_0}\varrho_{00}\right) - \frac{\eta V_{11}'}{(2\eta\Phi_{00})^{1/2}} + \frac{\eta V_{11}\Phi_{00}'}{2(2\eta)^{1/2}\Phi_{00}^{3/2}}\right]Y_n -$$
$$- \left[\frac{3}{16}\frac{\Phi_{00}'^2}{\Phi_{00}^2} + \frac{1}{4\Phi_{00}}\left(D + \frac{1}{\varepsilon_0}\varrho_{00}\right) - \frac{\eta V_{11}}{(2\eta\Phi_{00})^{1/2}}\right]Y_n' \qquad 24.37$$

The final results are

$$X_{n+1} = \left[1 - \frac{3}{32}\frac{\Phi_{00}'^2}{\Phi_{00}^2}\Delta z^2 - \frac{1}{8\Phi_{00}}\left(-D + \frac{1}{\varepsilon_0}\varrho_{00}\right)\Delta z^2 - \right.$$
$$\left. - \frac{\eta V_{11}}{2(2\eta\Phi_{00})^{1/2}}\Delta z^2\right]X_n + \Delta z X_n' \qquad 24.38$$

$$X_{n+1}' = \left[-\frac{3}{16}\frac{\Phi_{00}'^2}{\Phi_{00}^2}\Delta z - \frac{1}{4\Phi_{00}}\left(-D + \frac{1}{\varepsilon_0}\varrho_{00}\right)\Delta z - \right.$$
$$- \frac{\eta V_{11}}{(2\eta\Phi_{00})^{1/2}}\Delta z - \frac{3}{16}\frac{\Phi_{00}'\Phi_{00}''}{\Phi_{00}^2}\Delta z^2 + \frac{3}{16}\frac{\Phi_{00}'^3}{\Phi_{00}^3}\Delta z^2 - \frac{1}{8\Phi_{00}} \times$$
$$\times \left(-D' + \frac{1}{\varepsilon_0}\varrho_{00}'\right)\Delta z^2 + \frac{\Phi_{00}'}{8\Phi_{00}^2}\left(-D + \frac{1}{\varepsilon_0}\varrho_{00}\right)\Delta z^2 -$$
$$\left. - \frac{\eta V_{11}'}{2(2\eta\Phi_{00})^{1/2}}\Delta z^2 + \frac{\eta V_{11}\Phi_{00}'}{4(2\eta)^{1/2}\Phi_{00}^{3/2}}\Delta z^2\right]X_n + \left[1 - \frac{3}{32}\frac{\Phi_{00}'^2}{\Phi_{00}^2}\Delta z^2 - \right.$$
$$\left. - \frac{1}{8\Phi_{00}}\left(-D + \frac{1}{\varepsilon_0}\varrho_{00}\right)\Delta z^2 - \frac{\eta V_{11}}{2(2\eta\Phi_{00})^{1/2}}\Delta z^2\right]X_n' \qquad 24.39$$

$$Y_{n+1} = \left[1 - \frac{3}{32}\frac{\Phi_{00}'^2}{\Phi_{00}^2}\Delta z^2 - \frac{1}{8\Phi_{00}}\left(D + \frac{1}{\varepsilon_0}\varrho_{00}\right)\Delta z^2 + \right.$$
$$\left. + \frac{\eta V_{11}}{2(2\eta\Phi_{00})^{1/2}}\Delta z^2\right]Y_n + \Delta z\, Y_n' \qquad 24.40$$

$$Y_{n+1}' = \left[-\frac{3}{16}\frac{\Phi_{00}'^2}{\Phi_{00}^2}\Delta z - \frac{1}{4\Phi_{00}}\left(D + \frac{1}{\varepsilon_0}\varrho_{00}\right)\Delta z + \right.$$
$$+ \frac{\eta V_{11}}{(2\eta\Phi_{00})^{1/2}}\Delta z - \frac{3}{16}\frac{\Phi_{00}'\Phi_{00}''}{\Phi_{00}^2}\Delta z^2 + \frac{3}{16}\frac{\Phi_{00}'^3}{\Phi_{00}^3}\Delta z^2 - \frac{1}{8\Phi_{00}} \times$$

$$\times \left(D' + \frac{1}{\varepsilon_0}\,\varrho'_{00}\right) \varDelta z^2 + \frac{\varPhi'_{00}}{8\varPhi^2_{00}}\left(D + \frac{1}{\varepsilon_0}\,\varrho_{00}\right) \varDelta z^2 +$$

$$+ \frac{\eta\,V'_{11}}{2(2\eta\varPhi_{00})^{1/2}}\,\varDelta z^2 - \frac{\eta\,V_{11}\,\varPhi'_{00}}{4(2\eta)^{1/2}\varPhi^{3/2}_{00}}\,\varDelta z^2 \bigg]\,Y_n + \bigg[1 - \frac{3}{32}\,\frac{\varPhi'^2_{00}}{\varPhi^2_{00}}\,\varDelta z^2 -$$

$$- \frac{1}{8\varPhi_{00}}\left(D + \frac{1}{\varepsilon_0}\,\varrho_{00}\right) \varDelta z^2 + \frac{\eta\,V_{11}}{2(2\eta\varPhi_{00})^{1/2}}\,\varDelta z^2 \bigg]\,Y'_n \qquad\qquad 24.41$$

Note: When performing calculations with the given formulae, the following must be considered. If the region is densely divided, the terms multiplied by $\varDelta z^2$ may be disregarded [the region is considered densely divided if the sparsely performed control calculations (at each 5–10 points) confirm that the terms multiplied by $\varDelta z^2$ can actually be disregarded]. In favourable cases adequate accuracy can be obtained with sparse division of the region, but in this case a reliable control cannot be obtained from the given formulae. Approximative formulae of higher order can also be produced in the manner described.

25. DIFFERENCE METHOD

One highly important method of approximative solution of equations of motion is the difference equation method. According to this method, *the derivative of the unknown function in the differential equation to be solved are substituted by difference quotients, similarly to the method* given for solution of the potential equations. The information given there is also valid here with the only difference that instead of two variables, only one variable is present.

The division of the reg.. . shown in figure I.15.

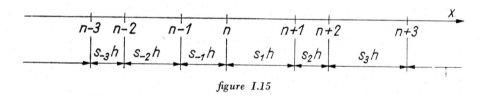

figure I.15

The *Taylor* series for solution of the equation of motion is

$$y = \sum_{\nu=0}^{\infty} \frac{y_n^{(\nu)}}{\nu!}\,(x - x_n)^\nu \qquad\qquad 25.1$$

and as an example, the value of the function pertaining to the division point $(n + 1)$ is

$$y_{n+1} = \sum_{\nu=0}^{\infty} \frac{y_n^{(\nu)}}{\nu!}\,s_1^\nu\,h^\nu \qquad\qquad 25.2$$

The (central) difference quotients required in the present case are determined by the well-known method

$$hy_n' = \frac{1}{s_{-1} + s_1} (y_{n+1} - y_{n-1}) \tag{25.3}$$

$$h^2 y_n'' = \frac{2}{s_{-1}s_1(s_{-1} + s_1)} [s_{-1}y_{n+1} - (s_{-1} + s_1) y_n + s_1 y_{n-1}] \tag{25.4}$$

which, in case of uniform division of the region, become the following

$$hy_n' = \frac{1}{2} (y_{n+1} - y_{n-1}) \tag{25.5}$$

$$h^2 y_n'' = y_{n+1} - 2y_n + y_{n-1} \tag{25.6}$$

Substituting the difference quotients 25.3, 25.4 into the differential equations, the solutions of the thus formed system of equations will form the solutions of the differential equations [11, 98].

Due to the resultant rapidity and simplicity of the calculations, numerous variants of this simple method have been developed and are in use [21, 595].

Very many highly accurate methods have been developed for solution of first-order differential equations of the form

$$y' = f(x, y) \tag{25.7}$$

Equations 22.12 and 21.13 are of first order from the beginning. Equations 22.13, 21.14, 21.15 belong to the type of

$$u'' = g(x, u, u') \tag{25.8}$$

with initial conditions

$$u(x_0) = u_0; \; u'(x_0) = u_0' \tag{25.9}$$

Now, instead of 25.8, 25.9 we introduce [154] the following system of first-order differential equations

$$u' = v = f(x, u, v); \quad v' = g(x, u, v) \tag{25.10}$$

with initial conditions

$$u(x_0) = u_0; \quad v(x) = v_0 = u_0' \tag{25.11}$$

Among the numerous methods of first-order equation and equation system solutions, we shall describe one method—based on central difference— by which a step-by-step integration is possible [6, 21].

Integrating equation 25.7

$$y_{n+1} = y_{n-1} + \int_{x_{n-1}}^{x_{n+1}} f(x, y) \, dx \tag{25.12}$$

For an approximation of $f(x, y)$ in the integral contained in equation 25.12, we employ *Stirling*'s interpolation polynomial [6, 11]. We assume that the function values $y_k(x_k)$ in the interpolation polynomial are known. If the values y_k are not known, they must be determined using, for example the *Taylor* series expansion (system of initial values). By integrating with the interpolation polynomial instead of $f(x, y)$, y_{n+1} can be determined.

Interpretation of the differences contained in *Stirling*'s interpolation formula is given in table I.2.

TABLE I.2

x_n	y_n	Δy_n	$\Delta^2 y_n$	$\Delta^3 y_n$	$\Delta^4 y_n$
x_{-3}	y_{-3}				
		Δy_{-3}			
x_{-2}	y_{-2}		$\Delta^2 y_{-3}$		
		Δy_{-2}		$\Delta^3 y_{-3}$	
x_{-1}	y_{-1}		$\Delta^2 y_{-2}$		$\Delta^4 y_{-3}$
		Δy_{-1}		$\Delta^3 y_{-2}$	
x_0	y_0		$\Delta^2 y_{-1}$		$\Delta^4 y_{-2}$
		Δy_0		$\Delta^3 y_{-1}$	
x_1	y_1		$\Delta^2 y_0$		$\Delta^4 y_{-1}$
		Δy_1		$\Delta^3 y_0$	
x_2	y_2		$\Delta^2 y_1$		
		Δy_2			
x_3	y_3				

Using the notation

$$t = \frac{x - x_0}{h} \qquad 25.13$$

the interpolation formula is

$$S(t) = y_0 + \frac{\Delta y_0 + \Delta y_{-1}}{2} \frac{t}{1!} + \Delta^2 y_{-1} \frac{t^2}{2!} +$$

$$+ \frac{\Delta^3 y_{-2} + \Delta^3 y_{-1}}{2} \frac{t(t^2 - 1)}{3!} + \Delta^4 y_{-2} \frac{t^2(t^2 - 1)}{4!} \ldots \qquad 25.14$$

Introducing the notation
$$F_n = f(x_n, y_n) \qquad 25.15$$
we obtain
$$S(t) = F_n + \frac{\Delta F_n + \Delta F_{n-1}}{2} \frac{t}{1!} + \Delta^2 F_{n-1} \frac{t^2}{2!} +$$

$$+ \frac{\Delta^3 F_{n-2} + \Delta^3 F_{n-1}}{2} \frac{t(t^2 - 1)}{3!} + \Delta^4 F_{n-2} \frac{t^2(t^2 - 1)}{4!} + \dots \qquad 25.16$$

From equation 25.13 we have

$$x = x_0 + th; \quad dx = h \, dt \qquad 25.17$$

and the integral 25.12 becomes

$$y_{n+1} = y_{n-1} + h \int_{-1}^{1} S(t) dt \qquad 25.18$$

The integrals appearing are

$$\int_{-1}^{1} dt = 2 ; \quad \int_{-1}^{1} t \, dt = 0 ; \quad \frac{1}{2} \int_{-1}^{1} t^2 \, dt = \frac{1}{3} ; \quad \frac{1}{6} \int_{-1}^{1} (t^3 - t) \, dt = 0 ;$$

$$\frac{1}{24} \int_{-1}^{1} (t^4 - t^2) \, dt = -\frac{1}{90} \qquad 25.19$$

Substituting the latter integrals into equation 25.18, we obtain

$$y_{n+1} = y_{n-1} + h \left(2 F_n + \frac{1}{3} \Delta^2 F_{n-1} - \frac{1}{90} \Delta^4 F_{n-2} + \dots \right) \qquad 25.20$$

The first-order equations and systems of equations can be solved with the formula 25.20.

Further formulae [582, 583] (special individual properties; greater accuracy at the cost of increased calculation work, etc.) are to be found in the literature [21].

It is not obligatory that the second-order equations be treated as a system of first-order equations. For direct calculations, among others, the following formulae, similarly based on central differences, may be employed [21]

$$y_{n+1} = 2y_n - y_{n-1} + h^2 \left(F_n + \frac{1}{12} \Delta^2 F_{n-1} - \frac{1}{240} \Delta^4 F_{n-2} + \dots \right) \qquad 25.21$$

$$y'_{n+1} = y'_{n-1} + h \left(2 F_n + \frac{1}{3} \Delta^2 F_{n-1} - \frac{1}{90} \Delta^4 F_{n-2} + \dots \right) \qquad 25.22$$

26. OTHER METHODS

The procedures discussed in the preceding paragraphs should be considered as the most important as they are used for virtually all approximative trajectory calculations. The following can also be used, although they occur more seldom. The principle discussed in item *b*) in particular has numerous variants which can be adapted to the individual cases.

(a) Method of indefinite coefficients

This method also belongs to the group of series expansion methods. The initial conditions pertaining to the differential equation to be solved are usually given the point x_0. With linear transformation of the independent variable, x_0 is made coincident with the origin of the coordinate system. Then the initial conditions are $y(0)$ and $y'(0)$ [instead of $y(x_0)$ and $y'(x_0)$]. The solution is given by its infinite series

$$y(x) = a_0 + a_1 x + a_2 x^2 + \ldots \qquad 26.1$$

In equation 26.1 the coefficients a_0 and a_1 are determined in such a manner as to satisfy the initial conditions $y(0)$ and $y'(0)$. Thereafter all differential and other expressions contained in the differential equation are determined with the help of equation 26.1 and are substituted into the differential equation to be solved. The relation so obtained is reduced to zero and the coefficients of the various powers of x are made equal to zero, whereby the coefficients, in harmony with the initial conditions, are produced in succession. These are functions of the potentials, space-charge, etc. contained in the differential equation [105, 106, 107].

(b) Approximation of the variable coefficients

The solution of equations of motion is made more difficult by the presence of variable coefficients. Let us now divide the region of integration into sufficiently small sections so that the variable coefficients within these can be considered as constants [557, 558], either linear or of second order [594, 595]. The differential equation thus obtained is easier to solve [569, 584]. By matching the solutions obtained within the sections, the solution referred to the entire region can be received.

(c) Approximation by given functions

The solution of equations of motion can be approximated by using a series of given functions. Determination of the solution is identical with determination of the constants contained in the series. In publications [556, 577] the solution is approximated by means of a sine series, and in [571, 586] with *Legendre* polynomial series.

(d) Miscellaneous methods

Among the numerous trajectory computation methods, that are treated in article [589] is worthy of mention, which employs the predictor corrector method; and communication [570] which employs only the predictor formula for the manual procedure; similarly, the paper [590] deals with a manual process in which the calculation of trajectories forming in the field of a lens consisting of two cylinders is found. Among the innumerable articles dealing with trajectory calculation, the paper [592] bases trajectory calculation on data gained from the electrolytic tank and the space-charge is also taken into account; consideration of space-charge figures in other works also [573–575]; the paper [563] uses path calculation for the calculation of magnetic lenses. Article [576] distinguishes permissible and non-permissible trajectories in a given space section, and calculates trajectories occurring in a magnetic field formed by current flowing through a straight wire, by a numerical method.

All trajectory calculation methods are cumbersome, involving considerable laborious work, and hence efforts are being made to develop computer methods.

As far as possible, it is desirable to perform the calculations by means of paraxial equations. The relevant conditions have been worked out in detail, and these are dealt with in detail by the electron-optical books listed in the bibliography.

For example, article [565] investigates the region near to the cathode within the subject matter of paraxiality. Thus, for instance, paraxial equations are valid at the cathode if the longitudinal forces are greater than the transversal forces, and furthermore, if the transversal velocity is also low (according to another viewpoint: if the radius of curvature of the cathode is great, in comparison with the paraxiality region dimensions). In some cases the above suffer modification [572].

Among the computer methods there is the (in conjunction with the electrolytic tank) analogous trajectory computation [600], and also [597] which employ solid dielectrics for the field computation. Paper [604] employs analogous and digital methods combined (trajectory computation is performed with the aid of *Liebman*'s method). The multitude of trajectories forming in a magnetron are computed in total by the digital method [585]. A combination of measurement and computation can also be used [580]. Digital computation is gradually becoming the absolute method, mainly since with the correct equipment, arbitrary tasks can be solved, while the same does not apply with analog methods. Further data respecting employment of digital computers: article [579] employs the digital computer for trajectory tracing, and article [588] describes solution of *Poisson*'s equation and trajectory computation, both by means of the FORTRAN IV program.

(G) DETERMINATION OF TRAJECTORIES
BY MEASUREMENT

Solution of the electron-optical problems finally requires determination of multitudes of trajectories. Although in the preceding sections we have described numerous exact calculation methods which are available by means of computers [585], yet we must deal also with trajectory tracing based on field-determining methods [619, 636, 660].

27. BASIC METHODS OF THE DETERMINATION OF TRAJECTORIES
BY MEASUREMENT

(a) Trajectory tracing by rubber membrane

The rubber membrane dealt with in § 16 is also suitable for trajectory tracing. The projection, onto the basic plane, of the trajectory of balls rolling down the surface of the rubber membrane corresponds to the electron trajectories [632, 644]. It is customary to photograph the rolling balls from a direction perpendicular to the basic plane, usually with uniform interruptions of exposure time, since in this case the time of travel of the trajectory becomes known. The noteworthy articles [608, 609, 613] are suitable for orientation.

(b) Trajectory tracing by electrolytic tank

The field-strength values are determined with the help of probes from the potential field formed in the electrolytic tank, and with the help of computers the probes are motioned along electron trajectories in accordance with the measured field strengths. The solution of this, connected mainly with electronics and control problems, is found in the literature [612, 629, 643].

Numerous publications [610, 639, 647, 649] deal with trajectory plotting solutions realised by means of an electrolytic tank. According to an old and original method the electron trajectory is plotted by a mechanical tracer [619], based on the circle method. The above *Gabor* trajectory tracer is used for the determination of trajectories forming in crossed fields [631]. The space-charge effect is naturally taken into account by the electron ray tracers: article [640] investigates the planar case, while article [628] investigates trajectories forming in millimetre wave tubes, taking space-charge into consideration. Paper [630] deals in detail with gradient plotting and trajectory tracing with aid of electrolytic tank. A demand for automatic tracing has appeared, together with corresponding papers [634, 635]. Measurements of trajectories by electrical trajectory tracer are now invariably automatic [638, 648], including some with means suitable for measurements made in superimposed fields [623] and these are coming more generally in use, displacing the older mechanical trajectory tracer [646].

(c) Trajectory tracing with resistance network

For the determination of trajectories by resistance network, the potential field is scanned by a scanner as in the case of the electrolytic tank. Due to the broken distribution of the field points, the scanner is a multi-position selector-switch. The trajectory may be calculated by either analog or digital computer, which controls the switch mechanism also.

Another solution is also used, where the full potential field is stored in the memory unit of the computer. Details are given in the literature [621, 626, 653].

Among the trajectory tracers operating with resistance networks [624], some employ axis resistances lower than customary [618], another takes into account space-charge [627], others are connected with a digital computer [625].

Note

(i) The communications [597, 657] deal with the structural details and further development of the trajectory traces. The publication [652] shows application of the trajectory tracer for investigation of post-deflection accelerator systems. Varied problems (structural, application) are investigated in the publications [617, 651, 656].

(ii) Trajectory tracing by means of electrolytic tank and resistance network can be performed also in a magnetic field [611].

(ii) The common operation principle of trajectory tracers based on potential field determined by electrolytic tank or resistance network is readily understood on the basis of the block scheme shown by figure I.16.

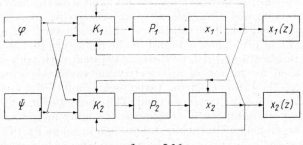

figure I.16

The electric or magnetic potential fields are determined by the units φ or ψ. The data of both potential fields enter switches K_1 and K_2, which, dependent upon the output of the trajectory tracer, connect the actually required potential values to units P_1 and P_2. Units P_1 and P_2 produce the field-strength components from the input potentials, and pass them to units x_1 and x_2. These determine the integrals of the equations of motion, and with the calculated function values, they control both the switches K_1 and K_2, and the trajectory tracers $x_1(z)$ or $x_2(z)$, or the table-preparing units. Among the cases describable with two variables (as we have discussed), the output signal of x_1 is required to operate x_2 (as shown in the figure) in axially symmetric and plane-symmetric cases. In case of motions occurring in quadrupole fields, the two motion components are independent, therefore this connection is not required (space-charge free case).

28. OTHER POSSIBILITIES OF DETERMINING TRAJECTORIES
BY MEASUREMENT

For determination of trajectories of electrons moving in the electric-magnetic field, including space-charge effects, in many cases suitable measurement is performed with the help of balls moving on isotimic surfaces, i.e. surfaces of equal worth, in either plane-symmetric or axially symmetric case. The effect of the space-charge is taken into consideration with the help of the function yielding the potential. The generalised potentials are determined with the help of equations 19.16 and 18.24 from the scalar and vector potentials. The surface characterising the generalised potential is made from a suitable material. Since the electron motion due to the generalised potential takes place according to equations 19.17 or 18.25, the paths of the balls moving on the isotimic surfaces give electron trajectories, similarly to the case of rubber membrane measurement. The method and its limitations are dealt with in greater detail in publications [72, 101, 614]. In the following, two further examples of trajectory plotting based on the mechanical model are mentioned, although the significance of trajectory plotters of this system is now reduced.

In addition to measurements based on the transmission-line analogy [620, 622], the determination of trajectories by measurement may also be performed using a mechanical integrator [650]. Trajectory determinations using this method are described in paper [659] with acceptable results, operating within an accuracy of ten per cent. Paths occurring in a magnetic field can be determined with the help of a mechanical model [646] with a ball moving on a rotating surface [658], but principally with a hodoscope (current flows through a flexible conductor placed in the magnetic field: the conductor takes up the shape of the trajectory) [637]. Due to its importance, numerous articles deal with the hodoscope [616, 641, 642], also the diploma [645]. Measurement of trajectories forming from the magnetic field are dealt with in article [633]. Paper [615] treats an automatic trajectory tracer. Trajectory tracers may be used in the solution of innumerable tasks. As an example, article [654] deals with gun design with the aid of trajectory tracer. Summarising works are also available [636, 656].

Electron-optical benches are the most suitable for detailed investigation of the trajectories, and in particular entire electron-optical systems. In these, the entire electrode system is produced, but on a different scale from reality. In the system placed in vacuum, all phenomena occur in accordance with the generally valid laws of similitude, and therefore the data of the original system can be calculated. Bibliographical data [661–673], among which communication [666] giving information on the electron-optical bench used with magnetic lenses, are emphasised. A simpler version exists [665], which operates with electric lenses only. An ion source employed with the electron-optical bench is described in paper [663], and communication [670] deals with an optical bench serving for electron-optical studies. Paper [669] is a diploma dissertation; communication [671] describes equipment suitable for research and demonstration purposes.

EXAMPLES OF SPECIAL PROBLEMS FROM
APPLICATION FIELDS

Prior to commencing a list of literature data pertaining to Chapter I, in order to avoid misunderstandings, it must be pointed out that although the present book treats a restricted region of electron optics, this region is nevertheless of great significance as concerns applications. In order to avoid the necessity of laborious research through electron-optics literature and supplementary mathematical, calculation technique, physics and special literature for the further development of this field, copious references covering the subject matter have been compiled.

Although not closely coupled to the material treated in our book, we consider it necessary to outline the potentialities of electron optics; in order to present an insight into certain fields, numerous observations are made, serving as examples only.

As a result of electron-optical investigations it has transpired for example that the magnetic electron lens is advantageous where the field is of rapid transition and is concentrated to short sections. This requirement brought about the design of pole shoes for the magnetic lenses, with which the desired effect may be obtained. For pole shoe concentration of the magnetic focusing lens field data serving rapid transition of the field are given e.g. in the series of articles [51–53]. Only twenty years after the formulation of the theoretical bases of electron optics [559], the communication [57] appeared, giving a complete summary of the dynamics of electron beams. Expounding of optical analogy is presented at the highest level, and derivation of the theorems relative to the multitude of flowing electrons, at the same time classifying the connection existing with fluid flow. Knowledge of the optical analogy automatically gives prominence to employment of the gauze lens. Employment of these is customary mainly where a sharp focus is not required [59], as for example for electron multipliers or electron accelerators. Among the third-order imaging aberrations occurring in electron-optical imaging systems, spherical aberration is the greatest [74–76]. It will be understood that great efforts have been made with a view to eliminating or at least reducing this aberration. As an example, the article [58] describes employment of a coaxial lens consisting of three electrodes for elimination of spherical aberration. Another solution is given in the paper [3]. A further aberration which may not be neglected and which is of salient magnitude, is chromatic aberration. A focusing system exists [63] which enables chromatic aberration-free imaging, while good results have been obtained by correction also [4]. In optics and in electron optics also, stigmatic imaging is aimed at, where the rays starting from a single point all converge into a single point. In optics, a lens of this type is the *Maxwell* fish-eye lens, and this is spherical symmetric, with inhomogeneous refractive index distribution. The electron-optical equivalent cannot be realised in a field excited by electrodes alone, since the resultant potential distribution does not satisfy *Laplace*'s equation. The article series [54–56] presents a principled solution of the problem with the aid of spherical symmetric inhomogeneous space-charge distribution. It cannot be denied that kinescopes have attained highly widespread use, neither that they are very large in size and occupy considerable space. For a long time the aim has been to produce a flat, small-size kinescope. Very considerable work has been invested in order to elaborate a special imaging system, a deflecting system, the trajectories and other structural details [1, 20, 137]. As a result of these diverse labours [65, 67], the possibility now exists of producing flat kinescopes, for black and white, and for colour [71]. Among the range of cathode-ray tubes, some are provided with postdeflection acceleration for increase of deflection sensitivity, or in the case of very high-frequency signals, the deflection inducing wave travels together with the electron ray on a slow-wave structure. Among the most significant discoveries of recent years is holography* [68], whose existence is due to research work

* In 1971 *Dennis Gabor*, well-known physicist of Hungarian origin, was awarded the Nobel prize for his discoveries in the field of holography.

conducted with the aim of eliminating spherical aberration, unacceptable in electron microscopy [60]. In addition to the highly successful optical experiments [61], numerous detail problems [62] and application problems [64] have become subjects of the investigations. Theoretical discussions on the interference of electrons have come up [66], the application of high resolving power X-ray microscopy and the solution of the phase problem [70] can also be found. In addition to the X-ray microscope, attention may be drawn to numerous other equipment types, e.g. the X-ray image intensifier tube, or the X-ray diffraction camera, but owing to lack of space, these cannot be treated. Paper [160] discusses electron microholography by the two-beam method. As a matter of interest, it may be mentioned that the aberrations of a deflecting unit may be determined by means of the deflected electron ray [170]. The possibilities of electron ray application are illustrated by further examples. Article [86] describes voltage regulation to an accuracy of a few millionth parts of a 50 kV d.c. source, with the aid of an electron velocity analyser. The communication [148] deals with calculations of the electron trajectories and the electric field of an equipment converting infrared radiation invisible to the human eye, into radiation in the visible region. Among the best known equipments serving for investigation of the surface properties of semiconductors is the low-energy electron diffraction equipment. Article [90] deals with the theory of this type of equipment, and realisation of the high accuracy and high resolving power is treated in article [35].

REFERENCES FOR CHAPTER I

a) *Electron Optics and Related Sciences*

1. AIKEN, W. R.: *Proc. Instn Radio Engrs.*, **45** (1957), 1599.
2. ALLEN, D. N. DE G.: *Relaxation Methods*. McGraw-Hill; New York, 1954.
3. ARCHARD, G. D.: *Proc. phys. Soc.*, **68-B** (1955), 156.
4. ARCHARD, G. D.: *Proc. phys. Soc.*, **68-B** (1955), 817.
5. ASTIN, A. V.–MARTON, L.: *Electron Physics*. Proceedings of the NBS Semicentennial Symposium on Electron Physics, US Department of Commerce, National Bureau of Standards, Circular 527.
6. BÁLINT, E.: Közelítő matematikai módszerek *(Approximative Mathematical Methods)*. Műszaki Könyvkiadó; Budapest, 1966.
7. BECKENBACH, E. F.: Modern matematika mérnököknek. I. *(Modern Mathematics for Engineers. I)*. Műszaki Könyvkiadó; Budapest, 1960.
8. BECKENBACH, E. F.: Modern matematika mérnököknek. II. *(Modern Mathematics for Engineers. II)*. Műszaki Könyvkiadó; Budapest, 1965.
9. BELLMANN, R.: *Introduction to Matrix Analysis*. McGraw-Hill; New York, 1960.
10. BINNS, K. J.–LAWRENSON, P. J.: *Analysis and Computation of Electric and Magnetic Field Problems*. Pergamon Press; Oxford, 1963.
11. BJEZIKOVICS, JA. SZ.: Közelítő számítások *(Approximative Calculations)*. Tankönyvkiadó; Budapest, 1952.
12. BORN, M.–WOLF, E.: *Principles of Optics*. Pergamon Press; Oxford, 1965.
13. BRONSHTEIN, I. N.–SEMENDYAYEV, K. A.: *A Guide-Book to Mathematics for Technologists and Engineers*. Pergamon Press; Oxford, 1964.
14. BRÜCHE, E.–RECKNAGEL, A.: Elektronengeräte. Prinzipien und Systematik. Springer; Berlin, 1941.
15. BRÜCHE, E.–SCHERZER, O.: Geometrische Elektronenoptik. Grundlagen und Anwendungen. Springer; Berlin, 1934.
16. BUCHHOLZ, H.: Elektrische und magnetische Potentialfelder. Springer; Berlin–Göttingen–Heidelberg, 1957.
17. BUCKINGHAM, R. A.: *Numerical Methods*. Pitman and Sons; London, 1966.
18. BUDO, Á.: Theoretische Mechanik. Deutscher Verlag der Wissenschaften; Berlin, 1963.
19. BUSCH, H.–BRÜCHE, E.: Beiträge zur Elektronenoptik. Vorträge von der Physikertagung 1936 sowie ergänzende Beiträge. Johann Ambrosius Barth; Leipzig, 1937.
20. CHIN, T. N.: *Proc. Instn Radio Engrs.*, **49** (1961), 832.
21. COLLATZ, L.: Numerische Behandlung von Differentialgleichungen. Springer; Berlin–Göttingen–Heidelberg, 1955.

22. COLLATZ, L.: Eigenwertaufgaben mit technischen Anwendungen. Akademische Ver-lagsgesellschaft Geest und Portig K.-G.; Leipzig, 1963.
23. CORBEN, H. C.–STEHLE, P.: *Classical Mechanics*. John Wiley and Sons; London, 1960.
24. COSSLETT, V. E.: *Introduction to Electron Optics*. Oxford University Press; Fairlawn, New Jersey, 1950.
25. COURANT, R.–HILBERT, D.: *Methods of Mathematical Physics. I*. Interscience Publishers; New York, 1953.
26. COURANT, R.–HILBERT, D.: *Methods of Mathematical Physics. II*. Interscience Publishers, a Division of John Wiley and Sons; New York, 1962.
27. DE BROGLIE, L.: Optique électronique et corpusculaire. Hermann; Paris, 1950.
28. DURAND, E.: Électrostatique et Magnétostatique. Masson et C-ie; Paris, 1953.
29. DURAND, E.: Électrostatique. Tome I. Les distributions. Masson et C-ie; Paris, 1964.
30. DURAND, E.: Magnétostatique. Masson et C-ie; Paris, 1968.
31. EISENHART, L. P.: *Treatise on the Differential Geometry of Curves and Surfaces*. Dover Publications; New York, 1960.
32. ERŐ, J.–SCHMIDT, G.: Elektrosztatika *(Electrostatics)*. Tankönyvkiadó; Budapest, 1954.
33. FANO, R. M.–CHU, L. J.–ADLER, R. B.: *Electromagnetic Fields, Energy and Forces*. John Wiley and Sons; New York, 1960.
34. FARAGÓ, P.–PÓCZA, J.: Elektronfizika *(Electron Physics)*. Akadémiai Kiadó; Budapest, 1954.
35. FARNSWORTH, H. E.–SCHLIER, R. E.–GEORGE, T. H.–BURGER, R. M.: *J. appl. Phys.*, **29** (1958), 1150.
36. FENYŐ, I.: Integrálegyenletek *(Integral Equations)*. Tankönyvkiadó; Budapest; 1957.
37. FENYŐ, I.–FREY, T.: Matematika villamosmérnököknek. I *(Mathematics for Electrical Engineers)*. Műszaki Könyvkiadó; Budapest, 1964.
38. FENYŐ, I.–FREY, T.: Matematika villamosmérnököknek. II *(Mathematics for Electrical Engineers)*. Műszaki Könyvkiadó; Budapest, 1964.
39. FISCHER, J.: Grössen und Einheiten der Elektrizitätslehre. Springer; Berlin–Göttingen–Heidelberg, 1961.
40. FLÜGGE, S.: Handbuch der Physik. Band I. Mathematische Methoden I. Springer; Berlin–Göttingen–Heidelberg, 1956.
41. FLÜGGE, S.: Handbuch der Physik. Band II. Mathematische Methoden II. Springer; Berlin–Göttingen–Heidelberg, 1955.
42. FLÜGGE, S.: Handbuch der Physik. Band XVI. Elektrische Felder und Wellen. Springer; Berlin–Göttingen–Heidelberg, 1958.
43. FLÜGGE, S.: Handbuch der Physik. Band XXIV. Grundlagen der Optik. Springer; Berlin–Göttingen–Heidelberg, 1956.
44. FLÜGGE, S.: Handbuch der Physik. Band XXV/1. Kristalloptik, Beugung. Springer; Berlin–Göttingen–Heidelberg, 1961.
45. FLÜGGE, S.: Handbuch der Physik. Band XXIX. Optische Instrumente. Springer; Berlin–Heidelberg–New York, 1967.
46. FLÜGGE, S.: Handbuch der Physik. Band XXXIII. Korpuskularoptik. Springer; Berlin–Göttingen–Heidelberg, 1956.
47. FORSYTHE, G. E.–WASOW, W. R.: *Finite-Difference Methods for Partial Differential Equations*. Applied Mathematics Series, Edited by I. S. SOKOLNIKOFF. John Wiley and Sons; New York, 1960.
48. FRANCKEN, J. C.: *Electron Optics of the Image Iconoscope*. Thesis, Delft, 1953.
49. FREY, T.: Végtelen sorozatok, sorok és szorzatok *(Infinite Sequences, Series and Products)*. Tankönyvkiadó; Budapest, 1965.
50. FUCHS, B. A.–SHABAT, B. V.: *Functions of a Complex Variable and Some of their Applications*. Pergamon Press; Oxford, 1964.
51. GABOR, D.: *Forsch. Hefte Stud. Ges. Höchstsp. Anl.*, **1** (1927), 7.
52. GABOR, D.: *Forsch. Hefte Stud. Ges. Höchstsp. Anl.*, **1** (1927), 47.
53. GABOR, D.: *Forsch. Hefte Stud. Ges. Höchstsp. Anl.*, **1** (1927), 62.
54. GABOR, D.: *Electron Engng.*, **15** (1942/43), 295.
55. GABOR, D.: *Electron Engng.*, **15** (1942/43), 328.
56. GABOR, D.: *Electron Engng.*, **15** (1942/43), 372.
57. GABOR, D.: *Proc. Instn. Radio Engrs.*, **33** (1945), 792.
58. GABOR, D.: *Nature, Lond.*, **158** (1946), 198.
59. GABOR, D.: *Nature, Lond.*, **159** (1947), 303.

60. Gabor, D.: *Nature*, Lond., **161** (1948), 777.
61. Gabor, D.: *Proc. R. Soc.*, **179**–A (1949), 454.
62. Gabor, D.: *Research*, Lond., **4** (1951), 107.
63. Gabor, D.: *Proc. phys. Soc.*, **64**–B (1951), 244.
64. Gabor, D.: *Proc. R. Soc.*, **64**–B (1951), 449.
65. Gabor, D.: *J. Telev. Soc.*, **8** (1956), 142.
66. Gabor, D.: *Rev. mod. Phys.*, **28** (1956), 260.
67. Gabor, D.: *Wireless Wld.*, **46** (1956), 570.
68. Gabor, D.: *Holography in 1970. An Overview.* Optosonic Press; New York, 1970.
69. Gabor, D.–Jull, D. W.: *Nature*, Lond., **175** (1955), 718.
70. Gabor, D.–Stroke, G. W.–Restrick, R.–Funkhouser, A.–Brumm, D.: *Phys. Lett.*, **18** (1965), 116.
71. Gabor, D.–Stuart, P. R.–Kalman, P. G.: *Proc. Instn Electr. Engrs.*, **105**–B (1958), 581.
72. Glaser, W.: Grundlagen der Elektronenoptik. Springer; Wien, 1952.
73. Glaser, W.: Elektronen- und Ionenoptik. *In:* Herausgegeben von S. Flügge: Handbuch der Physik. Band XXXIII. Korpuskularoptik. Springer; Berlin–Göttingen–Heidelberg, 1956.
74. Glaser, W.–Schiske, P.: *Optik Berlin*, **11** (1954), 422.
75. Glaser, W.–Schiske, P.: *Optik Berlin*, **11** (1954), 445.
76. Glaser, W.–Schiske, P.: *Optik Berlin*, **12** (1955), 233.
77. Goldstein, H.: *Classical Mechanics.* Addison-Wesley; Reading, Massachusetts, 1959.
78. (Govorkov, V. A.) Говорков, В. А.: Электрические и магнитные поля *(Electric and Magnetic Fields).* Госэнергоиздат; Москва, 1960.
79. (Gradshtein, I. S.–Ryzhik, I. M.) Градштейн, И. С.–Рыжик, И. М.: Таблицы интегралов, сумм, рядов и произведений *(Tables of Integrals, Sums, Series and Products).* Физматгиз; Москва, 1962.
80. (Grinberg, G. A.) Гринберг, Г. А.: Избранные вопросы математической теории электрических и магнитных явлений *(Selected Problems of the Mathematical Theory of Electric and Magnetic Phenomena).* Изд. Академии наук СССР; Москва–Ленинград, 1948.
81. Grivet, P.–Bernard, M. Y.–Bertein, F.–Castaing, R.–Gauzit, M.–Septier, A.: *Electron Optics.* Pergamon Press; Oxford, 1965.
82. Gröbner, W.–Hofreiter, N.: Integraltafel. 1. Teil. Unbestimmte Integrale. Springer; Wien–New York, 1965.
83. Gröbner, W.–Hofreiter, N.: Integraltafel. 2. Teil. Bestimmte Integrale. Springer; Wien, 1961.
84. Gutenmaher, L. I.: Elektromos modellek *(Electric Analogs).* Akadémiai Kiadó; Budapest, 1951.
85. Haine, M. E.–Cosslett, V. E.: *The Electron Microscope.* Spon; London, 1961.
86. Haine, M. E.–Jervis, M. W.: *Proc. Instn Elect. Engrs.* **102**–B (1955), 265.
87. Harman, W. W.: *Fundamentals of Electronic Motion.* McGraw-Hill; New York, 1953.
88. Henrici, P.: *Discrete Variable Methods in Ordinary Differential Equations.* John Wiley and Sons; New York, 1962.
89. Herzberger, M.: Strahlenoptik. Springer; Berlin, 1931.
90. Hirabayashi, K.–Takeishi, Y.: *Surf. Sci.*, **4** (1966), 150.
91. Infeld, L.–Pleransky, J.: *Motion and Relativity.* Pergamon Press — Panstwowe Wydawnictwo Naukowe; Oxford–Warsaw, 1960.
92. Jackson, J. D.: *Classical Electrodynamics.* John Wiley and Sons; New York, 1962.
93. Jacob, L.: *An Introduction to Electron Optics.* John Wiley and Sons; London, 1951.
94. Kamke, E.: Differentialgleichungen. Band I. Gewöhnliche Differentialgleichungen. Geest und Portig; Leipzig, 1962.
95. Kamke, E.: Differentialgleichungen. Band II. Partielle Differentialgleichungen. Geest und Portig; Leipzig, 1962.
96. Kamke, E.: Differentialgleichungen. Lösungsmethoden und Lösungen. Band I. Gewöhnliche Differentialgleichungen. Geest und Portig; Leipzig, 1959.
97. Kamke, E.: Differentialgleichungen. Lösungsmethoden und Lösungen. Band II. Partielle Differentialgleichungen erster Ordnung für eine gesuchte Funktion. Akademische Verlagsgesellschaft Geest und Portig K.-G.; Leipzig, 1959.
98. Kantorovich, L. V.–Krylov, V. I.: *Approximate Methods of Higher Analysis.* Interscience; New York, 1958.

99. KARPLUS, W. J.: *Analog Simulation, Solution of Field Problems.* McGraw-Hill; New York, 1958.
100. KARPLUS, W. J.–SOROKA, W. W.: *Analog Methods, Computation and Simulation.* McGraw-Hill Series in Engineering Sciences, Consulting Editors: S. H. CRANDALL and P. M. NAGHDI. McGraw-Hill; New York, 1959.
101. KELMAN, V. M.–JAVOR, SZ. JA.: Elektronoptika *(Electron Optics).* Akadémiai Kiadó; Budapest, 1965.
102. KING, L. V.: *On the Direct Numerical Calculation of Elliptic Functions and Integrals.* University Press; Cambridge, 1924.
103. KLEMPERER, O.: *Electron Optics.* University Press; Cambridge, 1953.
104. KLEMPERER, O.: *Electron Physics. The Physics of the Free Electron.* Butterworths; London, 1961.
105. KNESCHKE, A.: Differentialgleichungen und Randwertprobleme. Band I. Gewöhnliche Differentialgleichungen. Verlag Technik; Berlin, 1960.
106. KNESCHKE, A.: Differentialgleichungen und Randwertprobleme. Band II. Partielle Differentialgleichungen. Verlag Technik; Berlin, 1960.
107. KNESCHKE, A.: Differentialgleichungen und Randwertprobleme. Band III. Anwendungen der Differentialgleichungen. B. G. Teubner Verlagsgesellschaft; Leipzig, 1962.
108. KOBER, H.: *Dictionary of Conformal Representation.* Dover Publications; New York, 1952.
109. KUNZ, K. S.: *Numerical Analysis.* McGraw-Hill; New York, 1957.
110. LANCE, G. N.: *Numerical Methods for High-Speed Computers.* Mackay; London, 1960.
111. LANDAU, L. D.–LIFSHITZ, E. M.: *Mechanics.* Macmillan; New York, 1961.
112. LANDAU, L. D.–LIFSHITZ, E. M.: *The Classical Theory of Fields.* Pergamon Press; Oxford, 1962.
113. LAVRENTYEV, M. A.–LJUSTYERNYIK, L. A.: Variációszámítás *(Calculus of Variations).* Akadémiai Kiadó; Budapest, 1953.
114. LEHNERT, B.: *Dynamics of Charged Particles.* North-Holland Publishing Company; Amsterdam, 1964.
115. LIEBMANN, G.: *Field Plotting and Ray Tracing in Electron Optics. A Review of Numerical Methods. In:* MARTON, L. (ed.): Advances etc., 2 (1950), 101.
116. LIVINGSTON, M. S.–BLEWETT, J. P.: *Particle Accelerators.* McGraw-Hill; New York, 1962.
117. LUNEBURG, R. K.: *Mathematical Theory of Optics.* University of California Press; Berkeley–Los Angeles, California, 1964.
118. MALOFF, I. G.–EPSTEIN, D. W.: *Electron Optics in Television. With Theory and Application of Television Cathode-Ray Tubes.* McGraw-Hill; New York, 1938.
119. MIHLIN, S. G.: Integrálegyenletek *(Integral Equations).* Akadémiai Kiadó; Budapest, 1953.
120. MOON, P.–SPENCER, D. E.: *Field Theory for Engineers.* The Van Nostrand Series in Electronics and Communications. D. Van Nostrand; New Jersey, 1961.
121. MOON, P.–SPENCER, D. E.: *Field Theory Handbook.* Including Coordinate Systems, Differential Equations and their Solutions. Springer; Berlin–Göttingen–Heidelberg, 1961.
122. MORSE, P. M.–FESHBACH, H.: *Methods of Theoretical Physics. Part I.* International Series in Pure and Applied Physics. McGraw-Hill; New York, 1953.
123. MORSE, P. M.–FESHBACH, H.: *Methods of Theoretical Physics. Part II.* International Series in Pure and Applied Physics. McGraw-Hill; New York, 1953.
124. NAGY, GY. A.: A tértöltés elektronoptikája általános alappályán *(Electron Optics of the Space-Charge along the General Central Trajectory).* Kandidátusi értekezés (Candidature dissertation). Budapest, 1965.
125. NAGY, GY. A.: Az időben állandó villamos-mágneses mező származtatása egyetlen vektorból. Távközlési Kutató Intézet Évkönyve, 1966 (The Derivation of the Time-Constant Electric-Magnetic Field from a Single Vector. *Telecommunication Research Institute Yearbook,* 1966). Műszaki Könyvkiadó; Budapest, 1967.
126. NOVOBÁTZKY, K.–NEUGEBAUER, T.: Elektrodinamika és optika *(Electrodynamics and Optics).* Tankönyvkiadó; Budapest, 1961.
127. OLLENDORFF, F.: Die Potentialfelder der Elektrotechnik. Springer; Berlin, 1932.
128. OLLENDORFF, F.: Berechnung magnetischer Felder. Springer; Wien, 1952.
129. OLLENDORFF, F.: Elektronik des Einzelelektrons. Springer; Wien, 1955.

130. OLLENDORFF, F.: Elektronik freier Raumladungen. Springer; Wien, 1957.
131. OLLENDORFF, F.: Schwankungserscheinungen in Elektronenröhren. Springer; Wien, 1961.
132. PACH, ZS. P.–FREY, T.: Vektor és tenzoranalízis *(Vector and Tensor Analysis)*. Műszaki Kiadó; Budapest, 1964.
133. PICHT, J.: Einführung in die Theorie der Elektronenoptik. Johann Ambrosius Barth; Leipzig, 1963.
134. PLONSEY, R.–COLLIN, R. E.: *Principles and Applications of Electromagnetic Fields.* McGraw-Hill; New York, 1961.
135. RALSTON, A.: *A First Course in Numerical Analysis.* McGraw-Hill; New York, 1965.
136. RALSTON, A.–WILF, H. S. (Eds): *Mathematical Methods for Digital Computers.* John Wiley and Sons; New York, 1960.
137. RAMBERG, E. G.: *Proc. Instn Radio Engrs.,* **48** (1960), 1952.
138. RETTER, GY.: Magnetische Felder und Kreise. Deutscher Verlag der Wissenschaften; Berlin, 1961.
139. (RYAZANOV, G. A.) Рязанов, Г. А.: Опыты и моделирование при изучении электромагнитного поля *(Experiments and Modelling for Investigations of the Electromagnetic Field)*. Наука; Москва, 1966.
140. RICHTMEYER, R. D.: *Difference Methods for Initial Value Problems.* Interscience Publishers; New York, 1957.
141. ROGERS, A. E.–CONNOLLY, T. W.: *Analog Computation in Engineering Design.* McGraw-Hill Series in Information Processing and Computers, Consulting editor: NASH, J. P., McGraw-Hill; New York, 1960.
142. RUSTERHOLZ, A.: Elektronenoptik. Band I. Grundzüge der theoretischen Elektronenoptik. Birkhäuser; Basel, 1950.
143. SCHOUTEN, J. A.: *Tensor Analysis for Physicists.* Clarendon Press; Oxford, 1951.
144. SHAW, F. S.: *Relaxation Methods.* Dover Publications; New York, 1953.
145. SIMONYI, K.: Grundgesetze des elektromagnetischen Feldes. Deutscher Verlag der Wissenschaften; Berlin, 1963.
146. SIMONYI, K.: Theoretische Elektrotechnik. Deutscher Verlag der Wissenschaften; Berlin, 1966.
147. SIMONYI, K.: Elektronfizika *(Electron Physics)*. Tankönyvkiadó; Budapest, 1969.
148. SIMSCH, E.: *Telefunken-Röhre,* **47** (1967), 285.
149. SMYTHE, W. R.: *Static and Dynamic Electricity.* McGraw-Hill; New York, 1950.
150. SOUTHWELL, R. V.: *Relaxation Methods in Engineering Science.* Oxford University Press; Oxford, 1940.
151. SOUTHWELL, R. V.: *Relaxation Methods in Theoretical Physics.* Volume I. Clarendon Press; Oxford, 1946.
152. SOUTHWELL, R. V.: *Relaxation Methods in Theoretical Physics.* Volume II. Clarendon Press; Oxford, 1956.
153. SPANGENBERG, K. R.: *Vacuum Tubes.* McGraw-Hill; New York, 1948.
154. STEPANOW, W. W.: Lehrbuch der Differentialgleichungen. Deutscher Verlag der Wissenschaften; Berlin, 1956.
155. STILLE, U.: Messen und Rechnen in der Physik. Grundlagen der Grösseneinführung und Einheitsfestlegung. Friedrich Vieweg und Sohn; Braunschweig, 1955.
156. STRATTON, J. A.: *Electromagnetic Theory.* McGraw-Hill; New York, 1941.
157. STURROCK, P. A.: *Static and Dynamic Electron Optics. An Account of Focusing in Lens, Deflector and Accelerator.* University Press; Cambridge, 1955.
158. SYNGE, J. L.–SCHILD, A.: *Tensor Calculus.* University of Toronto Press; Toronto, 1961.
159. THOM, A.–APELT, C. J.: *Field Computations in Engineering and Physics.* D. Van Nostrand; London, 1961.
160. TOMITA, H.–MATSUDA, T.–KOMODA, T.: *J. appl. Phys.* **9** (1970), 719.
161. TORALDO DI FRANCIA, G.: *Electromagnetic Waves.* Interscience Publishers–Zanichelli; New York–Milan, 1956.
162. TSUKKERMAN, I. I.: *Electron Optics in Television.* Pergamon Press; Oxford, 1961.
163. TYCHONOFF, A. N.–SAMARSKI, A. A.: Differentialgleichungen der mathematischen Physik. Deutscher Verlag der Wissenschaften; Berlin, 1959.
164. URBANEK, J.: Egyenletek mértékfüggetlen írásmódja, a Giorgi-féle nemzetközi, abszolút MKS-rendszer *(Calibration Independent Writing Method for Equations, the Giorgi International, Absolute MKS System)*. Akadémiai Kiadó; Budapest, 1955.

165. VARGA, R. S.: *Matrix Iterative Analysis*. Prentice-Hall International; London, 1962.
166. VON ARDENNE, M.: Tabellen zur angewandten Physik. I. Band. VEB Deutscher Verlag der Wissenschaften; Berlin, 1962.
167. VON ARDENNE, M.: Tabellen zur angewandten Physik. II. Band. VEB Deutscher Verlag der Wissenschaften; Berlin, 1964.
168. WEBER, E.: *Electromagnetic Fields. Theory and Applications*. Volume I. Mapping of Fields. John Wiley and Sons; New York, Chapman and Hall; London, 1957.
169. WEIGAND, A.: Die angenäherte Berechnung ebener und rotationssymmetrischer Potentialfelder mit Hilfe des Differenzenverfahrens. Wissenschaftliche Berichte. Folge III. Elektrotechnik. Heft 5. VEB Verlag Technik; Berlin, 1953.
170. WENDT, G.: *Annls. Radioélect.*, **9** (1954), 286.
171. WENDT, G.: Statische Felder und stationäre Ströme. *In:* Herausgegeben von S. FLÜGGE: Handbuch der Physik. Band XVI. Elektrische Felder und Wellen. Springer; Berlin–Göttingen–Heidelberg, 1958.
172. WHITTAKER, E. T.: *A Treatise on the Analytical Dynamics*. Cambridge University Press; London, 1952.
173. WHITTAKER, E. T.–WATSON, G. N.: *A Course of Modern Analysis*. Cambridge University Press; London, 1927.
174. ZONNEVELD, J. A.: *Automatic Numerical Integration*. Mathematical Center; Amsterdam, 1964.
175. ZURMÜHL, R.: Matrizen. Springer; Berlin, 1958.
176. ZWORYKIN, V. K.–MORTON, G. A.–RAMBERG, E. G.–HILLIER, J.–VANCE, A. W.: *Electron Optics and the Electron Microscope*. John Wiley and Sons; New York, 1948.

b) *Field Calculation*

177. AMBOSS, K.: *J. Electron. Control*, **13** (1962), 545.
178. AMBOSS, K.: *IEEE Trans.*, **ED–12** (1965), 313.
179. BERZ, F.: *Phil. Mag.*, **41** (1950), 209.
180. BEURLE, R. L.–WREATHALL, W. M.–CARRÉ, B. A.: *Research on Electron-Optica Design*. English Electric Valve Co. Ltd., England, February 1962.
181. BEVC, V.–SÜSSKIND, C.: *Proc. Instn Radio Engrs.*, **47** (1959), 336.
182. BIRDSALL, C. K.: *Trans. IRE*, **ED–4** (1957), 132.
183. BIRKHOFF, G.–VARGA, R. S.–YOUNG, D.: *Adv. Comput.*, **3** (1962), 189.
184. BOERS, J. E.: *IEEE Trans.*, **ED–12** (1965), 425.
185. BREWER, G. R.: *J. appl. Phys.*, **28** (1957), 634.
186. CARRÉ, B. A.: *Comput. J.*, **4** (1961), 73.
187. CARRÉ, B. A.–WREATHALL, W. M.: *Radio Electron. Engr.*, **27** (1964), 446.
188. COLLINS, J. H.–DALY, P.: *J. Electron. Control*, **14** (1963), 361.
189. CRUISE, D. R.: *J. appl. Phys.*, **34** (1963), 3477.
190. DAVISSON, G. J.–CALBICK, C. J.: *Phys. Rev.*, **38** (1931), 585.
191. DAVISSON, G. J.–CALBICK, C. J.: *Phys. Rev.*, **42** (1932), 580.
192. DAYKIN, P. N.: *Br. J. appl. Phys.*, **6** (1955), 248.
193. DEIMEL, E.: *3rd MOGA*,* 493.
194. DOMMASCHK, W.: *Optik Berlin*, **23** (1966), 472.
195. DUBOIS, G. E. et al.: *Digital Computer Analysis of Axially Symmetric Solid-Beam Electron Guns*. RADC–TDR–64–119, University of Michigan, Ann Arbor, Michigan, 1964.
196. DURAND, E.: *C.R. Hebd. Séanc. Acad. Sci. Paris*, **244** (1957), 2355.
197. EGERVÁRI, E.: *Acta math. hung.*, **11** (1960), 341.
198. ERICKSON, E. E.–SUTHERLAND, A. D.: *4th MOGA*,* 533.
199. FLANDERS, D. A.–SHORTLEY, G.: *J. appl. Phys.*, **21** (1950), 1326.
200. FOX, L.: *Proc. R. Soc.*, **190–A** (1947), 31.
201. FOX, L.: *Q. Jl. Mech. appl. Math.*, **1** (1948), 253.
202. FRANKEL, S. P.: *Mathl Tabl. natn. Res. Com., Wash.*, **4** (1950), 65.

* Throughout these references the abbreviation MOGA has been used to refer to the Proceedings of the International Conferences on Microwave and Optical Generation and Amplification. (See p. 483.)

203. FROST, R. D.–PURL, O. T.–JOHNSON, H. R.: *Proc. Instn Radio Engrs.*, **50** (1962), 1800.
204. GARABEDIAN, P. R.: *Mathl Tabl. natn. Res. Com.*, *Wash.*, **10** (1956), 183.
205. GARABEDIAN, P. R.: *J. Math. Mech.*, **9** (1960), 905.
206. GARABEDIAN, P. R.–LIEBERSTEIN, H. M.: *J. aeronaut. Sci.*, **25** (1958), 109.
207. GERSCHGORIN, S.: *Z. angew. Math. Mech.*, **10** (1930), 373.
208. GROTH, T.–OLSEN, B.–PETTERSON, G.: *Nucl. Instrum. Meth.*, **56** (1967), 61.
209. HADAMARD, J.: *Lectures on Cauchy's Problem in Linear Partial Differential Equations.* Dover Publications; New York, 1952.
210. HAMZA, V.: NASA Rept. No. TN D–1711, Washington, D.C., 1963.
211. HAMZA, V.: *IEEE Trans.*, **ED–13** (1966), 485.
212. HAMZA, V.–KINO, G. S.: *IEEE Trans.*, **ED–14** (1967), 195.
213. HAMZA, V.–RICHLEY, E. A.: NASA Rept. No. TN D–1323, Washington, D.C., 1962.
214. HARKER, K. J.: *J. appl. Phys.*, **31** (1960), 2165.
215. HARKER, K. J.: *J. appl. Phys.*, **33** (1962), 1861.
216. HARKER, K. J.: *J. Mathl.Phys.*, **4** (1963), 993.
217. HARKER, K. J.–LLACER, J.: *Q. appl. Math.*, **21** (1963), 223.
218. HARRINGTON, R. F.: *Field Computation by Moment Methods.* Macmillan; New York, 1968.
219. HARRIS, L. A.: *Trans. IRE*, **ED–7** (1960), 46.
220. HARRISON, E. R.: *Br. J. appl. Phys.*, **5** (1954), 40.
221. HECHTEL, J. R.: *Telefunkenzeitung*, **28** (1955), 222.
222. HECHTEL, J. R.: *Arch. elekt. Übertr.*, **10** (1956), 535.
223. HERRMANNSFELDT, W. B.: *Poisson Equation Solving Program.* Report No. SLAC–51, Stanford Linear Accelerator Center, 1965.
224. HO, KUO-CHU–MOON, R. J.: *J. appl. Phys.*, **24** (1953), 1186.
225. HOCKNEY, R. W.: *A Fast Direct Solution of Poisson's Equation Using Fourier Analysis.* Stanford Electronic Laboratory Reports 0255–1; Stanford, California, 1964.
226. HORNSBY, J. S.: *A Computer Programme for the Solution of Elliptical Partial Differential Equations (Potential Problems).* CERN Reports 63–7; Geneva, 1963.
227. HYMAN, J.–ECKHARDT, W. O.–KNECHTLI, R. C.–BUCKEY, C. R.: *AIAA J*, **2** (1964), 1739.
228. KELLER, H. B.: *Q. appl. Math.*, **16** (1958), 209.
229. KINO, G. S.: *Trans. IRE*, **ED–7** (1960), 179.
230. KINO, G. S.–TAYLOR, N. J.: *Trans. IRE*, **ED–9** (1962), 1.
231. KIRSTEIN, P. T.: *Proc. Instn Radio Engrs.*, **46** (1958), 1716.
232. KIRSTEIN, P. T.: *IEEE Trans.*, **ED–12** (1965), 447.
233. KIRSTEIN, P. T.: *Int. J. Electron.*, **18** (1965), 95.
234. KIRSTEIN, P. T.–HORNSBY, J. S.: *4th MOGA*,* 566.
235. KIRSTEIN, P. T.–HORNSBY, J. S.: *IEEE Trans.*, **ED–11** (1964), 196.
236. KIRSTEIN, P. T.–KANTOR, R.–SZEGO, J.: *Numerical Solution to the Space-Charge Limited Flow Obtained by the Separation of Variables Method.* Microwave Laboratory Reports No. 714, Stanford University; Stanford, California, 1960.
237. KLOPFENSTEIN, R. W.: *J. Ass. comput. Mach.*, **8** (1961), 366.
238. KREYSZIG, E.: *Z. angew. Phys.*, **7** (1955), 13.
239. KULSRUD, H. E.: *Communs Ass. comput. Mach.*, **4** (1961), 184.
240. KULSRUD, H. E.: *RCAR*, **28** (1967), 351.
241. LIEBMANN, H.: Sitzungsberichte der Bayerischen Akademie der Wissenschaften, (1918), 385.
242. LINDSAY, P. A.: *J. Electron. Control*, **6** (1959), 415.
243. LOMAX, R. J.: *J. Electron. Control*, **3** (1957), 367.
244. LOMAX, R. J.: *J. Electron. Control*, **6** (1959), 39.
245. LOMAX, R. J.: *J. Electron. Control*, **7** (1959), 482.
246. LYLE, T. R.: *Phil. Mag.*, **3** (1902), 310.
247. MARTN, D. W.–TEE, G. J.: *Comput. J.*, **4** (1961), 242.
248. MELTZER, B.: *J. Electron. Control*, **8** (1960), 449.
249. MELTZER, G.–DINNIS, A. R.: *J. Electron. Control*, **4** (1958), 459.
250. MÜLLER, M.: *Arch. elekt. Übertr.*, **9** (1955), 20.
251. MÜLLER, M.: *J. Br. IRE*, **16** (1965), 83.

* See p. 483.

252. NELSON, R. B.: *6th MOGA,* * 60.
253. PEACEMAN, D. W.–RACHFORD, H. H.: *J. Soc. ind. appl. Math.*, **3** (1955), 28.
254. PETROVSKII, I. G.: *Lectures on Partial Differential Equations.* John Wiley and Sons, New York, 1954.
255. PICQUENDAR, J. E.–CAHEN, O.: *Revue techn. C.F.T.H.*, **32** (1960), 7.
256. PIERCE, J. R.: *J. appl. Phys.*, **11** (1940), 548.
257. PIERCE, J. R.: *Proc. Instn Radio Engrs.*, **29** (1941), 28.
258. PÖSCHL, K.–VEITH, W.: *Arch. elekt. Übertr.*, **12** (1958), 44.
259. PRINCE, D. C.–KUSKEVICS, G.–EDWARDS, R.: *Computer Evaluation of Ion Engines.* NAS 8–623, *G.E.*, Cincinnati, Ohio, 1962.
260. RADLEY, D. E.: *J. Electron. Control*, **4** (1958), 125.
261. REICHERT, K.: *Arch. Elektrotech.*, **52** (1968), 176.
262. RICHARDSON, L. F.: *Phil. Trans. R. Soc.*, **210–A** (1910), 307.
263. RICHARDSON, L. F.: *Proc. R. Soc.*, **83–A** (1910), 335.
264. RICHARDSON, L. F.: *Mathl. Gaz.*, **12** (1924/25), 415.
265. RUNGE, C.: *Z. Math. Phys.*, **56** (1908), 225.
266. SCHAGEN, P.–BRUINING, H.–FRANCKEN, J. C.: *Philips Res. Rep.*, **7** (1952), 119.
267. SCHÄFF, F.: *Z. angew. Phys.*, **23** (1967), 64.
268. SEITZ, W. E.–EILENBERG, S. L.: *J. appl. Phys.*, **38** (1967), 276.
269. SHORTLEY, G. H.–DARBY, P.–WELLER, R.–GAMBLE, E. H.: *J. appl. Phys.*, **18** (1947), 116.
270. SHORTLEY, G. H.–WELLER, R.: *J. appl. Phys.*, **9** (1938), 334.
271. SINGER, B.–BRAUN, M.: *IEEE Trans.*, **ED–17** (1970), 926.
272. SUGAI, I.: *Proc. Instn Radio Engrs.*, **47** (1959), 88.
273. SUGAI, I.: *IBM Jl Res. Dev.*, **3** (1959), 187.
274. TODD, E. G.–BREWER, G. R.: *IRE WESCON Conv. Rec.*, **3** (1959), 112.
275. WASOW, W.: *Z. angew. Math. Phys.*, **6** (1955), 81.
276. WEBER, C.: *Philips Tech. Rev.*, **24** (1962), 130.
277. WEBER, C.: *Proc. IEEE*, **51** (1963), 252.
278. WEBER, C.: *5th MOGA,* * 47.
279. YOUNG, D. M.: *Iterative Methods for Solving Partial Difference Equations of Elliptic Type.* Doctoral Thesis; Harvard University, 1950.
280. YOUNG, D. M.: *Trans. Am. math. Soc.*, **76** (1954), 92.
281. ZLOTYKAMIN, C.: *2nd MOGA,* ** 939.

c) *Electrolytic Tank*

282. AMMAN, F.–DADDA, L.: *Nuovo Cim.*, **3** (1956), 184.
283. ANDREWS, D. H.: *Electronics*, **27** (1954), 182.
284. BARKHAUSEN, H.–BRÜCK, J.: *Elektrotech. Z.*, **54** (1933), 175.
285. BOWMAN-MANIFOLD, M.–NICOLL, F. H.: *Nature, Lond.*, **142** (1938), 39.
286. BRACHER, A.: Thesis. Birmingham, 1950.
287. BRADFIELD, K. N. E.–HOOKER, S. G.–SOUTHWELL, R. V.: *Proc. R. Soc.*, **159** (1937), 315
288. BREWER, G. R.: *J. appl. Phys.*, **28** (1957), 7.
289. BURFOOT, J. C.: *Br. J. appl. Phys.*, **6** (1955), 67.
290. CHARLES, D.: *Annls. Radioélect.*, **4** (1949), 1.
291. COHN, S. B.: *Proc. Instn Radio Engrs.*, **39** (1951), 1416.
292. COOK, E. J.: *Proc. Instn Radio Engrs.*, **46** (1958), 497.
293. DAHLIN, E. B.: *Rev. Scient. Instrum.*, **25** (1954), 951.
294. DUKES, J. M. C.: *Proc. Instn elect. Engrs.*, **103–B** (1956), 319.
295. EINSTEIN, P. A.: *Br. J. appl. Phys.*, **2** (1951), 49.
296. FORTESCUE, C. L.–FARNSWORTH, S. W.: *Proc. Am. Instn elect. Engrs.*, **32** (1913), 757.
297. GERMAIN, C.: Thèse. Paris, 1955.
298. GERMAIN, C.: *C.R. Hebd. Séanc. Acad. Sci. Paris*, **240** (1955), 588.
299. GOUDET, G.–MUSSON-GENON, R.: *J. Phys. Radium Paris*, **6** (1945), 185.
300. GREEN, P. E.: *Rev. Scient. Instrum.*, **19** (1948), 646.
301. GREGORY, B. C.–SANDER, K. F.: *Proc. IEEE*, **3** (1964), 1766.

* See p. 484.
** See p. 483.

302. HARRIES, J. H. O.: *Proc. Instn Radio Engrs.*, **44** (1956), 236.
303. HARTILL, E. R.: *Elect. Energy*, **2** (1958), 118.
304. HEPP, G.: *Philips tech. Rdsc.*, **4** (1939), 235.
305. HIMPAN, J.: *Telefunken-Röhre*, **16** (1939), 198.
306. HIMPAN, J.: *Elektrotech. Z.*, **63** (1942), 349.
307. HOLLWAY, D. L.: *Aust. J. Phys.*, **8** (1955), 74.
308. HOLLWAY, D. L.: *Proc. IEEE*, **103–B** (1956), 155.
309. JACOBS, J. E.–LYON, J. A. M.: *Proc. natn. Electron. Conf.*, **6** (1950), 136.
310. KENNEDY, P. A.–KENT, G.: *Rev. scient. Instrum.*, **27** (1956), 916.
311. KENNELY, A. E.–WHITING, S. E.: *Electl. Wld.*, **48** (1906), 1239.
312. KIRCHHOFF, G. R.: *Annls Physik*, **64** (1845), 497.
313. KLEMPERER, O.: *J. scient. Instrum.*, **21** (1944), 88.
314. LIEBMANN, G.: *Proc. Phys. Soc.*, **66–B** (1953), 448.
315. LOMAX, R. J.: *J. Electron. Control*, **15** (1963), 229.
316. LOUKOCHCOFF, W. S.: *Vide*, **65** (1956), 328.
317. LOUKOCHKOW, V. S.: *1st MOGA,** Vol. II*, 154.
318. MAKAR, R.–BOOTHROYD, A. R.–CHERRY, E. C.: *Nature*, Lond., **161** (1948), 845.
319. MALAVARD, L.: *Onde élect.*, **36** (1956), 762.
320. MALAVARD, L.: *Onde élect.*, **36** (1956), 829.
321. MALAVARD, L.: *Onde élect.*, **36** (1956), 1046.
322. MET, V.: *Frequenz*, **9** (1955), 57.
323. MIROUX, J.: *Onde élect.*, **38** (1958), 450.
324. MURRAY, C. T.–HOLLWAY, D. L.: *J. scient. Instrum.*, **32** (1955), 481.
325. MUSSON-GENON, R.: *Annl. Télécommun.*, **2** (1947), 254.
326. MUSSON-GENON, R.: *Annl. Télécommun.*, **2** (1947), 298.
327. MUSSON-GENON, R.: *Onde élect.*, **28** (1948), 2; 236.
328. PEIERLS, R. E.: *Nature*, Lond., **158** (1946), 831.
329. PEIERLS, R. E.–SKYRME, T. H. R.: *Phil. Mag.*, **40** (1949), 269.
330. PÉRÈS, J.–MALAVARD, L.: *Bull. Soc. fr. Electns.*, **8** (1938), 715.
331. PETERS, C. J.: *Rev. scient. Instrum.*, **36** (1965), 174.
332. PICQUENDAR, J. E.–CAHEN, O.: *Rev. tech. C.F.T.H.* **32** (1960), 59.
333. PIERCE, J. R.: *J. appl. Phys.*, **11** (1940), 548.
334. REINIGER, F.: *Philips tech. Rdsch.*, **17** (1956), 220.
335. ROWE, J. E.–MARTIN, R. J.: *2nd MOGA,** 1024.
336. SAMUEL, A. L.: *Proc. Instn Radio Engrs.*, **33** (1945), 233.
337. SANDER, K. F.–OATLEY, C. W.–YATES, J. G.: *Proc. Instn elect. Engrs.*, **99–III** (1952), 169.
338. SANDER, K. F.–YATES, J. G.: *Proc. Instn elect. Engrs.*, **100–III** (1953), 167.
339. SANDER, K. F.–YATES, J. G.: *Proc. Instn elect. Engrs.*, **104–C** (1957), 81.
340. SCHMUDE, H.–SCHWENKHAGEN, H.: *Telefunken-Röhre*, **24–25** (1942), 47.
341. SPANGENBERG, K.–HELM, R.–FIELD, L. M.: *Electl Commun.*, **24** (1947), 101.
342. STRIEGEL, R.: *A.T.M.*, **No. 140** (1943), V312–1.
343. STRIEGEL, R.: *A.T.M.*, **No. 144** (1943), V312–2.
344. THEILE, R.–HIMPAN, J.: *Telefunken-Röhre*, **18** (1940), 50.
345. VAN DUZER, T.–BREWER, G. R.: *J. appl. Phys.*, **30** (1959), 291.
346. VAN DUZER, T.–BUCKEY, C. R.—BREWER, G. R.: *Rev. scient. Instrum.*, **34** (1963), 558.
347. VERSTER, J. L.: *On the Use of Gauzes in Electron Optics.* Thesis. Delft, 1963.
348. WESTON, M. K.: *J. scient. Instrum.*, **32** (1955), 367.

d) Resistance Network

349. ARCHARD, G. D.: *Resistance Networks in Aldermaston.* Assoc. Elect. Ind. Res. Lab., AEI Rept. A, Aldermaston, Berkshire, 1957.
350. CHARLES, D.: *Annl. Radioélect.*, **4** (1949), 1.
351. CHRISTENSEN, V.: *Techn. Mem.*, **71** (1959), Project Matterhorn, Princeton.
352. ČREŠMONIK, G.–STRUTT, M. J. O.: *Arch. Elektrotech.*, **43** (1957), 177.
353. CULVER, R.: *Br. J. appl. Phys.*, **3** (1952), 376.

* See p. 483.

354. DE PACKH, D. C.: *Rev. scient. Instrum.*, **18** (1947), 798.
355. (DER-SHVARTS, G. V.–NETREBENKO, K. A.) Дер-Шварц, Г. В.–Нетребенко, К. А.: *Изв. АН СССР, Сер. Физ.*, **23** (1959), 506.
356. DURAND, E.: *C.R. Hebd. Séanc. Acad. Sci. Paris*, **244** (1957), 2355.
357. FRANCKEN, J.: *Philips tech. Rev.*, **21** (1959), 10.
358. (GERSHGORIN, S. A.) Гершгорин, С. А.: *Ж. Приклад. Физ. СССР*, **6** (1929), 3.
359. HECHTEL, J. R.: *Telefunken-Röhre*, **31** (1953), 233.
360. HECHTEL, J. R.: *Telefunken-Röhre*, **32** (1955), 38.
361. HECHTEL, J. R.: *Telefunke n Z.*, **3 1** (1958), 124
362. HECHTEL, J. R.–SEEGER, J. A.:d*Proc. Instn Radio Engrs.*, **49** (1961), 933.
363. HENNEQUIN, J.: Diplôme d'étues supérieures. Paris, 1948.
364. HOGAN, T. K.: *J. Instn Engrs. Aust.*, **15** (1943), 89.
365. KARPLUS, W. J.: *Br. J. appl. Phys.*, **6** (1955), 356.
366. KRON, G.: *Elect. Engng.*, **67** (1948), 672.
367. LIEBMANN, G.: *Nature, Lond.*, **164** (1949), 149.
368. LIEBMANN, G.: *Proc. Phys. Soc.*, **62–B** (1949), 213.
369. LIEBMANN, G.: *Proc. Phys. Soc.*, **62–B** (1949), 753.
370. LIEBMANN, G.: *Phil. Mag.*, **41** (1950), 1143.
371. LIEBMANN, G.: *Br. J. appl. Phys.*, **1** (1950), 92.
372. LIEBMANN, G.: *Proc. Instn elect. Engrs.*, **99–IV** (1952), 260.
373. LIEBMANN, G.: *Br. J. appl. Phys.*, **4** (1953), 193.
374. LIEBMANN, G.: *Br. J. appl. Phys.*, **5** (1954), 362.
375. LIEBMANN, G.: *Br. J. appl. Phys.*, **5** (1954), 412.
376. LIEBMANN, G.: *Br. J. appl. Pyhs.*, **6** (1955), 145.
377. LIEBMANN, G.: *Trans. Am. Soc. mech. Engrs.*, **78** (1956), 655.
378. LIEBMANN, G.: *Trans. Am. Soc. mech. Engrs.*, **78** (1956), 1267.
379. LIEBMANN, G.–BAILEY, R.: *Br. J. appl. Phys.*, **5** (1954), 32.
380. REDSHAW, S. C.: *Proc. Instn mech. Engrs.*, **159** (1948), 55.
381. SUGATA, E.–TERADA, M.–HAMADA, H.: *J. Inst. elec. Commun. Engrs. Japan*, **42** (1959) 1088.
382. SUGATA, E.–TERADA, M.–HAMADA, H.: *Tech. Rep. Osaka Univ.*, **10** (1960), 39.
383. SUGATA, E.–TERADA, M.–HAMADA, H.: *Resistance Network Analog for Analysing Magnetic Field*. Meeting of Professional Group on Microwave Electron Tubes, Inst. elect. Commun. Engrs Japan, 1960.
384. SUGATA, E.–TERADA, M.–HAMADA, H.: *Resistance Network Analog for Analysing Magnetic Field*. Annual Meeting of the Inst. elect. Commun. Engrs, Japan, 1961.
385. TERMAN, F. E.: *Radio Engineers' Handbook*. McGraw-Hill; London, 1950.
386. TSCHOPP, P. A.: *Analogieverfahren zur Bestimmung von magnetischen Feldern in nicht-linearen nicht-isotropen Medien*. Thesis. Zürich, 1961.
387. TSCHOPP, P. A.: *Bull. schweiz. Elektrotech. Ver.*, **6** (1961), 185.
388. TSCHOPP, P. A.–FREI, H. A.: *Arch. Elektrotech.*, **44** (1959), 441.
389. WAKEFIELD, K. E.: Report PMS 23, 1958, Project Matterhorn, Princeton.
390. WEBER, C.: *Proc. Instn elect. Engrs.*, **51** (1963), 252.

e) *Rubber Membrane*

391. ALMA, G. A.–DIEMER, G.–GROENDIJK, H.: *Philips tech. Rev.*, **14** (1953), 336.
392. CLARK, J. W.–NEUBER, R. E.: *Proc. Instn Radio Engrs.*, **38** (1950), 521.
393. FREMLIN, J. H.–WALKER, J.: *J. scien. Instrum.*, **24** (1947), 50.
394. FULOP, W.: *Br. J. appl. Phys.*, **6** (1955), 21.
395. HARRIES, J. H. O.: *Proc. Instn Radio Engrs.*, **44** (1956), 236.
396. HOLLMANN, H. E.: *Proc. Instn Radio Engrs.*, **29** (1941), 70.
397. (KELMAN, V. M.–KRASNOV, I. F.) Кельман, В. М.–Краснов, И. Ф.: *Ж. Тех. Физ. СССР*, **25** (1955) 1714.
398. (KELMAN, V. M.–UTKIN, K. G.–LOGINOVA, L. N.) Кельман, В. М.–Уткин, К. Г.–Логинова, Л. Н.: *Ж. Тех. Физ. СССР*, **27** (1957) 2092.
399. (KRASNOV, I. F.–KELMAN, V. M.) Краснов, И. Ф.–Кельман, В. М.: *Ж. Тех. Физ. СССР*, **25** (1955) 1726.
400. MCGIVERN, J. G.–SUPPER, H. L.: *Trans. A.S.M.E.*, **56** (1934), 601.

401. McGivern, J. G.–Supper, H. L.: *J. Franklin Inst.*, **217** (1934), 491.
402. Smythe, W. R.–Rumbaugh, L. H.–West, S. S.: *Phys. Rev.*, **45** (1934), 724.
403. (Utkin, K. G.) Уткин, К. Г.: *Приборы Тех. Экспер. СССР*, **5** (1959), 111.
404. Walker, G. B.: *Proc. Instn elect. Engrs.*, **96–II** (1949), 319.
405. White, D. A.–Perry, D. L.: *Rev. scient. Instrum.*, **32** (1961), 730.
406. Wilson, L. H.–Miles, A. J.: *J. appl. Phys.*, **21** (1950), 532.

f) *Magnetic Field Measurement*

407. Adams, G. D.–Dressel, R. W.–Towsley, F. E.: *Rev. scient. Instrum.*, **21** (1950), 69.
408. Alekseev, A. G.–Gorelkin, A. S.–Mozalevskii, I. A.–Mozin, I. V.–Tarasov, B. I.–
　　Trokhachev, G. V.: *Instrums. exp. Tech.*, **4** (1962), 797.
409. Allen, G. P.–Sherry, M.: *J. Electron. Control*, **6** (1959), 264.
410. Alon, G. I.: *Onde élect.*, **42** (1962), 330.
411. Arnaud, M.–Cahen, O.: *Rev. Tech. C.F.T.H.*, **32** (1960), 43.
412. (Baranov, S. A.–Malov, A. F.–Shlyagin, K. N.) Баранов, С. А.–Малов, А. Ф.–
　　Шлягин, К. Н.: *Приборы Тех. Экспер. СССР*, **1** (1956), 3.
413. Barber, E.: Astronautics Information Literature Search No. 195. California Institute
　　of Technology, Pasadena, California, 1960.
414. Birss, R. R.–Fry, J. P.: *J. scient. Instrum.*, **37** (1960), 31.
415. Bloom, A. L.–Packard, M. E.: *Science*, **122** (1955), 738.
416. Brankhoff, K.: *Nachtech.*, **10** (1960), 247.
417. Braunersreuther, E.–Combe, J. C.–Hoffmann, L.–Morpurgo, M.: *CERN* Rept.
　　62–7 (1962).
418. Braunersreuther, E.–Kurth, F.–Lippmann, H. J.: *Z. Naturf.* **15–A** (1960), 795.
419. Brown, R. A.: *CERN* Rept 66–15 (1966).
420. Brown, W.–Sweer, J. H.: *Rev. Scient. Instrum.*, **16** (1945), 276.
421. Burson, S. B.–Martin, D. W.–Schmid, L. C.: *Rev. Scient. Instrum.*, **30** (1959), 513.
422. Buss, L.–Bogart, L.: *Rev. Scient. Instrum.*, **31** (1960), 204.
423. Caldecourt, V. J.–Adler, S. E.: *Rev. Scient. Instrum.*, **25** (1954), 953.
424. (Chechernikov, V. I.) Чечерников, В. И.: Магнитные измерения *(Magnetic Mea-*
　　surements). Московский Университет; Москва, 1963.
425. Cioffi, P. P.: *Rev. Scient. Instrum.*, **21** (1950), 624.
426. Cole, R. H.: *Rev. Scient. Instrum.*, **9** (1938), 215.
427. Cork, J. M.–Shreffler, R. G.–Shull, F. B.: *Rev. Scient. Instrum.*, **18** (1947), 315.
428. Cork, B.–Zajec, E.: University of California Radiation Laboratory Rept. UCRL–
　　2182 (1953).
429. Cragg, B. G.: *J. Scient. Instrum.*, **32** (1955), 385.
430. Daniltsev, E. N.–Plotnikov, V. K.: *Instrums. Exper. Tech.*, **3** (1963), 387.
431. Dayton, I. E.–Shoemaker, F. C.–Mozley, R. F.: *Rev. Scient. Instrum.*, **25** (1954), 485.
432. De Forest, R.: *Nucl. Instrum. Methods*, **18–19** (1962), 584.
433. (Denisov, Yu. N.) Денисов, Ю. Н.: *Приборы Тех. Экспер. СССР*, **5** (1958), 67.
434. Denisov, I. N.: *Instrums. Exper. Tech.*, **5** (1958), 658.
435. Denisov, I. N.: *Instrums. Exper. Tech.*, **7** (1960), 89.
436. De Raad, B.: *Dynamic and static measurements of strongly inhomogeneous magnetic*
　　fields. Thesis. Delft Institute of Technology, Holland 1958.
437. Dicke, R. H.: *Rev. Scient. Instrum.*, **19** (1948), 533.
438. (Dimov, G. I.) Димов, Г. И.: *Ж. Тех. Физ. СССР*, **29** (1959), 668.
439. Dolega, U.–Pfeifer, H.–Lösche, A.: *Z. angew. Phys.*, **7** (1955), 12.
440. Donnally, B.–Sanders, T. M.: *Rev. Scient. Instrum.*, **31** (1960), 977.
441. Dosse, J.: *Z. Phys.*, **117** (1941), 316.
442. Dosse, J.: *Z. Phys.*, **117** (1941), 437.
443. Dosse, J.: *Z. Phys.*, **117** (1941), 722.
444. Dosse, J.: *Z. Phys.*, **118** (1942), 375.
445. Driscoll, R. L.–Bender, P. L.: *Phys. Rev. Lett.*, **1** (1958), 413.
446. Dumin, D. J.: *Proc. Instn Radio Engrs.*, **50** (1962), 1825.
447. Durandeau, P.: *C.R. Hebd. Séanc. Acad. Sci. Paris*, **236** (1953), 366.
448. Edgar, R. F.: *Trans. Am. Inst. elect. Engrs.*, **56** (1937), 805.
449. Elmore, W. C.–Garrett, M. W.: *Rev. Scient. Instrum.*, **25** (1954), 480.

450. FECHTER, H. R.–RUBIN, S.: *Rev. Scient. Instrum.*, **26** (1955), 1108.
451. FELDMAN, D. W.: *Rev. Scient. Instrum.*, **31** (1960), 72.
452. FERT, C.–GAUTIER, P.: *C.R. Hebd. Séanc. Acad. Sci. Paris*, **233** (1951), 148.
453. FINLAY, E. A.–FOWLER, J. F.–SMEE, J. F.: *J. Scient. Instrum.*, **27** (1950), 264.
454. FÖRSTER, F.: *Z. Metallk.*, **46** (1955), 358.
455. FRAGSTEIN, C. V.: *Z. angew. Phys.*, **9** (1957), 268.
456. FRAZER, J. F.–HOFMANN, J. A.–LIVINGSTON, M. S.–VASH, A. M.: *Rev. Scient. Instrum.*, **26** (1955), 475.
457. FREEMAN, R.: *J. Scient. Instrum.*, **38** (1961), 318.
458. GABILLARD, R.: *Archs. Sci. Genève*, **9** (1956), 316.
459. GARRETT, M. W.: *J. appl. Phys.*, **22** (1951), 1091.
460. GAUTIER, P.: *C.R. Hebd. Séanc. Acad. Sci. Paris*, **235** (1952), 361.
461. GAUTIER, P.: *J. Phys. Radium, Paris* **15** (1954), 684.
462. GAUTIER, P.: *C.R. Hebd. Séanc. Acad. Sci. Paris*, **242** (1956), 1707.
463. GEIGER, W. A.: *Electronics*, **35** (1962), 48.
464. GERMAIN, C.: *Nucl. Instrum. Meth.*, **21** (1963), 17.
465. GIORDANO, S.–GREEN, G. K.–ROGERS, E. J.: *Rev. Scient. Instrum.*, **24** (1953), 848.
466. (GREKOV, N. N.–RYABOV, A. P.–GOLDIN, L. L.) Греков, Н. Н.–Рябов, А. П.–Голдин, Л. Л.: *Приборы Тех. Экспер. СССР*, **2** (1956), 29.
467. GRIVET, P.–SAUZADE, M.–STEFANT, R.: *Rev. gén. Elect.*, **70** (1961), 317.
468. GRIVET, P.–SEPTIER, A.: *Nuclear Instrum. meth.*, **6** (1960), 126.
469. GRIVET, P.–SEPTIER, A.: *Nuclear Instrum. meth.*, **6** (1960), 243.
470. HEDGRAN, A.: *Ark. Fys.*, **5** (1952), 1.
471. HENTSCHEL, E.–MEYER, A. F.: *Ann. Phys.*, **10** (1962), 207.
472. HERMANN, P. K.: *Arch. tech. Messen*, **345** (1964), 237.
473. HESSE, M. B.: *Proc. Phys. Soc.*, **61** (1949), 233.
474. HUBER, H. J.–ROGERS, K. C.: *Rev. Scient. Instrum.*, **35** (1964), 801.
475. HUDSON, E. D.–LORD, R. S.–MARSHALL, M. B.–SMITH, W. R.–RICHARDSON, E. G.: *Nuclear Instrum. meth.*, **18–19** (1962), 159.
476. HUTCHINSON, C. A.–PASTOR, R.: *Rev. Mod. Phys.*, **25** (1953), 285.
477. (INOZEMTSEV, K. V.–LATYSHEV, G. D.) Иноземцев, К. В.–Латышев, Г. Д.: *Изв. АН СССР, Сер. Физ.*, **13** (1949), 453.
478. JAN, J. P.: *Solid St. Phys.*, **5** (1957), 1.
479. JOUSSELIN, J.: *Atompraxis*, **8** (1962), 140.
480. JÜRGENS, B. F.: *Philips Tech. Rev.*, **15** (1953), 49.
481. JÜRGENS, B. F.–VAN DORSTEN, A. C.–FRANKEN, A. J. J.–BELJERS, H. G.: *Philips Tech. Rdsch.*, **14** (1953), 349.
482. KANDIAH, K.–BROWN, D. E.: *Proc. Instn elect. Engrs.*, **99–II** (1952), 314.
483. (KAPITSA, S. P.) Капица, С. П.: *Ж. Тех. Физ. СССР*, **25** (1955) 1307.
484. KELLY, J. M.: *Rev. Scient. Instrum.*, **22** (1951), 256.
485. KLEMPERER, O.–MILLER, H.: *J. Scient. Instrum.*, **16** (1939), 121.
486. KOHAUT, A.: *Z. tech. Phys.*, **18** (1937) 198.
487. KOLM, H.–LAX, B.–BITTER, F.–MILLS, R. (Eds): *High Magnetic Fields.* Proceedings of the International Conference on High Magnetic Fields, MIT, Cambridge, Massachusetts, 1961. MIT Press, Cambridge, Massachusetts and Wiley, New York, 1962.
488. KUHRT, F.: *Siemens-Z.*, **28** (1954), 370.
489. KUHRT, F.: *Elektron. Rdsch.*, **14** (1960), 10.
490. KUHRT, F.–HARTEL, W.: *Arch. Elektrotech.*, **43** (1957), 1.
491. KÜHNE, R.: *Arch. tech. Messen*, **199** (1952), 175.
492. LAMB, W. E.–RETHERFORD, R. C.: *Phys. Rev.*, **81** (1951), 222.
493. LANGER, L. M.–SCOTT, F. R.: *Rev. Scient. Instrum.*, **21** (1950), 522.
494. LANGNER, G.–LENZ, F.: *Optik, Berl.*, **11** (1954), 171.
495. LASLETT, L. J.: Rept. LJL–1. Brookhaven National Laboratory, Upton, New York, 1954.
496. LASLETT, L. J.: Rept. LJL–2. Brookhaven National Laboratory, Upton, New York, 1954.
497. LAUDET, M.: *J. Phys. Radium, Paris*, **18** (1957), 73A.
498. LENZ, F.: *Optik, Berl.*, **7** (1950), 243.
499. LENZ, F.: *Optik, Berl.*, **9** (1952), 3.
500. LEONTJEW, N. L.: *Nachtech. Z.*, **6** (1956), 351.

501. LIND, D. A.–RICKEY, M. E.–BARDIN, B. M.: *Nuclear Instrum. Meth.*, **18–19** (1962), 129.
502. LUSH, M. J.: *Instrums. Control. Syst.*, **37** (1964), 111.
503. McCUTCHEN, C. W.: *J. Scient. Instrum.*, **36** (1959), 471.
504. MONTAGUE, B. W.: *Mullard Tech. Commun.*, **2** (1955), 64.
505. MURAY, J. J.–SCHOLL, R. A.: Rept. SLAC–26. Stanford Linear Accelerator Center, Stanford University, California, 1964.
506. MURRMANN, H.: *Z. Phys.*, **165** (1961), 305.
507. NEUMANN, H.: *Arch. tech. Messen*, **222** (1954), 161.
508. OBERRETL, K.: *Elektrotech. Z.*, **84–A** (1963), 757.
509. OGUEY, H. J.: *Rev. Scient. Instrum.*, **31** (1960), 701.
510. PARKINSON, W. C.–GROVER, G. M.–CRANE, H. R.: *Rev. Scient. Instrum.*, **18** (1947), 734.
511. PARTON, J. E.–STAIRMAND, G. D.: *J. Scient. Instrum.*, **32** (1955), 464.
512. PEARSON, G. L.: *Rev. Scient. Instrum.*, **19** (1948), 263.
513. (PEREGUD, B. P.) Перегуд, Б. П.: *Приборы Тех. Экспер. СССР*, **3** (1957), 64.
514. PETERS, W. A. E.: *Elektrotech. Z.*, **71–A** (1950), 193.
515. PEUKERT, W.: *Elektrotech. Z.*, **31** (1910), 636.
516. POHM, A. V.–RUBENS, S. N.: *Rev. Scient. Instrum.*, **27** (1956), 306.
517. POPLE, J. A.–SCHNEIDER, W. G.–BERNSTEIN, H. J.: *High Resolution Nuclear Magnetic Resonance.* McGraw-Hill; New York, 1959
518. POUND, R. V.–FREEMAN, R.: *Rev. Scient. Instrum.*, **31** (1960), 96.
519. PUTLEY, E. H.: *The HALL Effect and Related Phenomena.* Butterworths; London–Washington, 1960.
520. RADKEVICH, I. A.–SOKOLOVSKII, V. V.–TALYZIN, A. N.–GOLDIN, L. L.–BYSHEVA, G. K.–GORYACHEV, Y. M.: *Instrums. exp. Tech. Pittsburgh*, **4** (1962), 848.
521. RADUS, R. J.: *J. appl. Phys.*, **31** (1960), 1865.
522. ROSHON, D. D.: *Rev. Scient. Instrum.*, **33** (1962), 201.
523. ROSS, I. M.–SAKER, E. W.–THOMPSON, N. A. C.: *J. Scient. Instrum.*, **34** (1957), 479.
524. SASAKI, H.: *Nucl. Instrum. Meth.*, **14** (1962), 252.
525. SAUZADE, M.: *C.R. Hebd. Séanc. Acad. Sci. Paris*, **246** (1958), 272.
526. SCHWAIBOLD, E.: *Arch. tech. Messen*, **246** (1956), 153.
527. SCHWINK, C.: *Z. Phys.*, **161** (1961), 560.
528. SHIRER, D. L.: *Rev. Scient. Instrum.*, **31** (1960), 1000.
529. SILVER, D. E. P.: *Electron. Engng.*, **36** (1964), 374.
530. SMITH, G. S.: *Elect. Engng.*, **56** (1937), 441.
531. SMITH, G. S.: *Elect. Engng.*, **56** (1937), 475.
532. SPIGHEL, M.: *J. Phys. Radium, Paris*, **18** (1957), 108A.
533. SPOKAS, O. E.–DANOS, M.: *Rev. Scient. Instrum.*, **33** (1962), 613.
534. STAHLKE, J. L.: *Nucl. Instrum. Methods*, **17** (1962), 157.
535. SYMONDS, J. L.: *Rep. Prog. Phys.*, **18** (1955), 83.
536. TENZER, R. K.: *Arch. tech. Messen*, **239** (1955), 285.
537. TICKLE, R. S.: *Nucl. Instrum. Methods*, **18–19** (1962), 98.
538. VAN DER WALT, N. T.: *Rev. Scient. Instrum.*, **24** (1953), 413.
539. VAN DORSTEN, A. C.: Symp. on El. Optics, Washington, 1951.
540. VAN DORSTEN, A. C.: 4. Jahrestagung der deutschen Ges. f. El. Mikroskopie, Tübingen, 1952.
541. VAN MENTS, M.: Report Technical University, Delft, 1946.
542. VAN MENTS, M.–LE POOLE, J. B.: *Appl. Scient. Res.*, **1–B** (1947), 3.
543. (VASILEVSKAYA, D. P.–DENISOV, YU. N.) Василевская, Д. П.–Денисов, Ю. Н.: *Приборы Тех. Экспер. СССР*, **3** (1959), 144.
544. VOELKER, P.–LEAVITT, M. A.: Rept. UCRL 3084. Radiation Laboratory, University of California, Berkeley, California, 1955.
545. WEISS, H.: *Z. Naturf.*, **11–A** (1956), 430.
546. WEISS, H.–WILHELM, M.: *Z. Phys.*, **176** (1963), 399.
547. WELKER, H.–WEISS, H.: *Solid. St. Phys.*, **3** (1956), 1 .
548. WILIMZIG, H.: *Arch. tech. Messen*, **302** (1961), 71.
549. WILLIAMSON, K. I.: *J. Scient. Instrum.*, **24** (1947), 242.
550. WILLS, M. S.: *J. Scient. Instrum.*, **29** (1952), 374.
551. WOLFF, O.: *Phys. Verh.*, **4** (1951), 69.
552. WOODBRIDGE, D. D.–WARNER, W. R.: *Am. J. Phys.*, **26** (1958), 490.

553. (ZHERNOVOY, A. I.–EGOROV, YU. S.–LATYSHEV, G. D.) Жерновой, А. И.–Егоров, Ю. С.–Латышев, Г. Д.: *Приборы Тех. Экспер. СССР,* **5** (1958), 71.
554. ZINGERY, W. L.: *Rev. Scient. Instrum.,* **32** (1961), 706.
555. ZUCKER, C.: *Am. J. Phys.,* **29** (1961), 577.

g) Path Calculation

556. BERNARD, M. Y.–GRIVET, P.: *Annls. Radioélect.,* **6** (1952), 3.
557. BERTEIN, F.: *C.R. Hebd. Séanc. Acad. Sci. Paris,* **234** (1952), 417.
558. BURFOOT, J. C.: *Br. J. appl. Phys.,* **3** (1952), 22.
559. BUSCH, H.: *Ann. Phys.,* **80** (1926), 974.
560. COLBURN, D. S.–HARKER, K. J.–KINO, G. S.: *AIAA J.,* **2** (1964), 322.
561. COTTE, M.: *Ann. Phys.,* **10** (1938), 333.
562. DORRESTEIN, R.: *Philips Res. Rep.,* **5** (1950), 116.
563. DURANDEAU, D.–FERT, C.: *Revue Opt. théor. instrumen.,* **36** (1957), 205.
564. FISSER, H.–KIPPENHAHN, R.: *Z. Naturf.,* **14a** (1959), 37.
565. FRANCKEN, J. C.–DORRESTEIN, R.: *Philips Res. Rep.,* **6** (1951), 323.
566. GABOR, D.: *Proc. Instn Radio Engrs.,* **33** (1945), 792
567. GABOR, D.: *Proc. Phys. Soc. Lond.,* **64–B** (1951), 244.
568. GABOR, D.: Light Optics, Electron Optics and Wave Mechanics. *In:* BORN, M.–WOLF, E. (Eds): *Principles of Optics.* Pergamon Press; Oxford, 1965, 738.
569. GANS, R.: *Z. tech. Phys.,* **18** (1937), 41.
570. GODDARD, L. S.: *Proc. Phys. Soc. Lond.,* **56** (1944), 372.
571. GRIVET, P.: *J. Phys. Radium Paris,* **13** (1952), 1A.
572. HASKER, J.–GROENDIJK, H.: *Philips Res. Rep.,* **17** (1962), 401.
573. HECHTEL, J. R.: *Telefunken-Röhre,* Festschrift zur 50Jahrfeier (1955), 233.
574. HECHTEL, J. R.–JOHNE, R.: *Telefunken-Röhre,* **36** (1959), 45.
575. HEITZ, R.: *Onde élect.,* **46** (1966), 1347.
576. HERTWECK, F.: *Z. Naturf.,* **14a** (1959), 47.
577. HUTTER, R. G. E.: *J. appl. Phys.,* **16** (1945), 678.
578. JENNINGS, J. C. E.–PRATT, R. G.: *Proc. Phys. Soc. Lond.,* **68–B** (1955), 526.
579. KIRSTEIN, P. T.–HORNSBY, J. S.: *IEEE Trans.,* **ED–11** (1964), 196.
580. KRAMER, N. B.–TODD, E. G.: *IEEE Trans.,* **ED–10** (1963), 394.
581. KRYLOFF, A. M.: *Méml. Artill. fr.,* **6** (1927), 353.
582. LAPEYRE, R.: *C.R. Hebd. Séanc. Acad. Sci. Paris,* **252** (1961), 3431.
583. LAPEYRE, R.–LAUDET, M.: *C.R. Hebd. Séanc. Acad. Sci. Paris,* **251** (1960), 679.
584. LAUDET, M.: *J. Phys. Radium, Paris,* **14** (1953), 604.
585. LEHR, C. G.–SILBERMAN, I.–LOTUS, J. W.: *3rd MOGA,** 195.
586. LENZ, F.: *Ann. Phys.,* **9** (1951), 245.
587. LIEBMANN, G.: *Proc. Phys. Soc.,* **62–B** (1949), 753.
588. LINN, H. J.–PÖSCHL, K.: *Arch. elektr. Übertr.,* **22** (1968), 146.
589. MILNE, W. E.: *Am. math. Mon.,* **40** (1933), 322.
590. MOTZ, H.–KLANFER, L.: *Proc. Phys. Soc,* **58** (1946), 30.
591. NAGY, GY. A.: A tértöltés elektronoptikája általános alappályán *(Electron Optics of the Space-Charge along the General Central Trajectory).* Kandidátusi értekezés (Candidature Dissertation), Budapest, 1965.
592. PICQUENDAR, J. E.: *Ann. Télécommun.,* **7** (1953), 173.
593. PORITSKY, H.–JERRAND, R. P.: *J. appl. Phys.,* **23** (1952), 928.
594. REGENSTREIF, E.: *Annls. Radioélect.,* **2** (1947), 348.
595. REGENSTREIF, E.: *Annls. Radioélect.,* **6** (1951), 51.
596. REGENSTREIF, E.: *Annls. Radioélect.,* **6** (1951), 164.
597. ROWE, J. E.–MARTIN, R. J.: *2nd MOGA,** 1024.
598. RÜDENBERG, R. J.: *J. Franklin Inst.,* **246** (1948), 311.
599. RÜDENBERG, R. J.: *J. Franklin Inst.,* **246** (1948), 377.
600. SANDER, K. F.–OATLEY, C. W.–YATES, J. G.: *Proc. Inst. electr. Engrs.,* **99–III** (1952), 169.
601. STÖRMER, C.: Congrès International des Mathématiques, Strasbourg, 1920. 242. Bibliothèque Universitaire de Toulouse, 1921.

* See p. 483.

602. Sturrock, P. A.: *Phil. Trans. R. Soc.*, **245–A** (1952–53), 155.
603. Van Ments, M.–Le Poole, J. B.: *Appl. Scient. Res.*, B **1** (1947). 3.
604. Vine, J.: *Comput. J.*, **2** (1959), 134.
605. Vine, J.: *IEEE Trans.*, **ED–13** (1966), 544.
606. (Vorobev, Yu. V.) Воробьев, Ю. В.: *Ж. Тех. Физ. СССР*, **22** (1952), 1166.
607. Wendt, G.: *Z. Phys.*, **120** (1942/43), 710.

h) *Path Measurement*

608. Allen, K. R.–Philips, K.: *Elect. Engng. N.Y.*, **27** (1955), 82.
609. Alma, G. A.–Diemer, G.–Groendijk, H.: *Philips tech. Rdsch.*, **15** (1953), 27.
610. Barber, M. R.–Sanders, K. F.: *J. Electron. Control*, **7** (1959), 465.
611. (Bleivas, I. M.) Блейвас, И. М.: Труды Конференции по электронике СВЧ. Госэнергоиздат; Москва, 1959, 133.
612. (Bleivas, I. M.) Блейвас, И. М.: *РИЭ СССР*, **8** (1963), 1764.
613. (Bobykin, B. V.–Kelman, V. M.–Kaminskiy, D. L.) Бобыкин, Б. В.–Кельман, В. М.–Каминский, Д. Л.: *Ж. Тех. Физ. СССР*, **22** (1952), 736.
614. Brüche, B. E.–Recknagel, A.: *Z. tech. Phys.*, **17** (1936), 126.
615. Cahen, O.: *Onde élect.*, **37** (1957), 1098.
616. Citron, A.–Farley, F. J.–Michaelis, E. L.–Øverås, H.: CERN 59–8, 1959.
617. Clark, J. W.–Neuber, R. E.: *Proc. Instn Radio Engrs.*, **38** (1950), 521.
618. De Boer, A. J. F.–Groendijk, H.–Verster, J. L.: *Philips tech. Rev.*, **23** (1961/62), 352.
619. Gabor, D.: *Nature, Lond.*, **139** (1937), 373.
620. Grivet, P.–Rocard, Y.: *Rev. Scient. Paris*, **11** (1949), 85.
621. Haine, M. E.–Vine, J.: *Proc. Instn elect. Engrs.*, **106–B** (1959), 517.
622. Hampikian, A.: *C.R. Hebd. Séanc. Acad. Sci. Paris*, **236** (1953), 1864.
623. Hart, W.–Steffen, D.–Claassen, M.: *Messtechnik*, **75** (1967), 396.
624. Hechtel, J. R.: *Telefunken-Röhre*, **32** (1955), 38.
625. Hechtel, J. R.: *Trans. IRE*, **ED–9** (1962), 62.
626. Hechtel, J. R.–Brauch, D. F.–Mizuhara, A.: *4th MOGA*,* 527.
627. Hechtel, J. R.–Johne, K. R.: *2nd MOGA*,* 917.
628. Henaff, J.–Le Mezec, J.: *Onde élect.*, **41** (1961), 36.
629. Hollway, D. L.: *Aust. J. Phys.*, **8** (1955), 74.
630. Hollway, D. L.: *Proc. Instn elect. Engrs.*, **103–B** (1956), 155.
631. Hollway, D. L.: *Proc. Instn elect. Engrs.*, **103–B** (1956), 161.
632. Kleijnen, P. H. J. A.: *Philips tech. Rundschau*, **2** (1937), 338.
633. (Kozodaev, M. S.–Tyapkin, A. A.) Козодаев, М. С.–Тяпкин, А. А.: *Приборы Тех. Экспер. СССР*, **7** (1962), 1.
634. Langmuir, D. B.: *Nature, Lond.*, **139** (1937), 1066.
635. Langmuir, D. B.: *RCAR*, **11** (1950), 143.
636. (Levin, G. E.–Prudkovskiy, G. P.) Левин, Г. Е.–Прудковский, Г. П.: *Приборы Тех. Экспер. СССР*, **1** (1956), 21.
637. Loeb, J.: *Onde élect.*, **27** (1947), 27.
638. Marvaud, J.: *C.R. Hebd. Séanc. Acad. Sci. Paris*, **226** (1948), 476.
639. Marvaud, J.: *C.R. Hebd. Séanc. Acad. Sci. Paris*, **234** (1952), 45.
640. Musson-Genon, R.: *Annls. Télécomm.*, **2** (1947), 254, 298.
641. Pinel, H.: *Ann. Radioélect.*, **14** (1959), 230.
642. Pinel, H.: *Ann. Radioélect.*, **15** (1960), 17.
643. Pizer, H. I.–Yates, J. G.–Sander, K. F.: *J. Electron*, **2** (1956), 65.
644. Rajchman, J.: *Arch. Sci. phys. nat.*, **20** (1938), 9.
645. Real, M.: Diplôme d'Études Supérieures. Paris, 1958.
646. Rose, A.: *J. appl. Phys.*, **11** (1940), 711.
647. Sander, K. F.–Oatley, C. W.–Yates, J. G.: *Nature, Lond.*, **163** (1949), 403.
648. Sander, K. F.–Oatley, C. W.–Yates, J. G.: *J. Instn elect. Engrs.*, **99–III** (1952), 169.
649. Sander, K. F.–Yates, J. G.: *Proc. Instn elect. Engrs.*, **11** (1953), 167.
650. Schiekel, M.: *Optik, Berl.*, **9** (1952), 145.
651. Spaven, W. J.: *Electronics*, **28** (1955), 174.

* See p. 483.

652. SPONSIER, G. C.: *J. appl. Phys.*, **26** (1955), 676.
653. SUGATA, E.– TERADA, M.–HAMADA, H.: *4th MOGA*,* 546.
654. VAN DUZER, T.–BREWER, G. R.: *J. appl. Phys.*, **30** (1959), 291.
655. VAN DUZER, T.–BUCKEY, C. R.–BREVER, G. R.: *Rev. Scient. Instrum.*, **34** (1963), 558.
656. VERSTER, J. L.: *Philips tech. Rev.*, **22** (1960–61), 245.
657. VINE, J.–TAYLOR, R. T.: *Proc. Instn elect. Engrs.*, **107–B** (1960), 181.
658. VINEYARD, G. H.: *J. appl. Phys.*, **23** (1952), 35.
659. WALTHER, A.–DREYER, H. J.: *Naturwissenschaften*, **36** (1949), 199.
660. ZWORYKIN, V. K.–RAJCHMAN, J. A.: *Proc. Instn Radio Engrs.*, **27** (1939), 558.

(a) *Electron-Optical Bench*

661. BAS, E. B.: *Z. angew. Phys.*, **6** (1954), 404.
662. BOERSCH, H.: *Z. Phys.*, **130** (1951), 517.
663. COUCHET, G.: *Annls. Phys.*, **9** (1954), 731.
664. FERT, C.: *C.R. Hebd. Séanc. Acad. Sci. Paris*, **252** (1951), 2085.
665. FISHWICK, W.: *J. Scient. Instrum.*, **32** (1955), 320.
666. MARTON, L.–MORGAN, M. M.–SCHUBERT, D. C.–SHAH, J. R.–SIMPSON, J. A.: *J. Res. natn. Bur. Stand.*, **47** (1961), 461.
667. MORPURGO, M.–SEPTIER, A.: *C.R. Hebd. Séanc. Acad. Sci. Paris*, **245** (1957), 2496.
668. NICOLL, F. H.: *Proc. Phys. Soc.*, **50** (1938), 891.
669. REISMAN, E.: Thesis. Cornell University, 1957.
670. REISNER, J. H.–PICARD, R. G.: *Rev. Scient. Instrum.*, **19** (1948), 556.
671. RUSKA, E.: Un nouveau banc d'optique électronique pour recherches et démonstrations avec des faisceaux d'électrons. Colloques Internationaux du Centre National de la Recherche Scientifique. Les techniques récentes en microscopie électronique et corpusculaire; Toulouse, 4–8 avril 1955, 253.
672. SEPTIER, A.: *C.R. Hebd. Séanc. Acad. Sci. Paris*, **245** (1957), 1406.
673. SEPTIER, A.: *C.R. Hebd. Séanc. Acad. Sci. Paris*, **246** (1958), 1983.

* See p. 483.

II. SPACE-CHARGE FLOW

GYULA ANDRÁS NAGY

We talk of space-charge flow when a large quantity of free charges (electrons, ions) flow in vacuum. The quantity of free charges is considered large if the value of its potential is not negligible compared with that of the electrodes. Two important cases of space-charge flow are considered in this chapter.

In the first case, *electrons pass through every point of a region limited by a closed electrode system*, and the space between the electrodes is completely filled by the flowing space-charge. For simplification, *this case is called space-charge flow.*

In the second case *electrons do not pass through every point of the region*, and even the electrode system is not necessarily closed; only a part of the space is filled by the flowing space-charge, *this case is called space-charge beam or electron beam.*

A further possibility of distinguishing these two flow problems is through their unknown quantities. *All the quantities* (electric-magnetic field, excitations, trajectory) are *unknowns in the problems of space-charge flow. In focusing problems generally only the trajectory is unknown*, the field is known and the excitations can be calculated in advance.

The basic equations given in Chapter I are used in the following discussions.

Charge flowing in vacuum can be used for numerous purposes, if the properties of the flow are known. This is the practical aspect, on account of which knowledge of the laws of space-charge flow is indispensable.

(A) GENERAL CHARACTERISTICS OF SPACE-CHARGE FLOW

29. SPACE-CHARGE LIMITED FLOW

Let us consider an arrangement given by the electrodes and their potentials. The emissivity of the electron-emitting electrodes is increased from zero, e.g. by the cathode temperature, whilst measuring the emitted current. Experimentally, it has been shown that the current attains a maximum value which cannot be increased by a further increase of the emissivity. *The flow* (pertaining to the maximum current) *formed under the conditions described, is known as space-charge limited flow.* (Space-charge flow may also be limited by other factors; however, knowledge of these factors is beyond the scope of the present work.)

The physical background of this phenomenon is very simple: the space-charge represented by the emitted electrons reduces the potential near to the emitter electrode to such an extent that the field strength over the entire surface of the electrode is reduced to zero. This state is considered a state of equilibrium insofar as the potential distribution derivative pertaining to the case without space-charge on the surface of the emitter electrode, and the potential distribution derivative on the surface of the emissive electrode originating only from space-charge, are of equal magnitude but of opposite sense.

10*

Let us denote the potential excited by the electrodes at the point of the investigated field with φ_v, and the potential excited by the space-charge with φ_ϱ. Hence

$$\varphi = \varphi_v + \varphi_\varrho \qquad 29.1$$

since the potentials of the different excitations are summed in accordance with equation 3.3. Differentiating equation 29.1, we obtain

$$-\text{grad } \varphi = -\text{grad } \varphi_v - \text{grad } \varphi_\varrho \qquad 29.2$$

In case of the space-charge limited flow we have on the electron-emitting surfaces

$$\mathbf{E} = -\text{grad } \varphi = 0 \qquad 29.3$$

i.e.

$$\mathbf{E} = -\text{grad } \varphi_v - \text{grad } \varphi_\varrho \qquad 29.4$$

$$\text{grad } \varphi_\varrho = -\text{grad } \varphi_v \qquad 29.5$$

Therefore, from equation 29.5 our qualitative description becomes quantitative. The foregoing is illustrated by a schematic drawing.

The potential distribution of the field between the parallel infinite planes [Chapter I: 126] in case of boundary conditions

$$\varphi(0) = 0; \quad \varphi(z_2) = \varphi_2 \qquad 29.6$$

is

$$\varphi = \frac{\varphi_2}{z_2} z \qquad 29.7$$

The case given by equation 29.7 is considered limiting in the value $I = 0$. The parameters of the curves shown in figure II.1 are the current values of $I_0 = 0 < I_1 < I_2 < I_3 < I_s = I_{max}$. The tangent of the curve with parameter I_s is horizontal at the point $z = 0$: the current is space-charge limited.

When investigating space-charge flow, the effects of numerous known factors are disregarded. In addition to the simplicity of this discussion, a further advantage is that the laws of space-charge flow appear cleared of other effects, and thus their special properties become prominent.

As stated, the electron-emitting electrodes are considered as having suitably high emissivity: they are therefore capable of supplying the current necessary in the given case.

The electrons do not leave the emitter electrodes with zero initial velocity, but with a velocity (and direction) distribution, however we shall only investigate those relations where the initial velocity is zero.

The flow conditions are only investigated in vacuum, gases or plasmas are excluded and, therefore, current can be carried only by electrons (or ions). Nevertheless, the results obtained can be used as an approximation for the case of low gas pressures, if the free path-length is greater than the largest electrode distance.

The number of electrons or ions is approximated by continuous charge distribution.

Magnetic field excitation by the flowing charges may be disregarded. *note*

Einstein's relativistic equations should be used instead of *Newton*'s equations of motion, in case of high-velocity motions, for this reason we are confining ourselves to low-velocity motions.

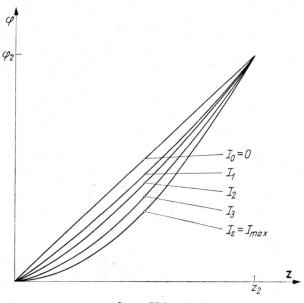

figure II.1

In addition to discussing stationary states, the investigation of transient flow is also important, but this matter is not treated.

The electrons incident on the collectors are capable of inducing emission of further electrons (secondary electron emission or secondary emission). The effect of the electrons thus produced is disregarded.

30. BASIC EQUATIONS OF SPACE-CHARGE FLOW

For determination of the field of the electron flow, we start from equations 2.4. 17.16, 1.5, which are now given again [32]

$$\Delta\varphi = -\frac{1}{\varepsilon_0}\varrho \qquad\qquad 30.1$$

$$\dot{\mathbf{r}}^2 = 2\eta\varphi \qquad\qquad 30.2$$

$$\mathbf{j} = \varrho\dot{\mathbf{r}} \qquad\qquad 30.3$$

Instead of the basic equations, one single equation may be used. Equation 30.3 is squared and substituted into equation 30.2

$$\mathbf{j}^2 = \varrho^2 \dot{\mathbf{r}}^2 = 2\eta\varphi\varrho^2 \qquad 30.4$$

From equation 30.4 ϱ is expressed

$$\varrho = \frac{\sqrt{\mathbf{j}^2}}{(2\eta\varphi)^{1/2}} \qquad 30.5$$

Equation 30.5 is substituted into 30.1

$$\Delta\varphi + K(\mathbf{r})\frac{1}{\sqrt{\varphi}} = 0 \qquad 30.6$$

where the meaning of the abbreviation $K(\mathbf{r})$ is

$$K(\mathbf{r}) = \frac{\sqrt{j^2}}{\varepsilon_0(2\eta)^{1/2}} \qquad 30.7$$

Under the discussed simplifying conditions and with knowledge of the boundary conditions, equation 30.6 is suitable for the solution of arbitrary space-charge flow problems. However, the solution is extremely difficult, not only since the absolute value of the current-density distribution must be known, but also since the equation is non-linear. In spite of the difficulties, solutions have been determined for numerous cases with important applications. In the following, we shall describe the more important solutions of the equation.

Note

(i) The system given by equations 30.1, 30.2, 30.3 can be used to determine the solution only with knowledge of the absolute value of the current density (in the opposite case the number of unknown functions would be greater than the number of independent equations).

(ii) The problem of space-charge flow can naturally be solved without previous knowledge of determined functions. The solution can be obtained with the help of the following equations [48]

$$\Delta\varphi = -\frac{1}{\varepsilon_0}\varrho \qquad 30.8$$

$$(\text{Grad } \dot{\mathbf{r}}) \cdot \dot{\mathbf{r}} = \eta \text{ grad } \varphi \qquad 30.9$$

$$\text{div}(\varrho\dot{\mathbf{r}}) = 0 \qquad 30.10$$

From the system of partial differential equations 30.8, 30.9, 30.10 (consisting of five equations), with knowledge of the supplementary conditions, the five unknown functions: three components of $\dot{\mathbf{r}}$, ϱ, φ can be determined. The left-hand side of equation 30.9 is the customary form of acceleration in flow fields [Chapter I: 132].

Equation 30.9 is given also in Cartesian coordinates

$$\dot{r}_1\frac{\partial\dot{r}_1}{\partial x_1} + \dot{r}_2\frac{\partial\dot{r}_1}{\partial x_2} + \dot{r}_3\frac{\partial\dot{r}_1}{\partial x_3} = \eta\frac{\partial\varphi}{\partial x_1} \qquad 30.11$$

$$\dot{r}_1 \frac{\partial \dot{r}_2}{\partial x_1} + \dot{r}_2 \frac{\partial \dot{r}_2}{\partial x_2} + \dot{r}_3 \frac{\partial \dot{r}_2}{\partial x_3} = \eta \frac{\partial \varphi}{\partial x_2} \qquad\qquad 30.12$$

$$\dot{r}_1 \frac{\partial \dot{r}_3}{\partial x_1} + \dot{r}_2 \frac{\partial \dot{r}_3}{\partial x_2} + \dot{r}_3 \frac{\partial \dot{r}_3}{\partial x_3} = \eta \frac{\partial \varphi}{\partial x_3} \qquad\qquad 30.13$$

(iii) Even the equations given in (ii) do not contain the effect of current density. An important point is that even space-charge flow problems considering current density can be solved.

31. B. MELTZER'S METHOD FOR DETERMINATION OF THE CHARACTERISTICS OF THE FLOW FIELD

Another method of discussion of the classical space-charge flow is also possible [112, 113]. This has its main use for curvilinear flows, where obvious assumptions can be made relative to the velocity field, and where there is no magnetic field.

Assuming an almost arbitrary velocity distribution $\dot{\mathbf{r}} = \dot{\mathbf{r}}(\mathbf{r})$ (the limitations will be treated later) all the characteristics of the flow field are determined with the help of the assumed velocity distribution.

According to [Chapter I: 132] the acceleration is

$$\ddot{\mathbf{r}} = (\text{Grad } \dot{\mathbf{r}}) \cdot \dot{\mathbf{r}} \qquad\qquad 31.1$$

The electric field strength is derived from equation 17.15

$$\mathbf{E} = \frac{-1}{\eta} (\text{Grad } \dot{\mathbf{r}}) \cdot \dot{\mathbf{r}} \qquad\qquad 31.2$$

The force acting upon the electron, from equation 17.9

$$\mathbf{F} = m(\text{Grad } \dot{\mathbf{r}}) \cdot \dot{\mathbf{r}} \qquad\qquad 31.3$$

The potential distribution by integration from equation 2.1

$$\varphi = \varphi_0 + \frac{1}{\eta} \int_{\mathbf{r_0}}^{\mathbf{r}} [(\text{Grad } \dot{\mathbf{r}}) \cdot \dot{\mathbf{r}}] \cdot d\mathbf{r} \qquad\qquad 31.4$$

The space-charge distribution from equation 1.2

$$\varrho = - \frac{\varepsilon_0}{\eta} \text{ div } [(\text{Grad } \dot{\mathbf{r}}) \cdot \dot{\mathbf{r}}] \qquad\qquad 31.5$$

The current-density distribution from equation 1.5

$$\mathbf{j} = - \frac{\varepsilon_0}{\eta} \dot{\mathbf{r}} \text{ div } [(\text{Grad } \dot{\mathbf{r}}) \cdot \dot{\mathbf{r}}] \qquad\qquad 31.6$$

The value of the current is obtained from equation 34.4

$$I = - \frac{\varepsilon_0}{\eta} \int_F \{\dot{\mathbf{r}} \text{ div } [(\text{Grad } \dot{\mathbf{r}}) \cdot \dot{\mathbf{r}}]\} \cdot d\mathbf{f} \qquad\qquad 31.7$$

The electric field has also been given with the help of function $\dot{\mathbf{r}}$, which must be in harmony with *Maxwell's* equations in order to obtain a real electric field. Due to this requirement, function $\dot{\mathbf{r}}$ is not entirely arbitrary. Due to equation 1.1

$$\text{curl } [(\text{Grad } \dot{\mathbf{r}}) \cdot \dot{\mathbf{r}}] = 0 \tag{31.8}$$

Due to equation 1.13

$$\text{div } \{\dot{\mathbf{r}} \text{ div } [(\text{Grad } \dot{\mathbf{r}}) \cdot \dot{\mathbf{r}}]\} = 0 \tag{31.9}$$

The requirement that space-charge distribution in the non zero case must be derivable from the assumed function $\dot{\mathbf{r}}$, in accordance with equation 31.5, is evident, since only then is the chosen velocity field identical with the space-charge flow velocity field.

This may also be used as approximation in the case pertaining to the space-charge distribution with zero value, when the space charge is negligible in the case of small currents or high voltages.

Several examples of the method described are discussed in papers [112, 113].

32. THE 3/2 LAW OF THE SPACE-CHARGE FLOW

This law is as follows:

The current density is proportional to the 3/2 power of the potential (also in the space-charge limited case).

This law can be derived from equation 30.6. Let us change the potential at every point to p-fold values (linear transformation). From equation 30.6 it can be established, by what scale should the current density be changed, in order that the equality shall remain valid. Let the necessary change of the current-density be s-fold

$$\Delta(p\varphi) + \frac{V(s\mathbf{j})^2}{\varepsilon_0(2\eta)^{1/2}} \frac{1}{(p\varphi)^{1/2}} = 0 \tag{32.1}$$

After transformation

$$\Delta\varphi + \frac{s}{p^{3/2}} \frac{V\mathbf{j}^2}{\varepsilon_0(2\eta)^{1/2}} \frac{1}{V\varphi} = 0 \tag{32.2}$$

The equation (and its solution) does not vary in relation to equation 30.6 if

$$\frac{s}{p^{3/2}} = 1 \tag{32.3}$$

This demonstrates that the relation

$$V\mathbf{j}^2 = g(\mathbf{r}, \mathbf{r}_0) \varphi^{3/2} \tag{32.4}$$

between the current density and the potential is valid (equation 32.3 is fulfilled). $g(\mathbf{r}, \mathbf{r}_0)$ is a function of the given geometric arrangement $(\mathbf{r}_0)$ and the position $(\mathbf{r})$: it is, therefore, important that this is not a constant. The foregoing is illustrated by three exactly solved cases of space-charge flow which are discussed in the present book.

In case of space-charge flow between infinite parallel planes from equations 34.43, 34.64 we have

$$j_z = -\frac{4\sqrt{2\varepsilon_0}\sqrt{\eta}}{9}\frac{1}{z^2}\varphi^{3/2} \qquad 32.5$$

In case of space-charge flow between coaxial infinite cylinders (from equations 35.31, 35.34)

$$j_r = -\frac{4\sqrt{2\varepsilon_0}\sqrt{\eta}}{9}\frac{1}{r^2 H^2(r)}\varphi^{3/2} \qquad 32.6$$

In case of space-charge flow between concentric spheres (from equations 36.27, 36.30)

$$j_r = -\frac{4\sqrt{2\varepsilon_0}\sqrt{\eta}}{9}\frac{1}{r^2 G^2(r)}\varphi^{3/2} \qquad 32.7$$

The functions $H^2(r)$ and $G^2(r)$ contained in equations 32.6, 32.7 may be selected from the tables pertaining to the respective space-charge flows.

The potential is a function of the boundary conditions (and current density)

$$\varphi(\mathbf{r}) = P[\mathbf{r}, \varphi_1(\mathbf{r}_0), \varphi_2(\mathbf{r}_0), \ldots] \qquad 32.8$$

In equation 32.8 P is the functional relation of the potential. Potentials φ_1, φ_2 appear on the surfaces (electrodes) given with the help of the variable $\mathbf{r}_0$. In case of only two electrodes where the cathode held at zero potential and the anode at potential φ_2, equation 32.8 becomes

$$\varphi(\mathbf{r}) = P_0(\mathbf{r}, \mathbf{r}_0)\varphi_2 \qquad 32.9$$

The statement 32.9 is clearly seen from equation 3.3, since the potential φ is a simple linear function of φ_2. In this case the following law can be stated:

The current density is proportional to the 3/2 power of the anode voltage (in the space-charge limited case also).

Substituting equation 32.9 into 32.4 we have

$$\sqrt{j^2} = g(\mathbf{r}, \mathbf{r}_0)P_0^{3/2}(\mathbf{r}, \mathbf{r}_0)\varphi_2^{3/2} \qquad 32.10$$

by which the law may be considered as proved.

The above law is true with regard to the current also:

The current is proportional to the 3/2 power of the anode voltage (as in the space-charge limited case).

This latter statement becomes clear when we consider that the current is derived from the current density by a homogeneous linear functional operation (see equation 34.4).

33. THE SCALING LAW OF THE SPACE-CHARGE FLOW

In practice it may become necessary to investigate space-charge flow between the elements of an electrode system similar in two senses, to be described later, to a realised fully calculated electrode system. The scaling law permits us to omit the repetition of the calculation, provided that the calculations relative to the already realised system are available.

When the ratio of the corresponding dimensions of the two systems is identical in all cases, we speak of a case of geometric similarity. Let us denote this ratio with g.

When the ratio of the voltages applied to the corresponding electrodes of the two systems is identical in all cases, we speak of the case of similarity of voltages applied to the electrodes. Let this ratio be p.

Figures II.2 and II.3 illustrate the generating curves of a symmetrical electrode system of cylindrical geometry. The characteristic data of the derived system are marked by crosses.

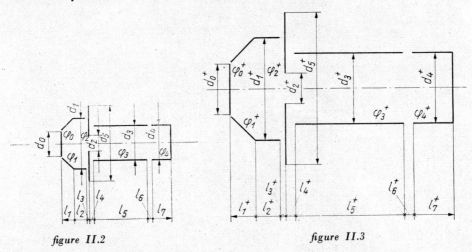

figure II.2   figure II.3

The geometrical similarity exists when

$$\frac{d_0^+}{d_0} = \frac{d_1^+}{d_1} = \frac{d_2^+}{d_2} = \frac{d_3^+}{d_3} = \frac{d_4^+}{d_4} = \frac{d_5^+}{d_5} = g \qquad 33.1$$

$$\frac{1_1^+}{1_1} = \frac{1_2^+}{1_2} = \frac{1_3^+}{1_3} = \frac{1_4^+}{1_4} = \frac{1_5^+}{1_5} = \frac{1_6^+}{1_6} = \frac{1_7^+}{1_7} = g \qquad 33.2$$

The similarity of voltages exists when

$$\frac{\varphi_0^+}{\varphi_0} = \frac{\varphi_1^+}{\varphi_1} = \frac{\varphi_2^+}{\varphi_2} = \frac{\varphi_3^+}{\varphi_3} = \frac{\varphi_4^+}{\varphi_4} = p \qquad 33.3$$

It is evident that *this similarity does not affect the mass, charge, and charge to mass ratio of the electron and the dielectric constant of free space*

$$m^+ = m; \quad e^+ = e; \quad \eta^+ = \eta; \quad \varepsilon_0^+ = \varepsilon_0 \qquad\qquad 33.4$$

The position vectors and the potentials vary according to definitions

$$\mathbf{r}^+ = g\mathbf{r}; \quad \varphi^+ = p\varphi \qquad\qquad 33.5$$

The characteristics of the flow field of the system marked with crosses can be calculated from the following formulae, with knowledge of the characteristics of the system without crosses

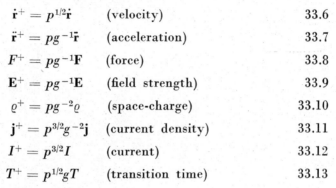

$$\dot{\mathbf{r}}^+ = p^{1/2}\dot{\mathbf{r}} \qquad \text{(velocity)} \qquad\qquad 33.6$$

$$\ddot{\mathbf{r}}^+ = pg^{-1}\ddot{\mathbf{r}} \qquad \text{(acceleration)} \qquad\qquad 33.7$$

$$F^+ = pg^{-1}F \qquad \text{(force)} \qquad\qquad 33.8$$

$$\mathbf{E}^+ = pg^{-1}\mathbf{E} \qquad \text{(field strength)} \qquad\qquad 33.9$$

$$\varrho^+ = pg^{-2}\varrho \qquad \text{(space-charge)} \qquad\qquad 33.10$$

$$\mathbf{j}^+ = p^{3/2}g^{-2}\mathbf{j} \qquad \text{(current density)} \qquad\qquad 33.11$$

$$I^+ = p^{3/2}I \qquad \text{(current)} \qquad\qquad 33.12$$

$$T^+ = p^{1/2}gT \qquad \text{(transition time)} \qquad\qquad 33.13$$

The relations 33.6 to 33.13 can be derived from the relations 17.11, 17.15, 17.9, 2.1, 2.4, 1.5, 34.4 [Chapter I: 153]. As an example, the derivation of the field strength is given

$$\mathbf{E}^+ = -\text{grad}^+ \varphi^+ \qquad\qquad 33.14$$

$$\text{grad}^+ = \frac{d}{d\mathbf{r}^+} = \frac{1}{g}\frac{d}{d\mathbf{r}} = \frac{1}{g}\text{grad} \qquad\qquad 33.15$$

Using the second equation of 33.5, we obtain

$$\mathbf{E}^+ = -\frac{p}{g}\text{grad}\,\varphi = \frac{p}{g}\mathbf{E} \qquad\qquad 33.16$$

The scaling law may also be used when the characteristics of the original system have been determined by means of numerical or graphical approximation.
In more simple cases *the formulae of the scaling law may be used for approximate calculations.* Namely, if the geometric arrangement remains qualitatively unchanged, and quantitatively is changed only in the sense that instead of the single factor *g* several are present, but they are approximately equal, and similarly, but not necessarily, for *p*, then the formulae 33.6 to 33.13 may be used for approximate calculation of the characteristics of the flow field. The formulae may naturally be used also in cases when e.g. only the voltages change, in a way determinable by several factors *p* which are approximately equal.

From this we must emphasise equation 33.12 which is treated as a separate law. This is the law of geometric similarity:

The current remains constant if the dimensions of a system with given geometry are increased by a factor g and the potentials remain unchanged.

This law can be readily recognized in the following manner: due to the change in the system, the current density changes by a factor g^{-2}; the surfaces change by a factor g^2. Their product or the integral 34.4 remains constant.

(B) IMPORTANT CASES OF SPACE-CHARGE FLOW

34. SPACE-CHARGE FLOW BETWEEN PARALLEL
INFINITE PLANE SURFACES

Let us assume that the equation of the electron-emitting plane is $z = 0$, and that of the electron-collecting plane is $z = z_2$, both planes are of infinite extent. With the given arrangement the potential and the other field characteristics are dependent only on the coordinate z, perpendicular to the planes. All the vectors have only one component each. Under these conditions the basic equations 30.1, 30.2, 30.3 are

$$\frac{d^2\varphi}{dz^2} = -\frac{1}{\varepsilon_0}\varrho \qquad\qquad 34.1$$

$$\dot{z}^2 = 2\eta\varphi \qquad\qquad 34.2$$

$$j_z = \varrho\dot{z} \qquad\qquad 34.3$$

Introducing the current I passing through surface A which is a plane surface parallel to the two basic planes, and placed between them, instead of the current density, the individual field characteristics will be expressed by a quantity more readily accessible for measurement purposes. The relation between the current and the current density is

$$I = \int_A \mathbf{j} \cdot d\mathbf{f} \qquad\qquad 34.4$$

In case of electron flow, I is of negative value, consequent on equation 1.5. In the present case the integration may be substituted by multiplication

$$I = -j_z F \qquad\qquad 34.5$$

In equation 34.5 F is the area of the surface section A. From 34.5

$$j_z = -\frac{I}{F} \qquad\qquad 34.6$$

Equation 34.6 is now substituted into 34.3 and ϱ is expressed

$$\varrho = -\frac{1}{\dot{z}}\frac{I}{F} \qquad\qquad 34.7$$

Substituting equation 34.3 into 34.7

$$\varrho = -\frac{I}{\sqrt{2\eta}\sqrt{F}}\frac{1}{\sqrt{\varphi}} \qquad 34.8$$

Substituting equation 34.8 into 34.1

$$\varphi'' - K\frac{1}{\sqrt{\varphi}} = 0 \qquad 34.9$$

where

$$K = \frac{I}{\sqrt{2}\sqrt{\eta}\varepsilon_0 F} \qquad 34.10$$

To solve the non-linear equation 34.9 we multiply it by $2\varphi'$

$$2\varphi'\varphi'' - 2K\frac{\varphi'}{\sqrt{\varphi}} = 0 \qquad 34.11$$

After transformation

$$\frac{d}{dz}(\varphi'^2) - 4K\frac{d}{dz}(\varphi^{1/2}) = 0 \qquad 34.12$$

Integrating

$$\varphi'^2 - 4K\varphi^{1/2} = C_1 \qquad 34.13$$

Expressing φ'

$$\varphi' = (C_1 + 4K\varphi^{1/2})^{1/2} \qquad 34.14$$

A new variable is introduced

$$u = C_1 + 4K\varphi^{1/2} \qquad 34.15$$

Applying equation 34.15 for 34.14

$$2\frac{u - C_1}{4K}\frac{u'}{4K} = u^{1/2} \qquad 34.16$$

Transforming equation 34.16

$$-\frac{C_1}{8K^2}\frac{u'}{u^{1/2}} + \frac{1}{8K^2}u^{1/2}u' = 1 \qquad 34.17$$

$$-\frac{C_1}{8K^2}\frac{d}{dz}(u^{1/2}) + \frac{1}{12K^2}\frac{d}{dz}(u^{3/2}) = 1 \qquad 34.18$$

Integrating

$$z = -\frac{C_1}{4K^2}(C_1 + 4K\varphi^{1/2})^{1/2} + \frac{1}{12K^2}(C_1 + 4K\varphi^{1/2})^{3/2} - C_2 \qquad 34.19$$

where z is again a function of the earlier variable.

In the potential theory only the boundary problem is of significance, but in certain cases a solution may be obtained mathematically by the initial-value problem, too. Such is the present case.

Prescriptions of the initial-value problem

$$\varphi(z_1) = \varphi_1; \quad \varphi'(z_1) = \varphi_1' \tag{34.20}$$

By applying the conditions 34.20 to equations 34.13 and 34.19, the constants of integration C_1 and C_2 can be determined

$$C_1 = \varphi_1'^2 - 4K\varphi_1^{1/2} \tag{34.21}$$

$$C_2 = -z_1 + \frac{1}{K}\varphi_1'\varphi_1^{1/2} - \frac{1}{6K^2}\varphi_1'^3 \tag{34.22}$$

Substituting equations 34.21 and 34.22 into 34.19, the general solution pertaining to the general initial conditions 34.20 is obtained

$$z = z_1 + \frac{1}{K^2}\left[\frac{1}{6}\varphi_1'^2 - K\varphi_1^{1/2}\right]\varphi_1' + \frac{1}{12K^2}[4K(\varphi^{1/2} - \varphi_1^{1/2}) + \varphi_1'^2]^{3/2} +$$

$$+ \frac{4K\varphi_1^{1/2} - \varphi_1'^2}{4K^2}[4K(\varphi^{1/2} - \varphi_1^{1/2}) + \varphi_1'^2]^{1/2} \tag{34.23}$$

Instead of the general boundary problem

$$\varphi(z_1) = \varphi_1; \quad \varphi(z_2) = \varphi_2 \tag{34.24}$$

let us consider the special boundary problem

$$\varphi(0) = 0; \quad \varphi(1) = 1 \tag{34.25}$$

That is, the electron-emitting surface may be chosen as plane $z = 0$; the value of the potential on the plane may be taken as zero, since when producing the accelerating voltage, this value is cancelled from the potentials referred to φ_1; in other words, the zero-potential surface may be freely chosen from the equipotential surfaces; z_2 may be chosen as the distance unit and φ_2 as the potential unit. Now, instead of solving the complicated system of equations

$$z_1 = -\frac{C_1}{4K_2}[C_1 + 4K\varphi_1^{1/2}]^{1/2} + \frac{1}{12K^2}[C_1 + 4K\varphi_1^{1/2}]^{3/2} - C_2 \tag{34.26}$$

$$z_2 = -\frac{C_1}{4K^2}[C_1 + 4K\varphi_2^{1/2}]^{1/2} + \frac{1}{12K^2}[C_1 + 4K\varphi_2^{1/2}]^{3/2} - C_2 \tag{34.27}$$

we need only solve the simpler system of equations

$$0 = -\frac{C_1^{3/2}}{4K^2} + \frac{C_1^{3/2}}{12K^2} - C_2 \tag{34.28}$$

$$1 = -\frac{C_1}{4K^2}(C_1 + 4K)^{1/2} + \frac{1}{12K^2}(C_1 + 4K)^{3/2} - C_2 \qquad 34.29$$

This is difficult, too, since although C_2 is easily expressed by C_1

$$C_2 = \frac{-1}{6K^2} C_1^{3/2} \qquad 34.30$$

however, for determination of the unknown C_1 a sixth-degree equation arises.

Returning to the solution pertaining to the initial conditions, we now seek the solution pertaining to the initial conditions

$$q(0) = 0; \quad \varphi'(0) = 0 \qquad 34.31$$

which appears in case of space-charge limited flow.

The solution is

$$z = \frac{2}{3K^{1/2}} \varphi^{3/4} \qquad 34.32$$

Solving the function 34.32 for φ we obtain

$$\varphi = \left(\frac{9K}{4}\right)^{2/3} z^{4/3} \qquad 34.33$$

We substitute now the value of K from equation 34.10 and summarise the field characteristics

$$\varphi = \left[\frac{9I}{4\sqrt{2}\sqrt{\eta\varepsilon_0}F}\right]^{2/3} z^{4/3} \qquad 34.34$$

$$\dot{z} = \left[\frac{9\eta I}{2\varepsilon_0 F}\right]^{1/3} z^{2/3} \qquad 34.35$$

$$\varrho = -\left[\frac{2\varepsilon_0 I^2}{9\eta F^2}\right]^{1/3} z^{-2/3} \qquad 34.36$$

$$j_z = -\frac{I}{F} = \text{constant} \qquad 34.37$$

$$E_z = -\left[\frac{\sqrt{6}\,I}{\sqrt{\eta\,\varepsilon_0}F}\right]^{2/3} z^{1/3} \qquad 34.38$$

$$F_z = \left[\frac{e^{3/2}\sqrt{6}\,I}{\sqrt{\eta\,\varepsilon_0}F}\right]^{2/3} z^{1/3} \qquad 34.39$$

$$\ddot{z} = \left[\frac{\sqrt{6}\,\eta I}{\varepsilon_0 F}\right]^{2/3} z^{1/3} \qquad 34.40$$

The transformation from the initial-value problem to the boundary-value problem is performed as follows. If a potential $\varphi = \varphi_2$ is required in position $z = z_2$, the following relation between the current and the potential is obtained from equation 34.34

$$\varphi_2 = \left[\frac{9I}{4\sqrt{2}\,\sqrt{\eta}\,\varepsilon_0 F} \right]^{2/3} z_2^{4/3} \qquad\qquad 34.41$$

Expressing current I from 34.41 we obtain

$$I = \frac{4\sqrt{2}\,\sqrt{\eta}\,\varepsilon_0 F}{9 z_2^2}\, \varphi_2^{3/2} \qquad\qquad 34.42$$

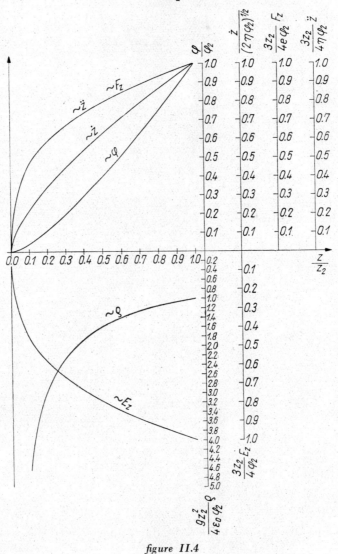

figure II.4

Equation 34.42 is the 3/2 law relative to space-charge flow between parallel infinite plane surfaces. The characteristics of space-charge limited flow may be written as follows

$$\varphi = \frac{\varphi_2}{z_2^{4/3}} z^{4/3} \qquad\qquad 34.43$$

$$\dot{z} = \left[\frac{2\eta\varphi_2}{z_2^{4/3}}\right]^{1/2} z^{2/3} \qquad\qquad 34.44$$

$$\varrho = -\frac{4\varepsilon_0\varphi_2}{9z_2^{4/3}} z^{-2/3} \qquad\qquad 34.45$$

$$j_z = -\frac{\sqrt{42}\,\varepsilon_0\sqrt{\eta}}{9z_2^2} \varphi_2^{3/2} = \text{constant} \qquad\qquad 34.46$$

$$E_z = -\frac{4\varphi_2}{3z_2^{4/3}} z^{1/2} \qquad\qquad 34.47$$

$$F_z = \frac{4e\varphi_2}{3z_2^{4/3}} z^{1/3} \qquad\qquad 34.48$$

$$\ddot{z} = \frac{4\eta\varphi_2}{3z_2^{4/3}} z^{1/3} \qquad\qquad 34.49$$

The field characteristics are shown in figure II.4 as functions of z/z_2. The values of these functions are given in table II.1.

TABLE II.1

z/z_2	$[z/z_2]^{1/3}$	$[z/z_2]^{2/3}$	$[z/z_2]^{-2/3}$	$[z/z_2]^{4/3}$
0.00	0.0000	0.0000	∞	0.0000
0.05	0.3684	0.1357	7.3681	0.0184
0.10	0.4642	0.2154	4.6417	0.0464
0.15	0.5313	0.2823	3.5422	0.0977
0.20	0.5848	0.3420	2.9237	0.1170
0.25	0.6300	0.3969	2.5198	0.1575
0.30	0.6694	0.4482	2.2312	0.2008
0.35	0.7047	0.4966	2.0135	0.2467
0.40	0.7368	0.5429	1.8419	0.2947
0.45	0.7663	0.5872	1.7035	0.3448
0.50	0.7937	0.6300	1.5873	0.3969
0.55	0.8193	0.6713	1.4900	0.4510
0.60	0.8434	0.7114	1.4057	0.5061
0.65	0.8662	0.7504	1.3327	0.5631
0.70	0.8879	0.7884	1.2684	0.6218
0.75	0.9086	0.8255	1.2114	0.6814
0.80	0.9283	0.8618	1.1604	0.7427
0.85	0.9473	0.8973	1.1144	0.8052
0.90	0.9655	0.9322	1.0728	0.8690
0.95	0.9831	0.9664	1.0348	0.9339
1.00	1.0000	1.0000	1.0000	1.0000

The characteristics of space-charge limited flow are determined by the solution of the initial-value problem. *It may occur that the emissivity of the electron-emitting electrode is of such low value that it is incapable to emit the current necessary for space-charge limited flow. In this case the flow is no longer space-charge limited, and the solution can be reached only by direct solution of the boundary problem:* we, therefore, seek the solution with boundary conditions 34.27, with the further reservation that j_z is of specified value, but lower than that given by equation 34.46.

Note: Equation 34.19 may be solved for φ. Let us introduce the notations

$$x = 4K^2(z + C_2); \qquad y = C_1 + 4K\varphi^{1/2} \qquad\qquad 34.50$$

Thereafter, the function $y = y(x)$ is obtained by solving equation

$$y^3 - 6C_1y^2 + 9C_1^2y - 9x^2 = 0 \qquad\qquad 34.51$$

and φ is

$$\varphi = \frac{1}{16K^2}(y - C_1)^2 \qquad\qquad 34.52$$

Example

Let the specified data be

a) $z_2 = 2 \times 10^{-2}$ m
$\varphi_2 = 10^3$ V
$I = 0.37$ A

b) $z_2 = 2 \times 10^{-2}$ m
$\varphi_2 = 10^3$ V
$I = 1.39$ A

The area of the cathode surface is yielded by equation 34.41

$$F = 2 \times 10^{-3} \text{ m}^2 \qquad\qquad F = 7.5 \times 10^{-3} \text{ m}^2$$

Current density is given by 34.46

$$j_z = 184.7 \text{ Am}^{-2} \qquad\qquad j_z = 184.7 \text{ Am}^{-2}$$

The two current values facilitate comparison with the flows between cylinders and spheres.

35. SPACE-CHARGE FLOW BETWEEN COAXIAL INFINITE CYLINDRICAL SURFACES

Let the equation of the electron-emitting cylinder be $x^2 + y^2 = R_1^2$, the equation of the electron-collecting cylinder be $x^2 + y^2 = R_2^2$, and the lengths of both cylinders be infinite. With the given arrangement the potential and the other field characteristics can be described by the variation along a straight line, intersecting axis z and perpendicular to the cylindrical surfaces. All the vectors can be given by their components along the given straight line. The geometric arrangement calls for introduction of cylindrical coordinates. In cylindrical coordinates the basic equations 30.1, 30.2, 30.3 referred to the present case are

$$\frac{1}{r}\frac{d}{dr}\left(r\frac{d\varphi}{dr}\right) = -\frac{1}{\varepsilon_0}\varrho \qquad\qquad 35.1$$

$$\dot{r}^2 = 2\eta\varphi \qquad\qquad 35.2$$

$$j_r = \varrho\dot{r} \qquad\qquad 35.3$$

We introduce current I flowing through to surface A, a cylindrical surface coaxial with the two basic cylinders and located between them, and express the individual field characteristics as functions of I. In this case the direction of the current density is perpendicular to the cylindrical surface, and since it is dependent on r only, the value of the integral 34.4 can be calculated by multiplication. Hence, the current flowing through a cylindrical surface of radius r is

$$I = -j_r 2\pi rL \qquad\qquad 35.4$$

In equation 35.4 L is the length of surface section A. From 35.4

$$j_r = -\frac{I}{2\pi L}\frac{1}{r} \qquad\qquad 35.5$$

We now substitute equation 35.5 into 35.3 and express ϱ

$$\varrho = -\frac{I}{2\pi L}\frac{1}{r\dot{r}} \qquad\qquad 35.6$$

Substituting 35.2 into 35.6

$$\varrho = -\frac{I}{2\sqrt{2\pi}\sqrt{\eta}\,L}\frac{1}{r}\frac{1}{\sqrt{\varphi}} \qquad\qquad 35.7$$

Substituting equation 35.7 into 35.1

$$r\varphi'' + \varphi' - K\frac{1}{\sqrt{\varphi}} = 0 \qquad\qquad 35.8$$

where

$$K = \frac{I}{2\sqrt{2\pi\varepsilon_0}\sqrt{\eta}\,L} \qquad\qquad 35.9$$

For solution of (non-linear) equation 35.8 the transformation

$$\varphi = \left[\frac{9}{4}K\right]^{2/3} r^{2/3}H^{4/3} \qquad\qquad 35.10$$

is performed, where $H(r)$ is the new function. After transformation, equation 35.8 becomes

$$r^2H'^2 + 3r^2HH'' + 7rHH' + H^2 - 1 = 0 \qquad\qquad 35.11$$

A new independent variable is introduced

$$u = \ln\frac{r}{R_1} \qquad\qquad 35.12$$

11*

Transforming equation 35.11 to the new variable

$$H'^2 + 3HH'' + 4HH' + H^2 - 1 = 0 \qquad 35.13$$

Equation 35.8 is to be solved with initial conditions

$$\varphi(R_1) = 0; \quad \varphi'(R_1) = 0 \qquad 35.14$$

The conditions referred to H can be determined from equations 35.10 and 35.13. From 35.10

$$H(0) = 0 \qquad 35.15$$

The value of $H'(0)$ cannot be determined from 35.10, since

$$\varphi' = \frac{2}{3}\left[\frac{9}{4}K\right]^{2/3} r^{-1/3} H^{4/3} + \frac{4}{3}\left[\frac{9}{4}K\right]^{2/3} r^{2/3} H^{1/3} H' \qquad 35.16$$

and due to 35.15, H' may be of arbitrary value. H' can be determined from equation 35.13. Its value appears as

$$H'(0) = \pm 1 \qquad 35.17$$

The value $+1$ is chosen since the initial velocity is zero, and proceeding towards the collecting electrode the potential increases, therefore

$$H'(0) = 1 \qquad 35.18$$

Equation 35.13 is solved by means of a *Taylor* series expansion. The differentiated coefficients of the series expansion are determined from the derivatives of equation 35.13

$$H''(0) = -\frac{4}{5}; \quad H'''(0) = \frac{11}{20}; \quad H^{(IV)}(0) = -\frac{376}{1100};$$

$$H^{(V)}(0) = \frac{31\,033}{154\,000} \qquad 35.19$$

The *Taylor* series of H is

$$H(u) = \sum_{\nu=0}^{\infty} \frac{H^{(\nu)}(0)}{\nu!} u^{\nu} \qquad 35.20$$

into which the differentiated coefficients 35.15, 35.18, 35.19 are substituted. Returning to variable r, the solution is

$$H(r) = \ln\frac{r}{R_1} - \frac{2}{5}\ln^2\frac{r}{R_1} + \frac{11}{120}\ln^3\frac{r}{R_1} -$$

$$- \frac{47}{3300}\ln^4\frac{r}{R_1} + \frac{31\,033}{1\,848\,000}\ln^5\frac{r}{R_1} - \dots \qquad 35.21$$

The value of K is substituted from equation 35.9 and the field character-istics are summarised

$$\varphi = \left[\frac{9I}{8\sqrt{2\pi\varepsilon_0}\sqrt{\eta L}} \right]^{2/3} r^{2/3} H^{4/3}(r) \qquad\qquad 35.22$$

$$\dot{r} = \left[\frac{9\eta I}{4\pi\varepsilon_0 L} \right]^{1/3} r^{1/3} H^{2/3}(r) \qquad\qquad 35.23$$

$$\varrho = -\left[\frac{\varepsilon_0 I^2}{18\pi^2 \eta L^2} \right]^{1/3} r^{-4/3} H^{-2/3}(r) \qquad\qquad 35.24$$

$$j_r = -\frac{I}{2\pi L}\frac{1}{r} \qquad\qquad 35.25$$

$$E_r = -\left[\frac{\sqrt{3}I}{4\pi\varepsilon_0\sqrt{\eta L}} \right]^{2/3} r^{-1/3} H^{1/3}(r) \left[H(r) + 2\frac{dH}{du} \right] \qquad\qquad 35.26$$

$$F_r = \left[\frac{\sqrt{3}e^{3/2}I}{4\pi\varepsilon_0\sqrt{\eta L}} \right]^{2/3} r^{-1/3} H^{1/3}(r) \left[H(r) + 2\frac{dH}{du} \right] \qquad\qquad 35.27$$

$$\ddot{r} = \left[\frac{\sqrt{3}\eta I}{4\pi\varepsilon_0 L} \right]^{2/3} r^{-1/3} H^{1/3}(r) \left[H(r) + 2\frac{dH}{du} \right] \qquad\qquad 35.28$$

The transformation from the initial-value problem to the boundary-value problem is performed in the following manner. If the potential $\varphi = \varphi_2$ is required in position $r = R_2$, the following relation between the current and the potential is given by equation 35.22

$$\varphi_2 = \left[\frac{9R_2 H^2(R_2)}{8\sqrt{2\pi\varepsilon_0}\sqrt{\eta L}} \right]^{2/3} I^{2/3} \qquad\qquad 35.29$$

Expressing current I from equation 35.29

$$I = \frac{8\sqrt{2\pi\varepsilon_0}\sqrt{\eta L}}{9R_0 H^2(R_2)} \varphi_2^{3/2} \qquad\qquad 35.30$$

Equation 35.30 is the 3/2 law of space-charge flow between coaxial infinite cylindrical surfaces. With the help of equation 35.30 the characteristics of space-charge limited flow may be written as follows

$$\varphi = \left[\frac{\varphi_2^{3/2}}{R_2 H^2(R_2)} \right]^{2/3} r^{2/3} H^{4/3}(r) \qquad\qquad 35.31$$

$$\dot{r} = \left[\frac{2\eta\varphi_2}{R_2^{2/3} H^{4/3}(R_2)} \right]^{1/2} r^{1/3} H^{2/3}(r) \qquad\qquad 35.32$$

$$\varrho = -\frac{4\varepsilon_0\varphi_2}{9R_2^{2/3} H^{4/3}(R_2)} r^{-4/3} H^{-2/3}(r) \qquad\qquad 35.33$$

TABLE II.2

r/R_1	$H^2(r)$	r/R_1	$H^2(r)$	r/R_1	$H^2(r)$	r/R_1	$H^2(r)$
1.00	0.00000	2.50	0.4121	6.5	0.8635	120	1.0726
1.01	0.00010	2.60	0.4351	7.0	0.8870	140	1.0677
1.02	0.00039	2.70	0.4571	7.5	0.9074	160	1.0634
1.04	0.00149	2.8	0.4780	8.0	0.9253	180	1.0596
1.06	0.00324	2.9	0.4980	8.5	0.9410	200	1.0562
1.08	0.00557	3.0	0.5170	9.0	0.9548	250	1.0494
1.10	0.00842	3.2	0.5526	9.5	0.9672	300	1.0440
1.15	0.01747	3.4	0.5851	10	0.9782	350	1.0397
1.20	0.02875	3.6	0.6148	12	1.0122	400	1.0362
1.30	0.05589	3.8	0.6420	14	1.0352	500	1.0307
1.40	0.08672	4.0	0.6671	16	1.0513	600	1.0266
1.50	0.11934	4.2	0.6902	18	1.0630	800	1.0209
1.60	0.1525	4.4	0.7115	20	1.0715	1 000	1.0171
1.70	0.1854	4.6	0.7313	30	1.0908	1 500	1.0114
1.80	0.2177	4.8	0.7496	40	1.0946	2 000	1.0082
1.90	0.2491	5.0	0.7666	50	1.0936	5 000	1.0020
2.00	0.2793	5.2	0.7825	60	1.0910	10 000	0.9999
2.10	0.3083	5.4	0.7973	70	1.0878	30 000	0.9990
2.20	0.3361	5.6	0.8111	80	1.0845	∞	1.0000
2.30	0.3626	5.8	0.8241	90	1.0813		
2.40	0.3879	6.0	0.8362	100	1.0782		

$R_1 < R_2$; $R_1 < r < R_2$
The function-values are positive numbers.

TABLE II.3

R_1/r	$H^2(r)$	R_1/r	$H^2(r)$	R_1/r	$H^2(r)$	R_1/r	$H^2(r)$
1.00	0.00000	2.3	1.3712	5.4	11.601	50	450.23
1.01	0.00010	2.4	1.5697	5.6	12.493	60	582.14
1.02	0.00040	2.5	1.7792	5.8	13.407	70	721.43
1.04	0.00159	2.6	1.9995	6.0	14.343	80	867.11
1.06	0.00356	2.7	2.2301	6.5	16.777	90	1018.5
1.08	0.00630	2.8	2.4708	7.0	19.337	100	1174.9
1.10	0.00980	2.9	2.7214	7.5	22.015	120	1501.4
1.15	0.02186	3.0	2.9814	8.0	24.805	140	1843.5
1.20	0.03849	3.2	3.5293	8.5	27.701	160	2199.4
1.3	0.08504	3.4	4.1126	9.0	30.698	180	2567.3
1.4	0.14856	3.6	4.7298	9.5	33.791	200	2946.1
1.5	0.2282	3.8	5.3795	10	36.976	250	3934.4
1.6	0.3233	4.0	6.0601	12	50.559	300	4973.0
1.7	0.4332	4.2	6.7705	14	65.352	350	6054.1
1.8	0.5572	4.4	7.5096	16	81.203	400	7172.1
1.9	0.6947	4.6	8.2763	18	97.997	500	9502.2
2.0	0.8454	4.8	9.0696	20	115.64	∞	∞
2.1	1.0086	5.0	9.887	30	214.42		
2.2	1.1840	5.2	10.733	40	327.01		

$R_1 > R_2$; $R_1 > r > R_2$
The function-values are negative numbers.

$$j_r = -\frac{4\sqrt{2}\,\varepsilon_0\sqrt{\eta}\varphi_2^{3/2}}{9R_2H^2(R_2)}\frac{1}{r}$$ 35.34

$$E_r = \frac{2}{3}\left[\frac{\varphi_2^{3/2}}{R_2H^2(R_2)}\right]^{2/3}r^{-1/3}H^{1/3}(r)\left[H(r)+2\frac{dH}{du}\right]$$ 35.35

$$F_r = \frac{2}{3}\left[\frac{e^{3/2}\varphi_2^{3/2}}{R_2H^2(R_2)}\right]^{2/3}r^{-1/3}H^{1/3}(r)\left[H(r)+2\frac{dH}{du}\right]$$ 35.36

$$\ddot{r} = \frac{2}{3}\left[\frac{\eta^{3/2}\varphi_2^{3/2}}{R_2H^2(R_2)}\right]^{2/3}r^{-1/3}H^{1/3}(r)\left[H(r)+2\frac{dH}{du}\right]$$ 35.37

The function $H(r)$ figuring in the equations is summarised in tables II.2 and II.3.

Figures II.5 and II.6 illustrate the functions given in tabulated form.

In accordance with the above *table II.2* is used when space-charge flows *outwards from inside*, and *table II.3* when space-charge flows *inwards from outside*.

If the emissivity of the electron-emitting electrode is so low that it is incapable of emitting the current required for space-charge limited flow, the flow is no longer space-charge limited, and the solution can be reached only by direct solution of the boundary problem. The solution is sought with normalised boundary conditions

$$\varphi(1) = 0; \quad \varphi(R_2) = \varphi_2$$ 35.38

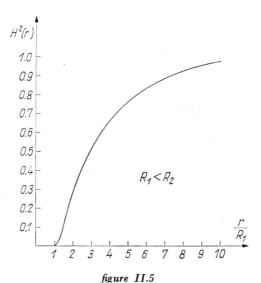

figure II.5

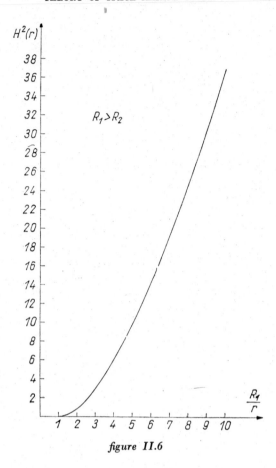

figure II.6

with the reservation that j_r is of specified value (but lower than that given by equation 35.34).

Example

1. *Flow inwards*

Let the specified data be

$R_1 = 3 \times 10^{-2}$ m ;

$R_2 = 10^{-2}$ m ;

$\varphi_2 = 10^3$ V;

$I = 0.37$ A

The length of the cathode cylinder is given by equation 35.29

$L = 2.38 \times 10^{-2}$ m

The current density is given by 35.34

$j_r = 82.5$ Am^{-2} (on the cathode surface)

2. *Flow outwards*

Let the specified data be

$R_1 = 10^{-2}$ m ;

$R_2 = 3 \times 10^{-2}$ m ;

$\varphi_2 = 10^3$ V;

$I = 1.39$ A

The length of the cathode cylinder is given by 35.29

$L = 4.65 \times 10^{-2}$ m

The current density is given by 35.34

$j_r = 476$ Am^{-2} (on the cathode surface)

36. SPACE-CHARGE FLOW BETWEEN CONCENTRIC SPHERICAL SURFACES

Let the equation of the electron-emitting sphere be $x^2 + y^2 + z^2 = R_1^2$; and that of the electron-collecting sphere be $x^2 + y^2 + z^2 = R_2^2$. With this given arrangement the potential and the other field characteristics may be described by the variation along a straight line passing through the common centre. Spherical coordinates are introduced. The basic equations 30.1, 30.2, 30.3, are

$$\frac{1}{r^2} \frac{d}{dr}\left(r^2 \frac{d\varphi}{dr}\right) = -\frac{1}{\varepsilon_0}\varrho \qquad 36.1$$

$$\dot{r}^2 = 2\eta\varphi \qquad 36.2$$

$$j_r = \varrho\dot{r} \qquad 36.3$$

The current I flowing through surface A (surface A is a concentric spherical surface between the two basic spheres) is introduced instead of the current density. The following appear similarly to the procedure followed during investigation of flow between cylindrical surfaces

$$I = -j_r 4\pi r^2 \qquad 36.4$$

$$j_r = -\frac{I}{4\pi}\frac{1}{r^2} \qquad 36.5$$

$$\varrho = -\frac{I}{4\pi}\frac{1}{r^2\dot{r}} = -\frac{I}{4\sqrt{2\pi}\sqrt{\eta}}\frac{1}{r^2}\frac{1}{\sqrt{\varphi}} \qquad 36.6$$

$$r^2\varphi'' + 2r\varphi' - K\frac{1}{\sqrt{\varphi}} = 0 \qquad 36.7$$

$$K = \frac{I}{4\sqrt{2\pi\varepsilon_0}\sqrt{\eta}} \qquad 36.8$$

With the transformation of

$$\varphi = \left[\frac{9}{4}K\right]^{2/3} G^{4/3} \qquad\qquad 36.9$$

$G(r)$ being the new function, we obtain

$$r^2G'^2 + 3r^2GG'' + 6rGG' - 1 = 0 \qquad\qquad 36.10$$

With the new independent variable

$$u = \ln\frac{r}{R_1} \qquad\qquad 36.11$$

we obtain

$$3GG'' + G'^2 + 3GG' - 1 = 0 \qquad\qquad 36.12$$

We now wish to solve equation 36.7 with initial conditions

$$\varphi(R_1) = 0; \quad \varphi'(R_1) = 0 \qquad\qquad 36.13$$

From 36.10

$$G(0) = 0 \qquad\qquad 36.14$$

and from 36.12, according to the motivation given with regard to flow between cylinders, we obtain

$$G'(0) = 1 \qquad\qquad 36.15$$

Coefficients required for the *Taylor* series expansion

$$G''(0) = -\frac{3}{5}; \quad G'''(0) = \frac{18}{40}; \quad G^{(\mathrm{IV})}(0) = -\frac{189}{550};$$

$$G^{(\mathrm{V})}(0) = -\frac{39\,933}{154\,000} \qquad\qquad 36.16$$

The solution is

$$G(r) = \ln\frac{r}{R_1} - \frac{3}{10}\ln^2\frac{r}{R_1} + \frac{3}{40}\ln^3\frac{r}{R_1} - $$

$$- \frac{63}{4400}\ln^4\frac{r}{R_1} + \frac{13\,311}{6\,160\,000}\ln^5\frac{r}{R_1}\cdots \qquad\qquad 36.17$$

The value of K is substituted from 36.8 and the field characteristics are summarised

$$\varphi = \left[\frac{9I}{16\sqrt{2\pi\varepsilon_0}\sqrt{\eta}}\right]^{2/3} G^{4/3}(r) \qquad\qquad 36.18$$

$$\dot{r} = \left[\frac{9\eta I}{8\pi\varepsilon_0} \right]^{1/3} G^{2/3}(r) \tag{36.19}$$

$$\varrho = - \left[\frac{\varepsilon_0 I^2}{72\pi^2\eta} \right]^{1/3} \frac{1}{r^2} G^{-2/3}(r) \tag{36.20}$$

$$j_r = - \frac{I}{4\pi} \frac{1}{r^2} \tag{36.21}$$

$$E_r = - \left[\frac{\sqrt{3}I}{2\sqrt{2\pi\varepsilon_0}\sqrt{\eta}} \right]^{2/3} \frac{1}{r} G^{1/3}(r) \frac{dG}{du} \tag{36.22}$$

$$F_r = \left[\frac{\sqrt{3}e^{3/2}I}{2\sqrt{2\pi\varepsilon_0}\sqrt{\eta}} \right]^{2/3} \frac{1}{r} G^{1/3}(r) \frac{dG}{du} \tag{36.23}$$

$$\ddot{r} = \left[\frac{\sqrt{3}\eta I}{2\sqrt{2\pi\varepsilon_0}} \right]^{2/3} \frac{1}{r} G^{1/3}(r) \frac{dG}{du} \tag{36.24}$$

Requiring the potential $\varphi = \varphi_2$ in the position $r = R_2$

$$\varphi_2 = \left[\frac{9G^2(R_2)}{16\sqrt{2\pi\varepsilon_0}\sqrt{\eta}} \right]^{2/3} I^{2/3} \tag{36.25}$$

from which the space-charge limited current is

$$I = \frac{16\sqrt{2\pi\varepsilon_0}\sqrt{\eta}}{9G^2(R_2)} \varphi_2^{3/2} \tag{36.26}$$

Equation 36.26 is the 3/2 law. With equation 36.26 the characteristics of the space-charge limited flow are

$$\varphi = \frac{\varphi_2}{G^{4/3}(R_2)} G^{4/3}(r) \tag{36.27}$$

$$\dot{r} = \left[\frac{2\eta\varphi_2}{G^{4/3}(R_2)} \right]^{1/2} G^{2/3}(r) \tag{36.28}$$

$$\varrho = - \frac{2\varepsilon_0\varphi_2}{9G^{4/3}(R_2)} \frac{1}{r^2} G^{-2/3}(r) \tag{36.29}$$

$$j_r = - \frac{4\sqrt{2\varepsilon_0}\sqrt{\eta}\varphi_2^{3/2}}{9G^2(R_2)} \frac{1}{r^2} \tag{36.30}$$

$$E_r = - \frac{4\varphi_2}{3G^{4/3}(R_2)} \frac{1}{r} G^{1/3}(r) \frac{dG}{du} \tag{36.31}$$

$$F_r = \frac{4e\varphi_2}{3G^{4/3}(R_2)} \frac{1}{r} G^{1/3}(r) \frac{dG}{du} \tag{36.32}$$

$$\ddot{r} = \frac{4\eta\varphi_2}{3G^{4/3}(R_2)} \frac{1}{r} G^{1/3}(r) \frac{dG}{du} \tag{36.33}$$

TABLE II.4

r/R_1	$G^2(r)$	r/R_1	$G^2(r)$	r/R_1	$G^2(r)$	r/R_1	$G^2(r)$
1.00	0.0000	2.6	0.543	7.0	1.453	140	3.903
1.05	0.0023	2.7	0.576	7.5	1.516	160	4.002
1.10	0.0086	2.8	0.608	8.0	1.575	180	4.089
1.15	0.0180	2.9	0.639	8.5	1.630	200	4.166
1.20	0.0299	3.0	0.669	9.0	1.682	250	4.329
1.25	0.0437	3.2	0.727	9.5	1.731	300	4.462
1.30	0.0591	3.4	0.783	10	1.777	350	4.573
1.35	0.0756	3.6	0.836	12	1.938	400	4.669
1.40	0.0931	3.8	0.886	14	2.073	500	4.829
1.45	0.1114	4.0	0.934	16	2.189	600	4.960
1.5	0.1302	4.2	0.979	18	2.289	800	5.165
1.6	0.1688	4.4	1.022	20	2.378	1 000	5.324
1.7	0.208	4.6	1.063	30	2.713	1 500	5.610
1.8	0.248	4.8	1.103	40	2.944	2 000	5.812
1.9	0.287	5.0	1.141	50	3.120	5 000	6.453
2.0	0.326	5.2	1.178	60	3.261	10 000	6.933
2.1	0.364	5.4	1.213	70	3.380	30 000	7.693
2.2	0.402	5.6	1.247	80	3.482	100 000	8.523
2.3	0.438	5.8	1.280	90	3.572		
2.4	0.474	6.0	1.311	100	3.652		
2.5	0.509	6.5	1.385	120	3.788		

$R_1 < R_2$; $R_1 < r < R_2$
The function-values are positive numbers.

TABLE II.5

R_1/r	$G^2(r)$	R_1/r	$G^2(r)$	R_1/r	$G^2(r)$	R_1/r	$G^2(r)$
1.000	0.000	2.3	1.193	4.6	6.712	20	93.24
1.025	0.0006	2.4	1.358	4.8	7.334	30	178.2
1.050	0.0024	2.5	1.531	5.0	7.976	40	279.6
1.075	0.0052	2.6	1.712	5.2	8.636	50	395.3
1.10	0.0096	2.7	1.901	5.4	9.315	60	523.6
1.15	0.0213	2.8	2.098	5.6	10.01	70	663.3
1.20	0.0372	2.9	2.302	5.8	10.73	80	813.7
1.25	0.0571	3.0	2.512	6.0	11.46	90	974.1
1.30	0.0809	3.1	2.729	6.5	13.35	100	1 144
1.35	0.1084	3.2	2.954	7.0	15.35	120	1 509
1.40	0.1396	3.3	3.185	7.5	17.44	140	1 907
1.45	0.1740	3.4	3.421	8.0	19.62	160	2 333
1.5	0.2118	3.5	3.664	8.5	21.89	180	2 790
1.6	0.2968	3.6	3.913	9.0	24.25	200	3 270
1.7	0.394	3.7	4.168	9.5	26.68	250	4 582
1.8	0.502	3.8	4.429	10	29.19	300	6 031
1.9	0.621	3.9	4.696	12	39.98	350	7 610
2.0	0.750	4.0	4.968	14	51.86	400	9 303
2.1	0.888	4.2	5.528	16	64.74	500	13 015
2.2	1.036	4.4	6.109	18	78.56		

$R_1 > R_2$; $R_1 > r > R_2$
The function-values are negative numbers.

The values of function $G(r)$ appearing in the equations are given in tables II.4 and II.5.

Figures II.7 and II.8 illustrate the functions given in the tables.

Table II.4 is used *when space-charge flows outwards from inside*, and table II.5 *when space-charge flows inwards from outside*.

The solution of non-space-charge limited flow with the normalised boundary conditions is also sought here

$$\varphi(1) = 0; \quad \varphi(R_2) = \varphi_2 \qquad\qquad 36.34$$

and with the specified value of j_r.

Example

1. *Flow inwards*

   Specified data

   $R_1 = 3 \times 10^{-2}$ m ;

   $R_2 = 10^{-2}$ m ;

   $\varphi_2 = 10^3$ m

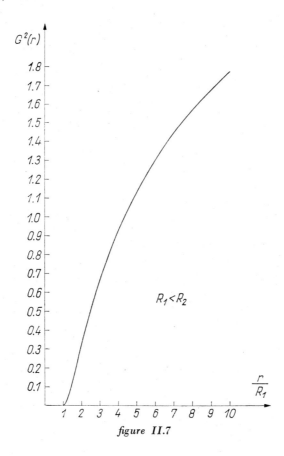

figure II.7

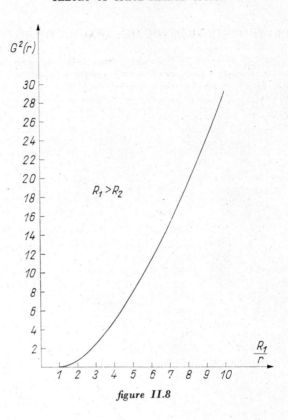

figure II.8

The (space-charge limited) current is obtained from equation 36.25

$I = 0.37$ A

The current density is obtained from equation 36.30

$j_r = 32.6$ Am^{-2} (on the cathode surface)

2. *Flow outwards*

Specified data

$R_1 = 10^{-2}$ m ;

$R_2 = 3 \times 10^{-2}$ m ;

$\varphi_2 = 10^3$ V

The (space-charge limited) current is obtained from equation 36.25

$I = 1.39$ A

The current density is obtained from equation 36.30

$j_r = 1110$ Am^{-2} (on the cathode surface)

(C) SPECIFIC PROBLEMS OF SPACE-CHARGE FLOW

The most important cases of space-charge flow (between parallel planes, coaxial cylinders, concentric spheres) which have frequent applications will now be complemented by investigation of space-charge flow between surfaces of other geometrical arrangements. In the majority of cases these also aid the practical application of the three most important cases of space-charge flow, since by these the scope of application of the basic cases can be defined. With the help of these cases the modifications, imperfect operation, caused by innccurate manufacture and mounting, occurring in the basic cases, can be calculated in advance, and thereby the permissible tolerances can be controlled with appropriate reliability. Information concerning the relation of work conducted in connection with flows of this type is given in the References [32]. The present work gives only a schematic description of one of the simplest cases (§ 37) [79, 141].

In spite of their importance, the basic cases of space-charge flow are in fact only very special cases: e.g. the three basic cases can be described by one single variable. The knowledge of the space-charge flow can be expected only by investigation of the most general cases, as the case discussed in § 38, where a general outline may be expected. In addition to the foregoing, justification of this paragraph is given by the differentiation of the space-charge flow and focusing subjects, without debating. Debates can be easily avoided by the presentation of an actual case [98]. § 39 deals with some errors to be found in the respective literature.

37. SPACE-CHARGE FLOW BETWEEN NON-PARALLEL INFINITE PLANE SURFACES

Discussion of the flow problem is carried out in cylindrical coordinate system due to the geometrical properties, using the notations of figure II.9 with the following simplifying assumptions:

(i) the intersecting line ($r = 0$) of the electrodes subtending an angle α_2 is excluded from the region under investigation (the two electrodes may not contact each other);

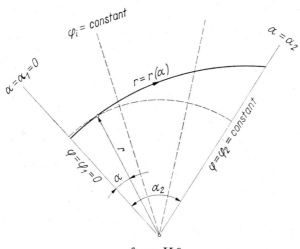

figure II.9

✳   (ii) the effect of the magnetic field is negligible (low-velocity motions);
(iii) the electrons leave the cathode with zero initial velocity (zero velocity pertains to zero potential);

(iv) the electrodes are infinitely great, therefore, the electric field strength has no component in z direction (in case of electrodes of finite size, the effect of the omitted parts and that of the space-charge are substituted by the effect of auxiliary electrodes);

(v) consequent upon the conditions (iii) and (iv), the flow field is independent of coordinate z, therefore, the trajectory of a chosen electron can be described with planar polar coordinates; the current density has no component in z direction.

With the conditions stated in the foregoing, equation 30.8, the first integral of 30.9 (energy equation), and equation 30.10 become

$$\frac{1}{r}\frac{\partial}{\partial r}\left(r\frac{\partial\varphi}{\partial r}\right) + \frac{1}{r^2}\frac{\partial^2\varphi}{\partial\alpha^2} = -\frac{1}{\varepsilon_0}\varrho \qquad 37.1$$

$$r^2 + r^2\dot\alpha^2 = 2\eta\varphi \qquad 37.2$$

$$\frac{\partial}{\partial r}(\varrho r\dot r) + \frac{\partial}{\partial\alpha}(\varrho r\dot\alpha) = 0 \qquad 37.3$$

The statement that each of the unknown functions is dependent only on the variables, r and α, is an obvious consequence of the foregoing. Equations 37.2 and 37.3 suggest application of B. Meltzer's method. The velocity field is non-rotational, this requirement is most easily satisfied by defining the velocity distribution as a gradient of a basic function W

$$\dot{\mathbf r} = \operatorname{grad} W \qquad 37.4$$

The potential is given with the help of equation 37.2, from the arbitrarily chosen W, and must assume a constant value on the electrodes. We shall demonstrate that the basic function, $f(\alpha)$ being the function to be determined, of the form

$$W = rf(\alpha) \qquad 37.5$$

satisfies the requirements. With regard to the equation

$$\dot{\mathbf r} = \dot r\mathbf e_r + r\dot\alpha\mathbf e_\alpha = \frac{\partial W}{\partial r}\mathbf e_r + \frac{1}{r}\frac{\partial W}{\partial\alpha}\mathbf e_\alpha \qquad 37.6$$

we can calculate the velocity components $\dot r$ and $r\dot\alpha$ representing the differentiation with respect to α by primes. Substituting these into equation 37.2, equation

$$f^2 + f'^2 = 2\eta\varphi \qquad 37.7$$

is obtained, from which it is evident that potential φ is independent of r, thus e.g. the value $\varphi_2 = $ constant pertains to the value $\alpha_2 = $ constant. But $\alpha_2 = $ constant is exactly the equation of the surface representing the anode.

Differentiating equation 37.7 and substituting into 37.1

$$\frac{1}{\eta r^2}(f'^2 + ff'' + f''^2 + f'f''') = -\frac{1}{\varepsilon_0}\varrho \qquad 37.8$$

Expressing ϱ from equation 37.8 and substituting into 37.3, we obtain the differential equation referring to f

$$(f - f'')(f^2 + f'^2)'' - f'(f^2 + f'^2)''' = ff'^2 + f^2f'' - f''^3 -$$
$$- 4f'^2f'' - 4f'f''f''' - f'^2f^{(VI)} = 0 \qquad 37.9$$

The characteristics of the flow field derivable from the single function $f(\alpha)$ are given in the following, similarly to the basic flow cases

$$\varphi(\alpha) = \frac{1}{2\eta}(f^2 + f'^2) \qquad 37.10$$

$$v_r(\alpha) = \dot{r} = f \qquad 37.11$$

$$v_\alpha(\alpha) = r\dot\alpha = f' \qquad 37.12$$

$$\varrho(r, \alpha) = -\frac{\varepsilon_0}{\eta}(f'^2 + ff'' + f''^2 + f'f''')\frac{1}{r^2} \qquad 37.13$$

$$j_r(r, \alpha) = -\frac{\varepsilon_0}{\eta}(f'^2 + ff'' + f''^2 + f'f''')\frac{f}{r^2} \qquad 37.14$$

$$j_\alpha(r, \alpha) = -\frac{\varepsilon_0}{\eta}(f'^2 + ff'' + f''^2 + f'f''')\frac{f'}{r^2} \qquad 37.15$$

$$E_r(r, \alpha) = -\frac{\partial\varphi}{\partial r} \equiv 0 \qquad 37.16$$

$$E_\alpha(r, \alpha) = -\frac{1}{r}\frac{\partial\varphi}{\partial r} = -\frac{1}{\eta}(f + f'')\frac{f'}{r} \qquad 37.17$$

$$F_r(r, \alpha) = -eE_r \equiv 0 \qquad 37.18$$

$$F_\alpha(r, \alpha) = -eE_\alpha = m(f + f'')\frac{f'}{r} \qquad 37.19$$

Since in basic flow cases the trajectories were straight lines with known positions, determination of the equation of the trajectories was not necessary. In case of space-charge flow between non-parallel planes, the trajectories are, however, generally curves, knowledge of which is necessary for the applications. From the ratio of equations 37.11 and 37.12 we have

$$\frac{\dot{r}}{r\dot\alpha} = \frac{1}{r}\frac{dr}{d\alpha} = \frac{f}{f'} \qquad 37.20$$

Integrating $[r_0 = r(\alpha_0)]$

$$r(\alpha) = r_0 \exp\left[\int_{\alpha_0}^{\alpha} \frac{f}{f'} \, d\alpha \right] \qquad 37.21$$

The current is obtained from equation 34.4, with an anode-plate height of L in the direction of z, and a length of $R_2 - R_1$ in the direction of r

$$I = \int_0^L \int_{R_1}^{R_2} j_\alpha(r, \alpha_2) \, dr dz =$$

$$= -\frac{\varepsilon_0 L}{\eta} \; |(f'^2 + ff'' + f''^2 + f' f''') f'|_{\alpha=\alpha_2} \int_{R_1}^{R_2} \frac{dr}{r^2} =$$

$$= -\frac{\varepsilon_0 L(R_2 - R_1)}{\eta R_1 R_2} \; |(f'^2 + ff'' + f''^2 + f' f''')f'|_{\alpha=\alpha_2} \qquad 37.22$$

Finally, the solution of the differential equation 37.9 must be given. The coefficients pertaining to the conditions of space-charge limited flow

$$\varphi(0) = 0; \; \varphi'(0) = 0 \qquad 37.23$$

are calculated by the series-expansion method applied in § 35. From these conditions, the new conditions

$$[f(0) + f''(0)]f'(0) = 0; \; f^2(0) + f'^2(0) = 0 \qquad 37.24$$

are obtained with the use of equations 37.10 and 37.17. On the cathode the electrons may have zero velocity, giving rise to the conditions

$$f(0) = 0; \; f'(0) = 0 \qquad 37.25$$

by using equations 37.11 and 37.12. Due to the first equation of 37.24, $f''(0)$ may be chosen as an arbitrary value. Therefore, with the arbitrary constant N, the first three coefficients of the *Taylor* series are

$$f(0) = f'(0) = 0; \; f''(0) = N \qquad 37.26$$

As a result of the calculation, the following coefficients have been obtained

$$f'''(0) = 0; \; f^{(\mathrm{IV})}(0) = -\frac{8}{13} N; \; f^{(\mathrm{V})}(0) = 0;$$

$$f^{(\mathrm{VI})}(0) = \frac{5602}{5239} N; \; f^{(\mathrm{VII})}(0) = 0; \; f^{(\mathrm{VIII})}(0) = -\frac{338\,938\,288}{6\,560\,427\,731} N \qquad 37.27$$

Using the calculated coefficients

$$f(\alpha) = N \left\{ \frac{1}{2} \alpha^2 - \frac{1}{39} \alpha^4 + \frac{2801}{1\,886\,040} \alpha^6 - \right.$$

$$\left. - \frac{21\,183\,643}{16\,532\,277\,882\,120} \alpha^8 + \ldots \right\} = N\,S(\alpha) \qquad 37.28$$

where the function appearing in brackets is denoted with $S(\alpha)$. The value of the constant N will be definite when the specification

$$\varphi(\alpha_2) = \varphi_2 \qquad 37.29$$

is made

$$N = \left[\frac{2\eta\varphi_2}{S^2(\alpha_2) + S'^2(\alpha_2)} \right]^{1/2} \qquad 37.30$$

With the determined value of N, the space-charge limited current (T is the abbreviation of the expression of the constants) is obtained from equation 37.22

$$T = = \frac{2\sqrt{2}\,\varepsilon_0 \sqrt{\eta}\,L(R_2 - R_1)}{R_1 R_2} \qquad 37.31$$

$$I = T \frac{[S'^2(\alpha_2) + S(\alpha_2)S''(\alpha_2) + S''^2(\alpha_2) + S'(\alpha_2)S'''(\alpha_2)]\,S'(\alpha_2)}{[S^2(\alpha_2) + S'^2(\alpha_2)]^{3/2}} \, \varphi_2^{3/2}$$

$$37.32$$

Now the entire flow field (with all characteristics) is known. Owing to lack of space, we do not give the flow-field characteristics as functions of φ_2, since with the help of equation 37.32, they can readily be written similarly to the basic cases.

38. THE FIELD OF THE SPACE-CHARGE FLOW IN THE VICINITY OF A GIVEN PLANE SURFACE

The axially symmetric flow has been chosen, since the practical significance of this case is beyond doubt the greatest, and with the help of equations 30.8, 30.9, 30.10, the schematic investigation of the problem can be performed [98].

Let us now consider a circular plate of finite diameter, which emits electrons. The flow pattern will be axially symmetric, and therefore we write our equations in an axially symmetric system. In the axially symmetric system the velocity vector is

$$\dot{\mathbf{r}} = \dot{r}\mathbf{e}_r + r\dot{\alpha}\mathbf{e}_\alpha + \dot{z}\mathbf{e}_z \qquad 38.1$$

The components of the velocity vector are now functions of the position. The potential equation in the axially symmetric system is

$$\frac{1}{r}\frac{\partial}{\partial r}\left(r\frac{\partial\varphi}{\partial r}\right) + \frac{1}{r^2}\frac{\partial^2\varphi}{\partial\alpha^2} + \frac{\partial^2\varphi}{\partial z^2} = -\frac{1}{\varepsilon_0}\varrho \qquad 38.2$$

12*

The equations of motion in the axially symmetric system are

$$\dot{r}\,\frac{\partial \dot{r}}{\partial r} + r\dot{\alpha}\,\frac{1}{r}\,\frac{\partial \dot{r}}{\partial z} + \dot{z}\,\frac{\partial \dot{r}}{\partial z} = \eta\,\frac{\partial \varphi}{\partial r} \qquad\qquad 38.3$$

$$\dot{r}\,\frac{\partial (r\dot{\alpha})}{\partial r} + r\dot{\alpha}\,\frac{1}{r}\,\frac{\partial (r\dot{\alpha})}{\partial \alpha} + \dot{z}\,\frac{\partial (r\dot{\alpha})}{\partial z} = \eta\,\frac{1}{r}\,\frac{\partial \varphi}{\partial \alpha} \qquad\qquad 38.4$$

$$\dot{r}\,\frac{\partial \dot{z}}{\partial r} + r\dot{\alpha}\,\frac{1}{r}\,\frac{\partial \dot{z}}{\partial \alpha} + \dot{z}\,\frac{\partial \dot{z}}{\partial z} = \eta\,\frac{\partial \varphi}{\partial z} \qquad\qquad 38.5$$

The continuity equation in the axially symmetric case is

$$\frac{1}{r}\,\frac{\partial}{\partial r}\,(r\varrho\dot{r}) + \frac{1}{r}\,\frac{\partial}{\partial \alpha}\,(\varrho r\dot{\alpha}) + \frac{\partial}{\partial z}\,(\varrho\dot{z}) = 0 \qquad\qquad 38.6$$

There is no energy equation among the basic equations; however, owing to its simplicity, we are using it. The energy equation in the axially symmetric system is

$$\dot{r}^2 + r^2\dot{\alpha}^2 + \dot{z}^2 = 2\eta\varphi \qquad\qquad 38.7$$

Owing to the axially symmetric flow pattern, no function is dependent on α. Equations 38.1 to 38.7 become, therefore, greatly simplified. Since we have now four unknown functions, we must choose four independent equations from among the simpler equations yielded, and we choose the four simplest. Using the simplifying method of writing $\dot{r} = u$ and $\dot{z} = v$, the four equations for the determination of the four unknown functions are

$$\frac{1}{r}\,\frac{\partial}{\partial r}\left(r\,\frac{\partial \varphi}{\partial r}\right) + \frac{\partial^2 \varphi}{\partial z^2} = -\frac{1}{\varepsilon_0}\,\varrho \qquad\qquad 38.8$$

$$u\,\frac{\partial u}{\partial r} + v\,\frac{\partial u}{\partial z} = \eta\,\frac{\partial \varphi}{\partial r} \qquad\qquad 38.9$$

$$\frac{1}{r}\,\frac{\partial}{\partial r}\,(r\varrho u) + \frac{\partial}{\partial z}\,(\varrho v) = 0 \qquad\qquad 38.10$$

$$u^2 + v^2 = 2\eta\varphi \qquad\qquad 38.11$$

Any misunderstanding will be avoided if we write the functions and their variables

$$\varphi = \varphi(r,z); \quad \varrho = \varrho(r,z); \quad u = u(r,z); \quad v = v(r,z) \qquad\qquad 38.12$$

We now differentiate equation 38.11 with respect to r and compare it with equation 38.9. The result of the comparison is

$$\frac{\partial u}{\partial z} = \frac{\partial v}{\partial r} \qquad\qquad 38.13$$

The characteristics of the flow field are given by their infinite series (using the parity requirements already known)

$$\varphi = \sum_{n=0}^{\infty} \varphi_{2n}(z)\, r^{2n} \tag{38.14}$$

$$\varrho = \sum_{n=0}^{\infty} \varrho_{2n}(z)\, r^{2n} \tag{38.15}$$

$$u = \sum_{n=0}^{\infty} u_{2n+1}(z)\, r^{2n+1} \tag{38.16}$$

$$v = \sum_{n=0}^{\infty} v_{2n}(z)\, r^{2n} \tag{38.17}$$

The axial component of the current density is given by a separate series

$$j_z = \varrho v = \sum_{n=0}^{\infty} j_{2n}(z)\, r^{2n} \tag{38.18}$$

We now wish to determine the space-charge limited flow, and we, therefore, choose the initial conditions

$$\varphi(r, 0) = 0; \quad \varphi_z'(r, 0) = 0 \tag{38.19}$$

from which the following conditions are obtained relevant to the coefficients of equation 38.14

$$\varphi_{2n}(0) = 0, \qquad n = 0, 1, 2, \ldots \tag{38.20}$$

$$\varphi_{2n}'(0) = 0, \qquad n = 0, 1, 2, \ldots \tag{38.21}$$

On the cathode surface ($z = 0$) the electrons may have no velocity and hence, using equations 38.16 and 38.17

$$u_{2n+1}(0) = 0, \qquad n = 0, 1, 2, \ldots \tag{38.22}$$

$$v_{2n}(0) = 0, \qquad n = 0, 1, 2, \ldots \tag{38.23}$$

are obtained.

In the case of space-charge limited flow the electron velocity on the cathode surface is zero and the space-charge density is infinite but in such a way that their product is of finite (limit) value. This well-known fact imposes the following prescriptions on the coefficients contained in equation 38.18

$$j_{2n}(0) = C_{2n}, \qquad n = 0, 1, 2, \ldots \tag{38.24}$$

where C_{2n} indicates a constant. The finite value of the current density is also expressive, since when calculated from equation 34.4, the current emitted by the (finite-sized) cathode. a finite value is to be obtained.

Now we substitute equations 38.14 and 38.15 into 38.8, with the result

$$\varphi_{2n+2} = -\frac{1}{4(n+1)^2}\left(\varphi_{2n}'' + \frac{1}{\varepsilon_0}\varrho_{2n}\right), \qquad n = 0, 1, 2, \ldots \quad 38.25$$

Substituting equations 38.16 and 38.17 into 38.13, the result is

$$v_{2n} = \frac{1}{2n}u_{2n-1}', \qquad n = 1, 2, \ldots \quad 38.26$$

Using the transformation [Chapter I: 49]

$$\sum_{\mu=0}^{\infty} a_\mu x^\mu \sum_{\nu=0}^{\infty} b_\nu x^\nu = \sum_{n=0}^{\infty}\left(\sum_{k=0}^{n} a_k b_{n-k}\right)x^n \qquad 38.27$$

the following are obtained by 38.10, taking 38.26 into consideration

$$\sum_{n=0}^{\infty} u_{2n+1} r^{2n} \sum_{n=0}^{\infty}\varrho_{2n}r^{2n} + \sum_{n=0}^{\infty}u_{2n+1}r^{2n+1}\sum_{n=0}^{\infty}2\,n\varrho_{2n}\,r^{2n-1} +$$

$$+ \sum_{n=0}^{\infty}\varrho_{2n}\,r^{2n}\sum_{n=0}^{\infty}(2n+1)\,u_{2n+1}\,r^{2n} + \sum_{n=0}^{\infty}j_{2n}'\,r^{2n} = 0$$

$$u_{2n+1} = -\frac{j_{2n}'}{2(n+1)\varrho_0} - \frac{1}{\varrho_0}\sum_{k=1}^{n}\varrho_{2k}\,u_{2n+1-2k}, \quad n = 1, 2, \ldots \quad 38.28$$

From equation 38.18, with the series 38.15 and 38.17, the transformation 38.27, and taking into consideration 38.26

$$\varrho_{2n} = \frac{j_{2n}}{v_0} - \frac{1}{2v_0}\sum_{k=0}^{n-1}\frac{1}{n-k}\varrho_{2k}u_{2n-1-2k}', \qquad n = 1, 2, \ldots \quad 38.29$$

is obtained.

Using 38.27, the series 38.16 and 38.17 are squared and substitnted inot equation 38.11. The identical satisfaction of this system of equations results in

$$\varphi_0 = \frac{1}{2\eta}v_0^2 \quad (n = 0) \qquad 38.30$$

$$\sum_{k=0}^{n-1}u_{2k+1}u_{2n-1-2k} + \sum_{k=0}^{n}v_{2k}v_{2n-2k} - 2\eta\varphi_{2n} = 0, \quad n = 1, 2, \ldots \quad 38.31$$

Substituting equation 38.25 and 38.26 into 38.31 we have

$$\varphi_{2n-2}'' = -\frac{1}{\varepsilon_0}\varrho_{2n-2} - \frac{4n^2}{\eta}v_0 v_{2n} - \frac{2n^2}{\eta}u_1 u_{2n-1} -$$

$$- \frac{2n^2}{\eta}\sum_{k=1}^{n-1}\left[u_{2k+1}u_{2n-1-2k} + \frac{1}{4k(n-k)}u_{2k-1}'u_{2n-1-2k}'\right], \quad n = 1, 2, \ldots \quad 38.32$$

For equation 38.32 the rule 5.55 must be taken into consideration.

Between the functions φ, ϱ, u, v, j_z unknown in flow problems, equations 38.8, 38.9, 38.10, 38.11 and 38.18 gave the relations. Between the coefficients figuring in the unknown functions, the systems of equations 38.25, 38.26, 38.28, 38.29 and 38.32 indicate the relations (equation 38.30 is supplementary). By giving the n indices of the equations of increasing values, the unknown coefficients, functions, can be determined. Two facts, however, must be noted: equation $j_0 = \varrho_0 v_0$ must figure among the equations, and they include not only differential equations, but algebraic equations also.

Seven equations with ten unknown functions pertain to the first step of the solution, therefore, three functions may be chosen arbitrarily; conditions 38.20 to 38.24 must naturally be enforced. The three arbitrarily chosen functions indicate the numerous flow types which may be formed. For example, we can give the velocity distribution (u_1, v_0) of the electrons leaving the cathode and the current density j_0. The work [98] gives an example calculated throughout for an actual case.

39. OTHER CASES AND PROBLEMS RELATING TO
SPACE-CHARGE FLOW

Discussion of the more complex space-charge flow problems (which, in the majority of cases, can be written only with two or three variables) is difficult, due to the mathematical problems involved. Investigation of the transient space-charge flow falls beyond the scope of our subject matter, and therefore we are dealing with steady space-charge flow only. Fortunately, we are able to use the space-charge concept, as an approximation, instead of separate treatment of the very numerous particular particles, since in our case the mutual repulsion of electrons may be written with continuous space-charge approximation. Even with steady flow, the exact solution of the space-charge problem counts as a rarity. The space-charge field-density functions, intensity functions, naturally can easily be derived from the precise solution, even in the case of non-laminar space-charge flow, planar or spatial motions, as for example space-charge distribution, which is obviously non-uniform space-charge distribution. Knowledge of the space-charge flow solution enables, for example, the calculation of space-charge density and thereby calculation of the charge, or calculation of potential, and hence the electric field calculation. Direct calculation of the axis potential is possible with the practically most important axially symmetric space-charge flow. For example, the calculation of space-charge flow gives the degree of electric condensation, or in the space-charge limited case, the infinite space-charge density. Although infinite space-charge has appeared at several points on the cathodes, in reality this cannot appear. Consequently, space-charge calculation in a region quite close to the cathode cannot be performed with the given equations. In any case, electric compression is realised with symmetrical arrangements, in which case the diagram of flow lines yields the semi-angle of beam convergence. Non-space-charge limited current seldom occurs from the partial space-charge conditions. The solution of this flow is more difficult than that of the space-charge limited flow, since fewer homogeneous conditions exist among the related conditions. The majority of space-charge flow tasks display plane-, cylindrical and spherical symmetry, and among the flow types, principally axial, radial and azimuthal space-charge flows occur. The investigation of turbulent flows belongs on the one hand to the analysis of space-charge flows, and on the other hand, to the consideration of space-charge flow perturbations. Turbulence investigation is necessary in the first place for validity control of our approximative calculations, and flow perturbations are investigated for determination of a dimension, or the permissible deviation in practice of any characteristic value. It should be mentioned further that complex formulation of space-charge flow equations also occurs.

In cases which cannot be exactly solved, approximative solutions of space-charge problems are sought. Similarly to other subject matters, in the field of space-charge flow, digital computers form a mainstay and determine the arithmetical solutions of space-charge flow equations. Space-charge simulation is no longer a formidable task, and calculations of space-charge flow can be performed with ease. Flow computation also opens the way to current density computation or to recognition of charge distribution. Computations can be performed in almost arbitrary symmetry cases. For example, axially symmetric flow, radial flow etc. can be determined. Both numerical computations and exact calculations can be employed for solution of special tasks, for example a potential maximum plane can be determined, e.g. in a given region without boundary; or the time of flight between two points.

Within the subject matter of space-charge flow, measurements are also of significance, in addition to exact and approximative calculations. Let us consider in the first place that we are not always able to solve a given problem with accuracy, and secondly that the given problem may be complex to such a degree that instead of numerical calculation, a solution by measurement may be quicker and less costly. As already seen in the headings dealing with field measurements, methods are available which enable potential plotting or measurement of electric field strength. With methods of measurements iteration, the possibility is opened for measurement of current density, and this already provides the possibility of current intensity measurement. With knowledge of the flow field velocity distribution (this appears automatically in the iterations) the space-charge density measurement has in fact been performed.

Space-charge flow forms a fine example of electron physics from the theoretical aspect, and is widely employed. The low-, medium- and high-power flows which, issuing from low-, medium- and high-power guns realise the low-, medium- and high-power beams, represent the practical raw material for solution of the technical tasks. A thorough knowledge of all behaviours and properties of the charged particles is indispensable for proper setting of equipment operating with electron beams, and efficiency enhancement in the event of further developments. In the first place, it is important to know the regularities of thermionic emission, since the emission brings about the space-charge flow medium. This subject matter, however, is not included in the material covered by the present book, and is only referred to. It is most important to know that emission is constrained by temperature. Arbitrary current cannot be taken from the emitting surface, since the electron current density is univocally determined by the cathode temperature, with knowledge of the emitting material work function. Temperature-dependent current-density limit forms one of the reasons why curvilinear motions are permissible instead of rectilinear motions, and it became necessary to resort to low-, medium- and high-convergence flows. These flows originate in sequence from low-, medium- and high-convergence guns, and induce low-, medium- and high-convergence beams relative to the gun region. The position is further complicated and although the cathode is equipotential, the cathode temperature distribution is not constant on the cathode surface, and therefore the cathode emission density is also not constant. A non-uniform emission density emerges instead of the uniform emission density. The geometric faults of the cathode surface inhomogeneities appearing in the material form sources of further faults, where e.g. smoothness of emission cannot be realised. These (and other unmentioned) symptoms encumber the calculation of current density.

In addition to the temperature-limited current, space-charge limitation also occurs. With a given gun type, a certain current value—the space-charge limited current—expressly pertains to the geometrical dimensions and the potential distribution arising. The limited current value is maximum, and from the given gun type, only the maximum current or a smaller current can be drawn. Limited flow within the given sense can take place only if limitation caused by the temperature is not yet effective.

The applications demanded employment of a triode gun (etc.) in addition to the diode gun. Due to the effect of the edges and the anode aperture, and the further electrode in the case of the triode, the potential distribution and with it the field-strength distribution deviate from the ideal. The cathode loading is not uniform since the limiting current density varies from point to point on the cathode surface, and for example in the case of axially symmetric systems we speak of emitting radius on the cathode, in addition to which there is no further emission. Then, with knowledge of the emitting radius, the total net current leaving the cathode gives only the mean cathode loading and nothing is known of the peak cathode loading. The net current found in the electron flow naturally varies with the electrode voltage. The current limitation caused by the space-charge was the other reason for being compelled to employ conical flows originating from converging electron guns, and appearing as converging electron beams in the gun region. It is interesting to note that the semi-angle of the beam cone is greater than 90° in radially injected currents too.

Unfortunately, we are continually meeting the limit concept in the subject matter of space-charge flow. A new important limit concept is thermal limitation. With regard to its origin we shall give later a few words concerning the *Langmuir* bounding expression giving the thermal velocity limit, according to which the current density in a given plane cannot exceed a maximum value. This vitally important limitation which was determined in 1937 with regard to the *Langmuir* flows induced by thermal electrons [213], can easily be derived from the sine law attributed to *Abbé* (1873), but actually derived by *Clausius* (1863) and later by *Helmholtz* (1873). As, for example, homogeneous initial velocity distribution does in effect not occur, and inhomogeneous initial velocity distribution is general, similarly, the current distribution emitted by the cathode is also not homogeneous. Angular current distribution can be written with approximation as *Lambert*'s law of emission, meaning in fact that the current density value in a given direction is proportionate to the cosinus of the angle subtended by the surface normal. The initial velocities of the electrons carrying the current are naturally removed from the uniform initial velocities and are definitely non-uniform velocities. In practice, the *Maxwellian* initial velocity distribution is used. Together with the *Maxwellian* emission equation all data are now available for the derivation of the *Abbé* theorem from the conservation of energy principle.

As has already been seen, the thermal velocities limit the current density obtainable on a given surface. It would be in vain to design various low-, medium- and high-density electron guns based on the basic equations of space-charge flow, the current density of the resultant low-, medium- and high-density electron flow would not attain the designed values. Therefore, the design work must be refined, and the thermal velocities must be taken into account as new factors. The measurement results demonstrate that the calculated values closely approach reality with regard to low-, medium- and high-current density flows, if the thermal velocity is taken into account. The results are practically faultless, when taking into account the *Maxwellian* distribution. It is customary to perform the calculations of the electron beams with paraxial approximation, although the conditions of paraxiality are almost never fulfilled. Besides the optical theory [Chapter VI: 327] of beam calculations, the single-velocity electron beam is introduced as an approximation, and single-velocity analysis [Chapter VI: 318], although the electron beam is in fact a multi-velocity electron beam, for the investigation of which a multi-velocity analysis is necessary. Without doubt, the latter method will provide the most reliable results for low-, medium- and high-current flows.

Supplementary to the concrete material of the preceding paragraphs, comments are given herewith, to aid formation of a more general understanding. These comments are based upon the available literature.

Attention is drawn first to an article [27] of historical interest, appearing under *a)* of the bibliography, which deals with the generation of space-charge flow medium—electron multitude—with the aid of thermionic emission. The communication published in 1903, about seventy years ago, clearly demonstrates, on the one hand, the immeasurable value of the pioneer work and, on the other hand, the zeal and equivalent scientific knowledge of the successors. The successors enjoyed the backing of the pioneers and can now prepare for planetary orbiting. The problem of emission is highly complicated, and now also engages the attention of researchers. As an example we mention article [6], in which it is established that current from rough-surface cathodes is limited by breakdown.

Study of space-charge flow is of interest in obtaining a theoretical basis for the design of electron guns. These guns include for instance, the medium current gun, or more frequently the high-current gun, according to the practical demand. We may add that with increasing applications, the low current or low-current density guns are gaining a more significant role. With consideration of the medium values, knowledge of a medium voltage electron flow enables design of the medium voltage electron gun. As regards other fields, again a knowledge of space-charge flow data enables theoretical recognition of diode characteristics or triode characteristics. Attention is drawn to some of the more important among the many problem groups, by reference to respective articles. The design of electron guns may be performed with consideration of the space-charge [16], for application in equipments requiring laminar beam [4], for obtaining high compression [13], for attainment of high μ (with non-intercepting current control grids) [2], for reduction of beam noisiness [25] (multi-anode types; potential minimum away from the cathode), for hollow beam-producing guns [1], as applied in ion engines, etc.

The practical application of space-charge flow is facilitated by scaling to a considerably greater degree than is suggested by the respective brief part of the present book. The characteristics of the derived tube can already be known from simple calculations: this represents an advantage which has induced the researchers to conduct thorough elaboration of the details of

this subject matter. The two main cases of scaling are those without consideration of thermal velocities and those involving thermal velocities. Two
sub-cases of the first main case: scaling without initial velocities and without
space-charge, or respectively scaling without initial velocities and with
space-charge. The two sub-cases of the second main case are: scaling with
initial velocities and without space-charge, or respectively scaling with
initial velocities and with space-charge. From among the series of communications dealing with scaling, mention should be made of work [11, 12]
performed earlier and by an author known from achievements also in
other fields [19]. These works are being continued [17], and are now dealing
with the most varied fields (energy converters) of application [22]. Following the example of cathode-ray tubes, a highly detailed communication [23]
treats the problem of scaling, and a special article is devoted to transverse
scaling [15]. The majority of book publications provide information on
scaling, as for example the recently published book [5].

Among the books figuring in item a) of the bibliography, in addition to
those dealing directly with space-charge flow [3, 26, 28], those treating
fluid mechanics and hydrodynamics are undoubtedly of the greater importance [21]. Due to the close connection between space-charge and fluid flow,
the methods and theses of hydrodynamics can generally be applied without
any change. Similarly, the connection between plasma physics, and principally thermal flow is also close, and this enables the aid of plasma physical
methods [7, 30]. The works [9, 10] review, on the one hand, the peripheral
field of emission phenomenon, and, on the other hand, that of gas discharges
(plasma physics). Further volumes investigate gun design [24], vacuum
tubes (equivalent diodes; thermal triodes; etc.) [29], the base of electron
motion [14], capacity reduction caused by space-charge [20], a certain
space-charge flow case (a cylindrical cathode between two parallel plane
anodes) as a part of contents [8], and related problems.

Reference is made to summarised publications, under item b) of the
bibliography. These include article [33], the first summary. The publication
[32] covers a wide field, while article [35] presents a brief, albeit very excellent summary of the subject matter. A summary of earlier results of
thermal flow is given in the article [36]. A large-scale review of the same field
is presented in the paper [34], and the summarised publication [31] covers
the entire field of dense electron beams, including thermal cases also.

Recently, the space-charge flow occurring in simultaneously acting electric-
magnetic fields has been increasingly dealt with [Chapter VI: 255]. The
relative basic equations provide relations between eight unknown functions

$$\Delta\varphi = -\frac{1}{\varepsilon_0}\varrho \qquad\qquad 39.1$$

$$\Delta\mathbf{A} = -\mu_0\varrho\dot{\mathbf{r}} \qquad\qquad 39.2$$

$$\operatorname{div}(\varrho\mathbf{r}) = 0 \qquad\qquad 39.3$$

$$(\operatorname{Grad}\dot{\mathbf{r}})\cdot\dot{\mathbf{r}} = \eta\operatorname{grad}\varphi - \eta\dot{\mathbf{r}}\times\operatorname{curl}\mathbf{A} \qquad\qquad 39.4$$

The eight unknown functions are: φ, ϱ, the three components of $\dot{\mathbf{r}}$, the three components of $\mathbf{A}$. The above system of equations is highly complex (among others, it is non-linear), yet it is widely investigated, principally in general curvilinear coordinate systems. The 'paraxial equations of space-charge flow' have been derived [Chapter VI: 255].

We now mention that *we can speak of 'paraxial' space-charge flow only if all the characteristics are known in a space section close to any surface, representing boundary condition, and not in the entire region.*

However, in the literature the focusing problems of electron beams based upon a curvilinear central trajectory are named incorrectly (see reference [124] given in the bibliography for Chapter I) 'problems of paraxial space-charge flow'. For discussion of focusing problems relating to a curvilinear central trajectory, essentially the same data are necessary as for discussions of problems of focusing based on a rectilinear central trajectory: the central trajectory, the course of the potential and its derivatives along the central trajectory, the magnetic and the electric field along the central trajectory. Knowledge of the data permits the determination of the electron trajectories near to the central trajectory, but in the paraxial case only; for example, in the axially symmetric case discussed in the present work the data are: (central trajectory) axis z, axis potential, axis induction.

Looking at the problem from another angle, this statement will again be recognised. The potential along the central trajectory can be given only with knowledge of the entire flow pattern, since the resultant potential is given by summation. On the other hand, if the potential is already given, determination of the flow field cannot be considered, only that of the focusing problem.

The thermal velocities must also be taken into consideration, in addition to the magnetic field, if we desire a better approach to reality. Although the problem of space-charge flow without thermal velocity has been dealt with in general, investigation of the discussed flow, taking into consideration thermal velocities, is still failing in such basic cases as space-charge flow between concentric spheres, with *Maxwellian* velocity distribution. The effect of thermal velocities is considerable, investigation of these effects is therefore important, and will represent the timely investigations of the present and the future.

In the following we shall present further literature information, and we refer to item *c)* of the bibliography. A number of articles on space-charge flow has been published in the literature. In numerous cases the problems of basic flow have been solved and the specific functions have been recalculated.

The most important flow problems form the subject matter of § 34, 35 and 36. These problems represented the commencement, following which not only theoretical, but articles relating to experimentation also appeared [96]. We make mention of the articles dealing with flow between planes [52, 99–101], flow between cylinders [47, 102, 125], flow between spheres [37, 103, 128].

The flow cases listed are such where the electron trajectories are straight lines. In the case of electrodes of other form the flow is curvilinear. Non-parallel planes [79, 141] are dealt with, the flow between non-coaxial cylinders [55, 77], and the effects caused by deviations resulting in practice are taken into consideration. Flow between electrodes of other form are also dealt with [8, 69], including several which may give more precise information relative to operation of the classical electron tubes [72, 73, 97]. The flow of non-space-charge limited flow between planes [40, 43, 49] and between cylinders [57, 58, 78] also form the subjects of research. The transit time between planes [53], cylinders [63, 65], spheres [66] can be calculated with the help of the references given.

The following works deal with generally valid laws e.g. $^3/_2$ law, relative to flows [33, 42, 64, 142]. Numerous articles deal also with curved-line flows and flows between non-real electrodes [94, 133, 143]. The same subject matter is dealt with under a different name in the articles discussing non-laminar flows [Chapter I: 198] and flows in magnetic fields [93; Chapter VI: 255]. Other articles are also presented, which discuss, for example, calculation of potential distribution pertaining to a given space-charge distribution [51], approximation methods [81, 82, 111, 123], complex variable method of description [90], method of separating variables [95, Chapter I: 236], numerical calculation methods [106], capacity calculations [20], determining whether the desired flows are possible [108], properties of three-dimensional flow [129], calculation of equivalent diodes [140], and azimuthal flow between spheres [144]. Computers may also be employed [Chapter I: 193].

Among the information required for discussion of space-charge flow is the problem of whether the individual interaction between the electrons may or may not be neglected. By calculations [38, 118] and experiments [39] it has been confirmed that the individual intereffect may be neglected. Virtually all space-charge flow results are valid for small-dimension flows only [116], among others they are not valid for large-size diodes, and the *Pierce* gun designing method can also not be employed if the beam diameter is large. Basic equations describing the flow are available within the limits of validity [48, 135], and the general equations of space-charge flow are available even in the time-dependent case [86, 127]. The communication [83] gives the space-charge flow differential equation written by the action function, with additive separation. In article [137] the action-function method is employed in several flow cases, as for example with the thin-grid wire placed opposite the cathode, or the effect of the anode hole in the planar diode. In article [92] the action-function-method is considerably more generalised, and, for example, the toroidal gun is derived from the cylindrical gun. The articles [117, 120, 121] deal with space-charge flow occurring along the orthogonal trajectories of the equipotential surfaces. This type of flow occurs rarely. Communication [114] deals with curvilinear space-charge flow; and similarly, the single-component space-charge flow is treated in article [115]. The papers [54, 70], together with others, endeavour to determine the shape of the electrodes from the prescriptions given along the central trajectory. Viewing the problem in principle, it is our opinion that the electrode shape cannot be determined from the central trajectory prescriptions, and therefore such statements should be considered

erroneous. In connection with this, we are again presenting a brief per-
spective of the subject.

Mistakes of this type, unfortunately, are fairly frequent. Formation of the
mistakes is due to the fact that the structure of numerous flows is somewhat simple, and in the cases employed most in practice these can be described using one or two variables. Nevertheless, either one or two variables,
the flows remain space flows. Electric-magnetic phenomena are automatically of space, and, e.g., introduction of the planar electric field is an abstraction only (for example, conformal mapping). Choosing the electric field
as an example, the spatial, i.e., the real potential field cannot be determined
univocally from the potential distribution given by a planar or even a
spatial curve. Surface integrals cannot be substituted by line integrals.
This is true even if one of the variables is constant and integration is reduced
to multiplication: in this case only one line integral is apparently calculated.
When in the axially symmetric case the potential is given along a curve, in
the meridian plane, it is in fact given on a surface of rotation. In the plane-
symmetric case, when given along the generating curve, it corresponds to
being given on a cylinder surface. If we now consider the closed surfaces,
it becomes apparent that the form of the given curves cannot be arbitrary.
A further difficulty is that neither the path nor the potential distribution
and the field-strength distribution along the path, nor the induction distribution along it can be taken arbitrarily, since interrelations exist between
them. Details of this problem are given in the candidature thesis, by the
author of this chapter [Chapter I: 124]. It is interesting to note that the
majority of the mistakes in the subject matters discussed in the book are
due to inadequate knowledge relating to the potential theory. In the first
chapter: at the field calculations, boundary conditions given on closed
surfaces are required for unique solution of the elliptic equations occurring
in field calculations; in the second chapter: potentials given with the help
of quadratures can be obtained only at the cost of surface integral calculations, and line-integrals cannot be employed. This latter is true
either the field is plane- or axially symmetric. The fact that with knowledge
of the axis potentials, or axis-induction (values given on one 'curve') the
potential may be calculated with regard to each point of the space, or the
field strength with closed expressions also, appears as contradictory to the
foregoing. This fact is actually a structural property of the axially symmetric
or the plane-symmetric field—see also the quadrupole field—, but first the
axis potential or the axis induction must be determined with the use of
boundary conditions. These may not be posited arbitrarily since the field
calculated from these does not necessarily (but may accidentally) satisfy
Laplace's equation, namely the field calculated with their aid is neither
an electric nor a magnetic field.

Now let us view the problem of electrode-shape determination from a
different aspect. First, we refer to the energy equation 17.16 given in the
first chapter. On the left side of the equations is a one-variable (time)
vector function, a time derivative of the vector-scalar function describing
the path. On the right-hand side of the equation, apart from a constant
multiplier, is the potential. This potential, however, is not of three, but of

only one variable, since the potential values have to be calculated in the path curve points given in the function of time. However, the equation may be taken as suitable for calculation of the potential, i.e. for determination of a three-variable function. This conception is however obviously erroneous, since a three-variable function, the potential, and through this the electrode shape can in no case be obtained from the one-variable function on the left side of the equation. Between the sharply distinguished subject matters of focusing and space-charge flow, already at the beginning of the present chapter, the problem of electrode shape determination with expectations of uniqueness and success can occur in the latter only. In spite of the foregoing it is not denied that with arbitrary data, or with approximating intentions only, more or less useful results can be obtained. We now revert to a review of the more interesting articles dealing with the problems of space-charge flow.

The space-charge flow task has already been solved with regard to the toroidal diode [75], from which the cylindrical and the spherical diode emerge as a marginal case. Solution with approximation of the space-charge flow between inclined plane electrodes is also accessible [80]. Space-charge flow between non-symmetrical electrodes is investigated in the paper [124]. As an item of interest we mention investigation of space-charge flow occurring in triodes [50] and tetrodes [109]. Knowledge of the axially symmetric space-charge flow from finite-dimension planar cathodes is of great importance in the near cathode space section [98]. The space-charge problem has been solved for example, between infinite planes, from a cathode of r radius [105]. Investigations have been conducted of the flow picture, when the angle of the beam forming electrode deviates from the *Pierce* angle [107]. Article [134] deals with beam investigations, assuming that the beam originates from a *Pierce* gun. According to article [74] the space-charge flow equations are solved by digital computers, but also electrolytic tank measurements are used for determining the electrodes of the hollow beam. Communications [61, 88] deal with magnetron-injection guns and flows emerging from these with consideration of low-voltage and low-noise guns [146]. The paper [138] investigates the effect of the planar diode anode hole in the case of dense electron beams. The communication [89] treats the solution of curvilinear space-charge flow tasks by separation, and also numerical calculations. An older [46] and a later [87] paper deal with space-charge flows occurring in crossed fields, and the guns developed from these. Communications [60, 145] deal with calculation of space-charge flow originating from cone-formed cathodes serving for producing hollow beams.

Finally, we give an account of the subject matter of the more important articles listed under *d)* in the bibliography.

The real cases of space-charge flow are in connection with thermal velocities. Basic knowledge relating to limitations caused by temperature can be obtained from the articles [34, 213, 227], while the effect of simultaneous presence of the magnetic field is discussed in article [149]. Effects caused by thermal velocities are of considerable significance and therefore discussions of this subject matter were commenced earlier and numerous articles have been published [155, 182, 242]. The basic cases consist of the homogeneous and the *Maxwellian* velocity distribution. Flow between planes, with homogeneous thermal velocities appear in articles [183, 226, 230], and with *Maxwellian* thermal velocities, in articles [187, 188, 259]. The case of cylinders with homogeneous thermal velocities is dealt with in the articles [157, 160, 176], and with *Maxwellian* thermal velocities, in articles [33, 154, 258]. Flow between spheres is at present accessible only with homogeneous thermal velocities [158, 161, 203]. Numerous works deal with the problem of stability. Some of these are: [229, 239, 260]. Finally, transit time [195, 256], Q factor [217] and other problems are also dealt with in works [177, 255, Chapter VI: 322].

Current density integrals (tabulated form) were presented in paper [240] fairly long ago. The work [199] of experimental nature again presents the phenomenon of current limitation. One early illustration of the difficulties presented by thermal velocities is related to the projection kinescope [216]. Communication [228] demonstrates that the limiting stable current increases in the presence of positive ions, which decrease the effect of the negative space-charge. The flow characteristics are given in the function of space-charge, thermal velocity and transit time in the compilation [211]. The diploma thesis [219] presents the potential distribution forming in the hollow cylinder in the case of radially injected current. Article [249] presents the results of computations performed by computer during investigation of thermal diode instability and the related noise, in the one-dimensional case. Communication [224] investigates the planar diode flow field as related to the *Langmuir* limit (*Maxwellian* thermal velocity). The investigation of instability and noise is presented with calculations in the communication [220], in the one-dimensional case. Work [164] also deals with instabilities, with consideration of plasma converters. This is a uniformed and summarised discussion, in the case of arbitrary currents and initial velocities between planes, cylinders and spheres [251]. Current limit, neutralisation and stability in the presence of a longitudinal magnetic field are investigated in the paper [150]. Communication [170] is of theoretical character in which multi-velocity electron flow is discussed as single-velocity flow, using the method of stress-tensor approximation. A later stability and noise calculation (one-dimensional case) is presented in papers [181] and [165]. The limit caused by thermal velocity is investigated in paper [218], with consideration of current density. Neutralisation is indispensable for ion-plasma engines, as given in the communication [252] according to results based on two-dimensional calculations. The great significance of the *Langmuir* limit is indicated by the fact that the paper [171] investigates influences caused by space-charge.

REFERENCES FOR CHAPTER II

a) *Space-Charge Flow and Related Sciences*

1. ANDERSON, J. R.–ETTER, J. E.–GALLEGHER, H. E.: *AIAA J*, **1** (1963), 582.
2. ASHLEY, J. R.–SUTHERLAND, A. D.–KOLB, W. P.: *5th MOGA,** 223.
3. BIRDSALL, C. K.–BRIDGES, W. B.: *Electron Dynamics of Diode Regions.* BOOKER, H. G.–CLARIS, N. DE (Eds): Electrical Science, A Series of Monographs and Texts, Academic Press; New York–London, 1966.
4. CUTTING, A. B.–FRASER, I.: *Vide*, **67** (1957), 74.
5. BULL, C. S.: *Fluctuations in Stationary and Non-Stationary Electron Currents.* Butterworths; London, 1966.
6. CRANBERG, L.: *J. appl. Phys.*, **23** (1952), 518.
7. DELCROIX, J. L.: *Plasma Physics.* John Wiley and Sons; New York, 1965.
8. DOW, W. G.: *Fundamentals of Engineering Electronics.* John Wiley and Sons; New York, 1952.
9. FLÜGGE, S. (Ed.): Handbuch der Physik. Band XXI. Elektronen-Emission, Gasentladungen I. Springer; Berlin–Göttingen–Heidelberg, 1956.
10. FLÜGGE, S. (Ed.): Handbuch der Physik. Band XXII. Gasentladungen II. Springer; Berlin–Göttingen–Heidelberg, 1956.
11. FRY, T. C.: *Phys. Rev.*, **17** (1921), 441.
12. FRY, T. C.: *Phys. Rev.*, **22** (1923), 445.
13. GEPPERT, D. V.: *IRE Wescon Conv. Rec.*, Pt. 3 (1960), 77.
14. HARMAN, W. W.: *Fundamentals of Electronic Motion.* McGraw-Hill; New York, 1953.
15. HERRMANN, G.: *J. appl. Phys.*, **28** (1957), 474.
16. HUBER, G.: *Annls. Radioélect.*, **4** (1949), 26.
17. IVEY, H. F.: *In: Advances etc.*, edited by MARTON, L.: **6** (1954), 137.
18. KIRSTEIN, P. T.–KINO, G. S.–WATERS, W. E.: *Space-Charge Flow.* McGraw-Hill; New York–San Francisco–Toronto–London–Sydney, 1967.
19. LANGMUIR, I.: *Phys. Rev.*, **21** (1923), 419.
20. LLEWELLYN, F. B.: *Electron Inertia Effects.* Cambridge University Press; London–New York, 1941.
21. MILNE-THOMSON, L. M.: *Theoretical Hydrodynamics.* Macmillan; New York, 1950.
22. MOSS, H.: *J. Electron. Control*, **2** (1957), 305.
23. MOSS, H.: *J. Brit. Instn. Radio Engrs.*, **22** (1961), 313.
24. MOSS, H.: Narrow Angle Electron Guns and Cathode Ray Tubes. MARTON, L. (Ed.): *Advances in Electronics and Electron Physics.* Supplement 3. Academic Press; New York–London, 1968.
25. MUELLER, W. M.: *Proc. Instn Radio Engrs.*, **49** (1961), 642.
26. PIERCE, J. R.: *Theory and Design of Electron Beams.* D. Van Nostrand; Toronto–New York–London, 1954.
27. RICHARDSON, D. W.: *Phil. Trans. R. Soc.*, **201** (1903), 497.
28. ROTHE, H.–KLEEN, W.: Grundlagen und Kennlinien der Elektronenröhren. Akademische Verlagsgesellschaft; Leipzig, 1944.
29. SPANGENBERG, K. R.: *Vacuum Tubes.* McGraw-Hill; New York, 1948.
30. SPITZER, L.: Physics of Fully Ionized Gases. MARSHAK, R. E. (Ed): *Interscience Tracts on Physics and Astronomy*, Interscience Publishers; New York–London, 1962.

b) *Summarising Publications*

31. AMBOSS, K.: The Analysis of Dense Electron Beam. *In: Advances etc.*, edited by MARTON, L., **26** (1969), 1.
32. IVEY, H. F.: Space-Charge Limited Currents. *In: Advances etc.*, edited by MARTON, L., **6** (1954), 137.
33. LANGMUIR, I.–COMPTON, K. T.: *Rev. mod. Phys.*, **3** (1931), 273.
34. LINDSAY, P. A.: Velocity Distribution in Electron Streams. *In: Advances etc.*, edited by MARTON, L., **13** (1960), 181.

* See p. 484.

35. Meltzer, B.: *Brit. J. appl. Phys.*, **10** (1959), 391.
36. Petrie, D. P. R.: *Electl. Commun.*, **20** (1941), 100.

c) *Space-Charge Flow*

37. Abdelkader, M. A.: *J. Electron. Control*, **15** (1963), 561.
38. Ash, E. A.: *J. appl. Phys.*, **26** (1955), 327.
39. Ash, E. A.–Gabor, D.: *Proc. R. Soc.*, **228–A** (1955), 477.
40. Barbour, J. P.–Dolan, W. W.–Trolan, J. K.–Martin, E. E.–Dyke, W. P.: *Phys. Rev.*, **92** (1953), 45.
41. Bartlett, W. S.: *Phys. Rev.*, **37** (1931), 279.
42. Bartlett, W. S.: *Phys. Rev.*, **37** (1931), 959.
43. Barut, A. O.: *Z. angew. Math. Phys.*, **2** (1951), 35.
44. Barut, A. O.: *Phys. Rev.*, **81** (1951), 274.
45. Bell, D. A.–Berktay, H. O.: *J. Electron.*, **2** (1956–57), 425.
46. Benham, E.: *Proc. Phys. Soc. Lond.*, **47** (1935), 1.
47. Bottenberg, H.–Zinke, O.: *Arch. elekt. Übertr.*, **18** (1964), 335.
48. (Breitman, V. M.–Kuznetsov, V. S.) Брейтман, В. М.–Кузнецов, В. С.: *РИЭ СССР*, **6** (1961), 993.
49. Brubaker, W. M.: *Phys. Rev.*, **83** (1951), 274.
50. Buneman, O.: *1st MOGA,** 24.
51. Cady, W. G.: *J. appl. Phys.*, **6** (1935), 10.
52. Child, C. D.: *Phys. Rev.*, **32** (1911), 492.
53. Cockburn, R.: *Proc. Phys. Soc. Lond.*, **47** (1935), 810.
54. Colburn, D. S.–Harker, K. J.–Kino, G. S.: *4th MOGA,** 572.
55. Coomes, E. A.–Buck, J. S.: *Proc. Instn Radio Engrs.*, **37** (1949), 626.
56. Copeland, P. L.–Eggenberger, D. N.: *J. appl. Phys.*, **20** (1949), 1148.
57. Copeland, P. L.–Eggenberger, D. N.: *Phys. Rev.*, **80** (1950), 298.
58. Copeland, P. L.–Eggenberger, D. N.: *J. appl. Phys.*, **23** (1952), 280.
59. Crank, J.–Hartree, D. R.—Ingham, J.–Sloane, R. W.: *Proc. Phys. Soc. Lond.*, **51–A** (1939), 952.
60. Dryden, V. W.: *J. appl. Phys.*, **33** (1962), 3118.
61. Dryden, V. W.: *4th MOGA,** 587.
62. Ferris, W. R.: *Proc. Instn Radio Engrs.*, **24** (1936), 82.
63. Fortescue, C. L.: *Wireless Engr.*, **12** (1935), 310.
64. Frank, N. H.: *Phys. Rev.*, **39** (1932), 226.
65. Gold, L.: *J. Electron.*, **3** (1957), 567.
66. Gold, L.: *J. Electron.*, **4** (1958), 335.
67. (Grinberg, G. A.–Pevzner, A.) Гринберг, Г. А.–Певзнер, А: *Ж. Тех. Физ. СССР*, **11** (1941), 1322.
68. Hamaker, H. C.: *Physics*, **9** (1942), 135.
69. Hardie, A. M.: *Wireless Engr.*, **30** (1953), 196.
70. Harker, K. J.: *Int. J. Electron.*, **18** (1965), 43.
71. Harker, K. J.–Colburn, D. S.: *Exact Solutions of the Equations of Space-Charge Limited Flow*. Microwave Laboratory Report No. 858, Stanford University, Stanford, California, 1961.
72. Harris, I. A.: *Wireless Engr.*, **18** (1941), 45.
73. Harris, I. A.: *Wireless Engr.*, **18** (1941), 153.
74. Harris, I. A.: *J. appl. Phys.*, **30** (1959), 826.
75. Hartnagel, H.: *J. Electron. Control*, **17** (1964), 425.
76. Huber, H.–Kleen, W.: *Arch. Elektrotech.*, **39** (1949), 394.
77. Ivey, H. F.: Westinghouse Research Memo BL–931–1, Dec. 1948.
78. Ivey, H. F.: *Phys. Rev.*, **76** (1949), 554.
79. Ivey, H. F.: *J. appl. Phys.*, **23** (1952), 240.
80. Ivey, H. F.: *J. appl. Phys.*, **24** (1953), 227.
81. Ivey, H. F.: *J. appl. Phys.*, **24** (1953), 1466.
82. Ivey, H. F.: *J. appl. Phys.*, **25** (1954), 543.

* See p. 483.

83. IWATA, G.: *Prog. theor. Phys. Osaka*, **15** (1956), 513.
84. JAFFE, G.: *Annls. Phys.*, **63** (1920), 145.
85. (KAN, V. L.) Кан, В. Л.: *Ж. Тех. Физ. СССР*, **18** (1948), 483.
86. KENT, G.: *J. appl. Phys.*, **33** (1962), 683.
87. KINO, G. S.: *IEEE Trans.*, **ED–7** (1960), 179.
88. KINO, G. S.–TAYLOR, N. J.: *IRE Trans.*, **ED–9** (1962), 1.
89. KIRSTEIN, P. T.: *Curvilinear Space-Charge Flow with Application to Electron Guns.* Microwave Laboratory Report No. 440, Stanford University. Stanford, California, 1958.
90. KIRSTEIN, P. T.: *J. Electron.*, **4** (1958), 425.
91. KIRSTEIN, P. T.: *J. Electron. Control*, **4** (1958), 425.
92. KIRSTEIN, P. T.: *J. Electron. Control*, **5** (1958), 33.
93. KIRSTEIN, P. T.: *J. Electron. Control*, **7** (1959), 417.
94. KIRSTEIN, P. T.: *J. appl. Phys.*, **30** (1959), 967.
95. KIRSTEIN, P. T.–KINO, G. S.: *J. appl. Phys.*, **29** (1958), 1758.
96. KLEEN, W.: *Telefunken-Röhre*, H9 (1937), 66.
97. KUSUNOSE, Y.: *Proc. Instn Radio Engrs.*, **17** (1929), 1706.
98. (KUZNETSOV, V. S.) Кузнецов, В. С.: *РИЭ СССР*, **7** (1962), 1379.
99. LANGMUIR, I.: *Phys. Rev.*, **2** (1913), 450.
100. LANGMUIR, I.: *Phys. Z.*, **15** (1914), 348.
101. LANGMUIR, I.: *Phys. Z.*, **15** (1914), 516.
102. LANGMUIR, I.–BLODGETT, K. B.: *Phys. Rev.*, **22** (1923), 347.
103. LANGMUIR, I.–BLODGETT, K. B.: *Phys. Rev.*, **24** (1924), 49.
104. LANGMUIR, I.–COMPTON, K. T.: *Rev. mod. Phys.*, **3** (1931), 191.
105. (LEVINTOV, I. I.) Левинтов, И. И.: *ДАН СССР*, **85** (1952), 1247.
106. LINDSAY, P. A.: *J. Electron. Control*, **6** (1959), 415.
107. LOMAX, R. J.: *J. Electron. Control*, **6** (1959), 39.
108. LUCAS, A. R.–MELTZER, B.–STUART, G. A.: *J. Electron.*, **4** (1958), 160.
109. (LUKOSHKOV, V. S.) Лукошков, В. С.: *Ж. Тех. Физ. СССР*, **6** (1936), 624.
110. MATHESON, R. M.–NERGAARD, L. S.: *J. appl. Phys.*, **23** (1952), 869.
111. MATRICON, M.–TROUVÉ, S.: *Onde élect.*, **30** (1950), 510.
112. MELTZER, B.: *Proc. Phys. Soc.*, **62–B** (1949), 431.
113. MELTZER, B.: *Proc. Phys. Soc.*, **62–B** (1949), 813.
114. MELTZER, B.: *Electron*, **29** (1956), 118.
115. MELTZER, B.: *J. Electron.*, **2** (1956), 118.
116. MELTZER, B.: *J. Electron. Control*, **6** (1959), 550.
117. MELTZER, B.–LUCAS, A. R.: *J. Electron. Control*, **4** (1958), 454.
118. MOTT-SMITH, H. M.: *J. appl. Phys.*, **24** (1953), 249.
119. MUELLER, W. M.: Electronics Research Laboratory Report, Series No. 60, Issue No. 143, 1957, University of California, Berkeley, California.
120. MUELLER, W. M.: *J. Electron. Control*, **6** (1959), 499.
121. MUELLER, W. M.: *J. Electron. Control*, **8** (1960), 111.
122. OERTEL, L.: *Telefunken-Röhre*, H10 (1939), 164.
123. O'NEILL, G. D.: *Sylvania Technol.*, **3** (1950), 22.
124. O'NEILL, G. D.: *J. appl. Phys.*, **26** (1955), 1034.
125. PAGE, L.–ADAMS, N. I.: *Phys. Rev.*, **68** (1945), 126.
126. PAGE, L.–ADAMS, N. I.: *Phys. Rev.*, **76** (1949), 381.
127. PEASE, M. C.: *J. appl. Phys.*, **31** (1960), 70.
128. (POPLOVSKIY, R. P.) Попловский, Р. П.: *Ж. Тех. Физ. СССР*, **20** (1950), 149.
129. ROSENBLATT, J.: *J. appl. Phys.*, **31** (1960), 1371.
130. SCHOTTKY, W.: *Phys. Z.*, **15** (1914), 526.
131. SCHOTTKY, W.: *Phys. Z.*, **15** (1914), 624.
132. SCHOTTKY, W.: *Phys. Z.*, **15** (1914), 656.
133. SPANGENBERG, K.: *J. Franklin Inst.*, **232** (1941), 365.
134. SPANGENBERG K.–HELM, R.–FIELD, L. M.: *Electl. Commun.*, **24** (1947), 101.
135. (SYROVOY, V. A.) Сыровой, В. А.: *Приклад. Мех. Тех. Физ. СССР*, **3** (1963), 26.
136. STERN, F.–GOSSLING, B.–FOWLER, R. H.: *Proc. R. Soc.*, **124–A** (1929), 699.
137. STUART, G. A.–MELTZER, B.: *J. Electron. Control*, **3** (1957), 51.
138. STUART, G. A.–MELTZER, B.: *Proc. Inst. elect. Engrs.*, **105–B** (1959), 928.
139. TAYLOR, N. J.: *4th MOGA*,* 583.

* See p. 483.

140. WALKER, G. B.: *Wireless Engr.*, **24** (1947), 5.
141. WALKER, G. B.: *Proc. Phys. Soc. Lond.*, **63–B** (1950), 1017.
142. WATERMAN, A. T.: *Phys. Rev.*, **38** (1931), 1497.
143. WATERS, W. E.: *J. appl. Phys.*, **29** (1958), 100.
144. WATERS, W. E.: *J. appl. Phys.*, **30** (1959), 368.
145. WATERS, W. E.: *Magnetron Guns — An Exact Theoretical Treatment.* Diamond Ordnance Fuze Lab., Rept. No. TR–843. Washington, D.C., 1960.
146. WATERS, W. E.: *IEEE Trans.*, **ED–10** (1963), 226.
147. WHEATCROFT, E. L. E.: *Proc. Leeds phil. lit. Soc.*, **3** (1938), 498.
148. WRIGHT, D. A.–WOODS, J.: *Proc. Phys. Soc. Lond.*, **65–B** (1952), 134.

d) Space-Charge Flow in the Presence of Thermal Velocities

149. ASH, E. A.: *J. appl. Phys.*, **35** (1964), 298.
150. ATKINSON, H. H.: *4th MOGA,** 559.
151. AUER, P. L.–HURWITZ, H.: *J. appl. Phys.*, **30** (1959), 161.
152. BARUT, A. O.: *Z. angew. Math. Phys.*, **2** (1951), 35.
153. BARUT, A. O.: *Phys. Rev.*, **81** (1951), 274.
154. BELL, D. A.–BERKTAY, H. O.: *J. Electron.*, **2** (1956), 425.
155. (BELLUSTIN, S. V.) Беллустин, С. В.: *ДАН СССР,* **16** (1937), 299.
156. (BELLUSTIN, S. V.) Беллустин, С. В.: *Ж. Экспер. Теор. Физ. СССР,* **9** (1939), 742.
157. (BELLUSTIN, S. V.) Беллустин, С. В.: *Ж. Экспер. Теор. Физ. СССР,* **9** (1939), 840.
158. (BELLUSTIN, S. V.) Беллустин, С. В.: *Ж. Экспер. Теор. Физ. СССР,* **9** (1939), 857.
159. (BELLUSTIN, S. V.) Беллустин, С. В.: *Ж. Физ. СССР,* **1** (1939), 251.
160. (BELLUSTIN, S. V.) Беллустин, С. В.: *Ж. Экспер. Теор. Физ. СССР,* **13** (1943), 230.
161. (BELLUSTIN, S. V.) Беллустин, С. В.: *Ж. Экспер. Теор. Физ. СССР,* **13** (1943), 238.
162. BELOW, F.: *Z. Fernmeldetech.*, **9** (1928), 113.
163. BELOW, F.: *Z. Fernmeldetech.*, **9** (1928), 136.
164. BIRDSALL, C. K.–BRIDGES, W. B.: *J. appl. Phys.*, **32** (1961), 2611.
165. BRIDGES, W. B.–BIRDSALL, C. K.: *J. appl. Phys.*, **34** (1963), 2946.
166. BULL, C. S.: *J. Instn elect. Engrs.*, **92–III** (1945), 86.
167. BULL, C. S.: *J. Instn elect. Engrs.*, **95–III** (1948), 17.
168. BULL, C. S.: *J. Instn elect. Engrs.*, **95–III** (1948), 362.
169. BULL, C. S.: *Proc. Inst. elect. Engrs.*, **97–III** (1950), 159.
170. CARROLL, J. E.: *J. Electron. Control*, **14** (1963), 403.
171. CHISHOLM, T.: *IEEE Trans.*, **ED–15** (1968), 374.
172. COCKBURN, R.: *Proc. Phys. Soc. Lond.*, **47** (1935), 810.
173. COCKBURN, R.: *Proc. Phys. Soc. Lond.*, **50** (1938), 298.
174. COCKBURN, R.: *Proc. Phys. Soc. Lond.*, **50** (1938), 476.
175. COPELAND, P. L.–SACHS, L. M.: *Am. J. Phys.*, **22** (1954), 102.
176. CRANK, J.–HARTREE, D. R.–INGHAM, J.–SLOANE, R. W.: *Proc. Phys. Soc.*, **51–A** (1939), 952.
177. DANIELSON, W. E.–ROSENFELD, J. L.–SALOOM, J. A.: *BSTJ*, **35** (1956), 375.
178. DAVISSON, C. I.: *Phys. Rev.*, **25** (1925), 808.
179. DIEMER, G.–DIJKGRAAF, H.: *Philips Res. Rep.*, **7** (1952), 45.
180. DUNN, D. A.–BORGHI, R. P.–MORWOOD, R. C.: *4th MOGA,** 610.
181. DUNN, D. A.–HO, I. T.: *AIAA J.*, **1** (1963), 2770.
182. EPSTEIN, P. S.: *Verh. dt. phys. Ges.*, **21** (1919), 85.
183. FAY, C. E.–SAMUEL, A. L.–SHOCKLEY, W.: *BSTJ*, **17** (1938), 49.
184. FERRIS, W. R.: *RCAR*, **10** (1949), 134.
185. FERRIS, W. R.: *RCAR*, **11** (1950), 568.
186. FREEMAN, J. J.: *J. Res. nat. Bur. Stand.*, **42** (1949), 75.
187. FRY, T. C.: *Phys. Rev.*, **17** (1921), 441.
188. FRY, T. C.: *Phys. Rev.*, **22** (1923), 445.
189. FÜRTH, R.: *Proc. Phys. Soc. Lond.*, **64–B** (1951), 404.
190. GANS, R.: *Annls. Phys.*, **69** (1922), 385.
191. GANS, R.: *Annls. Phys.*, **70** (1923), 625.
192. GEHRTS, A.: *Phys. Rev.*, **40** (1932), 434.

193. GILL, E. W. B.: *Phil. Mag.*, **49** (1925), 993.
194. GILL, E. W. B.: *Phil. Mag.*, **10** (1930), 134.
195. GUNDLACH, F. W.: *Philips Res. Rep.*, **8** (1953), 419.
196. HAHN, W. C.: *Proc. Instn Radio Engrs.*, **36** (1948), 1115.
197. HARRIES, J. H. O.: *Wireless Engr.*, **13** (1936), 190.
198. HARRIES, J. H. O.: *Wireless Engr.*, **13** (1936), 315.
199. HARRIES, J. H. O.: *Television Soc.*, **2** (1936), 106.
200. HARRIES, J. H. O.: *Wireless Engr.*, **15** (1938), 212.
201. HARRIES, J. H. O.: *Electron. Eng.*, **14** (1942), 586.
202. HERNQUIST, K. G.–KANEFSKY, M.–NORMAN, F. H.: *RCAR*, **19** (1958), 244.
203. ITZKAN, I.: *J. appl. Phys.*, **31** (1960), 652.
204. JAFFE, G.: *Phys. Rev.*, **65** (1944), 91.
205. JAFFE, G.: *Phys. Rev.*, **66** (1944), 30.
206. JONKER, J. L. H.: *Wireless Engr.*, **16** (1939), 274.
207. JONKER, J. L. H.: *Philips Tech. Rev.*, **5** (1940), 131.
208. JONKER, J. L. H.: *Philips Res. Rep.*, **4** (1949), 357.
209. KLEEN, W.–ROTHE, H.: *Z. Phys.*, **104** (1937), 711.
210. KLEIJNEN, P. H. A.: *Philips Res. Rep.*, **1** (1946), 81.
211. KNIPP, J. K.: *Space-Charge between Parallel Plane Grids.* Radiation Laboratory Reports No. 534. Cambridge, Massachusetts, 1944.
212. KNOL, K. S.–DIEMER, G.: *Philips Res. Rep.*, **5** (1950), 131.
213. LANGMUIR, D. B.: *Proc. Instn Radio Engrs.*, **25** (1937), 977.
214. LANGMUIR, I.: *Phys. Rev.*, **21** (1923), 419.
215. LANGMUIR, I.–MOTT-SMITH, H.: *Gen. Elect. Rev.*, **27** (1924).
216. LAW, R. R.: *Proc. Instn Radio Engrs.*, **25** (1937), 954.
217. LAW, R. R.: *Proc. Instn Radio Engrs.*, **30** (1942), 103.
218. LICHTENBERG, A. J.: *J. appl. Phys.*, **35** (1964), 315.
219. LOB, C.: *Potential Distribution in a Hollow Cylinder with Radially Injected Current.* M. S. Thesis, University of Illinois, 1949.
220. LOMAX, R. J.: *J. Electron. Control*, **9** (1960), 127.
221. LOOSJES, R.–VINK, H. J.: *Philips Res. Rep.*, **4** (1949), 449.
222. MACDONALD, D. K. C.–FÜRTH, R.: *Proc. Phys. Soc.*, **59** (1947), 375.
223. MOSS, H.: *Wireless Engr.*, **22** (1945), 316.
224. MOSS, H.: *J. Electron. Control*, **6** (1959), 403.
225. MOTT-SMITH, H.–LANGMUIR, I.: *Phys. Rev.*, **28** (1926), 727.
226. PAGE, L.–ADAMS, N. I.: *Phys. Rev.*, **76** (1949), 381.
227. PIERCE, J. R.: *J. appl. Phys.*, **10** (1939), 715.
228. PIERCE, J. R.: *J. appl. Phys.*, **15** (1944), 721.
229. PIERCE, J. R.: *Phys. Rev.*, **66** (1944), 29.
230. PLATO, G.–KLEEN, W.–ROTHE, H.: *Z. Phys.*, **101** (1936), 509.
231. PORITSKY, H.: *IRE Trans.*, **ED-2** (1953), 60.
232. RAKSHIT, H.: *Phil. Mag.*, **9** (1930), 80.
233. RAMBERG, E. G.–MALTER, L. M.: *J. appl. Phys.*, **23** (1952), 1333.
234. RODDA, S.: *Electron. Engr.*, **17** (1945), 541.
235. RODDA, S.: *Electron. Engr.*, **17** (1945), 589.
236. RODDA, S.: *Electron. Engr.*, **17** (1945), 649.
237. RODDA, S.: *Wireless Engr.*, **23** (1946), 140.
238. RODDA, S.: *Wireless Engr.*, **23** (1946), 202.
239. RODDA, S.: *Electron. Engr.*, **25** (1948), 33.
240. SAKAMOTO, S.: *Lpz. Ber.*, **80** (1928), 217.
241. SALZBERG, B.–HAEFF, A. V.: *RCAR*, **2** (1938), 336.
242. SCHOTTKY, W.: *Verh. dt. Phys. Ges.*, **16** (1914), 490.
243. SCHOTTKY, W.: *Phys. Z.*, **15** (1914), 526.
244. SCHOTTKY, W.: *Phys. Z.*, **15** (1914), 624.
245. SCHOTTKY, W.: *Annls. Phys.*, **44** (1914), 1011.
246. SPENKE, E.: *Wiss. Veröff. Siemens-Werke*, **16** (1937), 19.
247. STRUTT, M. J. O.–VAN DER ZIEL, A.: *Physica*, **5** (1938), 705.
248. STRUTT, M. J. O.–VAN DER ZIEL, A.: *Physica*, **6** (1939), 977.
249. TIEN, P. K.–MOSHMAN, J.: *J. appl. Phys.*, **27** (1956), 1067.
250. TONKS, L.: *Phys. Rev.*, **30** (1927), 501.

251. Tschopp, P. A.: *Scientia elect.*, **7** (1961), 3.
252. Wadhwa, R. P.–Buneman, O.–Brauch, D. F.: *AIAA J.*, **3** (1965), 1076.
253. Walker, G. B.: *Wireless Engr.*, **22** (1945), 157.
254. Walker, G. B.: *Wireless Engr.*, **22** (1945), 212.
255. Walker, G. B.: *Wireless Engr.*, **22** (1945), 276.
256. Wallmark, J. T.: *J. appl. Phys.*, **23** (1952), 1096.
257. Wheatcroft, E. L. E.: *J. Instn elect. Engrs.*, **86** (1940), 473.
258. Wheatcroft, E. L. E.: *J. Instn elect. Engrs.*, **87** (1940), 691.
259. Van der Ziel, A.: *Philips Res. Rep.*, **1** (1946), 91.
260. Van der Ziel, A.: *Appl. scient. Res.*, **1** (1948), 105.

III. ELECTRON GUNS

MIKLÓS SZILÁGYI

In this chapter electron guns, i.e. systems producing electron beams with high current density, are briefly surveyed.

In cathode-ray tubes, electron microscopes, etc. we have currents from a few microamperes to several milliamperes, while the voltages are several kilovolts. Such electron beams may be produced by systems consisting of a cathode, a *Wehnelt's* cylinder and an accelerating electrode. Electrons leaving the cathode are focused by the electric field of the *Wehnelt's* cylinder and the accelerating electrode. At the same time the electrons gain sufficient energy from the accelerating field, to produce the beam. For the calculation of such systems approximative methods are mostly used. We shall not deal with these methods here. The reader can find adequate data in the literature [1–10].

With the appearance of the microwave tubes, electron-beam technology, etc. electron beams with high currents and relatively low voltages became necessary. In these beams space-charge plays a role of great importance. Electron guns used for low-current beams are not suitable for producing high-current electron beams. It was necessary to look for a new principle.

It was J. R. Pierce who solved this problem ingeniously. The *Pierce* gun has become almost the unique solution of the problem. Up to now, no significant *fundamental* idea has appeared in this field. However, great progress has been achieved in improvement of the guns, by taking new effects into account and developing new methods of calculation. For this reason we shall consider in detail the theory and different types of the *Pierce* gun.

40. THE BASIC PRINCIPLE OF THE PIERCE GUN

We have dealt with the theory of space-charge flow in Chapter II. If we consider only a certain group of particles in the flow, i.e. a beam taken out of the flow, while the other electrons are abandoned, the form of the beam will be altered by the absence of the abandoned space-charge. It was Pierce's idea in 1940 [36] to represent the influence of the electrons of the region outside the beam by the electric field of electrodes with suitably chosen forms and potentials. In that way an electron beam of arbitrary form may be produced if only we can find a suitable space-charge flow, of which the given beam may be taken out.

The electron flow inside the beam should be exactly the same as it was when the beam was surrounded by the electrons of the region outside the beam. Obviously, we can achieve this requirement only by using additional forces in the charge-free region. The conditions of the electron flow will not be altered if the following requirements are satisfied:

(i) The potential distribution inside the beam should be determined by the original space-charge flow.

(ii) There should not exist forces in the beam acting normally to the direction of the flow.

These requirements are valid inside the beam as well as at its boundaries. If one solves the *Laplace* equation

$$\Delta\varphi = 0$$

for the charge-free region surrounding the beam with these boundary conditions, the distribution of the electric field representing the abandoned flow can be calculated. With the knowledge of this distribution one can determine the electrode shapes of the *Pierce* gun. This is the complete solution of the problem.

The solution of *Laplace*'s equation with the boundary conditions of the above type is the well-known *Cauchy* problem. This problem can be solved in terms of tabulated functions only in a few instances [31, 38]. It can be shown that, if there exists a solution, this is the only solution. The solution is usually highly sensitive to the alterations of the boundary conditions [34]. The solution is given in most cases in the form of a convergent series. It is also possible to transform the problem into a *Dirichlet* problem. Numerical solutions are less convenient, in our opinion, for this type of problem, because of the above-mentioned sensitivity to the alterations of the boundary conditions. However, an advantage of this sensitivity can be mentioned: minor alterations of the electrode shapes (especially the shape of the electrode held at higher potential) by technological reasons do not cause considerable disturbances in the operation of the gun: the beam adjusts itself to the new electrodes.

Thus, the *Pierce* gun consists of a cathode emitting the electrons (this is usually an oxide-coated cathode) and electrodes, the shapes of which are determined by the above method. The shape of the cathode depends on the form of the given beam, i.e. the kind of the space-charge flow taken as a starting point. The emission of the cathode must be very high. The design of an electron gun is based on the 3/2-power law of the space-charge flow (see § 32). This means that the accelerating voltage determines the current of the beam produced by an electron gun with given geometric dimensions.

The most practically important types of electron guns will now be surveyed. We shall consider electron beams only with straight edge trajectories, so the appropriate kinds of rectilinear space-charge flow will serve as starting points. We should like to emphasise that our treatment of electron guns is based on the approximations outlined in the Preface and stated in detail in § 47. The most important of these approximations is that the influence of the initial velocity distribution of the electrons (thermal velocities) is neglected.

(A) ELECTRON GUNS PRODUCING PARALLEL BEAMS

41. PRODUCTION OF STRIP ELECTRON BEAMS

For its simplicity, the *Pierce* gun producing strip electron beams will be considered first [35, 36]. (Strip beams are used in some types of microwave tubes.) The strip beam is formed by electrons moving along parallel rectilinear paths. The cross-section of the beam is a rectangle extended in the direction of the x axis (figure III.1). The space-charge forces are practically not acting in that direction (with the exception of the edges), so the whole analysis can be limited to the (y, z) plane. This is the case if the condition

$$W \gg y_0$$

is satisfied (see figure III.1).

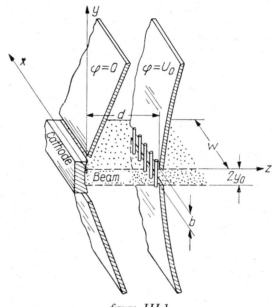

figure III.1

It is obvious in this case that we must start from the rectilinear space-charge flow between two parallel boundless planes (§ 34). The two conditions given in § 40 require in this case that at the edge of the beam, i.e. in the plane $y = 0$:
1. the potential distribution should be given by 34.34 and
2. the field strength should not have a component in the y direction.
Thus, the problem is to solve the *Laplace* equation

$$\frac{\partial^2 \varphi}{\partial y^2} + \frac{\partial^2 \varphi}{\partial z^2} = 0 \qquad\qquad 41.1$$

with the following boundary conditions

$$\left.\begin{array}{l} \varphi(0, z) = \varPhi(z) = Az^{4/3} \\[2mm] \dfrac{\partial \varphi}{\partial y}\bigg|_{y=0} = 0 \end{array}\right\} \qquad\qquad 41.2$$

where

$$A = \left(\frac{9I}{8\sqrt{2}\sqrt{\eta}\varepsilon_0 W y_0} \right)^{2/3} = 5.69 \times 10^3 \ j^{2/3} \quad [Vm^{-4/3}] \qquad 41.3$$

Solving this equation we obtain the electric field distribution necessary for the production of a strip beam. The electrode shapes are to be calculated from this distribution. The result does not depend on the beam width; the boundary conditions are the same in the plane $y = -2y_0$, so the result of the solution will also be the same at the opposite edge of the beam.

The solution of this problem is given by [2]

$$\varphi(y, z) = Re[\Phi(z + iy)] = \frac{1}{2} [\Phi(z + iy) + \Phi(z - iy)] \qquad 41.4$$

This potential distribution can be realised by two pairs of suitably shaped electrodes (figure III.1). Usually, one pair of electrodes adjoins the cathode held at zero potential while the other adjoins the anode held at potential U_0. Our task is to determine the equipotential surfaces as the electrode shapes coincide with these surfaces. Let us substitute 41.2 for Φ in 41.4, obtaining the following expression

$$\varphi(y, z) = Re[A(z + iy)^{4/3}] \qquad 41.5$$

If R is the absolute value and α is the argument of the complex number $(z + iy)$ we have

$$R = (y^2 + z^2)^{1/2} \quad \text{and} \quad \alpha = \arctan \frac{y}{z} \qquad 41.6$$

Using this notation, the following well-known formula can be written as

$$(z + iy)^{4/3} = R^{4/3} \left(\cos \frac{4}{3} \alpha + i \sin \frac{4}{3} \alpha \right)$$

Hence

$$\varphi(y, z) = A R^{4/3} \cos \frac{4}{3} \alpha \qquad 41.7$$

is the solution of equation 41.1. Substituting $\varphi = $ const. in 41.7 we obtain the form of the equipotential surfaces.

The electrode held at zero potential adjoins the cathode which is situated at the origin of the coordinate system used in figure III.1. The electrode shape is determined by 41.6 and 41.7 as follows

$$\alpha = \arctan \frac{y}{z} = \frac{3}{4} \frac{\pi}{2} (2k + 1) \qquad 41.8$$

Considering the value of the integer k to be equal to zero we find that the section of the zero potential electrode by the plane (y, z) is a straight line starting from the origin and having an angle of

$$\alpha = \frac{3\pi}{8} = 67.5 \quad \text{deg} \tag{41.9}$$

with the z axis. The value 67.5 deg is characteristic of all *Pierce* guns: although the zero potential electrode is not plane in other cases, this electrode always reaches the beam boundary at the same angle [38]. The influence of an alteration of this initial angle has been investigated [33].

Substituting $k = 1$ in 41.8 we obtain $\alpha = 202.5$ deg; the equipotential line is continued in the third quadrant (figure III.2). Expression 41.8 is not valid for $k \geq 2$.

Let us suppose that the plane of the anode held at potential U_0 is situated at a distance d from the cathode. Then, using 34.43, one can rewrite 41.3 as follows

$$A = \frac{U_0}{d^{4/3}} \tag{41.10}$$

The equation of the U_0 equipotential surface is

$$U_0 = \frac{U_0}{d^{4/3}} R^{4/3} \cos^{4/3} \alpha \tag{41.11}$$

Taking 41.6 into consideration, this equation can be rewritten as follows

$$\left[\left(\frac{z}{d} \right)^2 + \left(\frac{y}{d} \right)^2 \right]^{2/3} \times \cos \left[\frac{4}{3} \arctan \frac{\left(\dfrac{y}{d} \right)}{\left(\dfrac{z}{d} \right)} \right] = 1 \tag{41.12}$$

It is obvious from the form of this expression that the shape of the equipotential surface does not depend on U_0 and d. This means that the second electrode can be separated from the cathode by any distance and held at any potential. Thus, the U_0 potential electrode starts from the point with coordinates $(0, d)$. Its shape will be determined by the solution of the transcendental equation 41.12.

Substituting $\varphi = aU_0$ in equation 41.7 we obtain

$$\left[\left(\frac{z}{d} \right)^2 + \left(\frac{y}{d} \right)^2 \right]^{2/3} \times \cos \left[\frac{4}{3} \arctan \frac{\left(\dfrac{y}{d} \right)}{\left(\dfrac{z}{d} \right)} \right] = a \tag{41.13}$$

The shape of an arbitrary equipotential surface is determined by this equation (a being an arbitrary real number). We should like to note that calculating the value of $\alpha = \arctan [(y/d)/(z/d)]$ one must always take into

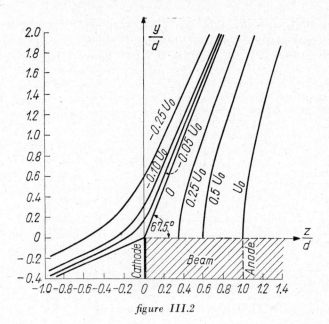

figure III.2

consideration the quadrant in which the given point with coordinates (y, z) is situated.

The shapes of the equipotential surfaces calculated by the above method are shown in figure III.2 [35].

There exists a relationship between the parameters of the gun and the electron beam, derived from 34.42

$$P = \frac{I}{U_0^{3/2}} = \frac{8\sqrt{2}\sqrt{\eta}\varepsilon_0 W y_0}{9d^2} = 4.67 \times 10^{-6} \frac{W y_0}{d^2} \; [\mathrm{AV}^{-3/2}] \qquad 41.14$$

where P is the ratio of the beam current and the 3/2 power of the accelerating voltage. This ratio is usually called the *perveance* of the system. Expression 41.14 gives us the characteristic property of a *Pierce* gun, i.e. the perveance of the beam produced by an electron gun is fully determined by the geometric dimensions of the gun and the beam. Except for geometric data, only the current *or* the voltage can be given arbitrarily; the other value follows from the given parameters. Naturally, this argument is also valid inversely: the relationship between geometric data of the electron gun being fully determined by the perveance. This means that only four of the five parameters in 41.14 can be given as starting data for the gun design.

It also follows from 41.14 that the maximum value of the beam perveance is about 10^{-6} A/V$^{3/2}$ in this type of electron gun. This is so because $y_0 \ll d$ and the beam width W is usually of the same order of magnitude as the distance d.

Thus, the gun consists of a flat cathode in the form of an extended rectangle, a pair of zero potential electrodes (beam-forming electrodes) and a pair of electrodes held at potential U_0 (see figure III.1). (Negative equipotentials can also be chosen for the beam-forming electrodes). This system enables the rectilinear motion of the electron beam emitted by the cathode to be normal to its surface direction, parallel with the axis.

A gun of this type produces a strip electron beam with given cross section moving in the direction of the z axis and accelerated to a voltage U_0.

We have to draw the reader's attention to a very important circumstance. This treatment is strictly valid only when the beam moves between two *plane surfaces*. But this is possible only if the output slit of the gun is closed by a metal surface held at potential U_0; then the electrons cannot leave the gun. Because of this, a metal grid or mesh should be used at the output of the gun (see figure III.1). Although even this system has great disadvantages: it disturbs the potential and picks up a considerable part of the beam current. For this reason the grid is not used in practice. We introduce a slit between the two anode electrodes, instead of a surface held at potential U_0. Although this is not the case we have dealt with, if the slit is sufficiently narrow, the difference is not too great. In this case one can assume that the gun produces the same electron beam, with the output slit acting as a divergent lens. The larger the slit aperture b compared with the distance d, the stronger the lens effect. This must be taken into account in the gun design.

The value of the focal length (defined as the distance between the principal plane and the respective focal plane of a lens) of a narrow slit is given by [4]

$$f = \frac{2U_0}{E_1 - E_2} + \frac{b}{2} \qquad 41.15$$

where E_1 and E_2 are the electric field strengths on the left and right side of the slit, respectively.

If there is a uniform potential U_0 after the anode electrodes, we have $E_2 = 0$. The value of E_1 can be calculated from 41.2 and 41.10. Hence

$$E_1 = -\frac{d\Phi}{dz}\bigg|_{z=d} = -\frac{4U_0}{3d} \quad \text{and} \quad E_2 = 0 \qquad 41.16$$

Naturally, these expressions are approximative because the anode slit has an effect on the potential distribution, too. We obtain from 41.15 and 41.16

$$f = -\frac{3}{2} d \left(1 - \frac{b}{3d}\right) \qquad 41.17$$

The focal length is negative (divergent lens), a divergent beam leaves the gun, and the spreading of the beam increases further due to space-charge forces in the uniform potential region (see § 54). For the calculation of the spreading, 41.17 should be substituted for the focal length and 41.14 for the perveance in expression 54.12. Using 54.2, 54.3 and 54.7 one can obtain the form of the beam from 54.12. Thus, we have succeeded in separating the diverging effect of the slit and the space-charge effect from each other and the gun. This is an important method for simplifying the design of guns. It should once again be emphasised that this method is applicable only for small values of b/d.

If one wishes to maintain the cross section of the beam constant in the region behind the gun, a further focusing device must be used. This problem will be dealt with in detail in Chapters V and VI.

42. PRODUCTION OF CYLINDRICAL ELECTRON BEAMS

The rectilinear space-charge flow between parallel boundless planes can be used for the production of cylindrical beams. In this case a cylinder with constant radius r_0 is taken from the flow. The influence of the abandoned space charge is represented by the electric field of properly shaped electrodes (figure III.3) [35]. The system is axially symmetric, thus the cylindrical

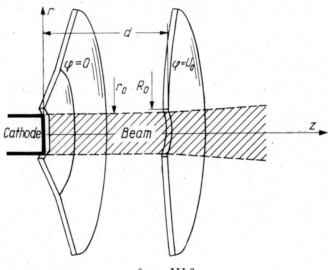

figure III.3

system of coordinates r, α, z is convenient: the whole analysis can be carried out using only two coordinates (r and z). In order to find the necessary electrode shapes we must solve the *Laplace* equation

$$\frac{1}{r}\frac{\partial\varphi}{\partial r} + \frac{\partial^2\varphi}{\partial r^2} + \frac{\partial^2\varphi}{\partial z^2} = 0 \qquad\qquad 42.1$$

in the region $r_0 \leq r < \infty$ (r_0 is the radius of the beam). As in the previous case, we have the following two boundary conditions

$$\left.\begin{array}{l} \varphi(r_0, z) = A\, z^{4/3} \\[2mm] \dfrac{\partial \varphi}{\partial r}\Big|_{r=r_0} = 0 \end{array}\right\} \qquad 42.2$$

where

$$A = \left(\frac{9I}{4\sqrt{2\pi}\sqrt{\eta \varepsilon_0 r_0^2}}\right)^{2/3} = 5.69 \times 10^3\, j^{2/3} \quad [\text{Vm}^{-4/3}] \qquad 42.3$$

Let us write the solution in the following way [15]

$$\varphi(r, z) = A\, z^{4/3} \sum_{n=0}^{\infty} \left(\frac{r_0}{z}\right)^n F_n\left(\frac{r}{r_0}\right) \qquad 42.4$$

Thus, the problem is reduced to the determination of the functions F_n. Let us calculate the appropriate derivatives of 42.4 and substitute them into equation 42.1 to obtain

$$\sum_{n=0}^{\infty} \left\{ \frac{z^2}{r}\left(\frac{r_0}{z}\right)^n \frac{dF_n}{dr} + z^2 \left(\frac{r_0}{z}\right)^n \frac{d^2 F_n}{dr^2} + \right.$$
$$\left. + \left(\frac{1}{3} - n\right)\left(\frac{4}{3} - n\right)\left(\frac{r_0}{z}\right)^n F_n \right\} = 0 \qquad 42.5$$

This equality is satisfied if the sums of the terms with like powers of z are equal to zero, i.e.

$$\frac{1}{r}\frac{dF_0}{dr} + \frac{d^2 F_0}{dr^2} = 0 \qquad 42.6$$

$$\frac{1}{r}\frac{dF_1}{dr} + \frac{d^2 F_1}{dr^2} = 0 \qquad 42.7$$

and

$$r_0^2 \left(\frac{1}{r}\frac{dF_{k+2}}{dr} + \frac{d^2 F_{k+2}}{dr^2}\right) + \left(\frac{1}{3} - k\right)\left(\frac{4}{3} - k\right) F_k = 0 \qquad 42.8$$

$$(k = 0, 1, 2, ..)$$

From the boundary conditions 42.2 we obtain

$$\left.\begin{array}{l} F_0(1) = 1 \\ F_{k+1}(1) = 0 \\ \dfrac{dF_k}{dr}(1) = 0 \end{array}\right\} \qquad 42.9$$

Using 42.9 we can easily find the solution of equations 42.6 and 42.7

$$F_0\left(\frac{r}{r_0}\right) = 1 \qquad\qquad 42.10$$

and

$$F_1\left(\frac{r}{r_0}\right) = 0 \qquad\qquad 42.11$$

Let us deal now with the solution of equation 42.8. It is seen immediately that for the case of odd indices the result is zero

$$F_{2m+1}\left(\frac{r}{r_0}\right) = 0 \qquad\qquad 42.12$$

$$(m = 0, 1, 2, \ldots)$$

The solution of equation 42.8 can be obtained by variation of constants in case of even indices

$$F_2\left(\frac{r}{r_0}\right) = -\frac{1}{9}\left[\left(\frac{r}{r_0}\right)^2 - 2\log\frac{r}{r_0} - 1\right] \qquad 42.13$$

and

$$F_4\left(\frac{r}{r_0}\right) = \frac{5}{648}\left\{\left(\frac{r}{r_0}\right)^4 - 8\left(\frac{r}{r_0}\right)^2\left(\log\frac{r}{r_0} - \frac{1}{2}\right) - 4\log\frac{r}{r_0} - 5\right\} \qquad 42.14$$

The functions F_2 and F_4 are listed in table III.1 for several values of r/r_0. (Values of $r/r_0 < 1$ will be needed in the next section.)

It can be seen from table III.1 and equation 42.4 that at large values of z and small values of r the series quickly converges. Thus, the equipotential surfaces near the beam edge and far from the cathode can be found with sufficient accuracy, neglecting the terms with powers $n \geq 5$ in the series

TABLE III.1

$\dfrac{r}{r_0}$	$F_2\left(\dfrac{r}{r_0}\right)$	$F_4\left(\dfrac{r}{r_0}\right)$
0.1	-0.4016	0.0342
0.2	-0.2508	0.0166
0.4	-0.1103	0.0039
0.6	-0.0423	0.0006
0.8	-0.0096	0.0002
1.0	0.0000	0.0000
1.5	-0.0488	0.0088
2.0	-0.1793	0.0158
3.0	-0.6448	0.2219
4.0	-1.3586	1.020
5.0	-2.3090	3.022

42.4. Let us consider, for example, an equipotential surface which cuts the beam at a distance z_0 from the cathode. According to 42.2, the potential of this surface is equal to

$$\varphi = A \, z_0^{4/3}$$

Substituting this into 42.4 and taking the foregoing into account, we obtain

$$\left(\frac{\dfrac{z_0}{r_0}}{\dfrac{z}{r_0}} \right)^{4/3} \approx 1 + \left(\frac{r_0}{z} \right)^2 F_2 \left(\frac{r}{r_0} \right) + \left(\frac{r_0}{z} \right)^4 F_4 \left(\frac{r}{r_0} \right) \qquad 42.15$$

where the functions F_2 and F_4 are given in 42.13 and 42.14. Expression 42.15 determines the shape of an equipotential surface near the beam edge and far from the cathode.

Comparing 42.15 with 41.13, one notices an essential difference. In the case of the strip beam the electrode shape does not depend on the cathode–anode distance d. However, in the case of the cylindrical beam we have obtained the electrode shape in r_0 units. That means that the form of the equipotential surface depends on the value of the ratio d/r_0, the value of d being independent of r_0.

The series 42.4 is divergent for small values of z. Thus, the shapes of the equipotential surfaces near the cathode are to be determined in another way. If we restrict the analysis to the region near the beam edge, the solution of equation 42.1 will be as follows [15]

$$\varphi(r, z) \approx A \, R^{4/3} \left[\cos \frac{4}{3} \alpha + \frac{R}{4r_0} \left(\sin \frac{\alpha}{3} - \frac{1}{7} \sin \frac{7\alpha}{3} \right) + \right.$$

$$\left. + \left(\frac{R}{2r_0} \right)^2 \left(\frac{9}{28} \cos \frac{10\alpha}{3} + \frac{3}{7} \cos \frac{4\alpha}{3} - \frac{3}{4} \cos \frac{2\alpha}{3} \right) \right] \qquad 42.16$$

where

$$R = [(r - r_0)^2 + z^2]^{1/2} \qquad 42.17$$

and

$$\alpha = \arctan \frac{r - r_0}{z} \qquad 42.18$$

Expression 42.16 is valid for $R < r_0$. We obtain the equation determining the shape of the zero potential electrode by making 42.16 equal to zero. This electrode adjoins the cathode, having an angle of 67.5 deg with the edge of the beam. In this case the plane section of the electrode is not a straight line.

We can determine the electrode shapes near the beam edge by means of the approximate expressions 42.15 and 42.16. The solution is more complicated for larger values of r [15, 38]. One can obtain the solution also by other approximate methods [20, 27]. The shape of the anode electrode can be approximated to a spherical surface with a radius of curvature $6d$.

As we can see, the determination of the electrode shapes is a very complicated problem even in the case of an approximate solution. In fact, at best the solution is given in the form of a transcendental equation. It takes troublesome calculations to get actual numerical results from such a solution. For this reason the analog method which was also proposed by Pierce [36] is of great practical importance. He obtained the electrode shapes by means of an ordinary electrolytic tank, without any special technique for the simulation of space-charge. The method is very ingenious and simple. A piece of insulating material inserted in the electrolyte represents the electron beam. This insures that the radial component of the field will be zero, as the current lines in the electrolyte are always parallel to the boundaries of the insulating material near these boundaries. So, there will be no radial force at the beam edge.

The only task now is to insure the potential distribution determined by 42.2 along the beam edge. Suitably adjusting the shapes and positions of the electrodes in the tank, we have to measure the potential distribution along the insulating material, until it coincides strictly with that given by 42.2. We then have rectilinear parallel space-charge flow in the beam.

The shapes of the equipotential surfaces obtained in this way are shown in figure III.4 [35]. The two electrodes usually adjoin the cathode and the gun output held at potential U_0. The values of the potentials are not given in the figure, as the value of the ratio d/r_0 can be chosen arbitrarily (if the beam perveance is not given *a priori*) and the shape of the equipotential U_0 will be different in every case.

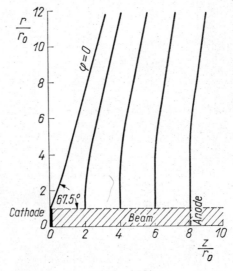

figure III.4

The equipotential lines given in the figure closely coincide near the beam edge with those calculated by means of 42.15 and 42.16.

We should like to note that the potential distribution given by 42.2 can also be obtained by means of a series of suitably situated diaphragms [37].

The following relationship can be derived from 34.42 between the parameters of the gun and the electron beam under discussion

$$P = \frac{I}{U_0^{3/2}} = \frac{4\sqrt{2}\pi\sqrt{\eta}\varepsilon_0 r_0^2}{9d^2} = 7.33 \times 10^{-6} \frac{r_0^2}{d^2} \quad [\mathrm{AV}^{-3/2}] \qquad 42.19$$

As in most cases $r_0 \ll d$, the maximum value of the beam perveance cannot exceed 10^{-6} A/V$^{3/2}$ in this type of electron guns. Naturally, only three of the four parameters in 42.19 can be given as arbitrary starting data for the gun design.

In this case the gun consists of a flat cathode of the form of a disc, a mostly zero potential beam-forming electrode and an electrode held at potential U_0. The electrodes are axially symmetric, their intersected axonometric projection is shown in figure III.3. This gun produces a solid cylindrical electron beam with given cross section moving in the direction of the z axis and accelerated to a voltage U_0.

We should like to draw the reader's attention once again to the fact that the above treatment is strictly valid only in the case when the beam moves between two *plane surfaces*. As in practice we have a hole in the anode electrode at the output of the gun, we will not have a surface held exactly at potential U_0. Though if the radius R_0 of the hole is small enough, the variation from this will not be great. In this case we assume that the gun produces the same electron beam but the hole in the second electrode acts as a divergent lens (circular diaphragm). The larger is the ratio of R_0/d, the stronger is the lens effect.

The focal length of a circular diaphragm is given by [4]

$$f = \frac{4U_0}{E_1 - E_2} + \frac{4R_0}{\pi} \qquad 42.20$$

where E_1 and E_2 are the electric field strengths on the left and right side of the diaphragm, respectively.

If we have a uniform potential U_0 behind the hole, the approximate expressions 41.16 can be used and

$$E_1 = -\frac{4U_0}{3d} \quad \text{and} \quad E_2 = 0 \qquad 42.21$$

We obtain from 42.20 and 42.21

$$f = -3d \left(1 - \frac{4}{3\pi}\frac{R_0}{d}\right) \qquad 42.22$$

The focal length of this divergent lens is nearly twice as large as that of the two-dimensional slit in case of a strip beam. The diverging effect of the hole is weaker.

14*

Thus, a divergent beam leaves the gun. The spreading of the beam further increases due to space-charge forces in the uniform potential drift region. In this U_0 uniform potential region behind the gun the motion of the beam can be calculated using § 53. For the calculation of the spreading, 42.22 should be substituted for the focal length and 42.19 for the perveance in 53.30. Using values from table IV.2, 53.2, 53.3 and 53.24 we can obtain the beam profile from 53.30. Thus, we have separated the diverging effect of the hole and the space-charge effect from each other and both of them from the gun, in case of small values of the ratio R_0/d.

If we wish to maintain the cross section of the beam constant in the region behind the gun, a further focusing device must be used (see Chapters V and VI).

43. PRODUCTION OF HOLLOW ELECTRON BEAMS

Let us cut out a tubular beam confined by an external cylinder with radius b and an internal cylinder with radius a of the rectilinear space-charge flow between parallel boundless planes (figure III.5). The influence of the abandoned space-charge is to be represented by the electric field of properly shaped electrodes. This is a *Pierce* gun producing a hollow electron beam.

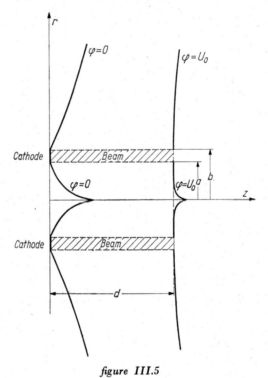

figure III.5

It is easy to see that this type is a special case of the gun producing a cylindrical electron beam.

Indeed, the *Laplace* equation 42.1 is to be resolved in the region outside the beam and the boundary conditions 42.2 are to be satisfied on the beam-edge surfaces, where

$$A = \left[\frac{9I}{4\sqrt{2\pi}\sqrt{\eta}\,\varepsilon_0(b^2 - a^2)} \right]^{2/3} \tag{43.1}$$

Naturally, the solution will coincide with the results obtained in the previous section. The electrode shapes outside the beam will again be the same as shown in figure III.4. (Of course, in this case b must be substituted for r_0.) In order to insure the given beam configuration it is necessary now to use electrodes also in the charge-free region inside the beam (figure III.5).

The electrode shapes inside the beam can be determined also from the results of § 42 substituting a for r_0 in the formulae. The only essential difference between the external and internal electrodes is that $r \geq b$ for the external electrodes, while $r \leq a$ in case of the internal electrodes. That causes a difference in the shapes of the equipotential surfaces, although the same formulae can be used in both cases. The shapes of the internal equipotential surfaces determined by expressions 42.15 and 42.16 and table III.1 are shown in figure III.6 [15]. (The approximations lead in this case to very correct results because of smallness of r.) It is seen in the figure that the zero potential electrode has an angle of 67.5 deg with the edge of the beam from inside, too. The values of the potentials are not given in this figure, either, as the shape of the equipotential U_0 depends on the value of the ratio of d/a.

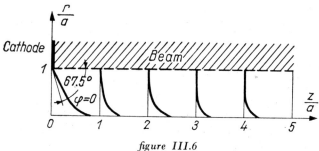

figure III.6

We have the following relationship between the parameters of the gun and the electron beam

$$P = \frac{I}{U_0^{3/2}} = \frac{4\sqrt{2\pi}\sqrt{\eta}\,\varepsilon_0(b^2 - a^2)}{9d^2} =$$

$$= 7.33 \times 10^{-6} \frac{b^2 - a^2}{d^2} \quad [\text{AV}^{-3/2}] \tag{43.2}$$

Only four of the five parameters in 43.2 can be chosen arbitrarily. The maximum value of the beam perveance is relatively small in this electron gun type.

The gun consists of a flat cathode of the form of a ring, the external and internal beam-forming electrodes and the external and internal electrodes held at potential U_0. The section of the gun is shown in figure III.5. The gun produces a hollow electron beam with constant annular cross section moving in the direction of the z axis and accelerated to voltage U_0.

The annular hole between the anode electrodes acts as a divergent lens in this case, too. The larger is the value of the ratio $[(b-a)/a]$, the stronger is the lens effect. A divergent electron beam leaves the gun. The spreading of the beam increases further due to space-charge forces. If we have a uniform potential region behind the gun the beam motion can be calculated by the use of § 55. If one wishes to maintain the cross section of the beam constant in the region behind the gun, a further focusing device must be used.

This type of electron gun is commonly used because hollow beams are desirable in many electron-beam devices. Electron guns producing hollow beams have been investigated by a number of authors [19, 21–23, 25, 30, 32, 41–43].

(B) ELECTRON GUNS PRODUCING CONVERGENT BEAMS

44. PRODUCTION OF PLANE-SYMMETRIC CONVERGENT BEAMS
(WEDGE-BEAMS)

Let us suppose that we need a strip beam in which the electrons are moving not along parallel paths but along converging rectilinear paths. In this case we must start from the rectilinear space-charge flow between two coaxial cylinders (§ 35). We shall assume that the electrons flow from the external cylindrical surface held at zero potential and having a radius R_k towards the internal cylinder held at potential U_0 with radius R_a. We shall use the rectangular Cartesian coordinate system, the x axis of which is directed parallel to the common axis of the cylinders. If the length L of the cylinders is large enough, the whole analysis can be carried out in the (y, z) plane (figure III.7), normal to the axis.

Let us cut out a wedge with half angle α_0 of the system, so that the edge should coincide with the common axis of the cylinders. If we represent the influence of the abandoned space-charge by the electric field of properly shaped electrodes, the rectilinear space-charge flow inside the wedge beam will be maintained unaltered.

Naturally, the beam current I will be smaller than the current occurring in § 35 because the cross section of the flow is smaller. The current density remains unaltered. Hence, the beam current can be calculated from the following expression

$$I = \frac{\alpha_0}{\pi} I_t \qquad\qquad 44.1$$

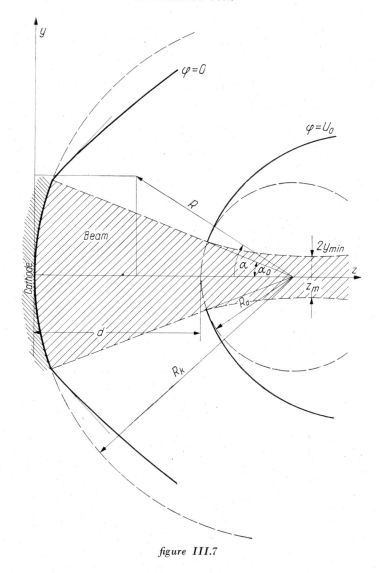

figure III.7

where I_t is the total current determined by expression 35.4. The relationship 44.1 must be taken into account in the following treatment.

For the determination of the electrode shapes it is convenient to introduce the polar coordinate system R, α the origin of which coincides with the intersection point of the common axis of the cylinders with the y, z plane (figure III.7). We have

$$R = [y^2 + (R_k - z)^2]^{1/2} \quad \text{and} \quad \alpha = \arctan \frac{y}{R_k - z} \qquad 44.2$$

The problem is then to solve the *Laplace* equation

$$\frac{1}{R}\frac{\partial\varphi}{\partial R} + \frac{\partial^2\varphi}{\partial R^2} + \frac{1}{R^2}\frac{\partial^2\varphi}{\partial\alpha^2} = 0 \qquad 44.3$$

in the region $\alpha \geq \alpha_0$. (It is sufficient to find the solution only on one side of the beam because of the symmetry.) The boundary conditions require that at the beam edge forces should not act in the α direction and the potential distribution should follow 35.10. Using 44.1 we obtain

$$\varphi(R, \alpha_0) = BR^{2/3} [H(R)]^{4/3}$$

and

$$\left.\frac{\partial\varphi}{\partial\alpha}\right|_{\alpha=\alpha_0} = 0 \qquad\qquad 44.4$$

where

$$B = \left[\frac{9I}{8\sqrt{2}\,\varepsilon_0\sqrt{\eta}L\alpha_0}\right]^{2/3} \qquad 44.5$$

$H(R)$ is the function determined by 35.21 and given in table II.3 $(R_1 = R_k)$. The solution of the problem is given by [38]

$$\varphi(R, \alpha) = \mathrm{Re}\left\{B\omega^{4/3}\sum_{n=1}^{\infty} b_n\omega^{n-1}\right\} \qquad 44.6$$

where

$$\omega = \log\frac{R}{R_k} + i(\alpha - \alpha_0) \qquad 44.7$$

and the first six values of the coefficients b_n are listed in table III.2. The solution has been found in another form by [13, 29].

The shapes of the equipotential lines are shown in figure III.8 [38]. The shape of the anode electrode held at potential U_0 depends on the value of the ratio R_k/R_a. The scale of the figure is given in R_k units.

TABLE III.2

n	b_n
1	1.0000
2	0.1333
3	0.02444
4	0.003924
5	0.0005298
6	0.00006972

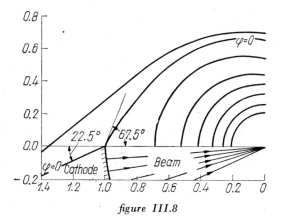

figure III.8

We have the following relationship between the parameters of the gun and the electron beam, using 35.30 and 44.1

$$P = \frac{I}{U_0^{3/2}} = \frac{8\sqrt{2}\varepsilon_0\sqrt{\eta}L\alpha_0}{9R_aH^2(R_a)} = 4.67 \times 10^{-6}\,\frac{L\alpha_0}{R_aH^2(R_a)} \quad [AV^{-3/2}] \quad 44.8$$

The gun design should be carried out on the basis of this formula.

The gun consists of a cylindrical cathode, a pair of zero-potential beam-forming electrodes and a pair of electrodes held at potential U_0 (figure III.7). The gun produces a plane-symmetric electron beam moving in the direction of the z axis and accelerated to voltage U_0.

The diverging effect of the slit between the anode electrodes causes the angle of the beam edge with the z axis to be altered at the output of the gun. One can assume approximately that the divergent lens formed by the anode slit is superimposed on a convergent lens with focal length R_a, for the beam was originally converging towards the axis. The resultant focal length of these two lenses determines the initial condition for the further motion of the electron beam. If there is a uniform potential region behind the gun, the beam motion can be described with the use of § 54. The convergence of the beam will gradually decrease due to space-charge forces until the beam becomes divergent [11, 28] (figure III.7). If we wish to get an electron beam with uniform cross section from the gun, the focusing device should be adjusted to the position of the minimum cross section of the beam (z_m).

45. PRODUCTION OF AXIALLY SYMMETRIC CONVERGENT BEAMS
(CONICAL BEAMS)

This electron gun type will be analysed in detail because axially symmetric convergent beams are used the most frequently.

We shall start from the rectilinear space-charge flow between two concentric spheres (§ 36). We shall assume that the electrons flow from the external spherical surface held at zero potential and having a radius R_k towards the internal spherical surface with radius R_a and potential U_0. Let us cut out a cone of the system, with half angle ϑ_0, so that the apex of the cone should coincide with the common centre of the spheres (figure III.9). In order to maintain the rectilinear space-charge flow, the abandoned space-charge must be represented by the electric field of properly shaped electrodes. By doing this one can see that a convergent axially symmetric electron beam will be formed in which the electrons will be moving along recti-linear paths.

The beam current I will again be smaller than the current occurring in § 36 because the cross section of the flow is smaller. The solid angle of a cone with half-angle ϑ_0 is equal to

$$\Omega = 2\pi(1 - \cos\vartheta_0) \qquad 45.1$$

The cross section of this flow is to the cross section of the flow between total spheres as $\Omega : 4\pi$. The current density remains unaltered. Thus, the beam current can be calculated by the following expression obtained from 45.1

$$I = \frac{1 - \cos\vartheta_0}{2} I_t \qquad 45.2$$

where I_t is the total current determined by 36.4. During the following treatment the relationships obtained in § 36 can be used but expression 45.2 must always be taken into account.

For the determination of the electrode shapes it is convenient now to introduce the spherical coordinate system $(R, \vartheta, \varkappa)$, the origin of which coincides with the common centre of the spheres (figure III.9). Then, because of the axial symmetry of the gun, the whole analysis can be carried out using only two coordinates (R and ϑ). (The radius R measured from the centre of the spheres should not be confused with radius r measured from the z axis !)

The problem is then to solve the *Laplace* equation

$$\frac{1}{R^2}\frac{\partial}{\partial R}\left(R^2\frac{\partial\varphi}{\partial R}\right) + \frac{1}{R^2\sin\vartheta}\frac{\partial}{\partial\vartheta}\sin\vartheta\frac{\partial\varphi}{\partial\vartheta} = 0 \qquad 45.3$$

in the region $\vartheta \geq \vartheta_0$. The boundary conditions require that at the beam edge forces should not act in the ϑ direction and the potential distribution should be determined by 36.9. Taking 45.2 into account we obtain

$$\varphi(R, \vartheta_0) = D[G(R)]^{4/3}$$

and

$$\left.\frac{\partial\varphi}{\partial\vartheta}\right|_{\vartheta=\vartheta_0} = 0 \qquad\qquad 45.4$$

where

$$D = \left[\frac{9I}{8\sqrt{2}\pi\varepsilon_0\sqrt{\eta}} \cdot \frac{I}{1 - \cos\vartheta_0}\right]^{2/3} \qquad 45.5$$

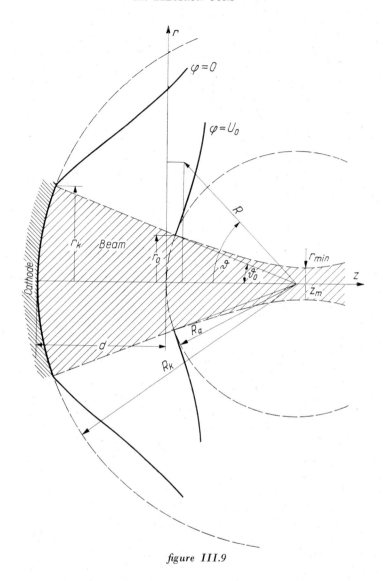

figure III.9

$G(R)$ is the function determined by 36.17 and given in table II.5 ($R_1 = R_k$). The approximate solution of the problem is given by [38]

$$\varphi(R, \vartheta) \approx D \sqrt{\frac{\sin \vartheta_0}{\sin \vartheta}} \, \omega^{4/3} \left[\cos \frac{4\psi}{3} - \frac{2\omega}{5} \cos \frac{7\psi}{3} + \right.$$

$$\left. + \frac{3\omega}{56} (7 \cotan \vartheta_0 + \cotan \vartheta) \sin \frac{7\psi}{3} \right] \qquad 45.6$$

where

$$\omega = \left| \log \frac{R_k}{R} + i(\vartheta - \vartheta_0) \right|$$

45.7

and

$$\psi = \arctan \frac{\vartheta - \vartheta_0}{\log \dfrac{R_k}{R}}$$

45.8

The solution can be found also in other forms [16–18]. A very accurate solution obtained by complicated analytical and numerical calculations is given by [39]. Sensitive numerical methods have been used for the determination of the electrode shapes by [12, 14, 24].

Using the method described in § 42, the electrode shapes can also be determined by means of an electrolytic tank [26]. The shapes of the equipotential lines obtained in this way are shown in figures III.10–13 for four different values of ϑ_0. The shape of the anode electrode held at potential U_0 depends on the value of the ratio R_k/R_a. These values are given in the figures by the corresponding curves. The arrangement of the coordinate system depends on the value of the ratio R_k/R_a.

The beam-forming electrode has always an angle of 67.5 deg with the beam edge. It should be remarked that from practical point of view the shape of the beam-forming electrode is to be formed with great accuracy;

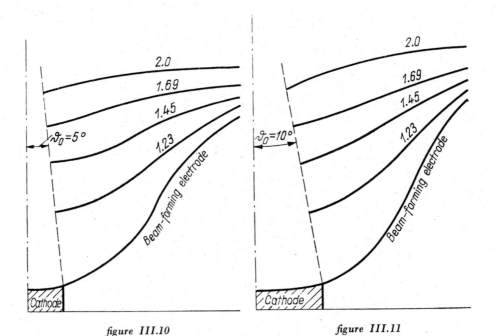

figure III.10   figure III.11

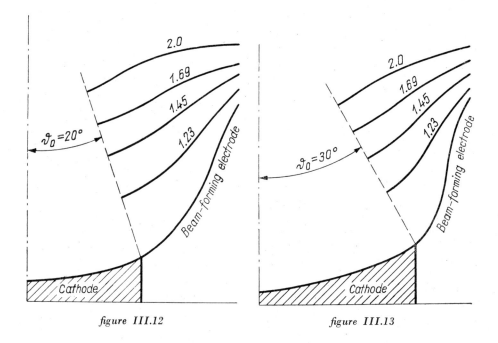

figure III.12   figure III.13

the shape of the anode electrode is not so sensitive to alterations. Sometimes better results can be achieved by using a beam-forming electrode held at negative potential.

The perveance characterising the given gun as a function of the geometrical parameters can be obtained from 36.26 and 45.2

$$P = \frac{I}{U_0^{3/2}} = \frac{8\sqrt{2\pi\varepsilon_0}\sqrt{\eta}}{9} \frac{1 - \cos\vartheta_0}{G^2(R_a)} =$$

$$= 14.67 \times 10^{-6} \frac{1 - \cos\vartheta_0}{G^2(R_a)} \quad [\text{AV}^{-3/2}] \qquad\qquad 45.9$$

The correspondence between the angle ϑ_0 and the ratio d/R_k at different values of the perveance are shown in figure III.14 [40]. The curves are calculated on the basis of expression 45.9. The values of the perveance are given by the corresponding curves in 10^{-6} A/V$^{3/2}$ units. The parameter

$$d/R_k = 1 - R_a/R_k$$

figures in 45.9 through the function G. When the value of the ratio d/R_k increases, the value of G^2 increases, too. The increase of the angle ϑ_0 causes the increase of $(1 - \cos\vartheta_0)$. These facts have the following consequences:

(i) If the angle ϑ_0 of the convergence is given, the perveance decreases with the increase of d/R_k.

(ii) If the value of d/R_k is given, the perveance increases with the increase of ϑ_0.

(iii) If the perveance is given, the greater is the value of d/R_k, the greater should be the value of ϑ_0.

These consequences must be taken into consideration at the gun design.

Thus, the gun consists of a spherical cathode, a beam-forming electrode and an anode electrode held at potential U_0 and situated at a distance d from the cathode (figure III.9). The electrodes are axially symmetric. The gun produces an axially symmetric electron beam moving in the direction of the z axis and accelerated to voltage U_0.

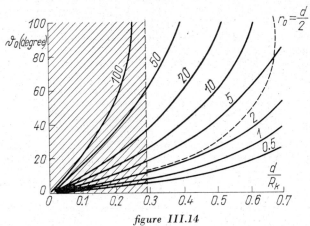

figure III.14

Let us now consider the beam profile in detail [35]. There is a diverging effect from the anode hole in this case, too. If we have a uniform potential region behind the gun, the beam spreading will occur due to space-charge forces. It should be remarked that at large values of the ratio r_0/d (where r_0 is the radius of the anode hole) the anode hole cannot simply be considered as a thin divergent lens. In this case the field distribution between the anode and the cathode is sufficiently disturbed and the conditions of the space-charge flow are changed. This results in a considerable decrease of the value of the beam perveance in comparison with the value determined by expression 45.9.

We can generally assume that the expression 45.9 is valid until the diameter $2r_0$ of the anode hole is comparable with the cathode–anode spacing d. One can see from figure III.9 that

$$\frac{d}{R_k} = 1 - \frac{R_a}{R_k} = 1 - \frac{r_0}{R_k \sin \vartheta_0} \qquad 45.10$$

If $2r_0 = d$, we have

$$\frac{d}{R_k} = 1 - \frac{d}{2R_k \sin \vartheta_0} \qquad 45.11$$

Hence

$$\frac{d}{R_k} = \frac{2 \sin \vartheta_0}{1 + 2 \sin \vartheta_0} \tag{45.12}$$

The relation between d/R_k and ϑ_0 is determined by 45.12 for the case $r_0 = d/2$. This function is given in figure III.14 by a dashed curve. Above the dashed curve (i.e. when the value of ϑ_0 is larger or the value of d/R_k is smaller than the values corresponding to the curve) the perveance is smaller than that determined by 45.9, because the potential distribution is altered by the large anode hole. This also causes a considerable decrease in the current density at the vicinity of the beam axis. The maximum practical value of the perveance is about 10^{-6} A/V$^{3/2}$ in this type of electron gun.

If the convergence angle ϑ_0 is small enough, the anode hole can be assumed as a diaphragm. According to 42.20, its diverging effect can be taken into account as a divergent lens with focal length

$$f = \frac{4U_0}{E_1 - E_2} + \frac{4r_0}{\pi} \tag{45.13}$$

The distances are measured from the anode hole and the direction of the z axis is considered positive (figure III.9).

If the divergent lens and the space-charge forces did not act, the beam would converge towards the centre of the spheres. Thus, we can make the approximate assumption that the divergent lens is superimposed on a convergent lens with focal length R_a. Let us denote the resultant focal length with F. Then we have

$$\frac{1}{F} = \frac{1}{R_a} = \frac{1}{f} \tag{45.14}$$

The focal length F determines the initial condition for the further motion of the electron beam. If there is a uniform potential region behind the gun, we have $E_2 = 0$.

Let us determine now the value of E_1. Firstly, we shall differentiate 45.4 with respect to R, obtaining

$$\frac{d\varphi}{dR} = \frac{4}{3} DG^{1/3}(R) \frac{dG}{dR} \tag{45.15}$$

The values of the function G are listed in table II.5 in the form of G^2 against R_k/R, consequently we shall slightly transform expression 45.15 to become

$$\frac{d(G^2)}{d\left(\frac{R_k}{R}\right)} = \frac{d(G^2)}{dR} \frac{dR}{d\left(\frac{R_k}{R}\right)} = -2G \frac{R^2}{R_k} \frac{dG}{dR} \tag{45.16}$$

whence

$$\frac{dG}{dR} = - \frac{R_k}{2GR^2} \frac{d(G^2)}{d\left(\dfrac{R_k}{R}\right)}. \qquad\qquad 45.17$$

We can rewrite expression 45.15 by using 45.17 and 36.27 in the following way

$$\frac{d\varphi}{dR} = - \frac{4U_0 R_k}{6R^2 G^{4/3}\left(\dfrac{R_k}{R_a}\right) G^{2/3}\left(\dfrac{R_k}{R}\right) d\left(\dfrac{R_k}{R}\right)} \qquad\qquad 45.18$$

It is easy now to calculate the value of E_1. We obtain

$$E_1 = - \frac{d\varphi}{dz}\bigg|_{z=0} = \frac{d\varphi}{dR}\bigg|_{R=R_a} =$$

$$= - \frac{4U_0 R_k}{6R_a^2 G^2\left(\dfrac{R_k}{R_a}\right) d\left(\dfrac{R_k}{R_a}\right)} \qquad\qquad 45.19$$

as the coordinate z is directed oppositely to R and originates from the centre of the anode hole. The values of the derivatives of G^2 can be determined numerically on the basis of table II.5.

For the calculation of E_1 we have just assumed that the potential distribution is not disturbed by the anode hole. This assumption is valid for small values of the angle ϑ_0. The same assumption makes it possible to neglect the second term of the expression 45.13. Then, using 45.13 and 45.19 we can rewrite formula 45.14 for the resultant focal length as follows

$$\frac{1}{F} = \frac{1}{R_a} - \frac{R_k}{6R_a^2 G^2\left(\dfrac{R_k}{R_a}\right) d\left(\dfrac{R_k}{R_a}\right)} \qquad\qquad 45.20$$

This expression can be transformed to the following form

$$\frac{R_a}{F} = 1 - \frac{R_k}{R_a} \frac{\dfrac{d(G^2)}{d\left(\dfrac{R_k}{R_a}\right)}}{6G^2\left(\dfrac{R_k}{R_a}\right)} \qquad\qquad 45.21$$

The value of R_a/F versus R_k/R_a is plotted in figure III.15 [35]. If R_a/F is positive, a convergent electron beam leaves the gun. Naturally, $R_a/F < 1$ because of the diverging effect of the anode hole. It is seen in the figure that the resultant focal length increases with the decrease of the ratio R_k/R_a, i.e. with the decrease of the cathode–anode spacing. When $R_k < 1.42R_a$ the beam becomes divergent $(R_a/F < 0)$. In the limiting case of $R_k/R_a = 1.42$ the beam leaves the gun parallel to the axis. According to 45.10, in this case the cathode–anode spacing $d = 0.29R_k$. If $d/R_k < 0.29$, a divergent beam leaves the gun. This interval has less practical importance; it is shown as the hatched portion of figure III.14.

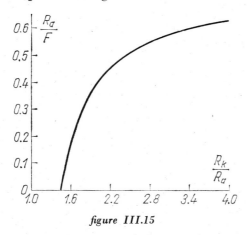

figure III.15

We have assumed that the value of the angle ϑ_0 is small. But then, according to figure III.9, we can write

$$\vartheta_0 \approx \sin \vartheta_0 = \frac{r_k}{R_k} = \frac{r_0}{R_a}$$

where r_k is the beam radius at the cathode. Hence

$$1 - \cos \vartheta_0 \approx \frac{\vartheta_0^2}{2} = \frac{1}{2}\left(\frac{r_0}{R_a}\right)^2$$

Substituting this into 45.9 we obtain

$$P = \frac{4\pi\varepsilon_0(2\eta)^{1/2}}{9}\frac{\left(\dfrac{r_0}{R_a}\right)^2}{G^2\left(\dfrac{R_k}{R_a}\right)} =$$

$$= 7.33 \times 10^{-6}\frac{\left(\dfrac{r_0}{R_a}\right)^2}{G^2\left(\dfrac{R_k}{R_a}\right)} \quad [\text{AV}^{-3/2}] \qquad\qquad 45.22$$

Expressions 45.21 and 45.22 determine the initial convergence and perveance of the beam, respectively. With knowledge of these values one can analyse the beam motion in the uniform potential region behind the gun on the basis of § 53. The diverging effect of the space-charge causes the spreading of the beam in this region. The initial radius of the beam in this region is equal to r_0, the dimensionless value of the initial convergence is determined by 53.30. Substituting 45.22 into 53.3 we obtain

$$Z = \frac{\sqrt{2}}{3} \frac{\dfrac{z}{R_a}}{\left[G^2 \left(\dfrac{R_k}{R_a} \right) \right]^{1/2}} \qquad 45.23$$

This is a convenient way to write the expression, as table II.5 gives values of G^2 versus R_k/R_a. The positive sign is to be considered before the square root.

Let us now substitute 45.23 into 53.30, giving the following result

$$R_0' = - \frac{3 \left[G^2 \left(\dfrac{R_k}{R_a} \right) \right]^{1/2}}{\sqrt{2}} \frac{R_a}{F} \qquad 45.24$$

where the value of R_a/F is determined by 45.21 and $F = z_f$.

It is now easy to determine the beam configuration by the use of 53.24 and table IV.2 (see figure III.9).

According to 45.24 and 53.7 the following value corresponds to the minimum beam radius

$$R_{\min} = \exp \left[-\frac{9}{2} \left(\frac{R_a}{F} \right)^2 G^2 \left(\frac{R_k}{R_a} \right) \right] \qquad 45.25$$

The position of the minimum beam cross section can be characterised by the following expression derived from 45.24 and 53.23

$$Z_m = 2F^* \left\{ \frac{3 \left[G^2 \left(\dfrac{R_k}{R_a} \right) \right]^{1/2}}{\sqrt{2}} \frac{R_a}{F} \right\} \qquad 45.26$$

where F^* is the function determined by expression 53.22. This function should not be confused with the focal length F in the brackets.

The beam radius at the cathode is given by

$$r_k = r_0 \frac{R_k}{R_a} \qquad 45.27$$

Let us introduce dimensionless coordinates z/R_k and r/r_k. From 45.23, 45.27 and 53.2, these coordinates can be determined as follows

$$\frac{z}{R_k} = \frac{3\left[G^2\left(\dfrac{R_k}{R_a}\right)\right]^{1/2}}{\sqrt{2}\,\dfrac{R_k}{R_a}}\, Z \qquad\qquad 45.28$$

and

$$\frac{r}{r_k} = \frac{r}{r_0}\frac{r_0}{r_k} = \frac{R}{\dfrac{R_k}{R_a}} \qquad\qquad 45.29$$

where $R = r/r_0$.

The following expression can be derived from 45.25 and 45.29 for the minimum beam radius

$$\frac{r_{\min}}{r_k} = \frac{R_{\min}}{\dfrac{R_k}{R_a}} = \frac{\exp\left[-\dfrac{9}{2}\left(\dfrac{R_a}{F}\right)^2 G^2\left(\dfrac{R_k}{R_a}\right)\right]}{\dfrac{R_k}{R_a}} \qquad\qquad 45.30$$

The values of G^2 versus R_k/R_a are listed in table II.5. The values of R_a/F versus R_k/R_a are plotted in figure III.15 on the basis of 45.21. The value of $r_{\min}/r_k$ depends only on the cathode to anode radii. This function is calculated using 45.30 and plotted in figure III.16 [35]. The value of $r_{\min}/r_k$ diminishes with the increase of the ratio R_k/R_a.

The distance of the minimum beam cross section from the anode related to the cathode radius is given by the following expression derived from 45.26 and 45.28

$$\frac{z_m}{R_k} = \frac{3\sqrt{2}\left[G^2\left(\dfrac{R_k}{R_a}\right)\right]^{1/2}}{\dfrac{R_k}{R_a}}\, F^*\left[\frac{3\left[G^2\left(\dfrac{R_k}{R_a}\right)\right]^{1/2}}{\sqrt{2}}\,\frac{R_a}{F}\right] \qquad 45.31$$

Here again, the values of G^2 and R_a/F versus R_k/R_a can be found from table II.5 and figure III.15, respectively, and z_m/R_k depends only on the ratio of the cathode to anode radii. The function calculated on the basis of 45.31 is plotted in figure III.17 (continuous curve) [35]. The values of F^* have been calculated with the aid of table IV.2 In the same figure the quantity F/R_k, i.e. the focal length without space-charge, is also plotted against R_k/R_a (dashed curve). This function is determined by the following expression

$$\frac{F}{R_k} = \frac{1}{\dfrac{R_a}{F}\dfrac{R_k}{R_a}}. \qquad\qquad 45.32$$

where the values of the ratio R_a/F are to be found in figure III.15.

15*

It is seen from figure III.17 that the focal length without space-charge diminishes when R_k/R_a is increased. At large values of R_k/R_a the effect of the space-charge appears in the increase of focal length $(z_m > F)$, for at large values of R_k/R_a the value of $|R_0'|$ is also large, as follows from 45.24.

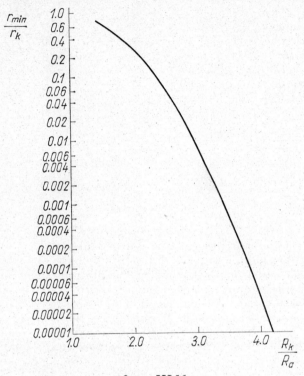

figure III.16

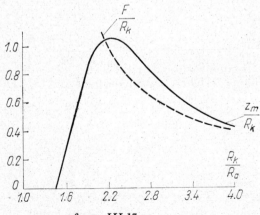

figure III.17

(See § 53.) Of course, beside this effect the focal point turns into a round spot, the radius of which is determined by 45.30. The larger the value R_k/R_a, the smaller the difference between F and z_m.

At small values of R_k/R_a the value of $|R_0'|$ is also small, and in this case space-charge forces cause a dispersion of the beam before the locus of the focal point present in the absence of space-charge ($z_m < F$). If $R_k/R_a = 1.42$ the beam leaves the gun parallel to the axis, i.e. $F \rightarrow \infty$ and $z_m = 0$.

The relation between r_{min} and z_m is rather complicated. If the value of the ratio R_k/R_a decreases, r_{min} increases, but z_m initially increases and then decreases. Naturally, $F > R_a$, but both $z_m > F$ and $z_m < R_a$ are possible.

Let us consider an example: $R_k = 30$ mm and $r_k = 5$ mm. For this case the values of R_a, F, z_m and r_{min} are listed against R_k/R_a in table III.3.

TABLE III.3

$\dfrac{R_k}{R_a}$	R_a mm	F mm	z_m mm	r_{min} mm
1.6	18.8	104	9.0	3.0
2.0	15.0	36.6	28.8	1.5
2.5	12.0	23.1	29.4	0.3

Thus, the beam profile behind the electron gun can be accurately calculated. The accuracy is determined by the physical assumptions, the calculations themselves are rigorous. The focusing device for the maintenance of the given constant cross section of the electron beam should be adjusted generally to the position of the minimum cross section of the beam z_m.

The anode-hole problem is a fundamental problem of the electron gun design, especially at large values of the convergence angle ϑ_0. This problem has been treated by many authors [44–57].

Although the influence of thermal velocities is not considered in this book, it must be pointed out once again that the above theory is valid only if the beam parameters are determined by *space-charge*. It is a very difficult problem to take both space-charge and thermal velocities into consideration [61, 64] but a limit up to which the beam parameters are *mainly* determined by space-charge can be estimated relatively easily. The calculations give the following result [35]: at cathode temperature 1160 °K the critical value of the accelerating voltage is

$$U_{0\,crit} = 0.1 \left[\frac{\left(\dfrac{r_k}{r_{min}}\right)^2}{0.39 \sin^2 \vartheta_0} - 1 \right] [\text{V}] \qquad 45.33$$

The above approximate theory is valid only in the case of $U_0 > U_{0\,crit}$. In this case the influence of space-charge is stronger than the influence of thermal velocities. If $U_0 < U_{0\,crit}$, the influence of thermal velocities is

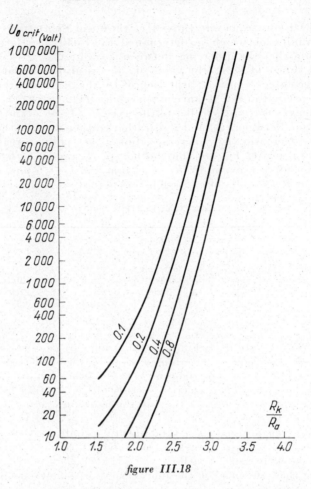

figure III.18

stronger than the influence of space-charge. Expression 45.33 must be taken into account at the gun design.

The value of $U_{0\,\mathrm{crit}}$ depends on the angle ϑ_0 and the ratio R_k/R_a, i.e. it is fully determined by the geometrical dimensions of the gun. If the ratio R_k/R_a is increased, the value of $r_k/r_{\min}$ increases and $U_{0\,\mathrm{crit}}$ becomes larger. On the other hand, the smaller is the value of the angle ϑ_0, the larger is the value of $U_{0\,\mathrm{crit}}$. The function $U_{0\,\mathrm{crit}}$ versus R_k/R_a calculated by means of 45.33 for four values of ϑ_0 is given in figure III.18 [35]. The values of $\sin \vartheta_0$ are given on the curves. It is seen from the figure that the space-charge theory described in this chapter is valid only for small values of the ratio R_k/R_a.

The effect of thermal velocities in electron guns has been investigated in detail by [49, 58–64].

We shall briefly summarise now how the *design* of an electron gun can be carried out. We have six parameters: the beam perveance P, the convergence angle ϑ_0, the cathode radius R_k, the anode radius R_a, the minimum beam radius $r_{\min}$ and the position z_m of the minimum beam cross section. These parameters are connected by the correlations given in figures III.14, 16 and 17. This means that only three of the six parameters can be given arbitrarily (this, of course, does not mean that *any* three parameters can be used as starting data !). The values of the three other parameters can be determined from the figures. It is also necessary to take into consideration figure III.18 in order to determine whether our design formulae are applicable. Attention should also be paid to the fact that in figure III.14 only the non-hatched region below the dashed curve is suitable for this method of calculation. Thus, it is desirable to have a small value of the angle ϑ_0 and a large value of the ratio R_k/R_a. This is also required to achieve small values of $r_{\min}/r_k$, but here there is a contradictory requirement: the ratio R_k/R_a should be small in order to achieve a large value of the perveance and also for the reasons seen in figure III.18. Consequently, the requirements are to be considered carefully and a compromise solution taken for the design of an electron gun. If a compromise is not possible, the effect of thermal velocities and of the large anode hole must be taken into account. The reader can find sufficient data for these problems in the literature referred to in this chapter.

Example

Let us design an electron gun with the following starting data: beam current $I = 10$ mA, anode voltage $U_0 = 600$ V, convergence angle $\vartheta_0 = 20$ deg and the minimum beam radius behind the gun $r_{\min} = 0.25$ mm.

We shall first calculate the beam perveance

$$P = \frac{I}{U^{3/2}} = 6.8 \times 10^{-7} \, \text{A/V}^{3/2} < 10^{-6} \text{A/V}^{3/2}$$

We have from 45.22

$$G^2 = \frac{7.33 \times 10^{-6} \, \vartheta_0^2}{P} = 1.31$$

The corresponding value of $R_k/R_a = 2.37$ can be found from table II.5. According to figure III.18 the space-charge-based calculation in this case can be assumed valid.

We have from figure III.16 that $r_{\min}/r_k = 0.1$. This means that $r_k = 2.5$ mm. We have obtained all the dimensions of the gun

$$R_k \approx \frac{r_k}{\vartheta_0} = 7.17 \text{ mm}$$

and

$$R_a = \frac{R_k}{2.37} = 3.02 \text{ mm}$$

Finally, we find from figure III.17 that $z_m/R_k = 1.04$. Therefore, $z_m = 7.47$ mm. The cathode should be chosen with an emission $j_k > I/\pi r_k^2 = 51$ mA/cm². The beam-forming electrode can be found from figure III.12. The shape of the electrode held at potential U_0, for the given value of the ratio R_k/R_a can be determined by means of an electrolytic tank.

46. A BRIEF SURVEY OF OTHER TYPES OF ELECTRON GUNS
PRODUCING HIGH CURRENT DENSITY BEAMS

The size of this book does not make it possible to describe in detail the novel and special types of electron guns. These will be given only schematically in this section. We have to confine ourselves to giving a reasonable selection of literature to the reader.

A recent development in this field is the appearance of electron guns suitable not only for the production of electron beams but also to allow for variation of the parameters (mainly the current) of the beam. This requirement can be fulfilled by means of additional electrodes (one or more), known as the *triode* electron gun with control electrode. The beam-forming electrode adjoining the cathode can also serve as the control electrode. In this case the beam current is controlled by the variation of the voltage of the beam-forming electrode. However, this method is effective only for small values of the perveance. If the perveance is large enough, additional control electrode or electrodes are used *(multianode electron guns)*, or special control grids are applied *(grid-controlled guns)* [65–84].

In some cases of magnetic focusing (see Chapter VI) the electron gun is immersed in the magnetic field. These *immersed-flow guns* are also used for the improvement of the gun parameters (mainly for the enhancement of beam stability and perveance) [85–101].

The *Heil* gun [154, 175] and the *Mueller* gun [54] have been composed experimentally. The electrode system of these guns is different from that of the *Pierce* gun in order to diminish the effect of the anode hole.

Electron guns producing relativistic dense electron beams are described by [158, 188].

The production of electron beams for crossed-field devices is a problem of great practical importance. *Magnetron injection guns* derived from different cases of curvilinear space-charge flow are used for this purpose. Papers [38, 102–123] are devoted to detailed analysis of this type of electron gun.

Electron guns for electron beam melting and welding are treated by [129, 141, 171, 172].

The results of experimental investigation of electron guns are given by [138, 142, 164].

The results of the efforts taken in the enhancement of the perveance of electron guns, new methods of calculation and investigation of electron guns, aberrations of electron guns and application of the guns in different electron-beam devices can be found in detail in the additional literature for this chapter [124–192]. More or less detailed reviews of high-intensity electron guns are given in [124, 136, 157, 163, 181, 184].

REFERENCES FOR CHAPTER III

a) *Classical Electron Guns*

1. (TSUKKERMAN, I. I.) Цуккерман, И. И.: Электронная оптика в телевидении *(Electron Optics in Television)*. Госэнергоиздат; Москва–Ленинград, 1958.
2. GLASER, W.: Grundlagen der Elektronenoptik, Springer; Wien, 1952.
3. HAINE, M. E.: *J. Brit. IRE*, **17** (1957) 4, 211.
4. (KELMAN, V. M.–YAVOR, S. YA.) Кельман, В. М.–Явор, С. Я.: Электронная оптика *(Electron optics)*. Изд. АН СССР; Москва–Ленинград, 1963.
5. MOSS, H.: *J. Brit. IRE*, **5** (1954), 10.
6. MOSS, H.: *J. Brit. IRE*, **5** (1945), 204.
7. MOSS, H.: *J. Brit. IRE*, **6** (1946), 99.
8. PLOKE, B. M.: *Z. angew. Phys.*, **3** (1951), 12, 441.
9. PLOKE, B. M.: *Z. angew. Phys.*, **4** (1952), 1, 1.
10. STEIGERWALD, K. H.: *Optik Berlin*, **5** (1949), 469.

b) *Theory of Pierce Guns*

11. (BAKHRAKH, L. E.–SULIMIN, A. D.) Бахрах, Л. Е.–Сулимин, А. Д.: *РИЭ СССР*, **6** (1961), 2, 333.
12. BERZ, F.: *Phil. Mag.*, **41** (1950), 209.
13. BOLZ, G.: *Nachrichtentechnik. Z.*, **12** (1959), 9, 464.
14. BREWER, G. R.: *J. appl. Phys.*, **28** (1957), 5, 634.
15. DAYKIN, P. N.: *Brit. J. appl. Phys.*, **6** (1955), 7, 248.
16. HARKER, K. J.: *J. appl. Phys.*, **31** (1960), 12, 2165.
17. HARKER, K. J.: *J. appl. Phys.*, **33** (1962), 5, 1861.
18. HARKER, K. J.: *J. Math. Phys.*, **4** (1963), 7, 993.
19. HARRIS, L. A.: *J. appl. Phys.*, **30** (1959), 6, 826.
20. HARRISON, E. R.: *Brit. J. appl. Phys.*, **5** (1954), 1, 40.
21. HARTNAGEL, H. L.: *Proc. IEE*, **111** (1964), 1, 57.
22. HARTNAGEL, H. L.: *Proc. IEE*, **111** (1964), 11, 1821.
23. HARTNAGEL, H. L.: *J. Electron. Control*, **17** (1964), 4, 425.
24. HECHTEL, R.: *Telefunkenzeitung*, **28** (1955), 110, 222.
25. HECHTEL, R.–MIZUHARA, A.: Microwave Tubes, Proc. 5th Intern. Conf., p. 227, Paris, 1964.
26. HELM, R.–SPANGENBERG, K.–FIELD, L. M.: *Electr. Commun.*, **24** (1947), 1, 101.
27. HO, K. C.–MOON, R. J.: *J. appl. Phys.*, **24** (1953), 9, 1186.
28. (IGNATENKO, V. P.) Игнатенко, В. П.: *Ж. Тех. Физ. СССР*, **31** (1961), 1443.
29. (IGNATENKO, V. P.) Игнатенко, В. П.: *Ж. Тех. Физ. СССР*, **32** (1962), 1, 63.
30. JOHNE, R.–HENNE, W.: *Telefunken-Röhre*, **38** (1960), 99.
31. KIRSTEIN, P. T.: *J. Electron. Control*, **5** (1958), 2, 163.
32. KRAMER, N. B.–TODD, E. G.: *IEEE Trans.*, **ED–10** (1963), 6, 394.
33. LOMAX, R. J.: *J. Electron. Control*, **6** (1959), 1, 39.
34. MELTZER, B.: *J. Electron. Control*. **8** (1960), 6, 449.
35. PIERCE, J. R.: *Theory and Design of Electron Beams*, Chapter X, Van Nostrand; New York, 1954.
36. PIERCE, J. R.: *J. appl. Phys.*, **11** (1940), 8, 548.
37. PIERCE, J. R.: *Bell Syst. tech. J.*, **24** (1945), 305.
38. RADLEY, D. E.: *J. Electron. Control*, **4** (1958), 2, 125.
39. RADLEY, D. E.: *J. Electron. Control*, **15** (1963), 5, 469.
40. SAMUEL, A. L.: *Proc. Instn Radio Engrs.*, **33** (1945), 4, 233.
41. SCHWARTZ: *IRE Nat. Conv. Rec.*, **6** (1958), 3, 13.
42. TODD, E. G.–KRAMER, N. B.–BREWER, G. R.: Microwaves, Proc. 4th Intern. Conf., p. 550, Eindhoven, 1962.
43. (TRENEVA, S. N.) Тренева, С. Н.: *РИЭ СССР*, **2** (1957), 7, 925.

c) Effect of the Anode Hole

44. Amboss, K.: *J. Electron. Control*, **13** (1962), 6, 545.
45. Birdsall, C. K.: *Trans. IRE*, **ED–4** (1957), 2, 132.
46. Brewer, G. R.: *J. appl. Phys.*, **28** (1957), 1, 7.
47. Brown, K. L.–Süsskind, C.: *Proc. Instn Radio Engrs.*, **42** (1954), 598.
48. Copeland, P. L.: *Amer. J. Phys.*, **10** (1942), 236.
49. Danielson, W. E.–Rosenfeld, J. L.–Saloom, J. A.: *Bell Syst. tech. J.*, **35** (1956), 2, 375.
50. Harris, L. A.: *Proc. Instn Radio Engrs.*, **46** (1958), 3, 615.
51. Harris, L. A.: *Proc. Instn Radio Engrs.*, **46** (1958), 9, 1655.
52. Harris, L. A.: *J. Electron. Control*, **8** (1960), 4, 241.
53. Müller, M.: *Arch. elekt. Übertr.*, **9** (1955), 20.
54. Müller, M.: *J. Brit. IRE*, **16** (1956), 1, 83.
55. Pöschl, K.–Veith, W.: *Arch. elekt. Übertr.*, **12** (1958), 1, 45.
56. Shipley, D. W.: *Trans. IRE*, **ED–7** (1960), 4, 195.
57. Stuart, G. A.–Meltzer, B.: *Proc. Inst. elect. Engrs.*, **105–B** (1959), 928.

d) Effect of Thermal Velocities in Electron Guns

58. (Batalin, V. A.) Баталин, В. А.: *Ж. Тех. Физ. СССР*, **36** (1966), 2, 313.
59. Cutler, C. C.–Hines, M. E.: *Proc. Instn Radio Engrs.*, **43** (1955), 3, 307.
60. Hasker, J.: *Philips Res. Rep.*, **21** (1966), 2, 122.
61. Kirstein, P. T.: Microwave Tubes, Proc. 5th Intern. Conf., p. 348, Paris, 1964.
62. Sugata, E. et al.: *Techn. Rep. Osaka Univ.* (Japan), **12** (1962), 73.
63. Sugata, E. et al.: *J. Inst. Electr. Commun. Engrs.* (Japan), **45** (1962), 11, 1572.
64. Weber, C.: Microwave Tubes, Proc. 5th Intern. Conf., p. 47, Paris, 1964.

e) Electron Guns with Additional Electrodes

65. Ashley, J. R.–Sutherland, A. D.–Kolb, W. P.: Microwave Tubes, Proc. 5th Conf., p. 223, Paris, 1964.
66. Bosch, B. G.–Niglas, K. B.: *Proc. Instn Radio Engrs.*, **50** (1962), 3, 324.
67. Bryant, J. H.–Antoniou, M. I.: *Nachtech. Fachber.*, **22** (1961), 473.
68. (Buryanov, P. D.) Бурянов, П. Д.: *РИЭ СССР*, **9** (1964), 1405.
69. (Buryanov, P. D.) Бурянов, П. Д.: *РИЭ СССР*, **11** (1966), 1579.
70. Eichenbaum, A. L.: *Proc. IEEE*, **52** (1964), 5, 613.
71. Gallagher, H. E.: *Trans. IRE*, **ED–6** (1959), 4, 390.
72. Gallagher, H. E.: *Trans. IRE*, **ED–9** (1962), 2, 234.
73. Harris, L. A.: *Trans. IRE*, **ED–7** (1960), 1, 46.
74. Hart, P. A. H.–Weber, C.: *Philips Res. Rep.*, **16** (1961), 4, 376.
75. Hasegawa, A.: *J. Inst. electr. commun. Engrs.* (Japan), **45** (1962), 1, 28.
76. Ho, K. C.: *Trans. IRE*, **ED–2** (1955), 3, 10.
77. Kaneda, S.: *J. Inst. electr. commun. Engrs.* (Japan), **44** (1961), 4, 485.
78. Meltzer, B.: *J. Electron. Control*, 7 (1959), 6, 491.
79. Robinson–Kompfner, R.: *Proc. Instn Radio Engrs.*, **39** (1951), 8, 918.
80. Simpson, J. A.–Kuyatt, C. E.: *Rev. Scient. Instr.*, **34** (1963), 3, 265.
81. (Treneva, S. N.) Тренева, С. Н.: *Приборы Тех. Экспер. СССР*, **8** (1963), 3, 177.
82. (Troitskiy, Yu. V.) Троицкий, Ю. В.: *РИЭ СССР*, **6** (1961), 8, 1402.
83. Wolkstein, H. J.: *RCA Rev.*, **21** (1960), 3, 389.
84. (Zybin, G. P.–Tregubov, V. F.) Зыбин, Г. П.–Трегубов, В. Ф.: *Изв. Ленинг. Электротех. Ин-та*, **53** (1964).

f) Electron Guns with Magnetic Field

85. (Alyamovskiy, I. V.) Алямовский, И. В.: *Радиотех. Электрон.* 7 (1962), 12, 2037.
86. Amboss, K.: *IEEE Trans.*, **ED–12** (1965), 6, 322.

87. CHEN, T. S.: *J. Electron. Control*, **4** (1958), 523.
88. CHODOROW, M.–SÜSSKIND, C.: *Proc. Instn Radio Engrs.*, **46** (1958), 2, 497.
89. COOK, E. J.: *J. appl. Phys.*, **30** (1959), 6, 860.
90. COOK, E. J.: *Trans. IRE*, **ED–8** (1961), 2, 140.
91. DUNN, D. A.–HOLADAY, R. E.: *Nachtech. Fachber.*, **22** (1961), 452.
92. VAN DUZER, T.–BUCKEY, C. R.–BREWER, G. R.: *Rev. Scient. Instrum.*, **34** (1963), 5, 558.
93. EICHENBAUM, A. L.–HAMMER, J. M.: *RCA Rev.*, **23** (1962), 3, 420.
94. EICHENBAUM, A. L.–PETER, R. W.: *RCA Rev.*, **20** (1959), 1, 18.
95. GEPPERT, D. V.: *IRE WESCON Conv. Rec.*, **4** (1960), 377.
96. (IGRITSKIY, A. L.) Игрицкий, А. Л.: *РИЭ СССР*, **8** (1963), 3, 440.
97. JOHNE, R.: *Telefunken-Röhre*, **36** (1959), 65.
98. PIERCE, J. R.: *Bell Syst. techn. J.*, **30** (1951), 825.
99. (TROITSKIY, YU. V.) Троицкий, Ю. В.: *Ж. Тех. Физ. СССР*, **30** (1960), 1, 25.
100. (TROITSKIY, YU. V.) Троицкий, Ю. В.: *Ж. Тех. Физ. СССР*, **30** (1960), 5, 512.
101. ZLOTYKAMIN, C.: *Proc. Inst. electr. Engrs.*, **105–B** (1958), 939.

g) Magnetron-Injection Electron Guns

102. ARFIN, B.: Microwaves, Proc. 4th Intern. Conf., p. 595, Eindhoven, 1962.
103. COOK, E. J.: *Proc. Instn Radio Engrs.*, **46** (1958), 2, 497.
104. DRYDEN, V. W.: *J. appl. Phys.*, **33** (1962), 10, 3118.
105. HOCH, O. L.–WATKINS, D. A.: *Trans. IRE*, **ED–6** (1959), 1, 18.
106. KINO, G. S.: *Trans. IRE*, **ED–7** (1960), 3, 179.
107. KINO, G. S.–TAYLOR, N. J.: *Trans. IRE*, **ED–9** (1962), 1, 1.
108. KIRSTEIN, P. T.: *Proc. Instn Radio Engrs.*, **46** (1958), 10, 1716.
109. KLÜVER, J. W.: *Proc. IEEE*, **51** (1963), 10, 1363.
110. LEBLOND: *Proc. Inst. electr. Engrs.*, **105–B** (1958), 1021.
111. LOMAX, R. J.: *J. Electron. Control*, **3** (1957), 4, 367.
112. LOMAX, R. J.: *J. Electron. Control*, **7** (1959), 6, 482.
113. LOMAX, R. J.: *J. Electron. Control*, **15** (1963), 3, 229.
114. MELTZER, B.: *J. Electron. Control*, **2** (1956), 118.
115. MIDFORD, T. A.–KINO, G. S.: *Trans. IRE*, **ED–8** (1961), 4, 324.
116. MIDFORD, T. A.–KINO, G. S.: *Trans. IRE*, **ED–9** (1962), 6, 431.
117. OKOSHI, T.: *Trans. IEEE*, **ED–11** (1964), 7, 349.
118. STAINSBY, A. G.: *Nachtech. Fachber.*, **22** (1961), 489.
119. SUGAI, I.: *Proc. Instn Radio Engrs.*, **47** (1959), 1, 87.
120. TAYLOR, N. J.: Microwaves, Proc. 4th Intern. Conf., p. 583, Eindhoven, 1962.
121. UNOTORO, T.: *Rev. elect. Commun. Lab.* (Tokyo), **9** (1961), 7–8, 497.
122. WATERS, W. E.: *J. appl. Phys.*, **30** (1959), 3, 368.
123. WATERS, W. E.: *Trans. IEEE*, **ED–10** (1963), 4, 226.

h) Additional References

124. (ALYAMOVSKIY, I. V.) Алямовский, И. В.: Электронные пучки и электронные пушки *(Electron Beams and Electron Guns)*. Советское Радио; Москва, 1966.
125. AMBOSS, K.: *Trans. IEEE*, **ED–12** (1965), 6, 313.
126. ARCHARD, G. D.: *Proc. Phys. Soc.*, **74** (1959), 2, 177.
127. BARBER, M. R.–SANDER, K. F.: *Proc. Inst. elect. Engrs.*, **106–B** (1959), 901.
128. BARBER, M. R.–SANDER, K. F.: *J. Electron. Control*, **7** (1959), 6, 465.
129. BAS, E. B.–GREMOSNIK, G.–LERCH, H.: *Schweizer Arch. angew. Wiss. Tech.*, **28** (1962), 3, 112.
130. BEAL, J. W.: *Trans. IEEE Nuclear Sci.*, **NS–14** (1967), 3, 93.
131. (BEREZIN, A. K. et al.) Березин, А. К. и др.: *Приборы Тех. Экспер. СССР*, **7** (1962), 2, 136.
132. BERGHAMMER, J.: *RCA Rev.*, **21** (1960), 3, 369.
133. (BEZVERKHIY–PINES) Безверхий–Пинес: *Ж. Тех. Физ. СССР*, **17** (1947), 1341.
134. BOERS, J. E.: *IEEE Trans.*, **ED–12** (1965), 7, 425.

135. Boring, K. L.–Stauffer, L. H.: *Proc. nat. Electron. Conf.*, **19** (1963), 535.
136. Brewer, G. R.: *High-intensity Electron Guns. Focusing of Charged Particles*, Vol.2, Chapter 3.2, p. 23, Academic Press; New York, 1967.
137. Chodorow, M. et al.: *Proc. Instn Radio Engrs.*, **41** (1953), 1584.
138. Climer, B. J.: *J. Electron. Control*, **13** (1962), 5, 385.
139. Colburn, D. S.–Harker, K. J.–Kino, G. S.: Microwaves, Proc. 4th Intern. Conf., p. 572, Eindhoven, 1962.
140. Colburn, D. S.–Kino, G. S.: *J. appl. Phys.*, **34** (1963), 5, 1568.
141. Cole, M.–Fischer, C.–Bucklow, I. A.: *Brit. J. appl. Phys.*, **12** (1961), 10, 577.
142. Cutler, C. C.–Saloom, J. A.: *Proc. Instn Radio Engrs.*, **43** (1955), 3, 299.
143. Deimel, E.: *Nachtech. Fachber.*, **22** (1961), 493.
144. Field, L. M.: *Rev. mod. Phys.*, **18** (1946), 353.
145. Frost, R. D.–Purl, O. T.–Johnson, H. R.: *Proc. Instn Radio Engrs.*, **50** (1962), 8, 1800.
146. Gabor, D.: *Proc. Instn Radio Engrs.*, **33** (1945), 11, 792.
147. Gallagher, W. J.: *Proc. IEEE*, **57** (1969), 1, 94.
148. Gregory, B. C.–Beck, A. H. W.: *Int. J. Electron.*, **21** (1966), 6, 561.
149. Hamza, V.: *IEEE Trans.*, **ED–13** (1966), 5, 485.
150. Hamza, V.: *IEEE Trans.*, **ED–13** (1966), 7, 551.
151. Hamza, V.–Kino, G. S.: *IEEE Trans.*, **ED–14** (1967), 4, 195.
152. Hasker, J.: *Philips Res. Rep.*, **24** (1969), 3, 231.
153. Hechtel, R.: *Arch. elektr. Übertr.*, **10** (1956), 12, 535.
154. Heil, O.–Ebers, J. J.: *Proc. Instn Radio Engrs.*, **38** (1950), 6, 645.
155. Henaff, J.: *Onde élect.*, **41** (1961), 406, 36.
156. Hoffmann, G.: *Optik Berlin*, **29** (1969), 5, 506.
157. (Ignatenko, V. P.) Игнатенко, В. П.: *Успехи Физ. Наук СССР*, **73** (1961), 2, 243.
158. (Ignatenko, V. P.) Игнатенко, В. П.: *РИЭ СССР*, **8** (1963), 1, 127.
159. Jakubowski, J.–Skladnik-Sadowska, E.: *Przegl. Elektron.*, **10** (1969), 1, 9.
160. (Kabanov, A. N.–Kafarov, A. A.–Starostin, E. P.) Кабанов, А. Н.–Кафаров, А. А.–Старостин, Е. П.: *Изв. АН СССР, Сер. Физ.*, **32** (1968), 7, 1192.
161. Kawamura, M.: *J. Inst. elect. Commun. Engrs. Japan*, **43** (1960), 6, 711.
162. Kirstein, P. T.–Hornsby, J. S.: *IEEE Trans.*, **ED–11** (1964), 5, 196.
163. Kirstein, P. T.–Kino, G. S.–Waters, W. E.: *Space-charge Flow* (Physical and quantum electronics series). McGraw-Hill Book Company; New York–San Francisco–London–Sydney, 1967.
164. Klemperer, O.: *Proc. Phys. Soc. Lond.*, **59** (1947), 302.
165. Linn, H. J.–Pöschl, K.: *Arch. elektr. Übertr.*, **22** (1968), 3, 146.
166. Mathias, L. E. S.–King, P. G. R.: *Trans. IRE*, **ED–4** (1957), 3, 280.
167. Milner, C. J.–Ausburn, K. J.: *Brit. J. appl. Phys.*, **12** (1961), 7, 346.
168. (Molokovskiy, S. I.) Молоковский, С. И.: *Изв. Ленингр. Электротех. Ин-та СССР*, **48** (1963), 76.
169. Morizuni, Y.: *J. Inst. elect. commun. Engrs.* (Tokyo), **50** (1967), 4, 664.
170. Nakai, A.: *Nucl. Instr. Meth.*, **54** (1967), 1, 57.
171. Nazarenko, O. K.: *Avtom. Svarka*, **6** (1961).
172. Nazarenko, O. K. et al.: *Avtom. Svarka*, **5** (1962).
173. Nishimaki, M.–Asaba, T.–Shimada, T.: Intern. Electron Devices Meeting, p. 124, Washington, 1967.
174. Picquendar, J. E.–Cahen, O.–Lapostolle, P.: Les effets de la charge d'espace dans les canons à électrons; Thomson–Houston; Paris, 1956.
175. Reed, E. D.: *Bell. Syst. tech. J.*, **34** (1955), 563.
176. Ruggles, P. C.: *Proc. IEE*, **105–B** (1958), 918.
177. Shimada, T.–Asaba, T.–Nishimaki, M.: *IEEE Trans.*, **ED–16** (1969), 7, 663.
178. Shimada, T.–Nishimaki, M.: *IEEE Trans.*, **ED–15** (1968), 11, 907.
179. (Shtyrov, A. I. et al.) Штыров, А. И. и др.: *РИЭ СССР*, **12** (1967), 7, 1286.
180. Sturrock, P. A.: *Proc. IEE*, **105–B** (1958), 1032.
181. Süsskind, C.: *Adv. Electronics Electron Phys.*, **8** (1956), 363.
182. (Syrovoy, V. A.) Сыровой, В. А.: *Ж. Прикл. Мех. Тех. Физ. СССР*, **2** (1964).
183. (Syrovoy, V. A.) Сыровой, В. А.: *Ж. Прикл. Мех. Тех. Физ. СССР*, **4** (1967). 3.
184. (Taranenko, V. P.) Тараненко, В. П.: Электронные пушки *(Electron Guns)*. Техника; Киев, 1964.

185. TORSTENSSON, L. et al.: *J. Inst. Telecommun. Engrs.* New Delhi, **6** (1960), 6, 245.
186. (VECHESLAVOV, V. V.–GORBUNOV, A.–KONONOV, V. I.) Вечеславов В. В.–Горбунов, А.–Кононов, В. И.: *РИЭ СССР*, **13** (1968), 8, 1472.
187. YADAVALLI, S.: *Proc. Instn Radio Engrs.*, **49** (1961), 6, 1098.
188. ZEPP, G.: *C. R. Acad. Sci. Paris*, **256** (1963), 16, 3426.
189. (ZINCHENKO, N. S.) Зинченко, Н. С.: *Ж. Тех. Физ. СССР*, **38** (1968), 1, 184.
190. (ZINCHENKO, N. S.) Зинченко, Н. С.: *Ж. Тех. Физ. СССР*, **38** (1968), 8, 1344.
191. (ZINCHENKO, N. S.) Зинченко, Н. С.: *Укр. Физ. Зап.*, **14** (1969), 2, 213.
192. (ZINCHENKO, N. S.–SOKOLOVA, V. A.) Зинченко, Н. С.–Соколова, В. А.: *РИЭ СССР*, **14** (1969), 2, 286.

IV. SPACE-CHARGE EFFECTS IN ELECTRON BEAMS

MIKLÓS SZILÁGYI

47. ELECTRON-BEAM CHARACTERISTICS; OUR ASSUMPTIONS; SPACE-CHARGE EFFECTS

In Chapter III, methods of production of high-intensity electron beams, electron beams with high current densities, were surveyed. In the following Chapters of this book long electron beams will be considered. Electrons move along nearly parallel paths in such beams. An electron beam is assumed 'long' if the beam length is much greater than the transverse dimension of the beam.

In Chapters V and VI the problem of maintenance of long electron beams will be treated. But first it is necessary to analyse the *properties of electron beams*, i.e. space-charge effects in high-intensity long electron beams. This is the task of Chapter IV. We shall list primarily the *requirements* for the electron beams, the *parameters* characterising the beams and the *assumptions* on which the analysis is based.

In modern electron-beam devices the production of a beam with given configuration is not satisfactory in itself. Different properties of the beam should also be taken into consideration. Let us consider, for example, microwave tubes where the following *requirements* should be met:

1. large value of the beam perveance;
2. long beam with given size and configuration, nearly constant cross section and strictly defined boundaries;
3. uniformity of the focusing and accelerating voltages;
4. great stability, because of strong high-frequency fields;
5. low noise level;
6. the geometrical dimensions of the focusing system must be in accordance with the construction of the tube. When the frequency is increased, the cross section of the beam and also the spacing between the beam edge and the microwave circuit must be reduced;
7. large value of the current transmission;
8. high vacuum, to reduce ionisation;
9. laminar flow.

The exact analysis of high-density electron beams is a very complicated problem. For the rigorous description of an electron beam it is necessary to have knowledge of the electron distribution in space and velocity, i.e. the distribution of the space-charge density $\varrho(\mathbf{r})$ and the velocity distribution $\mathbf{v}(\mathbf{r})$. For this knowledge we would have to solve the mechanical equations of motion, *Maxwell*'s equations and the equation of the conservation of energy, simultaneously. This is an unsolvable problem, not only in general form but even for the majority of special cases if we need rigorous solutions.

It is practically possible to obtain approximate solutions for some special cases. (The assumptions used for them will be described in detail below.) Usually, the following *parameters* can be given or measured and serve as starting data:

I = the total current of the beam;

U_0 = the accelerating potential of the beam;

$j(\mathbf{r})$ = the current-density distribution across the beam;

$\varphi(\mathbf{r})$ = the potential distribution inside and in the vicinity of the beam.

Geometrical dimensions: the beam length, initial sizes, the shape of the cross section of the beam.

The following characteristics are particularly important: *perveance, stability, current transmission.*

The ratio of the beam current in amperes to the 3/2 power of the accelerating voltage in volts is called *perveance* (P) (see § 41)

$$P = \frac{I}{U_0^{3/2}} \quad [\text{AV}^{-3/2}] \qquad\qquad 47.1$$

As we shall see, all the important effects of space charge depend on the value of the perveance. The perveance is an average quantity, it does not describe the electron distribution among velocities. On the basis of practical experience it is usually assumed that an electron beam is 'intensive', i.e. space-charge effects come to the front when

$$P \geq 10^{-8} \left[\frac{\text{A}}{\text{V}^{3/2}}\right]$$

In the limiting case of $P = 10^{-8}\,\text{A}/\text{V}^{3/2}$ the diameter of an axially symmetric electron beam becomes doubled due to space-charge only after passing a distance 63 times longer than the initial beam diameter. The values of the perveance calculated according to 47.1 are given in table IV.1 for several values of beam current and voltage.

TABLE IV.1

The values of perveance in $A/V^{3/2}$ units

U_0 (volt) \ I (mA)	1	5	10	50	100
300	1.92×10^{-7}	9.60×10^{-7}	1.92×10^{-6}	9.60×10^{-6}	1.92×10^{-5}
500	8.94×10^{-8}	4.47×10^{-7}	8.94×10^{-7}	4.47×10^{-6}	8.94×10^{-6}
1 000	3.16×10^{-8}	1.58×10^{-7}	3.16×10^{-7}	1.58×10^{-6}	3.16×10^{-6}
2 000	1.12×10^{-8}	5.60×10^{-8}	1.12×10^{-7}	5.60×10^{-7}	1.12×10^{-6}
3 000	6.09×10^{-9}	3.05×10^{-8}	6.09×10^{-8}	3.05×10^{-7}	6.09×10^{-7}
5 000	2.83×10^{-9}	1.42×10^{-8}	2.83×10^{-8}	1.42×10^{-7}	2.83×10^{-7}
10 000	10^{-9}	5.00×10^{-9}	10^{-8}	5.00×10^{-8}	10^{-7}

The *stability* is the resistance of the beam against external or random perturbations, i.e. for example, against variations of the initial conditions or instabilities of the focusing voltages. The stability depends on the 'stiffness' of the beam. The beam stiffness [93] is determined by the following two factors:

(a) the rate of change of restoring force as an edge electron is displaced from its equilibrium orbit;

(b) the magnitude of the restoring force.

The greater are the focusing forces, the better is the stability. Because of this, special constant defocusing forces are sometimes applied so that the space-charge forces play a minor role. The focusing forces have to balance the resultant of the defocusing forces and of the space-charge forces. The beam stability can be considerably increased in this way. For this reason electrostatically focused rotating beams are particularly stabile (see Chapter V).

The *current transmission* is the ratio of the current which passed through a given system to the current emitted by the cathode. This factor determines the practicability of the focusing system. Its value depends on the parameters of the focusing system and of the electron beam; this can be determined generally in an experimental way.

We shall generally make the following physical *assumptions* for the analysis of high-intensity long electron beams:

(1) We shall assume that the flow is laminar and the electron paths do not cross each other. Aberrations and thermal-velocity effects are automatically excluded by this assumption. It means also that the current inside any electron path is considered constant.

(2) We shall assume that the current density and space-charge density at a given distance from the cathode are constant across the beam and are equal to the respective values at the beam axis. The values of ϱ and j abruptly change to zero at the beam boundary. Obviously, this is a rather rough assumption. It has been observed experimentally that the transverse current-density distribution in electron beams with not too large value of the perveance generally can be assumed Gaussian. Because of the potential depression due to space-charge, the current-density distribution is also altered inside the beam. For this reason, in high-intensity beams the current density in the vicinity of the beam axis is lower than it would follow from the Gaussian distribution.

(3) As a consequence of the above two assumptions, the beam is considered a substance with definite boundaries. The beam boundary is determined by a given family of electron paths. In most cases only the motion of the boundary electrons is investigated.

(4) We shall not consider electron beams as statistical systems; the wave properties of the electrons will also be neglected. This means that there should not be a great deal of variations in the fields within distances comparable with *de Broglie*'s wavelength of the electrons.

(5) The influence of ions and secondary emitted electrons will be neglected.

(6) We shall consider only fields constant in time. The effect of high-frequency fields, sufficient in microwave tubes, on the focusing will be neglected as well as space-charge waves.

(7) We confine ourselves to electron beams in which the electron velocities are small in comparison with the velocity of light, thus, relativistic effects can be neglected.

(8) We shall assume that space-charge forces act radially or, in case of strip beams, in the direction of coordinate y. This assumption is strictly valid only if the electrons move exactly parallel to the z axis.

(9) The paraxial approximation will be frequently used. We shall generally assume that the beam is infinitely long.

These assumptions mean that the results of the calculations given in this book will compare with physical facts only with an accuracy of about 20%. But this is sufficient for engineering design. If one needs more accurate data, precise measurements should be carried out in order to improve the results.

The three most important *effects caused by space-charge* in electron beams are as follows:

(i) *The negative space-charge produced by the electrons causes the depression of the potential in the beam region.*

(ii) *Repulsive forces between electrons cause the spreading of the beam.*

(iii) *The beam current is limited by space-charge.*

These three effects will be treated in this Chapter for some simple cases: potential distribution, spreading and current limitation in cylindrical, hollow and sheet strip electron beams.

More or less detailed reviews of space-charge effects in electron beams are given by [1–19, 135, 136].

More general treatment of high-intensity electron beams can be found in papers [20–54, 144–146].

The scaling laws of space-charge optics are given by [28, 31, 136].

It is convenient to use the method of successive approximation for space-charge problems [40], but in many cases this method converges slowly [43]. Recently, computers have come into general use [21, 30, 37, 38, 154], but even these methods only make possible the solution of some of the special problems at the present time.

New methods of calculation and investigation of high-density electron beams appear regularly [123–154].

The scope of *applications* of high-intensity electron beams is increasing rapidly. It is sufficient to mention electron-beam melting, welding, machining, etc. [67]. Microwave tubes are typical examples as classical applications of space-charge optics. A very well arranged survey of the applications s given by [56].

(A) POTENTIAL DISTRIBUTION ACROSS ELECTRON BEAMS

48. THE POTENTIAL FIELD GENERATED BY THE SPACE-CHARGE OF AN ELECTRON BEAM

Let us suppose that an infinitely long electron beam is moving in a uniform external potential region—a *drifting beam*. The current density is constant across the beam and the space-charge spreading of the beam is compensated by a very strong magnetic field which makes the electrons move along paths parallel to the axis. Thus, we have an electron beam with uniform cross section. We shall analyse the potential distribution in the vicinity of the beam, which will be valid at any cross section of the beam, as the beam is assumed to be infinitely long.

It is obvious that the negative space-charge of the beam will cause a potential depression. The quantitative analysis of the potential distribution will be carried out in this Chapter for different types of electron beams. The problem is to solve *Poisson*'s equation in the region inside the beam and *Laplace*'s equation in the region outside the beam. It follows from equations 1.5 and 17.16 that if our assumptions are fulfilled, the value of space-charge density at a given point of the beam determined by radius vector **r** can be given by the following expression

$$\varrho(\mathbf{r}) = - \frac{I}{S_0[2\eta\varphi(\mathbf{r})]^{1/2}} \qquad 48.1$$

where I is the total beam current, S_0 is the area of the uniform cross section of the beam and $\varphi(\mathbf{r})$ is the potential at the given point determined by the field of the external electrodes and by space-charge.

For simplification of the mathematical treatment we shall generally assume that the space-charge density ϱ is constant across the whole beam. According to 48.1, this assumption causes the potential $\varphi(\mathbf{r})$ to become constant which seems a contradiction, for just the determination of the potential distribution $\varphi(\mathbf{r})$ is the aim of the analysis! But if the current density of the beam is not too large and the average value of the beam potential is not too small, we can assume as a first approximation that the term in the right-hand side of *Poisson*'s equation is constant. This means that we assume the space-charge density to be determined by the average potential U_0 of the beam. In this case we can write

$$\varrho = - \frac{I}{S_0(2\eta U_0)^{1/2}} = \text{constant} \qquad 48.2$$

Taking into account the distribution 48.1 of the space-charge density we shall meet with great mathematical difficulties which can be removed only by approximate solutions. We consider the method used in this chapter to be much more convenient and obtain the results without further mathematical simplifications, in a relatively simple way. The accuracy of our results is as good as those obtained in a reasonable time from approximate solutions. This method also has the advantage of simplicity and it clarifies the physical assumptions as well.

We should like to emphasise that in this part of Chapter IV only infinitely long, laminar electron beams confined by very strong magnetic fields will be treated and the results given here are valid only for such beams. When any other method of beam confinement is used, the potential distribution will be different from the present result. The determination of the actual potential distribution is a very complicated problem. Practically, it can be assumed that our formulae are approximately valid for all cases of beam focusing, if the value of the beam perveance is not too large, i.e. if the approximation $\varrho = \text{constant}$ can be used.

The potential distribution in axially symmetric electron beams has been treated in a more general way by [58].

The potential distribution in a solid beam of finite length [63] and the potential distribution in a hollow beam of finite length [107] have also been investigated. The potential distribution of electron beams moving in uniform electric fields has been analysed by [61, 106]. The longitudinal potential distribution in electron beams with infinite width and finite length can be found in [19]. Papers [90, 101] are devoted to determination of the potential distribution of axially symmetric electron bunches of finite length moving in metal cylinders. Potential distribution problems have also been treated by [10, 71]. The current-limiting effect of space charge in cylindrical and plane-symmetric electron beams has been analysed by [55, 62].

49. POTENTIAL DISTRIBUTION IN HOLLOW ELECTRON BEAMS*

A hollow beam is derived from a solid beam by the enclosing of given parts of the beam, i.e. by putting boundary surfaces inside the beam and taking out the parts of the beam surrounded by these surfaces. The most simple and widespread case is the axially symmetric hollow beam — a *tubular beam*. Its boundary surfaces are two coaxial cylinders.

We shall determine now the radial potential distribution in an infinitely long axially symmetric hollow electron beam for the case when *the beam moves between two coaxial cylinders held at different voltages*, parallel to the z axis, i.e. normal to the plane of figure IV. 1. We assume that the

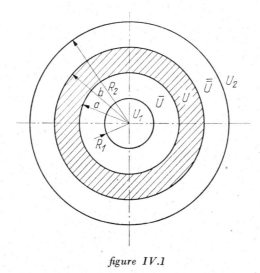

figure IV.1

* Departing from the order chosen in this book, we begin the treatment of potential distributions with that of the hollow beam because the potential distribution of the cylindrical solid beam will be derived from this case.

16*

space-charge density is constant across the whole beam. The geometrical dimensions of the beam and of the cylinders are given in the figure. The internal cylinder with radius R_1 is held at potential U_1, the external cylinder with radius R_2 is held at potential U_2. The beam boundaries are cylinders; the radius of the external boundary is equal to b while the radius of the internal boundary is a.

The potential within the beam will be denoted with U, between the beam and the internal cylinder with $\bar{U}$ and between the beam and the external cylinder with $\bar{\bar{U}}$. The problem is to determine the functions $U = U(r)$, $\bar{U} = \bar{U}(r)$ and $\bar{\bar{U}} = \bar{\bar{U}}(r)$. Owing to the infinite length and axial symmetry of the system, *Poisson*'s and *Laplace*'s equations can be written in cylindrical coordinate system with one independent variable.

Thus, we have the following equations in the respective intervals

$$R_1 \leq r \leq a \qquad \frac{1}{r} \frac{d}{dr} \left(r \frac{d\bar{U}}{dr} \right) = 0 \qquad\qquad 49.1$$

$$a \leq r \leq b \qquad \frac{1}{r} \frac{d}{dr} \left(r \frac{dU}{dr} \right) = - \frac{\varrho}{\varepsilon_0} \qquad\qquad 49.2$$

and

$$b \leq r \leq R_2 \qquad \frac{1}{r} \frac{d}{dr} \left(r \frac{d\bar{\bar{U}}}{dr} \right) = 0 \qquad\qquad 49.3$$

Integrating these equations once, we obtain

$$\frac{d\bar{U}}{dr} = \frac{C_1}{r} \qquad\qquad 49.4$$

$$\frac{dU}{dr} = - \frac{\varrho r}{2\varepsilon_0} + \frac{C_3}{r} \qquad\qquad 49.5$$

and

$$\frac{d\bar{\bar{U}}}{dr} = \frac{C_5}{r} \qquad\qquad 49.6$$

Integrating again, we obtain

$$\bar{U} = C_1 \log r + C_2 \qquad\qquad 49.7$$

$$U = - \frac{\varrho r^2}{4\varepsilon_0} + C_3 \log r + C_4 \qquad\qquad 49.8$$

and

$$\bar{\bar{U}} = C_5 \log r + C_6 \qquad\qquad 49.9$$

We have the following boundary conditions for the determination of the constants $C_1, \ldots, C_6$

$$\left.\begin{aligned}
\bar{U}(R_1) &= U_1 & \frac{d\bar{U}}{dr}\Big|_{r=a} &= \frac{dU}{dr}\Big|_{r=a}\\
\bar{U}(a) &= U(a) & \frac{d\bar{U}}{dr}\Big|_{r=a} &= \frac{dU}{dr}\Big|_{r=a}\\
\bar{\bar{U}}(b) &= U(b) & \frac{d\bar{\bar{U}}}{dr}\Big|_{r=b} &= \frac{dU}{dr}\Big|_{r=b}\\
\bar{\bar{U}}(R_2) &= U_2 & \frac{d\bar{\bar{U}}}{dr}\Big|_{r=b} &= \frac{dU}{dr}\Big|_{r=b}
\end{aligned}\right\}\qquad 49.10$$

(The potentials are given on the cylinders; the potential and the radial field strength are to be continuous at the beam boundaries.) Potentials $U(a)$ and $\bar{U}(b)$ are unknown; they should be determined from 49.8.

Thus, the following eight equations are determined by the boundary conditions

$$C_1 \log R_1 + C_2 = U_1 \qquad\qquad 49.11$$

$$C_5 \log R_2 + C_6 = U_2. \qquad\qquad 49.12$$

$$C_1 \log a + C_2 = U(a) \qquad\qquad 49.13$$

$$C_5 \log b + C_6 = U(b) \qquad\qquad 49.14$$

$$-\frac{\varrho a^2}{4\varepsilon_0} + C_3 \log a + C_4 = U(a) \qquad\qquad 49.15$$

$$-\frac{\varrho b^2}{4\varepsilon_0} + C_3 \log b + C_4 = U(b) \qquad\qquad 49.16$$

$$\frac{C_1}{a} = -\frac{\varrho a}{2\varepsilon_0} + \frac{C_3}{a} \qquad\qquad 49.17$$

and

$$\frac{C_5}{b} = -\frac{\varrho b}{2\varepsilon_0} + \frac{C_3}{b} \qquad\qquad 49.18$$

The values of the six constants and of $U(a)$ and $U(b)$ will be determined from these equations. We obtain the following results

$$C_1 = \frac{\varrho a^2}{2\varepsilon_0} + \frac{1}{\log \dfrac{R_2}{R_1}}\left[U_2 - U_1 + \frac{\varrho b^2}{2\varepsilon_0}\left(\log\frac{R_2}{b} + \frac{1}{2}\right) + \right.$$

$$\left. + \frac{\varrho a^2}{2\varepsilon_0}\left(\log\frac{a}{R_1} - \frac{1}{2}\right)\right] \qquad\qquad 49.19$$

$$C_2 = U_1 + \frac{\varrho a^2}{2\varepsilon_0}\log R_1 - \frac{\log R_1}{\log\dfrac{R_2}{R_1}}\left[U_2 - U_1 + \right.$$

$$\left. + \frac{\varrho b^2}{2\varepsilon_0}\left(\log\frac{R_2}{b} + \frac{1}{2}\right) + \frac{\varrho a^2}{2\varepsilon_0}\left(\log\frac{a}{R_1} - \frac{1}{2}\right)\right] \qquad\qquad 49.20$$

$$C_3 = \frac{1}{\log \dfrac{R_2}{R_1}} \left[U_2 - U_1 + \frac{\varrho b^2}{2\varepsilon_0} \left(\log \frac{R_2}{b} + \frac{1}{2} \right) + \right.$$

$$\left. + \frac{\varrho a^2}{2\varepsilon_0} \left(\log \frac{a}{R_1} - \frac{1}{2} \right) \right] \tag{49.21}$$

$$C_4 = U_1 - \frac{\varrho a^2}{2\varepsilon_0} \left(\log \frac{a}{R_1} - \frac{1}{2} \right) - \frac{\log R_1}{\log \dfrac{R_2}{R_1}} \left[U_2 - U_1 + \right.$$

$$\left. + \frac{\varrho b^2}{2\varepsilon_0} \left(\log \frac{R_2}{b} + \frac{1}{2} \right) + \frac{\varrho a^2}{2\varepsilon_0} \left(\log \frac{a}{R_1} - \frac{1}{2} \right) \right] \tag{49.22}$$

$$C_5 = - \frac{\varrho b^2}{2\varepsilon_0} + \frac{1}{\log \dfrac{R_2}{R_1}} \left[U_2 - U_1 + \right.$$

$$\left. + \frac{\varrho b^2}{2\varepsilon_0} \left(\log \frac{R_2}{b} + \frac{1}{2} \right) + \frac{\varrho a^2}{2\varepsilon_0} \left(\log \frac{a}{R_1} - \frac{1}{2} \right) \right] \tag{49.23}$$

$$C_6 = U_2 + \frac{\varrho b^2}{2\varepsilon_0} \log R_2 - \frac{\log R_2}{\log \dfrac{R_2}{R_1}} \left[U_2 - U_1 + \right.$$

$$\left. + \frac{\varrho b^2}{2\varepsilon_0} \left(\log \frac{R_2}{b} + \frac{1}{2} \right) + \frac{\varrho a^2}{2\varepsilon_0} \left(\log \frac{a}{R_1} - \frac{1}{2} \right) \right] \tag{49.24}$$

$$U(a) = U_1 - \frac{\varrho a^2}{2\varepsilon_0} \log \frac{a}{R_1} + \frac{\log \dfrac{a}{R_1}}{\log \dfrac{R_2}{R_1}} \left[U_2 - U_1 + \right.$$

$$\left. + \frac{\varrho b^2}{2\varepsilon_0} \left(\log \frac{R_2}{b} + \frac{1}{2} \right) + \frac{\varrho a^2}{2\varepsilon_0} \left(\log \frac{a}{R_1} - \frac{1}{2} \right) \right] \tag{49.25}$$

and

$$U(b) = U_2 + \frac{\varrho b^2}{2\varepsilon_0} \log \frac{R_2}{b} - \frac{\log \dfrac{R_2}{b}}{\log \dfrac{R_2}{R_1}} \left[U_2 - U_1 + \right.$$

$$\left. + \frac{\varrho b^2}{2\varepsilon_0} \left(\log \frac{R_2}{b} + \frac{1}{2} \right) + \frac{\varrho a^2}{2\varepsilon_0} \left(\log \frac{a}{R_1} - \frac{1}{2} \right) \right] \tag{49.26}$$

By the determination of the constants the problem is actually solved. Before writing the final expressions for the potential distribution we shall determine the potential gradient inside the beam. According to 49.5 and 49.21 we have

$$\frac{dU}{dr} = -\frac{\varrho r}{2\varepsilon_0} + \frac{1}{r \log \dfrac{R_2}{R_1}}\left[U_2 - U_1 + \frac{\varrho}{4\varepsilon_0}(b^2 - a^2) + \right.$$

$$\left. + \frac{\varrho}{2\varepsilon_0}\left(b^2 \log \frac{R_2}{b} + a^2 \log \frac{a}{R_1}\right)\right] =$$

$$= -\frac{1}{r}\frac{\varrho}{2\varepsilon_0}\left\{r^2 - \frac{1}{\log \dfrac{R_2}{R_1}}\left[\frac{2\varepsilon_0}{\varrho}(U_2 - U_1) + \right.\right.$$

$$\left.\left. + \frac{1}{2}(b^2 - a^2) + b^2 \log \frac{R_2}{b} + a^2 \log \frac{a}{R_1}\right]\right\} \qquad 49.27$$

Let us introduce the following quantity [66]

$$r_e^2 = \frac{1}{\log \dfrac{R_2}{R_1}}\left[\frac{2\varepsilon_0}{\varrho}(U_2 - U_1) + \frac{1}{2}(b^2 - a^2) + \right.$$

$$\left. + b^2 \log \frac{R_2}{b} + a^2 \log \frac{a}{R_1}\right] \qquad 49.28$$

Then we can rewrite 49.27 in the following way

$$\frac{dU}{dr} = -\frac{1}{r}\frac{\varrho}{2\varepsilon_0}(r^2 - r_e^2) \qquad 49.29$$

It is seen from this expression immediately that r_e is the radius at which the space-charge force is equal to zero, i.e. the minimum value of the potential inside the beam is at $r = r_e$. Hence the quantity r_e is called the 'equilibrium radius'. According to 48.2 we can write

$$\varrho = -\frac{I}{\pi(b^2 - a^2)(2\eta U_0)^{1/2}} \qquad 49.30$$

where U_0 is the average value of the potential inside the beam. Using this expression we obtain

$$\frac{dU}{dr} = \frac{\sqrt{2}\,I}{4\pi\varepsilon_0\sqrt{\eta}\sqrt{U_0}}\frac{1}{r}\frac{r^2 - r_e^2}{b^2 - a^2} \qquad 49.31$$

where

$$r_e^2 = \frac{1}{\log \frac{R_2}{R_1}} \left\{ b^2 \log \frac{R_2}{b} + a^2 \log \frac{a}{R_1} + \right.$$

$$\left. + \frac{b^2 - a^2}{2} \left[1 - \frac{8\pi\varepsilon_0 \sqrt{\eta}\sqrt{U_0}}{\sqrt{2I}} (U_2 - U_1) \right] \right\} \qquad 49.32$$

Let us now write the expressions for the potential distribution, using the equilibrium radius and substituting the values of the physical con- stants

$$\bar{U}(r) = U_1 - 3.03 \times 10^4 \frac{I}{\sqrt{U_0}} \frac{r_e^2 - a^2}{b^2 - a^2} \log \frac{r}{R_1} \qquad 49.33$$

$$U(r) = U_1 + 3.03 \times 10^4 \frac{I}{\sqrt{U_0}} \frac{1}{b^2 - a^2} \left(\frac{r^2 - a^2}{2} + \right.$$

$$\left. + a^2 \log \frac{a}{R_1} - r_e^2 \log \frac{r}{R_1} \right) \qquad 49.34$$

and

$$\bar{\bar{U}}(r) = U_2 - 3.03 \times 10^4 \frac{I}{\sqrt{U_0}} \frac{b^2 - r_e^2}{b^2 - a^2} \log \frac{R_2}{r} \qquad 49.35$$

The minimum value of the potential is equal to

$$U_{\min} = U(r_e) = U_1 + 3.03 \times 10^4 \frac{I}{\sqrt{U_0}} \times$$

$$\times \frac{1}{b^2 - a^2} \left(\frac{r_e^2 - a^2}{2} + a^2 \log \frac{a}{R_1} - r_e^2 \log \frac{r_e}{R_1} \right) \qquad 49.36$$

Let us consider an *example*. We shall determine the potential distribution of a hollow electron beam with perveance $P = 1.92 \times 10^{-6} \text{A/V}^{3/2}$ and the following geometrical parameters

$$\frac{a}{R_1} = 2, \qquad \frac{b}{R_1} = 3, \qquad \frac{R_2}{R_1} = 4$$

For simplicity we assume $U_1 = U_2 = U_0$. Then we shall have

$$\frac{r_e}{R_1} = 2.38 \quad \text{and} \quad \frac{U_{\min}}{U_0} = 0.9847$$

The potential depression due to space-charge does not exceed 1.53%, in this case. The potential distribution across the beam calculated on the basis of expressions 49.33–49.35 is given in figure IV.2. It is quite clear from the figure that the electrons are forced by space-charge to move outwards in a radial direction if $r > r_e$ and towards the axis if $r < r_e$.

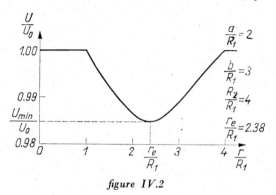

figure IV.2

Finally, we notice that in the special case when the electron beam is absent, the expression of the potential distribution in a cylindrical condenser can be obtained as follows

$$U(r) = U_1 + (U_2 - U_1) \frac{\log \dfrac{r}{R_1}}{\log \dfrac{R_2}{R_1}}$$

49.37

This expression can also be written as

$$U(r) = U_2 - (U_2 - U_1) \frac{\log \dfrac{R_2}{r}}{\log \dfrac{R_2}{R_1}}$$

49.38

These two expressions are identical. If r is calculated in R_1 units, it is convenient to use 49.37. If r is calculated in R_2 units, 49.38 is better.

Let us consider now another practically important case when *there is no electrode inside the hollow electron beam*. The beam moves in a tube with radius R and potential U_0. The notation of all the other parameters is the same as in the previous case (figure IV.3). The potential distribution is divided again into regions $\overline{U}$, U and $\widetilde{U}$. The equations are exactly the same as in the previous case. Boundary conditions will not change either, with the exception of the condition $\overline{U}(R_1) = U_1$. Instead of this condition the following new condition occurs because of the symmetry of the system

$$\left. \frac{d\overline{U}}{dr} \right|_{r=0} = 0$$

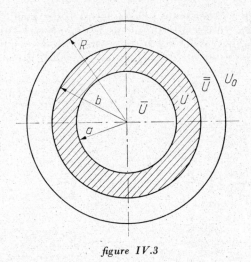

figure IV.3

It means that we have now

$$C_1 = 0$$

instead of 49.11. Expressions 49.12–49.18 are valid without any alteration. The potential distribution can easily be obtained after determination of the constants. We shall not give here the whole calculation because it is similar to the previous case. The final results are as follows

$$\bar{U} = U(0) = U(a) = U_{min} = U_0 - 3.03 \times 10^4 \frac{I}{\sqrt{U_0}} \times$$

$$\times \frac{1}{b^2 - a^2} \left[\frac{b^2 - a^2}{2} + b^2 \log \frac{R}{b} - a^2 \log \frac{R}{a} \right] = \text{const.} \qquad 49.39$$

$$U(r) = U_0 - 3.03 \times 10^4 \frac{I}{\sqrt{U_0}} \frac{1}{b^2 - a^2} \left[b^2 \log \frac{R}{b} - \right.$$

$$\left. - a^2 \log \frac{R}{r} + \frac{b^2 - r^2}{2} \right] \qquad 49.40$$

and

$$\bar{\bar{U}}(r) = U_0 - 3.03 \times 10^4 \frac{I}{\sqrt{U_0}} \log \frac{R}{r} \qquad 49.41$$

These formulae can also be obtained as special cases of expressions 49.33–49.55, by substituting $U_2 = U_0$, $U_1 = \bar{U}(0)$, $R_2 = R$ and $R_1 \to 0$ into these expressions. $U(0)$ is determined by 49.39. According to 49.32 we have $r_e = a$ in this case, i.e. the equilibrium radius coincides with the internal boundary radius of the beam. There is no force inside the beam, in the charge-free region. In the interior of the beam electrons are forced by space-charge forces to move outwards in radial direction. Expressions 49.39–49.41 have been obtained with the assumption that the value of the average beam potential is equal to U_0.

Comparing these two cases we see that the removal of the internal electrode causes an essential alteration in the potential distribution. But it can easily be proved that in case of a *given electrode system* the potential distribution caused by space-charge in the given electrode system can be separated from the potential distribution produced by the electric field of the electrodes themselves. The resultant potential distribution can be found by superposition of these two distributions (see 29.1). In case of more complicated electrode arrangements this method is frequently used for the simplification of the calculations.

Let us consider again the potential distribution of a hollow electron beam with perveance $P = 1.92 \times 10^{-6}$ A/V$^{3/2}$ in case of the absence of the internal electrode, as an example. Similarly to the previous case, the values of the geometrical parameters are as follows

$$\frac{a}{R} = \frac{1}{2} \quad \text{and} \quad \frac{b}{R} = \frac{3}{4}$$

In this case we have

$$\frac{U_{\min}}{U_0} = 0.9730$$

The potential depression due to space charge does not exceed 2.7% in this case. It is stronger than in the previous case: we have no internal electrode which could raise the value of the potential. The potential distribution calculated on the basis of expressions 49.39–49.41 is given in figure IV.4.

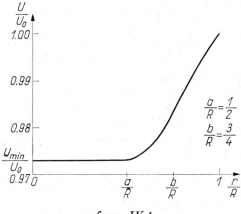

figure IV.4

As we have already mentioned, one of the most important space-charge effects is that *the beam current is limited by space-charge*. This effect arises in the ideally parallel beams considered in this section, too. It is easy to understand this fact: if the beam current were too large, the potential in the beam region would be so strongly non-uniform that different electrons of the same beam would move along paths with strongly different potentials and this would cause the collapse of the beam.

Let us consider this problem in detail. For the case of thin beams the method given by [73] can be applied. We shall consider a *hollow beam moving between two cylindrical tubes* (see figure IV).

We shall assume that the beam is a thin annular tube with radius r_e and potential U_{min}. The radial dimensions of the beam and the potential distribution inside the beam will be neglected. Potential U_{min} is determined by 49.36, the value of the radius r_e is determined by 49.32.

The value of the linear charge density of the beam is given by

$$q = \frac{I}{(2\eta)^{1/2} \sqrt{U_{min}}} \quad [\text{As m}^{-1}] \qquad 49.42$$

A charge of the same value is induced by this charge on the surface of the two tubes. It means that

$$q = C_1(U_1 - U_{min}) + C_2(U_2 - U_{min}) \qquad 49.43$$

where

$$C_1 = \frac{2\pi\varepsilon_0}{\log \dfrac{r_e}{R_1}} \quad [\text{Fm}^{-1}] \qquad 49.44$$

is the capacitance per unit length of the cylindrical condenser formed by the electron beam and the internal tube and

$$C_2 = \frac{2\pi\varepsilon_0}{\log \dfrac{R_2}{r_e}} \quad [\text{Fm}^{-1}] \qquad 49.45$$

is the capacitance per unit length of the cylindrical condenser formed by the electron beam and the external tube. (The capacitances are expressed in units of farad/m.)

We find from 49.42 and 49.43 that

$$I = (2\eta)^{1/2} C_1 \left[\sqrt{U_{min}} (U_1 - U_{min}) + C_2 \sqrt{U_{min}} (U_2 - U_{min}) \right] \quad 49.46$$

We have a maximum value of the beam current if the condition

$$\frac{dI}{dU_{min}} = 0 \qquad 49.47$$

is fulfilled. The optimum value of the potential U_{min} can be obtained from 49.46 and 49.47

$$U_{min\ opt} = \frac{U_1}{3}\left[1 - \frac{C_2}{C_1 + C_2}\left(1 - \frac{U_2}{U_1}\right)\right] \qquad 49.48$$

In case of $U_1 = U_2 = U_0$ we have $U_{min\ opt} = \dfrac{U_0}{3}$

Taking into account 49.44 and 49.45 we can rewrite 49.48 as follows

$$U_{min\ opt} = \frac{U_1}{3}\left[1 - \frac{\log \dfrac{r_e}{R_1}}{\log \dfrac{R_2}{R_1}}\left(1 - \frac{U_2}{U_1}\right)\right] \qquad 49.49$$

Expression 49.46 can be rewritten using 49.48 ás

$$I = (2\eta)^{1/2}\,(C_1 + C_2)\,U_1^{3/2}\sqrt{\frac{U_{min}}{U_1}\left(3\,\frac{U_{min\ opt}}{U_1} - \frac{U_{min}}{U_1}\right)} \qquad 49.50$$

From this expression we can easily obtain the value of I_{max}

$$I_{max} = 2(2\eta)^{1/2}\,(C_1 + C_2)U_{min\ opt}^{3/2} \qquad 49.51$$

Taking into account 49.44, 49.45, 49.49 and the values of the physical constants we obtain the final expression for the maximum beam current

$$I_{max} = 1.27 \times 10^{-5}\ U_1^{3/2}\ \frac{\log \dfrac{R_2}{R_1}}{\log \dfrac{r_e}{R_1}\log \dfrac{R_2}{r_e}}\left[1 - \frac{\log \dfrac{r_e}{R_1}}{\log \dfrac{R_2}{R_1}}\left(1 - \frac{U_2}{U_1}\right)\right]^{3/2}\ [\text{A}]$$

$$49.52$$

Expression 49.52 determines the value of the maximum beam current at given electrode potentials and geometric dimensions.

If the internal tube is removed (see figure IV.3), charge will be induced only on the external conductor, so we have $C_1 = 0$. In this case the following expression will determine the maximum beam current

$$I_{max} = 1.27 \times 10^{-5}\ \frac{U_0^{3/2}}{\log \dfrac{R}{b}}\ [\text{A}] \qquad 49.53$$

The problem of potential distribution and maximum current in hollow electron beams has been solved by means of numerical methods in [104]. We have compared the example given in [104] with our calculations and have found that our approximation leads to the results obtained by numerical calculations with an error of several percents. The potential distribution of a hollow electron beam has been calculated with space-charge density written in the form of an infinite series (see 5.43) by [74]. The first term of·this series corresponds to the approximation $\varrho = $ constant.

50. POTENTIAL DISTRIBUTION IN CYLINDRICAL
ELECTRON BEAMS

We shall determine now the potential distribution in an infinitely long axially symmetric solid continuous electron beam. The beam with radius b moves in a cylindrical metal tube with radius R and potential U_0 in the direction normal to the plane of figure IV.5.

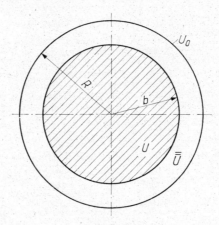

figure IV.5

Let us consider first the approximation $\varrho = $ constant. In this case we have from 48.2

$$\varrho = -\frac{I}{\pi b^2 (2\eta U_0)^{1/2}} \qquad 50.1$$

(We have assumed for simplicity that the velocity of the electrons in the beam is determined by the potential of the tube.)

This solid beam is a special case of the hollow beam without an internal electrode, treated in the second part of the previous section. We get a solid beam by considering the case $a = 0$. Substituting this value into expressions 49.39–49.41 we obtain

$$U_{\min} = U_0 - 3.03 \times 10^4 \frac{I}{\gamma U_0} \left(\frac{1}{2} + \log \frac{R}{b} \right) \qquad 50.2$$

The potential distribution inside the beam is given by

$$U(r) = U_0 - 3.03 \times 10^4 \frac{I}{\sqrt{U_0}} \left[\frac{1}{2} + \log \frac{R}{b} - \frac{1}{2} \left(\frac{r}{b} \right)^2 \right] \qquad 50.3$$

The potential distribution outside the beam is determined by the following expression

$$\bar{\bar{U}}(r) = U_0 - 3.03 \times 10^4 \frac{I}{\sqrt{U_0}} \log \frac{R}{r} \qquad 50.4$$

In this case $r_e = 0$; the equilibrium radius coincides with the beam axis where no force is acting. Inside the beam a repulsive force of the value

$$F_e = 3.03 \times 10^4 \frac{eI}{b^2 \sqrt{U_0}} r \quad \text{[Newton]} \qquad 50.5$$

is acting on the electrons. This force is proportional to the radius. This means that our approximation $\varrho = $ constant just corresponds to the *paraxial approximation*. It is seen from 50.2 that the fuller is the tube filled by the electron beam, the lesser is the potential depression in the beam. In the limiting case of $b = R$ we have

$$U_{\min}|_{b=R} = U_0 - 1.515 \times 10^4 \frac{I}{\sqrt{U_0}} \qquad 50.6$$

The value of the potential at the beam boundary is

$$U(b) = U_0 - 3.03 \times 10^4 \frac{I}{\sqrt{U_0}} \log \frac{R}{b} \qquad 50.7$$

We obtain from 50.2 and 50.7 the ratio of the potential depression inside the beam to the whole potential depression

$$U(b) - U_{\min} = \frac{U_0 - U_{\min}}{1 + 2 \log \frac{R}{b}} \qquad 50.8$$

Let us consider now our *example* in case of a solid beam. We have again

$$P = 1.92 \times 10^{-6} \text{ A/V}^{3/2} \quad \text{and} \quad \frac{b}{R} = \frac{3}{4}$$

The total potential depression in this case is equal to 4.6%. The potential depression inside the beam is equal to 2.9%. The potential depression due to space-charge in a solid beam is stronger than in a hollow beam. The potential distribution calculated on the basis of 50.2–50.4 is plotted in figure IV.6. As a comparison we remark that the total potential depression in an electron beam with the same value of the perveance is only 2.9% if the tube is completely filled by the electron beam.

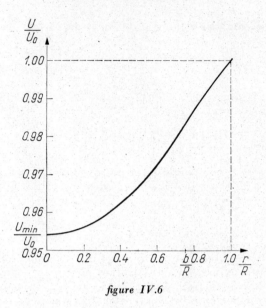

figure IV.6

We shall consider now in detail the case when *the tube is completely filled by the electron beam*, i.e. the diameter of the beam is equal to the diameter of the tube.

The exact value of the space-charge density ϱ at a distance r from the axis is given by 48.1

$$\varrho(r) = - \frac{I}{\pi b^2 \, [2\eta U(r)]^{1/2}} \qquad \qquad 50.9$$

where $U(r)$ is the value of the electric potential at a given value of r.

Due to the infinite length and the axial symmetry of the beam, *Poisson's* equation 5.8 will contain only derivatives with respect to r in this case, too. There is no charge-free region in this case; the only problem is to solve *Poisson's* equation

$$\frac{1}{r} \frac{d}{dr} \left(r \frac{dU}{dr} \right) = \frac{I}{\pi \varepsilon_0 b^2 \, [2\eta U(r)]^{1/2}} \qquad \qquad 50.10$$

Following the method given in [12], we have integrated this second-order nonlinear differential equation by means of a numerical method. The following dimensionless variables have been introduced

$$V = \frac{U(r)}{U_{min}} \qquad \qquad 50.11$$

and

$$\sigma = r \left[\frac{I}{\pi \varepsilon_0 b^2 (2\eta)^{1/2} U_{min}^{3/2}} \right]^{1/2} = 246 \sqrt{\frac{I}{U_{min}^{3/2}}} \, \frac{r}{b} \qquad \qquad 50.12$$

The greater is the perveance, the lesser value of r/b will correspond to a given value of σ. We have at the beam boundary that

$$\sigma = \sigma_{max} = 246 \sqrt{\frac{I}{U_{min}^{3/2}}}$$

Equation 50.10 can be rewritten with these variables as follows

$$\frac{1}{\sigma}\frac{d}{d\sigma}\left(\sigma\frac{dV}{d\sigma}\right) = V^{-1/2} \qquad\qquad 50.13$$

The boundary conditions at $\sigma = 0$ are

$$V_0 = 1 \quad \text{and} \quad \frac{dV}{d\sigma}\bigg|_0 = 0.$$

The numerical solution of equation 50.13 has been plotted in figure IV.7 (curve 1).

Naturally, the solution is valid only in the interval $\sigma < \sigma_{max}$. Therefore. only the initial part of the curve has a practical meaning. For example, in case of $I/U_{min}^{3/2} = 10^{-6}$ A/V$^{3/2}$ we have $\sigma_{max} = 0.246$. The curve given in [12] is not very practicable because the accuracy of its reading is too little at the initial region. The curve given in figure IV.7 has been calculated by the author.

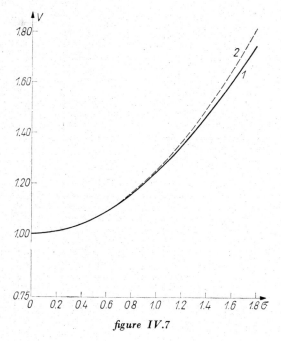

figure IV.7

It is seen in the figure that the potential is an increasing monotonic function of the distance from the axis. According to 50.12, the greater is the beam perveance, the greater is the rate of increase of the potential.

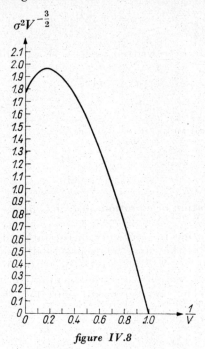

$$\sigma^2 V^{-\frac{3}{2}}$$

figure IV.8

It follows from 50.11 and 50.12 that the quantity

$$\sigma^2 V^{-3/2} = \frac{I r^2}{\pi \varepsilon_0 b^2 (2\eta)^{1/2} U^{3/2}(r)} \qquad\qquad 50.14$$

is proportional to the beam perveance. This quantity has been plotted against $1/V$, i.e. against the ratio of the potential along the axis to the potential at a radius r, in figure IV.8. (This dependence can easily be determined by means of curve 1 in figure IV.7.)

If $U_{\min} = 0$ we have $\sigma \rightarrow \infty$ and $V \rightarrow \infty$, independent of the value of r. Obviously, the solution is not valid in this case. It is easily seen, however, that in this case equation 50.10 can be satisfied by the following expression

$$U = \left(\frac{9I}{16\,\pi\varepsilon_0\,(2\eta)^{1/2}} \right)^{2/3} \left(\frac{r}{b} \right)^{4/3} \qquad\qquad 50.15$$

Thus, according to 50.14 and 50.15

$$\sigma^2 V^{-3/2} = \frac{16}{9} = 1.778$$

is the value corresponding to the case of

$$U_{\min} = \frac{1}{V} = 0$$

(see figure IV.8).

As we can see in the figure

$$(\sigma^2 V^{-3/2})_{\max} = 1.963$$

This maximum value corresponds to

$$\frac{1}{V_{\text{opt}}} = 0.174$$

Substituting these values as well as $r = b$ and $U = U_0$ into 50.14, we obtain the possible maximum value of the beam current

$$I_{\max} = 3.24 \times 10^{-5} U_0^{3/2} \quad [\text{A}] \qquad 50.16$$

If $U_{\min}/U_0 < 0.174$ the beam instability occurs. Thus, the maximum potential depression without a collapse of the beam is 5.75-fold.

Let us now compare this accurate solution with that obtained using the approximation $\varrho = \text{constant}$. Thus we shall have an estimate of the accuracy of this approximation. Instead of 50.1 we shall use

$$\varrho = - \frac{I}{\pi b^2 (2\eta U_{\min})^{1/2}} \qquad 50.17$$

i.e. we assume that the space-charge density is determined by the potential on the axis across the whole beam. Then, taking into account 50.12, we obtain for the variable V the following expression, using 50.17, 50.2, 50.3 and 50.11

$$V = 1 + \left(\frac{\sigma}{2}\right)^2 \qquad 50.18$$

The dependence 50.18 has been plotted in figure IV.7 (curve 2). Naturally, curve 2 is situated a little over curve 1, as in 50.17 the space-charge density is greater than the actual one, i.e., the value of V has been increased. But in the practically important initial region the two curves almost coincide with each other. It is a proof that for electron beams with not very high intensity the approximation $\varrho = \text{constant}$ is acceptable.

Obviously, at higher values of V the approximation becomes worse. Thus, calculating the dependence of $\sigma^2 V^{-3/2}$ versus $1/V$ on the basis of 50.18, we obtain a curve considerably different from that given in figure IV.8. We shall have $V_{\text{opt}} = 3$ and $(\sigma^2 V^{-3/2})_{\max} = 1.54$, whence $I_{\max} = 2.54 \times 10^{-5} U_0^{3/2}$. This result is a little bit worse than that obtained by accurate calculations, as it was to be expected.

If the tube is not filled completely by the electron beam we find that the value of $I_{\max}$ becomes smaller. The method used in the previous section

17*

can be applied for this case if $b \ll R$. The result coincides with that obtained for the hollow beam without internal conductor (49.53)

$$I_{max} = 1.27 \times 10^{-5} \frac{U_0^{3/2}}{\log \dfrac{R}{b}} \quad [A] \qquad\qquad 50.19$$

It follows from this that the value of the maximum current *density* is greater in a hollow beam than in a solid beam. The result is the same if one starts from space-charge distribution 48.1 [97]. The potential on the beam axis corresponding to the maximum value of the current is equal to

$$U_{min\,opt} = U_0/3$$

51. POTENTIAL DISTRIBUTION IN PLANE-SYMMETRIC
ELECTRON BEAMS

Let us consider now the potential distribution of an infinitely long sheet (strip) electron beam in the z, y plane for the case when the beam is extended in the direction of x axis ($W \gg y_0$). The approximation $\rho = $ constant will be used. The beam is moving in a box held at potential U_0, in the direction of the z axis. The width of the box is equal to $2g$. The cross section of the system is given in figure IV.9. In this approximation we have a problem

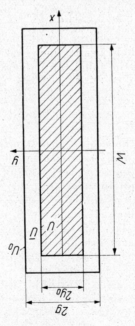

figure IV.9

with one independent variable; the potential distribution depends only on the coordinate y. The potential between the box and the beam will be denoted with $\bar{U}$, that within the beam will be denoted with U. We have the following equations

$$0 \leq y \leq y_0 \qquad \frac{d^2U}{dy^2} = -\frac{\varrho}{\varepsilon_0} \qquad\qquad 51.1$$

and

$$y_0 \leq y \leq g \qquad \frac{d^2\bar{U}}{dy^2} = 0 \qquad\qquad 51.2$$

Integrating these equations, we obtain

$$\frac{dU}{dy} = -\frac{\varrho}{\varepsilon_0}y + C_1 \qquad\qquad 51.3$$

and

$$\frac{d\bar{U}}{dy} = C_2 \qquad\qquad 51.4$$

Integrating once again, we obtain

$$U = -\frac{\varrho}{2\varepsilon_0}y^2 + C_1 y + C_3 \qquad\qquad 51.5$$

and

$$\bar{U} = C_2 y + C_1 \qquad\qquad 51.6$$

We have the following boundary conditions

$$\left. \frac{dU}{dy} \right|_{y=0} = 0 \qquad \bar{U}|_{y=g} = U_0 \left.\vphantom{\frac{dU}{dy}}\right\}$$
$$\qquad\qquad\qquad\qquad\qquad\qquad\qquad\qquad 51.7$$
$$U|_{y=y_0} = \bar{U}|_{y=y_0} \qquad \left. \frac{dU}{dy} \right|_{y=y_0} = \left. \frac{d\bar{U}}{dy} \right|_{y=y_0}$$

We shall determine now the constants from the boundary conditions

$$C_1 = 0 \qquad\qquad 51.8$$

$$C_2 = -\frac{\varrho}{\varepsilon_0}y_0 \qquad\qquad 51.9$$

$$C_3 = U_0 + \frac{\varrho}{2\varepsilon_0}y_0(2g - y_0) \qquad\qquad 51.10$$

and

$$C_4 = U_0 + \frac{\varrho}{\varepsilon_0} y_0 g \qquad\qquad 51.11$$

If we assume that the velocities of all the electrons of the beam are determined by the potential U_0 then, according to 48.2, we shall have

$$\varrho = -\frac{I}{2 W y_0 (2\eta U_0)^{1/2}} \qquad\qquad 51.12$$

Using 51.5, 51.6, 51.8–51.11 and 51.12 and substituting the values of the physical constants we obtain final expressions for the potential distribution

$$U(y) = U_0 - 4.75 \times 10^4 \frac{I}{W y_0 \sqrt{U_0}} (2g\, y_0 - y_0^2 - y^2) \qquad 51.13$$

and

$$\bar{U}(y) = U_0 - 9.5 \times 10^4 \frac{I}{W y_0 \sqrt{U_0}} y_0(g - y) \qquad 51.14$$

The minimum value of the potential is given by

$$U_{min} = U(0) = U_0 - 4.75 \times 10^4 \frac{I}{W \sqrt{U_0}} (2g - y_0) \qquad 51.15$$

As an *example* we shall determine now the potential distribution in a sheet beam with perveance $P = 1.92 \times 10^{-6}$ A/V$^{3/2}$ and the following geometrical dimensions

$$\frac{y_0}{g} = \frac{9}{16} \quad \text{and} \quad \frac{y_0}{W} = \frac{1}{10}$$

The value of the total potential depression is equal to 2.3% in this case. The potential depression inside the beam is 0.9%. The potential distribution is plotted in figure IV.10. As a comparison we remark that the total potential depression in an electron beam with that value of the perveance is only 0.9% if the box is completely filled by the electron beam.

For the determination of the maximum beam current the 'condenser' method can be applied if $y_0 \ll g$. The capacitance per unit length of the planar condenser formed by the box and the electron beam is given by

$$C = \frac{W \varepsilon_0}{g - y_0} \quad [\text{Fm}^{-1}] \qquad\qquad 51.16$$

Carrying out the calculations similar to those given in § 49, we obtain for the maximum value of the beam current

$$I_{max} = 4.05 \times 10^{-6} \frac{W}{g} U_0^{3/2} \quad [\text{A}] \qquad\qquad 51.17$$

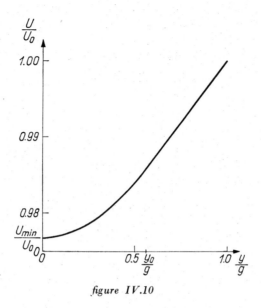

figure IV.10

The value of the potential on the axis corresponding to the maximum beam current is equal to $U_{\text{min opt}} = U_0/3$. The same result can be obtained by the accurate solution of the problem on the basis of space-charge distribution 48.1 [73]. It has been found that the value of I_{max} increases with an increase of the ratio y_0/g. If the box is completely filled by the electron beam ($y_0 = g$), the maximum value of the beam current is determined by

$$I_{\text{max}} = 9.35 \times 10^{-6} \frac{W}{g} U_0^{3/2} \qquad\qquad 51.18$$

The corresponding value of the potential on the axis is given by

$$U_{\text{min opt}} = \frac{U_0}{4}$$

(B) SPREADING OF ELECTRON BEAMS DUE TO SPACE-CHARGE

52. ELECTRON-BEAM MOTION IN UNIFORM POTENTIAL REGION (SPREADING OF A DRIFTING BEAM)

We shall now consider a long electron beam drifting in a uniform potential region. Due to space-charge, repulsive forces will occur between the electrons of the beam. These forces cause the transversal (normal to the direction of motion) dimensions of the beam to increase, i.e. *beam spreading* occurs. We shall give a quantitative analysis of beam spreading for different types of electron beams in the following. With the exception of hollow beams, the most important practical *paraxial approximation* will be used. The results obtained in that way can also be generalised for non-paraxial motion.

Besides the assumptions made in §47, here the potential distribution across the beam will also be neglected. Naturally, the beam spreading itself can be considered as a consequence of the potential depression due to space-charge. However, this potential depression in not very high-intensity electron beams is so insignificant in the beam region that it can be neglected as a separate effect. We have seen in § 50 that the total potential depression of a cylindrical electron beam with perveance $P = 1.92 \times 10^{-6} \, \text{A/V}^{3/2}$ amounts only to a few percent. But the cross section of the same beam increases not less than 4-fold after passing a distance only 4.5 times longer than the initial beam diameter. This example illustrates clearly that the beam spreading may be considerable even at comparatively small intensities when the potential depression can be neglected. We should like to remark that in Chapter V we shall assume that the electrostatic focusing potential is independent of the space-charge, i.e. satisfies *Laplace*'s equation. Space-charge shall be taken into account merely as a *force* acting on the electrons but at not too large values of the perveance its potential-depressing effect can always be neglected.

If the potential distribution across the beam is taken into account, the problem becomes much more complicated. Obviously, stronger beam spreading will occur than in the case of a uniform potential beam because the average velocity of the electrons will be less and it causes a greater influence of space-charge. But experimental investigations have shown that the additional effect due to the potential depression is roughly compensated by the effect of positive ions formed in the electron beam. Thus, this complicated analysis is not necessary at practical values of the beam perveance.

As it is well known, *magnetic attraction* occurs between particles moving in the same direction parallel to each other. The following question arises naturally: how are electrostatic repulsion forces between the electrons of the beam compensated by this attraction? This problem will be treated on the example of the axially symmetric solid beam. According to 50.5 a radial repulsive force of the value

$$F_e = \frac{eI}{2\pi\varepsilon_0 \, v_z b} \qquad\qquad 52.1$$

is acting on the edge electron of the beam. This formula is strictly valid only for beams consisting of electrons moving parallel to each other and only in the approximation $\varrho = \text{constant}$.

According to the *Biot–Savart* law, the beam current induces at a distance r from the axis the magnetic induction

$$B = \frac{\mu_0 I}{2\pi r} \qquad\qquad 52.2$$

in tangential direction. Thus, the radial *Lorentz* force acting on the edge electron is equal to

$$F_m = -\frac{\mu_0 e I v_z}{2\pi\, b} \qquad\qquad 52.3$$

where

$$v_z = (2\eta U_0)^{1/2}$$

is the electron velocity in axial direction.

Taking into account that

$$\frac{1}{(\mu_0\varepsilon_0)^{1/2}} = c \qquad\qquad 52.4$$

we obtain the resultant force

$$F = F_e + F_m = \frac{eI}{2\pi\varepsilon_0 v_z b}\left[1 - \frac{v_z^2}{c^2}\right] \qquad\qquad 52.5$$

As we see, the magnetic attraction is considerable only in the relativistic case. If the electrons move with the velocity of light, the magnetic force totally compensates the electrostatic repulsion force. As the relativistic treatment is not dealt with in this book, the magnetic attraction will always be neglected in the following. Detailed analysis of the relativistic effects in electron beams can be found in [108–122].

53. SPREADING OF CYLINDRICAL ELECTRON BEAMS

We shall consider the motion of an axially symmetric solid electron beam in a uniform Φ_0 potential drift space. We assume that there is no magnetic field and the electrons have no azimuthal component of initial velocity. Taking into account that in 50.1 $r(z)$ should be written instead of b, in this case the *paraxial equation* 21.14 of the *edge electron trajectory* $r(z)$ of the beam can be written as

$$\frac{d^2r}{dz^2} = \frac{1}{4\sqrt{2\pi\varepsilon_0}\sqrt{\eta}}\frac{I}{\Phi_0^{3/2}}\frac{1}{r} \qquad\qquad 53.1$$

As we have assumed that the value of the potential is not altered considerably by space-charge, let us consider $\Phi_0 = U_0$, where U_0 is the potential of the electrode surrounding the drift space. If there is no force except that of space-charge, the beam configuration determined by space-charge spreading is described by equation 53.1.

It can be seen immediately from equation 53.1 that in case of $r \to 0$ we have $r'' \to \infty$, i.e. the edge electron can never cross the axis of symmetry. A very important conclusion can be drawn from this fact: a point image can never be formed if space-charge is produced by the electron beam itself. Space-charge does not change *in principle* the image formation if space-charge density ϱ depends only on coordinate z. But we had to take into consideration in equation 53.1 that ϱ depends on the cross section of the beam, i.e. depends on r because in this case the cross section changes in the course of the motion.

For the integration of the paraxial ray equation 53.1 the following dimensionless variables will be introduced [12]

$$R = \frac{r}{r_0} \qquad\qquad 53.2$$

and

$$Z = \left[\frac{I}{2\sqrt{2\pi\varepsilon_0}\sqrt{\eta}\Phi_0^{3/2}}\right]^{1/2} \frac{z}{r_0} = 174\sqrt{P}\,\frac{z}{r_0} \qquad 53.3$$

where r_0 is the beam radius at the initial point $z = Z = 0$ and $P = I/\Phi_0^{3/2}$ is the perveance of the beam. Then equation 53.1 can be written as follows

$$\frac{d^2R}{dZ^2} = \frac{1}{2R} \qquad\qquad 53.4$$

Equation 53.4 will be integrated with the following initial conditions

$$Z = 0 \begin{cases} R = R_0 = 1 \\ R' = \dfrac{dR}{dZ} = R_0' = \dfrac{dR}{dZ}\Big|_{Z=0} \end{cases} \qquad 53.5$$

Let us multiply both sides of this equation by dR. We have

$$R' \times dR' = \frac{dR}{2R}$$

We can now integrate

$$R'^2 = R_0'^2 + \log R \qquad\qquad 53.6$$

It is immediately seen from this expression that if the beam is initially convergent, the minimum value of R is equal to

$$R_{min} = \exp(-R_0'^2) \qquad\qquad 53.7$$

Let us integrate now equation 53.6. The result is

$$Z = \int_1^R \frac{dR}{\pm(R_0'^2 + \log R)^{1/2}} \qquad\qquad 53.8$$

Integrating with respect to $u = R'$ instead of R, we can rewrite integral 53.8 in another form

$$Z = 2\exp(-R_0'^2) \int_{R_0'}^{R' = \pm(\log R + R_0'^2)^{1/2}} \exp(u^2)\,du \qquad 53.9$$

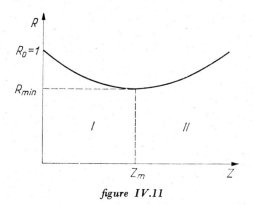

figure IV.11

If $R_0' < 0$ (initially convergent beam), the trajectory can be divided into two parts (figure IV.11). In the first region we have

$$u = R' \le 0, \qquad 0 \le Z \le Z_m \qquad \text{and} \qquad R \le 1 \qquad 53.10$$

Therefore, the negative sign must be chosen in the upper limit of integration 53.9. Then expression 53.9 can be written in the following form

$$Z = 2 \; \exp\left(-R_0'^2\right) \int_{R_0'}^{-(\log R + R_0'^2)^{1/2}} \exp\left(u^2\right) du \qquad 53.11$$

The integration should be carried out on the interval from a negative quantity to another negative quantity of lesser absolute value. As

$$f(x) = \int_0^x \exp\left(u^2\right) du \qquad 53.12$$

is an even function, we have

$$\int_{-x}^0 \exp\left(u^2\right) du = - \int_0^{-x} \exp\left(u^2\right) du = \int_0^x \exp\left(u^2\right) du$$

Therefore expression 53.11 can be written in the following form

$$Z = 2 \; \exp\left(-R_0'^2\right) \left[\int_0^{-R_0'} \exp\left(u^2\right) du - \int_0^{+(\log R + R_0'^2)^{1/2}} \exp\left(u^2\right) du \right] \qquad 53.13$$

We obtain for the location of the minimum cross section of the beam

$$Z_m = 2 \; \exp\left(-R_0'^2\right) \int_0^{-R_0'} \exp\left(u^2\right) du \qquad 53.14$$

The value of the minimum beam radius is given by 53.7.

In region II we have

$$Z_m \leq Z < \infty \qquad \text{and} \qquad R' \geq 0 \qquad\qquad 53.15$$

For this region the positive sign must be chosen in the upper limit of the integral 53.9. Expression 53.9 can be written then in the following form

$$Z = 2 \, \exp\left(-R_0'^2\right) \int\limits_{R_0'}^{+(\log R + R_0'^2)^{1/2}} \exp\left(u^2\right) du \qquad\qquad 53.16$$

The integration should be carried out on the interval from a negative value to a positive value. Therefore

$$Z = 2 \exp\left(-R_0'^2\right) \left[\int\limits_0^{-R_0'} \exp\left(u^2\right) du + \int\limits_0^{+(\log R + R_0'^2)^{1/2}} \exp\left(u^2\right) du \right] \qquad 53.17$$

Taking into account 53.14, it follows from expressions 53.13 and 53.17 that *the whole beam can be completely described by the following expression*

$$Z = Z_m \pm 2 \, \exp\left(-R_0'^2\right) f\left[(\log R + R_0'^2)^{1/2}\right] \qquad\qquad 53.18$$

where the negative sign is to be chosen in the converging region I, and the positive sign in the diverging region II, of the beam. $f(x)$ is an increasing monotonic function defined by 53.12. The values of this function are listed in table IV.2.

It follows from expression 53.18 that the beam is symmetrical with respect to its minimum cross section, in longitudinal direction.

If the beam enters the drift space parallel to the z axis ($R_0' = 0$), we obtain from expression 53.9 that

$$Z = 2 f (\sqrt{\log R}) \qquad\qquad 53.19$$

It also follows from 53.7 and 53.14 that in this case $Z_m = 0$ and $R_{\min} = R_0$, i.e. space-charge causes a monotonic spreading of the beam.

It follows from expressions 53.2, 53.3, 53.12 and 53.19 that

$$f\left(\sqrt{\log \frac{r}{r_0}}\right) = 87 \sqrt{P} \, \frac{z}{r_0} \qquad\qquad 53.20$$

Thus, the rate of the space-charge spreading increases with the increase of the beam perveance.

It follows from expression 53.20 that with the knowledge of the universal beam-spread curve $R(Z)$ [12] (figure IV.12) determined by 53.19 the spreading of the beam can be immediately obtained for any value of P.

Actually, we obtain from 53.3 that

$$\frac{z}{r_0} = \frac{Z}{174 \sqrt{P}} \qquad\qquad 53.21$$

TABLE IV.2

Values of the functions for the calculation of beam spreading

x	$\exp(x^2)$	$\exp(-x^2)$	f	F
0.00	1.000	1.0000	0.0000	0.0000
0.02	1.000	0.9996	0.0200	0.0200
0.04	1.002	0.9984	0.0400	0.0400
0.06	1.004	0.9964	0.0601	0.0599
0.08	1.006	0.9936	0.0802	0.0797
0.10	1.010	0.9901	0.1003	0.0993
0.12	1.015	0.9857	0.1206	0.1189
0.14	1.020	0.9806	0.1409	0.1382
0.16	1.026	0.9757	0.1614	0.1575
0.18	1.033	0.9681	0.1820	0.1762
0.20	1.041	0.9608	0.2027	0.1948
0.22	1.049	0.9528	0.2236	0.2130
0.24	1.059	0.9440	0.2447	0.2310
0.26	1.070	0.9346	0.2660	0.2486
0.28	1.082	0.9246	0.2875	0.2658
0.30	1.094	0.9139	0.3092	0.2826
0.32	1.108	0.9027	0.3313	0.2991
0.34	1.123	0.8918	0.3536	0.3154
0.36	1.138	0.8785	0.3762	0.3305
0.38	1.155	0.8655	0.3991	0.3454
0.40	1.174	0.8521	0.4224	0.3599
0.42	1.193	0.8377	0.4461	0.3737
0.44	1.214	0.8240	0.4701	0.3874
0.46	1.236	0.8093	0.4946	0.4003
0.48	1.259	0.7942	0.5196	0.4127
0.50	1.284	0.7788	0.5450	0.4244
0.52	1.310	0.7631	0.5709	0.4356
0.54	1.339	0.7471	0.5974	0.4463
0.56	1.368	0.7308	0.6245	0.4564
0.58	1.399	0.7143	0.6522	0.4659
0.60	1.433	0.6977	0.6805	0.4748
0.62	1.469	0.6809	0.7095	0.4831
0.64	1.506	0.6639	0.7393	0.4908
0.66	1.546	0.6469	0.7698	0.4980
0.68	1.588	0.6298	0.8011	0.5045
0.70	1.632	0.6126	0.8333	0.5105
0.72	1.679	0.5957	0.8664	0.5161
0.74	1.729	0.5783	0.9005	0.5208
0.76	1.782	0.5612	0.9356	0.5251
0.78	1.838	0.5442	0.9718	0.5289
0.80	1.897	0.5273	1.0091	0.5321
0.82	1.959	0.5105	1.0477	0.5348
0.84	2.024	0.4938	1.0875	0.5370
0.86	2.095	0.4773	1.1287	0.5387
0.88	2.169	0.4610	1.1713	0.5399
0.90	2.248	0.4449	1.215	0.5405
0.92	2.331	0.4290	1.261	0.5409
0.94	2.420	0.4133	1.309	0.5410
0.96	2.513	0.3979	1.358	0.5403
0.98	2.608	0.3827	1.409	0.5393
1.00	2.718	0.3679	1.463	0.5382
1.02	2.830	0.3533	1.518	0.5363
1.04	2.949	0.3391	1.576	0.5344
1.06	3.076	0.3249	1.636	0.5316

(Table IV.2 continued)

x	$\exp(x^2)$	$\exp(-x^2)$	f	F
1.08	3.210	0.3115	1.699	0.5292
1.10	3.354	0.2982	1.765	0.5263
1.12	3.506	0.2853	1.833	0.5229
1.14	3.668	0.2726	1.905	0.5194
1.16	3.841	0.2604	1.980	0.5156
1.18	4.025	0.2485	2.059	0.5116
1.20	4.221	0.2369	2.141	0.5073
1.22	4.430	0.2257	2.228	0.5029
1.24	4.653	0.2149	2.318	0.4981
1.26	4.892	0.2044	2.414	0.4935
1.28	5.147	0.1943	2.514	0.4885
1.30	5.420	0.1845	2.620	0.4834
1.32	5.711	0.1751	2.731	0.4782
1.34	6.023	0.1660	2.848	0.4729
1.36	6.357	0.1573	2.972	0.4675
1.38	6.715	0.1489	3.103	0.4621
1.40	7.099	0.1409	3.241	0.4565
1.42	7.511	0.1331	3.387	0.4509
1.44	7.953	0.1257	3.542	0.4453
1.46	8.428	0.1186	3.705	0.4396
1.48	8.939	0.1119	3.879	0.4339
1.50	9.488	0.1054	4.063	0.4282
1.52	10.078	0.0992	4.259	0.4226
1.54	10.715	0.0933	4.467	0.4169
1.56	11.400	0.0877	4.688	0.4112
1.58	12.139	0.0824	4.923	0.4056
1.60	12.936	0.0773	5.174	0.4000
1.62	13.796	0.0725	5.44	0.3943
1.64	14.726	0.0679	5.73	0.3891
1.66	15.731	0.0636	6.03	0.3834
1.68	16.817	0.0595	6.36	0.3782
1.70	17.993	0.0556	6.70	0.3724
1.72	19.267	0.0519	7.08	0.3675
1.74	20.648	0.0484	7.47	0.3618
1.76	22.145	0.0452	7.90	0.3568
1.78	23.770	0.0421	8.36	0.3517
1.80	25.534	0.0392	8.85	0.3466
1.82	27.451	0.0364	9.38	0.3417
1.84	29.537	0.0339	9.95	0.3369
1.86	31.804	0.0314	10.57	0.3323
1.88	34.275	0.0292	11.23	0.3277
1.90	36.966	0.0271	11.94	0.3230
1.92	39.901	0.0251	12.71	0.3185
1.94	43.103	0.0232	13.54	0.3141
1.96	46.600	0.0215	14.43	0.3097
1.98	50.420	0.0198	15.40	0.3054
2.00	54.598	0.0183	16.45	0.3014

Thus, the variation of P causes only a change of the scale of the figure. For example: if $P = 1.32 \times 10^{-6}$ A/V$^{3/2}$. we have

$$\frac{z}{r_0} = 5Z$$

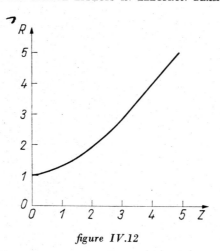

figure IV.12

We should like to remark, however, that at large values of r/r_0 expression 53.19 is a rough approximation because in this case our assumption on the radial direction of space-charge forces is not fulfilled.

Naturally, expression 53.21 is valid also in case of $R'_0 \neq 0$. It is sufficient to determine the dependence $R(Z)$ only once for each value of R'_0. The variation of the perveance P causes only a change of the scale of the abscissa, according to 53.21.

Let us introduce the following integral [84]

$$F(x) = \exp(-x^2) \int_0^x \exp(u^2)\, du \qquad 53.22$$

It is easy to prove that if $x \ll 1$, we have

$$F(x) \approx \int_0^x du = x$$

and if $x \gg 1$, then

$$F(x) = \frac{\int_0^x \exp(u^2)\, du}{\exp(x^2)} \xrightarrow[x \to \infty]{} \frac{\exp(x^2)}{2x \exp(x^2)} = \frac{1}{2x}$$

Using 53.22, we can rewrite expression 53.14 in the following form

$$Z_m = 2F(-R'_0) \qquad 53.23$$

The beam configuration can be determined for any value of R'_0 by mean of table IV.2 and expression 53.18. For this we shall turn 53.18 into the following form, by the use of 53.23

$$Z = 2F(-R'_0) \pm 2 \exp(-R'^2_0) f[(\log R + R'^2_0)^{1/2}] \qquad 53.24$$

Let us denote the argument of the function f with x

$$(\log R + R'^2_0)^{1/2} = x \qquad 53.25$$

Then

$$R = \exp(x^2) \exp(-R'^2_0) \qquad 53.26$$

We have from 53.24 the following expression

$$f(x) = \pm \frac{Z - 2F(-R'_0)}{2 \exp(-R'^2_0)} \qquad 53.27$$

Then we can determine the values of $F(-R'_0)$ and $\exp(-R'^2_0)$ from table IV.2. Now we calculate the function $f(x)$ for different values of Z and look up the respective values of the argument x in the table. After this the values of R can be determined by means of expression 53.26. Values of $\exp(x^2)$ necessary for the determination of R are also to be found in the table.

The values of R_{min} and Z_m are determined from expressions 53.7 and 53.23, respectively. These quantities are plotted versus R'_0 in figures IV.13 and 14.

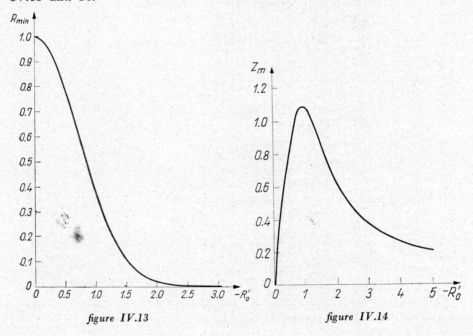

figure IV.13   figure IV.14

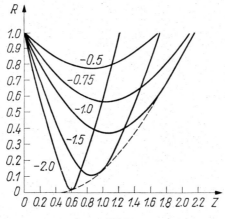

figure IV.15

In figure IV.15 the function $R(Z)$ determining the spreading of the beam is plotted for different values of R_0'. These values have been shown at the respective curves of the figure [12].

It follows from expressions 53.2 and 53.3 that

$$R_0' = \frac{dr}{dz}\bigg|_0 \frac{1}{174\sqrt{P}} \qquad\qquad 53.28$$

where $(dr/dz)|_0$ is the initial slope of the edge electron trajectory of the beam. Thus, the value of R_0' is uniquely defined by this slope and the perveance P. The greater is the beam perveance, the smaller is the value of R_0'.

Let us suppose that the initial slope of the originally parallel beam has been produced by an aberrationless *thin lens* placed in the plane $z = 0$. The focal length of this lens is denoted with z_f.

It is easy to see that in this case

$$\frac{dr}{dz}\bigg|_0 = -\frac{r_0}{z_f} \qquad\qquad 53.29$$

It follows from expressions 53.29, 53.28 and 53.3 that

$$R_0' = -\frac{r_0}{174\,z_f\sqrt{P}} = -\frac{z}{Z z_f} \qquad\qquad 53.30$$

We can see in figures IV.13 and IV.14 that the increase of the initial beam slope as well as the decrease of the perveance cause the decrease of the minimum beam radius R_{min}, while the value of Z_m first increases and then decreases.

If space-charge is negligible ($P \approx 0$), we have $R_0' \to \infty$, independently of the value of $(dr/dz)|_0$, i.e. $R_{min} \approx 0$. In this case we have a conical beam with apex angle defined by the value of $(dr/dz)|_0$. The focus of the beam will be formed in the apex of the cone. The greater is the value of $-(dr/dz)|_0$ the lesser is the focal length z_f. In case of $P = 0$ parameter Z cannot be used as $Z \equiv 0$, independent from the value of z. Nevertheless, figure IV.15 can be directly applied for comparison of the values z_m and z_f.

The correlation between the values of z_f and z_m can be found immediately by drawing a tangent to the curve in figure IV.15 with respective value of R'_0 at the initial point. Actually, if the abscissa is intersected by the tangent at a point Z_1, we have

$$-R'_0 = \frac{1}{Z_1} \qquad\qquad 53.31$$

On the other hand, it follows from expressions 53.29, 53.3 and 53.28 that

$$-\frac{dr}{dz}\bigg|_0 = \frac{r_0}{z_f} = \frac{174\sqrt{P}}{Z_f} = -174\sqrt{PR'_0} \qquad 53.32$$

Comparing 53.31 with 53.32 we find that

$$Z_1 = Z_f$$

Thus, it can be easily proved that it would be a wrong idea to think that at a given value of $(dr/dz)|_0$ the increase of the perveance would cause not only the increase of the minimum cross section but also the increase of the value of z_m. The inequality $z_m > z_f$ is valid only for small values of the beam perveance. When the perveance increases, the value of z_m first increases, too, but then it starts to decrease. At large values of the perveance we have $z_m < z_f$, i.e. the location of the minimum cross section is nearer to the lens than it would be without space-charge.

This method of calculation has been applied in § 45.

It can also be seen from figure IV.15 that at a given value of Z we can obtain a minimum cross section denoted as R_k with a value of R'_0 such that $Z_m \neq Z$ but with a certain value of R'_{0k} whose corresponding value $Z_{mk} = 2F(-R'_{0k})$ is less than Z.

The values of R_k corresponding to the given values of Z are given in figure IV.15 by the dotted curve. It is seen in the figure that the attainable minimum cross section is growing with Z, i.e. the farther is the given cross section and the greater is the perveance, the greater is the minimum cross section of the beam. Approximately [67], the following formula can be used

$$R_k = 0.148\, Z^{5/2}$$

More detailed analysis of this problem has been given by [68, 77, 78, 92, 96, 102].

If the beam is already diverging at the point $Z = 0$ ($R'_0 > 0$) then we only have region II in figure IV.11 and the integration in 53.16 is carried out over the interval from one positive quantity to another positive quantity of greater value. We have in this case

$$Z = 2\,\exp\,(-R'^2_0)[f(\log R + R'^2_0)^{1/2} - f(R'_0)] \qquad 53.33$$

There is a monotonic spreading of the beam in this case.

Let us determine now the *maximum beam current* which can be transmitted through a tube with diameter $D = 2r_0$ and length l [12], without any special focusing device.

The current-limiting effect of the beam spreading is a very important factor. It is frequently necessary, for example in klystrons, to transmit a possible maximum current through a tube with given geometrical dimensions without any special focusing. We shall assume that a converging electron beam enters the tube in the plane $z = 0$ (figure IV.11). Let us change the perveance of the beam. At very small values of the perveance we can choose the initial slope of the beam in such a way that the beam passes the tube so that it is not completely filled by the beam even at the output. If the value of the perveance is considerably increased, the spreading of the beam due to space-charge will be so strong that only a small fraction of the beam will pass the tube. There is an optimum value of the perveance at which the beam entirely passes the tube and the tube is completely filled by the beam at the output. As a consequence of the symmetry discussed above, the minimum cross section of the beam will be located in this case at the centre of the tube, i.e. in the plane $z_m = l/2$.

It follows from 53.3 that in this case the coordinate of the output of the tube is equal to

$$Z = 348 \sqrt{P} \, \frac{l}{D} = 2Z_m \qquad\qquad 53.34$$

But we have seen in figure IV.14 that Z_m has a maximum value

$$Z_{m\,max} = 1.08 \qquad\qquad 53.35$$

The corresponding optimal value of R_0' being

$$(-R_0')_{opt} = 0.92 \qquad\qquad 53.36$$

It follows from this that Z has a maximum value, too. Using this fact, the maximum value (P_{max}) of the perveance of a beam which can be transmitted through the tube can be calculated. Actually, considering the value of P as a variable in 53.34, we can see that a certain value of P_{max} corresponds to Z_{max}

$$P_{max} = \frac{Z_{max}^2}{348^2} \left(\frac{D}{l}\right)^2 \qquad [AV^{-3/2}] \qquad 53.37$$

where

$$Z_{max} = 2Z_{m\,max}$$

Thus, we have from 53.35 and 53.37 that

$$P_{max} = 3.85 \times 10^{-5} \left(\frac{D}{l}\right)^2 = 49 \times 10^{-6} \frac{S_0}{l^2} \qquad [AV^{-3/2}] \qquad 53.38$$

18*

where S_0 is the initial value of the area of the cross section of the beam. So, it is possible to transmit through a metal tube with diameter D, length l and potential U_0 an electron beam with current not more than

$$I_{max} = 3.85 \times 10^{-5} U_0^{3/2} \left(\frac{D}{l}\right)^2 \qquad \text{[A]} \qquad\qquad 53.39$$

because of the spreading of the beam.

We can easily obtain from 53.28, 53.38 and 53.36 that

$$\left(\frac{dr}{dz}\Big|_0\right)_{opt} = -\frac{D}{l}. \qquad\qquad 53.40$$

i.e. in order to achieve the maximum value (P_{max}) of the perveance determined by 53.38, the initial direction of the edge electron trajectory of the beam should coincide with the direction of the diagonal of a rectangle with width D and length l. The diameter of the beam will be of minimum value at the centre of the tube. According to 53.7 and 53.36 this value is equal to

$$\frac{d_{min}}{D} = R_{min} = 0.43 \qquad\qquad 53.41$$

The case when the electron beam passes two diaphragms with different diameters has been treated by [80].

We have carried out the analysis in paraxial approximation. Similar results can be obtained in the general case as well [59, 86, 87, 103].

The spreading of a cylindrical electron beam in uniform axial external electric field has been analysed by [83, 89, 91]. A numerical solution of the paraxial ray equation has been given by [58] for linear and quadratic potential distributions along the beam axis.

The spreading of non-homocentric electron beams has been treated by [105]. Papers [108, 112, 119] are devoted to the investigation of the spreading of relativistic electron beams. The beam spreading due to space-charge has been analysed by [81] making allowance for the simultaneous effect of thermal velocities.

54. SPREADING OF SHEET ELECTRON BEAMS

We shall consider now a sheet electron beam moving in the direction of z axis in a uniform Φ_0 potential drift space. We assume that there is no magnetic field and the electrons have no initial velocity component in the direction of x axis. Taking into consideration that in 51.12 $y(z)$ is to be written instead of y_0, the *paraxial equation* 22.13 of the *edge electron trajectory* $y(z)$ of the beam can be written as follows

$$\frac{d^2y}{dz^2} = \frac{1}{4\sqrt{2}\,\varepsilon_0 W \sqrt{\eta}} \frac{I}{\Phi_0^{3/2}} \qquad\qquad 54.1$$

As we have already mentioned, the beam can be considered two-dimensional if $W \gg y$ is valid for the whole beam. In this case the entire analysis can be carried out in the y, z plane. Thus, space-charge causes the increase of the thickness y of the beam (figure IV.16).

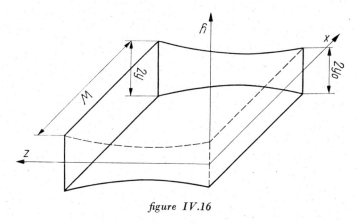

figure IV.16

The right-hand side of equation 54.1 is a constant. Even if Φ is a function of z this side depends only on the coordinate z. Therefore, we can conclude that it is possible in principle to form a linear image by a plane-symmetric electron beam even in the presence of space-charge.

The following dimensionless variables will be introduced [12]

$$Y = \frac{y}{y_0} \qquad\qquad 54.2$$

and

$$Z_s = \left(\frac{I y_0}{8 \sqrt{2} \, \varepsilon_0 W \sqrt{\eta} \Phi_0^{3/2}} \right)^{1/2} \frac{z}{y_0} = 154 \left(p \, \frac{y_0}{W} \right)^{1/2} \frac{z}{y_0} \qquad\qquad 54.3$$

(Index s in this notation serves only for distinction from variable Z used in the axially symmetric case.)

Then equation 54.1 can be written in the following form

$$\frac{d^2 Y}{dZ_s^2} = 2 \qquad\qquad 54.4$$

This equation can be integrated immediately with the following initial conditions

$$Z_s = 0 \begin{cases} Y = Y_0 = 1 \\[2mm] Y' = \dfrac{dY}{dZ_s} = Y_0' = \dfrac{dY}{dZ_s} \bigg|_{Z_s=0} \end{cases} \qquad\qquad 54.5$$

We have the following result

$$\frac{dY}{dZ_s} = 2Z_s + Y_0'$$
54.6

and

$$Y = Z_s^2 + Y_0' Z_s + 1$$
54.7

Thus, the longitudinal section of the beam is of parabolic form. If $Y_0' < 0$ (an initially converging beam), the vertex of the parabola is situated in the point with the following coordinates

$$(Z_s)_m = -\frac{Y_0'}{2} \quad \text{and} \quad Y_{\min} = 1 - \frac{Y_0'^2}{4}$$
54.8

The location and size of the minimum cross section are determined by this point. The parabola is symmetrical with respect to its minimum cross section.

The values of $(Z_s)_m$ and $Y_{\min}$ versus Y_0' are plotted in figure IV.17.

According to 54.8, with the increase of $-Y_0'$ the value of $(Z_s)_m$ increases linearly, while the value of $Y_{\min}$ decreases quadratically.

In figure IV.18, the function $Y(Z_s)$ determining the beam configuration is plotted for different values of Y_0', on the basis of 54.7. The corresponding values of Y_0' are shown at the curves. These curves are easily convertible into real coordinates. For this it is only necessary to choose the proper scale of the abscissa. We obtain from 54.3 that

$$\frac{z}{y_0} = \frac{Z_s}{154 \left(\dfrac{Py_0}{W}\right)^{1/2}}$$
54.9

It follows from expressions 54.2 and 54.3 that

$$Y_0' = \frac{1}{154} \left(\frac{W}{y_0 P}\right)^{1/2} \frac{dy}{dz}\bigg|_0$$
54.10

Thus, the value of Y_0' is uniquely defined by the perveance and geometrical parameters of the beam. The greater is the perveance, the greater must be the initial slope $(dy/dz)\big|_0$ at a given value of Y_0'.

If the initial slope of the originally parallel beam has been produced by an aberrationless *thin cylindrical lens* placed in the plane $z = 0$, the following expression will determine the dependence between this slope and the focal length z_f of the lens

$$\frac{dy}{dz}\bigg|_0 = -\frac{y_0}{z_f}$$
54.11

Thus, we have

$$Y_0' = -\frac{1}{154 z_f} \left(\frac{W y_0}{P}\right)^{1/2}$$
54.12

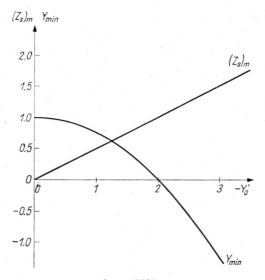

figure IV.17

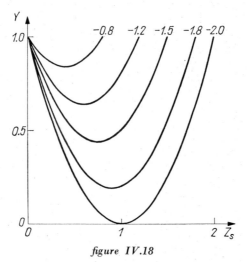

figure IV.18

As we have already mentioned, the linear image formation is possible in case of dense sheet beams. It follows from expression 54.7 that the beam is focused into a straight line parallel to the x axis if

$$Y = Z_s^2 + Y_0' Z_s + 1 = 0$$

i.e.

$$(Z_s)_f = \pm \left(\frac{Y_0'^2}{4} - 1 \right)^{1/2} - \frac{Y_0'}{2} \qquad\qquad 54.13$$

This is possible only if $-Y_0' \geq 2$. In the limiting case of $Y_0' = -2$ we have $(Z_s)_f = (Z_s)_m = 1$. In this case one focal line is formed; this corresponds to the minimum cross section $Y_{\min} = 0$. As it is seen from figure IV.17, in case of $-Y_0' > 2$ the coordinate of the vertex of the parabola is negative ($Y_{\min} < 0$). This contradicts to our assumption that the trajectories should not cross each other. Thus, only the case $Y_0' = -2$ can be considered for the linear image formation.

If space-charge is negligible ($P \approx 0$) the parameter Z_s cannot be used. In this case the smaller the value of $-(dy/dz)|_0$, the greater is the focal length z_f. If the value of the initial slope is given, the increase of the perveance first causes an increase in the focal length, according to 54.13. In the limiting case of the linear image formation ($Y_0' = -2$) it can be easily seen that $z_m = 2z_f$. If the perveance is further increased, the area of the minimum beam cross section increases and the value of z_m decreases, i.e. the minimum cross section comes closer to the plane $z = 0$. At large values of the perveance we have $z_m < z_f$ as in the axially symmetric case.

If the beam enters the drift space parallel to the z axis ($Y_0' = 0$), we obtain from 54.7 that

$$Y = Z_s^2 + 1 \qquad\qquad 54.14$$

This is the case of monotonic spreading of the beam. The rate of this spreading increases with the increase of the beam perveance, according to 54.3 and 54.14.

It is sufficient to determine the dependence $Y(Z_s)$ only once (figure IV.19). The variation of the perveance causes only a variation of the scale of the abscissa, according to 54.9.

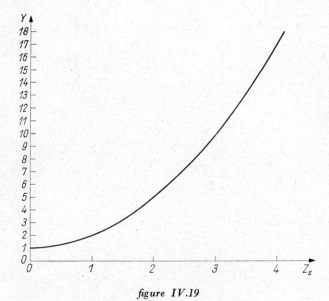

figure IV.19

If the beam is diverging already in the plane $z = 0$ ($Y_0' > 0$), we again have monotonic spreading according to 54.7.

Let us determine now the *maximum beam current* which can be transmitted through a metal box with length l, width W and thickness $N = 2y_0$, without any special focusing device. Following the idea described at the axially symmetric case, we shall consider as an optimum case when the box is just completely filled by the electron beam at its output. In this case the output plane is determined from the following expressions, according to 54.3

$$Z_s = 154\sqrt{P}\left(\frac{2l^2}{WN}\right)^{1/2} = 2(Z_s)_m \qquad 54.15$$

As the value of $(Z_s)_m$ increases linearly with the increase of $|Y_0'|$, it may seem that the perveance can be increased arbitrarily and no current limitation occurs. However, this is not so. In this case the current is limited by the fact that the electron trajectories must not cross each other. The current limitation occurs when the edge electron just crosses the z axis, i.e. when $Y_{\min} = 0$. According to figure IV.17 the corresponding values are as follows

$$(Z_s)_m = 1 \qquad \text{and} \qquad -Y_0' = 2 \qquad 54.16$$

Substituting the value of $(Z_s)_{m\,\max} = 1$ into 54.15, we obtain

$$(Z_s)_{\max} = 154\sqrt{P_{\max}}\left(\frac{2l^2}{WN}\right)^{1/2} = 2 \qquad 54.17$$

Hence

$$P_{\max} = 8.44\times10^{-5}\frac{WN}{l^2} = 84.4\times10^{-6}\frac{S_0}{l^2} \quad [\text{AV}^{-3/2}] \qquad 54.18$$

where S_0 is the initial value of the area of the cross section of the beam. Thus, it is possible to transmit through a metal box with length l, width W and thickness N and held at potential U_0 an electron beam with a current not more than

$$I_{\max} = 8.44\times10^{-5}\,U_0^{3/2}\frac{WN}{l^2} \quad [\text{A}] \qquad 54.19$$

We obtain from 54.10 and 54.16 that the optimum initial direction of the edge electron trajectory which is necessary in order to achieve the maximum value of the perveance ($P_{\max}$) determined by 54.18 is equal to

$$\left(\frac{dy}{dz}\Big|_0\right)_{\text{opt}} = -\frac{2N}{l} \qquad 54.20$$

The minimum cross section of the beam is located at the centre of the box. The theoretical value of its area is zero.

Comparing 53.38 with 54.18, we can see that more current can be transmitted in case of a plane-symmetric beam than in case of an axially symmetric beam. A more detailed analysis of this problem can be found in paper [69].

Carrying out the analysis for the general case, we obtain results similar to the paraxial case [60, 79, 82, 102].

The spreading of a sheet electron beam with finite width W has been investigated by [20]. The spreading of a sheet beam in crossed electric and magnetic fields has been dealt with in [72, 85]. The spreading of a sheet beam in uniform axial electric field has been analysed by [64, 102]. The motion of sheet electron beams in the field of parallel plate [94] and cylindrical condensers [95] has also been investigated.

Finally, let us compare the spreading of a cylindrical electron beam with that of a sheet beam [3]. We shall determine the ratio of the area of the cross section S of the beam at an arbitrary value of z to the area of the initial cross section S_0 for a beam which enters the drift space parallel to the z axis. Let us first express the variables Z and Z_s by the use of S_0. We have from 53.3 that

$$Z = 309 \left(\frac{P}{S_0} \right)^{1/2} z \qquad\qquad 54.21$$

and from 54.3 that

$$Z_s = 218 \left(\frac{P}{S_0} \right)^{1/2} z \qquad\qquad 54.22$$

If the areas of the initial cross sections S_0 are identical for both the cylindrical and the sheet beam, we can simply compare expressions 54.21 and 54.22. We obtain

$$Z_s = 0.706 \, Z \qquad\qquad 54.23$$

In the axially symmetric case we have

$$\frac{S}{S_0} = \frac{r^2}{r_0^2} = R^2 = [R(Z)]^2 \qquad\qquad 54.24$$

where the function $R(Z)$ is determined by expression 53.19. In the plane-symmetric case we obtain from 54.14 and 54.23 that

$$\frac{S}{S_0} = \frac{y}{y_0} = Y = 1 + \frac{Z^2}{2} \qquad\qquad 54.25$$

Thus, we have succeeded in expressing the rate of the space-charge spreading as a function of the same parameter for both cases. In figure IV.20 the dependence of the ratio S/S_0 versus Z is plotted. Curve 1 has been calculated from 54.24 for the axially symmetric case, while curve 2 calculated from 54.25 refers to the plane-symmetric case. We can see that in the case of identical initial conditions the rate of spreading of an axially symmetric electron beam is greater than that of a sheet beam. The difference increases with the increase of the beam perveance. Thus, sheet beams are advantageous from the point of both current limitation and beam spreading.

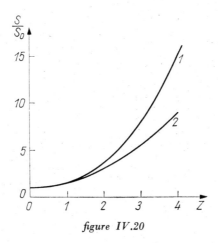

figure IV.20

55. SPREADING OF HOLLOW ELECTRON BEAMS

Let us consider a hollow electron beam moving between two coaxial metal tubes. The beam enters the drift space with uniform potential U_0 between the two cylinders parallel to the z axis. Thus, the potential of both cylinders is equal to U_0. We assume that there is no magnetic field. In this case the only force acting on the electron beam is that of space-charge. The cross section of the system is shown in figure IV.1.

As we have seen in § 49, in the case of $r > r_e$ space-charge forces act outwards in radial direction, in the case of $r < r_e$ they act towards the axis, while in the case of $r = r_e$ there is no force. The value of the equilibrium radius r_e has been defined by 49.28. Accepting the approximation $\varrho =$ constant, we can directly use the results given in § 49. The spreading will appear in the fact that the outer boundary of the beam will be displaced outwards and the inner boundary towards the axis of the system and so they become farther and farther from the equilibrium radius r_e. It is sufficient to analyse the motion of these edge electrons in order to get enough information on the spreading of a laminar hollow beam. If the beam thickness is small in comparison with the value of r_e the beam moves approxi-

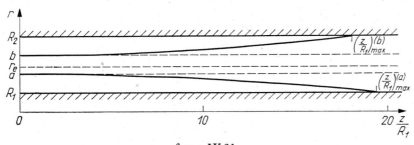

figure IV.21

mately parallel to the z axis and we can assume that only the edge electrons deviate from that direction (see figure IV.21). Then we can consider the motion of the edge electrons in the potential field generated by space-charge of a hollow electron beam with uniform thickness [99, 104].

The equation of motion of the *outer* edge electron can be written by the use of 49.35 as follows

$$\frac{d^2r}{dt^2} = \eta \frac{d\overline{U}}{dr} = 3.03 \times 10^4 \, \eta \, \frac{I}{\sqrt{U_0}} \frac{b^2 - r_e^2}{b^2 - a^2} \frac{1}{r} \qquad 55.1$$

Let us multiply both sides of this equation by $2\,dr$ and integrate for the interval from b to r $(r > b)$ with the following initial conditions

$$z = 0 \begin{cases} r = r_0 = b \\ \dfrac{dr}{dz} = 0 \end{cases} \qquad 55.2$$

We shall take into account that

$$\frac{dr}{dz} = \frac{1}{v_z} \frac{dr}{dt} \approx \frac{1}{(2\eta U_0)^{1/2}} \frac{dr}{dt} \qquad 55.3$$

The result of the first integration is

$$\left(\frac{dr}{dz}\right)^2 = 3.03 \times 10^4 \, \frac{1}{U_0^{3/2}} \frac{b^2 - r_e^2}{b^2 - a^2} \log \frac{r}{b} \qquad 55.4$$

Hence we have

$$\frac{dr}{dz} = + \left(3.03 \times 10^4 \, \frac{I}{U_0^{3/2}} \frac{b^2 - r_e^2}{b^2 - a^2} \log \frac{r}{b}\right)^{1/2} \qquad 55.5$$

The positive sign is chosen before the square root because the value of r increases with the increase of coordinate z. Integrating once again and carrying out some simple transformations, we obtain [104]

$$\frac{z}{b} = \frac{f \left(\log \dfrac{r}{b}\right)^{1/2}}{\left(7.58 \times 10^3 \, P \, \dfrac{1 - \left(\dfrac{r_e}{b}\right)^2}{1 - \left(\dfrac{a}{b}\right)^2}\right)^{1/2}} \qquad 55.6$$

where $f(x)$ is the function defined by 53.12.

The outer spreading of the hollow electron beam is determined by expression 55.6. The case of the axially symmetric solid beam is contained in this expression as a special case. Actually, substituting $a = r_e = 0$ and

$b = r_0$ into 55.6, we obtain exactly expression 53.20 which determines the spreading of the cylindrical solid beam. Comparing these two expressions 55.6 and 53.20, one can see that in the case of a hollow beam a somewhat lesser value of r/b corresponds to a given value of z/b than in the case of a solid beam. This means that the rate of spreading of a hollow beam is lesser than that of a solid beam. At the same time, assuming identical currents, the current density of the hollow beam is much higher. Thus, in the case of identical current densities the spreading of a hollow beam is much lesser than that of a solid beam. This is an advantage of using hollow electron beams.

Let us consider now the *inner* edge electron trajectory of the hollow beam [99]. According to 49.33 we have the following equation of motion

$$\frac{d^2r}{dt^2} = \eta \frac{d\bar{U}}{dr} = -3.03 \times 10^4 \, \eta \, \frac{I}{\sqrt{U_0}} \frac{r_e^2 - a^2}{b^2 - a^2} \frac{1}{r} \qquad 55.7$$

We have now to integrate from a to r ($r < a$), taking into account 55.3 and using the following initial conditions

$$z = 0 \begin{cases} r = a \\[2mm] \dfrac{dr}{dz} = 0 \end{cases} \qquad 55.8$$

After the first integration we obtain

$$\frac{dr}{dz} = -\left[-3.03 \times 10^4 \, \frac{I}{U_0^{3/2}} \frac{r_e^2 - a^2}{b^2 - a^2} \log \frac{r}{a} \right]^{1/2} \qquad 55.9$$

In front of the square root the negative sign should now be used because in this region the value of r decreases with the increase of coordinate z. Integrating equation 55.9 and carrying out some simple transformations, we obtain

$$\frac{z}{a} = \frac{\mathrm{erf}\left[\left(-\log \dfrac{r}{a} \right)^{1/2} \right]}{\left[9.65 \times 10^3 \, P \, \dfrac{\left(\dfrac{r_e}{a} \right)^2 - 1}{\left(\dfrac{b}{a} \right)^2 - 1} \right]^{1/2}} \qquad 55.10$$

where

$$\mathrm{erf}\, x = \frac{2}{\sqrt{\pi}} \int_0^x \exp\left(-u^2\right) du \qquad 55.11$$

is the error function. The inner edge trajectory is determined by expression 55.10. Now our problem is solved.

We can also determine the maximum possible value of the length of the beam, using expressions 55.6 and 55.10. The beam length is limited by the outer cylinder of radius R_2 and the inner one of radius R_1. If the outer radius of the beam becomes equal to R_2 or the inner radius equal to R_1 the beam is considered finished. The maximum possible beam perveance at a given value of the beam length can be calculated from the same conditions [98]. We obtain from 55.6 that

$$\left(\frac{z}{b}\right)_{max} = \frac{f\left[\left(\log\frac{R_2}{b}\right)^{1/2}\right]}{\left[7.58\times10^3\,P\,\dfrac{1-\left(\dfrac{r_e}{b}\right)^2}{1-\left(\dfrac{a}{b}\right)^2}\right]^{1/2}}$$ 55.12

The second condition follows from 55.10

$$\left(\frac{z}{a}\right)_{max} = \frac{\mathrm{erf}\left[-\log\left(\frac{R_1}{a}\right)^{1/2}\right]}{\left[9.56\times10^3\,P\,\dfrac{\left(\dfrac{r_e}{a}\right)^2-1}{\left(\dfrac{b}{a}\right)^2-1}\right]^{1/2}}$$ 55.13

That condition is valid from 55.12 and 55.13, which leads to the lesser value of z_{max}.

Finally, let us examine the spreading of the hollow beam considered as an *example* in § 49. So, we have

$$P=1.92\times10^{-6}\mathrm{A/V^{3/2}}; \quad \frac{a}{R_1}=2, \quad \frac{b}{R_1}=3 \quad \text{and} \quad \frac{R_2}{R_1}=4$$

As we have seen in § 49, in this case $r_e/R_1 = 2.38$. It follows from 55.12 that $(z/R_1)^b_{max} = 18.04$. We obtain from 55.13 that $(z/R_1)^a_{max} = 19.38$. Thus, the outer edge trajectory determines the maximum value of the length of the beam. The edge trajectories calculated on the basis of expressions 55.6 and 55.10, respectively, have been plotted in figure IV.21.

Space-charge spreading of hollow electron beams has been dealt with also by [75, 88].

56. SPREADING OF ELLIPTICAL-CROSS-SECTION ELECTRON BEAMS

Finally, we shall deal with the motion of a solid electron beam with elliptical cross section in a uniform U_0 potential drift space. It is an important case because electron beams focused by quadrupole lenses have elliptical cross section. On the other hand, space-charge of elliptical electron-beam drifting in uniform potential space also generates a quadrupole field (see 9.8).

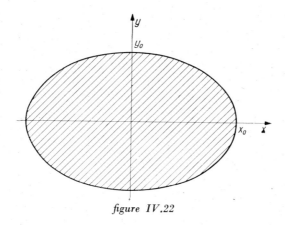

figure IV.22

If there is no magnetic field, the *paraxial equations* of the *edge electron trajectories* $[x(z),\ y \equiv 0]$ and $[y(z),\ x \equiv 0]$ of the beam can be written in the following way [65, 70]

$$\frac{d^2x}{dz^2} = \frac{b^2}{x+y} \qquad\qquad 56.1$$

and

$$\frac{d^2y}{dz^2} = \frac{b^2}{x+y} \qquad\qquad 56.2$$

where

$$b^2 = \frac{I}{2\sqrt{2\pi\varepsilon_0}\sqrt{\eta}\,U_0^{3/2}} \qquad\qquad 56.3$$

The location of the coordinate system is shown in figure IV.22. The beam moves in the direction z normal to the plane of the figure. Let us introduce the following new variables [57]

$$u = \frac{x+y}{2L} \qquad\qquad 56.4$$

and

$$v = \frac{x-y}{2L} \qquad\qquad 56.5$$

where L is a constant quantity having a dimension of length. We shall replace the independent variable by a dimensionless one, too, similar to 53.3

$$Z = b\frac{z}{L} \qquad\qquad 56.6$$

Equations 56.1 and 56.2 can be rewritten with these variables in the following form

$$\frac{d^2u}{dZ^2} = \frac{1}{2u} \qquad\qquad 56.7$$

and

$$\frac{d^2v}{dZ^2} = 0 \qquad\qquad 56.8$$

The functions $u(Z)$ and $v(Z)$ determining the trajectories $x(z)$ and $y(z)$, respectively, are solutions of these equations. We have the following initial conditions in the plane $Z = 0$

$$u_0 = \frac{x_0 + y_0}{2L} \qquad\qquad 56.9$$

$$v_0 = \frac{x_0 - y_0}{2L} \qquad\qquad 56.10$$

$$\frac{du}{dZ}\bigg|_0 = u_0' = \frac{1}{2b}\left(\frac{dx}{dz}\bigg|_0 + \frac{dy}{dz}\bigg|_0\right) \qquad\qquad 56.11$$

and

$$\frac{dv}{dZ}\bigg|_0 = v_0' = \frac{1}{2b}\left(\frac{dx}{dz}\bigg|_0 - \frac{dy}{dz}\bigg|_0\right) \qquad\qquad 56.12$$

Equation 56.7 coincides with equation 53.4. Only the initial condition 56.9 differs from its counterpart condition 53.5. Using this fact and taking into account 53.22, we obtain the solution of equation 56.7 on the basis of 53.24 as follows [100]

$$Z = 2u_0 \exp\left(-u_0'^2\right)\left[f(-u_0') \pm f\left[\left(\log\frac{u}{u_0} + u_0'^2\right)^{1/2}\right]\right] \qquad\qquad 56.13$$

where $f(x)$ is defined by 53.12. The sign should be chosen according as the slope of $u(Z)$ in the given point Z is positive or negative with respect to the direction of Z axis.

Equation 56.8 has the following solution

$$v = v_0 + v_0'Z \qquad\qquad 56.14$$

The edge electron trajectories $x(z)$ and $y(z)$ can be obtained from functions $u(Z)$ and $v(Z)$ which are determined by 56.13 and 56.14, respectively, with the use of expressions 56.4 and 56.5. We should like to emphasise that $x(z)$ and $y(z)$ are not projections of one trajectory but they are the *trajectories of two edge electrons* moving in the orthogonal medium planes x, z and y, z of the beam, respectively.

REFERENCES FOR CHAPTER IV

a) *Reviews of Space-Charge Effects*

1. (ALYAMOVSKIY, I. V.) Алямовский, И. В.: Электронные пучки и электронные пушки *(Electron Beams and Electron Guns)*. Советское Радио; Москва, 1966.
2. CHARLES, D.: *Annls. Radioélect.*, **4** (1949), 1, 33.
3. (GABOVICH, M. D.) Габович, М. Д.: *Усп. Физ. Наук*, **56** (1955), 2, 215.
4. (IGNATENKO, V. P.) Игнатенко, В. П.: *Усп. Физ. Наук*, **73** (1961), 2, 243.
5. IVEY, H. F.: *Advances in Electronics and Electron Physics*, **6** (1954), 137.
6. (LOPUKHIN, V. M.) Лопухин, В. М.: Возбуждение электромагнитных колебаний и волн электронными потоками *(Generation of Electromagnetic Oscillations and Waves by Means of Electron Beams)*. Гостехтеоретиздат; Москва, 1953.
7. MELTZER, B.: *Brit. J. appl. Phys.*, **10** (1959), 9, 391.
8. (MOLOKOVSKIY, S. I.–SUSHKOV, A. D.) Молоковский, С. И.–Сушков, А. Д.: Электронно-оптические системы приборов сверхвысоких частот *(Electron-Optical Systems for Microwave Devices)*. Энергия; Москва, 1965.
9. OLLENDORFF, F.: Elektronik freier Raumladungen. Springer-Verlag; Wien, 1957.
10. PETRIE, D. P. R.: *Electr. Commun.*, **20** (1941/42), 2, 100.
11. PICQUENDAR, J. E.: *Nachtech. Fachber.*, **22** (1961), 442.
12. PIERCE, J. R.: *Theory and Design of Electron Beams*, Chapter IX; Van Nostrand, New York, 1954.
13. ROTHE, H.–KLEEN, W.: Hochvakuum-Elektronenröhren, Bd. I. Akademische Verlagsgesellschaft; Frankfurt/Main, 1955.
14. ROTHE, H.–KLEEN, W.: *Z. tech. Phys.*, **17** (1936), 12, 635.
15. SCHWARZ, H.: *J. appl. Phys.*, **33** (1962), 12, 3464.
16. SPANGENBERG, K. R.: *Vacuum Tubes*. McGraw-Hill; New York–London–Toronto, 1948.
17. (TARANENKO, V. P.) Тараненко, В. П.: Электронные пушки *(Electron Guns)*. Техника; Киев, 1964.
18. THOMPSON, H. C.: *Proc. Instn Radio Engrs.*, **24** (1936), 10, 1276.
19. (ZINCHENKO, N. S.) Зинченко, Н. С.: Курс лекций по электронной оптике *(Electron Optics)*. Харьковский Университет; Харьков, 1961.

b) *General Theory of Electron Beams*

20. AHARONI, J.: *Phil. Mag.*, **35** (1944), 36.
21. (BREITMAN, V. M.–KUZNETSOV, V. S.) Брейтман, В. М.–Кузнецов, В. С.: *РИЭ СССР*, **6** (1961), 6, 993.
22. BUTCHER, P. N.: *Phil. Mag.*, **44** (1953), 971.
23. COOK, J. S.: *J. appl. Phys.*, **30** (1959), 6, 860.
24. (DANILOV, V. N.) Данилов, В. Н.: *РИЭ СССР*, **9** (1964), 12, 2140.
25. ERICKSON, E. E.–SUTHERLAND, A. D.: Microwaves, Proc. 4th Intern. Conf., p. 533. Eindhoven, 1962.
26. GABOR, D.: *Proc. Instn Radio Engrs.*, **33** (1954), 11, 792.
27. GATLAND, I. R.–GOLD, L.: *Int. J. Elect.*, **18** (1965), 3, 219.
28. HAINE, M. E.: *Brit. J. appl. Phys.*, **8** (1957), 1, 44.
29. HARRISON, E. R.: *Plasma Phys.* (Accels-Thermonucl. Res.) **5** (1963), 1, 23.
30. HECHTEL, J. R.–BRAUCH, D. F.–MIZUHARA, A.: Microwaves, Proc. 4th Intern. Conf., p. 527. Eindhoven, 1962.
31. HERRMANN, G.: *J. appl. Phys.*, **28** (1957), 474.
32. KIRSTEIN, P. T.: *J. Electron. Control*, **4** (1958), 5, 457.
33. KIRSTEIN, P. T.: *J. Electron. Control*, **5** (1958), 33.
34. KIRSTEIN, P. T.: *J. appl. Phys.*, **30** (1959), 7, 967.
35. (KORMILITSIN, B. T.–OVCHAROV, V. T.) Кормилицин, Б. Т.–Овчаров, В. Т.: *РИЭ СССР*, **5** (1960), 7, 1112.
36. LAWSON, J. D.: *Plasma Phys.* (Accels-Thermonucl. Res.), **1** (1959), 1–2, 31.
37. (LOMNEV, S. P.) Ломнев, С. П.: *ДАН СССР*, **141** (1961), 5, 1065.
38. (LOMNEV, S. P.) Ломнев, С. П.: *ДАН СССР*, **143** (1962), 6, 1309.
39. LUCAS, A. R.–MELTZER, B.–STUART, G. A.: *J. Electron. Control*, **4** (1958), 2, 160.

40. MALOFF, J.–EPSTEIN, D.: *Proc. Instn Radio Engrs.*, **22** (1934), 1386.
41. MELTZER, B.: *Proc. Phys. Soc. Lond.*, **B62** (1949), 431, 813.
42. MELTZER, B.: *J. Electron.*, **2** (1956), 118.
43. MELTZER, B.–BROWN, I.: *Nature, Lond.*, **181** (1957), 1384.
44. MELTZER, B.–LUCAS, A. R.: *J. Electron. Control*, **4** (1958), 454.
45. MILLER, M. H.: *J. appl. Phys.*, **31** (1960), 3, 607.
46. MUELLER, W.: *J. Electron. Control*, **6** (1959), 6, 499.
47. MUELLER, W.: *J. Electron. Control*, **8** (1960), 2, 111.
48. (OVCHAROV, V. T.) Овчаров, В. Т.: *ДАН СССР*, **107** (1956), 1, 47.
49. (OVCHAROV, V. T.) Овчаров, В. Т.: *РИЭ СССР*, **2** (1957), 6, 696.
50. (OVCHAROV, V. T.) Овчаров, В. Т.: *РИЭ СССР*, **4** (1959), 10, 1741.
51. (OVCHAROV, V. T.) Овчаров, В. Т.: *РИЭ СССР*, **7** (1962), 8, 1367.
52. SPANGENBERG, K.: *J. Franklin Inst.*, **232** (1941), 365.
53. WALKER, G. B.: *Proc. Phys. Soc.*, **B63** (1950), 12, 1017.
54. WAX, N.: *J. appl. Phys.*, **24** (1953), 6, 727.

c) *Space-Charge Effects in Long Electron Beams*

55. (BAKHRAKH, L. E.) Бахрах, Л. Е.: *РИЭ СССР*, **10** (1965), 6, 1104.
56. BAKISH, R. (Ed.): *Introduction to Electron Beam Technology*. Wiley; New York–London, 1962.
57. BICK, J. H.: *IEEE Trans.*, **ED–12** (1965), 7, 408.
58. BORGHI, R. P.–DUNN, D. A.: *J. appl. Phys.*, **34** (1963), 3, 692.
59. VAN BORRIES, B.–DOSSE, J.: *Arch. Elektrotech.*, **32** (1938), 221.
60. BOWERS, A.: *Physica*, **2** (1935), 145.
61. (BREITMAN, V. M.) Брейтман, В. М.: *РИЭ СССР*, **5** (1960), 10, 1619.
62. BRIDGES, W. B.–FREY, J. I.–BIRDSALL, C. K.: *IEEE Trans.*, **ED–12** (1965), 5, 264.
63. (BRODSKIY, V.) Бродский, В.: *Сб. Труд. Физ. Технол.*, (1948), 151.
64. (BURYANOV, P. D.) Бурянов, П. Д.: *РИЭ СССР*, **9** (1964), 8, 1405.
65. BURNOT, G.: *Nucl. Instrum. Meth.*, **27** (1964), 1, 77.
66. CHANG, K.: *Proc. Instn Radio Engrs.*, **45** (1957), 11, 1522.
67. FOTI, E.: *Elektrontechnológiák (Electron Beam Technology)*. Műszaki Könyvkiadó; Budapest, 1965.
68. (GABOVICH, M. D.) Габович, М. Д.: *Ж. Тех. Физ. СССР*, **21** (1951), 3, 363.
69. (GABOVICH, M. D.) Габович, М. Д.: *Ж. Тех. Физ. СССР*, **25** (1955), 8, 1458.
70. GLANCE, B.: Microwave Tubes, Proc. 5th Intern. Conf., p. 355, Paris, 1964.
71. GOUDET, M. G.–GRATZMULLER, A. M.: *J. Phys. Radium Paris*, **6** (1944), 142.
72. GUPTA, K. C.: *Int. J. Electr.*, **18** (1965), 2, 177.
73. HAEFF, A. V.: *Proc. Instn Radio Engrs.*, **27** (1939), 3, 586.
74. HARRIS, L. A.: *Proc. Instn Radio Engrs.*, **40** (1952), 6, 700.
75. HARRIS, L. A.: IRE Convention Record, pt. 3, p. 11 (1956).
76. HOLLWAY, D. L.: *Aust. J. sci. Res.*, **A5** (1952), 430.
77. HOLLWAY, D. L.: *Electronics* (Feb. 16, 1962).
78. HOLLWAY, D. L.: *J. Brit. IRE*, **24** (1962), 3, 209.
79. HOUTERMANNS, F. G.–RIEWE, K. H.: *Arch. Elektrotech.*, **35** (1941), 686.
80. HUTTER, R. G. E.–HARRISON, S. W.: *Sylvania Tech.*, **2** (1949).
81. (KAPCHINSKIY, I. M.) Капчинский, И. М.: *РИЭ СССР*, **8** (1963), 6, 985.
82. KLEMPERER, O.: *Proc. Phys. Soc. Lond.*, **59** (1947), 302.
83. (KUZNETSOV, V. S.) Кузнецов, В. С.: *РИЭ СССР*, **7** (1962) 8, 1385.
84. LASH-MILLER, W.–GORDON, A. R.: *J. phys. Chem. Ithaca*, **35** (1931), 2785.
85. (LIZHDVOI, K. YA.) Лиждвой, К. Я.: *РИЭ СССР*, **4** (1959), 1, 120.
86. (LUKOSHKOV, V. S.) Лукошков, В. С.: *Ж. Тех. Физ. СССР*, **6** (1936), 1, 26.
87. MACGREGOR-MORRIS, J. T.–MINES, R.: *J. Instn elect. Engrs.*, **63** (1925), 1101.
88. (MINENKO, L. I.–FOMENKO, G. P.) Миненко, Л. И.–Фоменко, Г. П.: *Ж. Тех. Физ. СССР*, **35** (1965), 705.
89. MOAK, C. D.: *Nucl. Instrum. Meth.*, **8** (1960), 1, 19.
90. (MOLOKOVSKIY, S. I.–SUSHKOV, A. D.) Молоковский, С. И.–Сушков, А. Д.: *РИЭ СССР*, **6** (1961), 3, 375.
91. MOSS, H.: *Wireless Eng.*, **22** (1945), 262, 316.

92. Moss, H.: *J. Brit. IRE*, **21** (1961), 1, 35.
93. Palmer, J. L.–Süsskind, C.: *J. Electron. Control*, **10** (1961), 5, 365.
94. (Shapovalov, A. S.) Шаповалов, А. С.: *Ж. Тех. Физ. СССР*, **35** (1965), 6, 1053.
95. (Shapovalov, A. S.) Шаповалов, А. С.: *Ж. Тех. Физ. СССР*, **36** (1966), 5, 920.
96. Schwartz, J. W.: *RCA Rev.*, **18** (1957), 1, 3.
97. Smith, L. P.–Hartman, P. L.: *J. appl. Phys.*, **11** (1940), 220.
98. Szilágyi, M.: *Tungsram Technische Mitteilungen*, **10** (1963), 433.
99. Szilágyi, M.: *Acta Phys. hung.*, **18** (1965), 4, 325.
100. Szilágyi, M.: *6th MOGA*,* 70.
101. (Sushkov, A. D.–Molokovskiy, S. I.) Сушков, А. Д.–Молоковский, С. И.: *Ж. Тех. Физ. СССР*, **33** (1963), 3, 326.
102. Thompson, B. J.–Headrick, L. B.: *Proc. Instn Radio Engrs.*, **28** (1940), 7, 318.
103. Watson, E. E.: *Phil. Mag.*, **3** (1927), 849.
104. Wax, N.: *J. appl. Phys.*, **20** (1949), 3, 242.
105. Wendt,: *Annls. Phys.*, **2** (1948), 256.
106. (Zinchenko, N. S.–Sayenko, V. I.) Зинченко, Н. С.–Саенко, В. И.: *Ж. Тех. Физ. СССР*, **33** (1963), 2, 154.
107. (Zinchenko, N. S.–Sorokina, V. M.) Зинченко, Н. С.–Сорокина, В. М.: *Ж. Тех. Физ. СССР*, **31** (1961), 9, 1073.

d) Relativistic Electron Beams

108. Boivin, M.: *J. Phys. Radium Paris*, **21** (1960), 11, 171 A.
109. Burgess, R. E.: *Wireless Eng.*, **23** (1946), 178.
110. Chodorow, M. et al.: *Proc. Instn Radio Engrs.*, **41** (1953), 1584.
111. Hartman, W.: *Proc. Instn Radio Engrs.*, **37** (1949), 1038.
112. (Ignatenko, V. P.) Игнатенко, В. П.: *РИЭ СССР*, **7** (1962), 7, 1175.
113. Lomax, R. J.: *J. Electron. Control*, **5** (1958), 563.
114. Lucas, A. R.: *J. Electron. Control*, **5** (1958), 3, 245.
115. Meltzer, B.: *J. Electron. Control*, **4** (1958), 350.
116. Meltzer, B.: *J. Electron. Control*, **5** (1958), 348.
117. Meltzer, B.: *Nature*, Lond., **181** (1958), 1332.
118. Meltzer, B.: *J. Electron. Control*, **6** (1959), 550.
119. Septier, A.: *J. Phys. Radium Paris*, **22** (1961), 6, 79 A.
120. Winwood, J. M.: *J. Electron. Control*, **5** (1958), 161.
121. Winwood, J. M.: *J. Electron. Control*, **6** (1959), 3, 258.
122. Yadavalli, S. V.: *J. Electron. Control*, **3** (1957), 65.

e) Recent Development

123. (Babich, Yu. F.–Pavlyuchenko, Yu. F.) Бабич, Ю. Ф.–Павлюченко, Ю. Ф.: *Изв Высш. Учеб. Завед. Радиоэлектрон. СССР*, **11** (1968), 12, 1312.
124. (Barantseva, O. D.) Баранцева, О. Д.: *Ж. Тех. Физ. СССР*, **38** (1968), 2, 268.
125. (Beilis, I. I. et al.) Беилис, И. И. и др.: *Ж. Тех. Физ. СССР*, **39** (1969), 9, 1650.
126. Chisholm, T.: *IEEE Trans.*, **ED–15** (1968), 6, 374.
127. Chisholm, T.: *Proc. IEEE*, **57** (1969), 3, 357.
128. Czarczynski, W.: *Pr. Przem. Inst. Elektron.* (Poland). **9** (1968), 1, 45.
129. (Danilov, V. N.) Данилов, В. Н.: *РИЭ СССР*, **14** (1969), 4, 719.
130. Dionisio, J. S.–De Lima, D. X.: *Nucl. Instr. Meth.*, **61** (1968), 1, 260.
131. Dobson, J.–Gallagher, W. J.: *IEEE Trans.*, **NS–16** (1969), 3, 227.
132. Einstein, P. E.: *Electron. Lett.*, **5** (1969), 22, 546.
133. Hara, E.: *Nuclear Instrum. Meth.*, **63** (1968), 3, 373.
134. Hartnagel, H. L.: *Proc. IEEE*, **54** (1966), 4, 684.
135. Hutter, R.: *Beams with Space-Charge. Focusing of Charged Particles*, Vol. 2, Chapter 3.1, p. 3. Academic Press, New York 1967.

* See p. 484.

136. KIRSTEIN, P. T.–KINO, G. S.–WATERS, W. E.: *Space-Charge Flow* (Physical and Quantum Electronics Series). McGraw-Hill Book Company; New York–San Francisco–Toronto–London–Sydney, 1967.
137. (KUZNETSOV, V. S.) Кузнецов, В. С.: *Ж. Тех. Физ. СССР*, **37** (1967), 5, 932.
138. (KUZNETSOV, V. S.) Кузнецов, В. С.: *Ж. Тех. Физ. СССР*, **38** (1968), 2, 274.
139. (KUZNETSOV, V. S.–FIDELSKAYA, R. P.) Кузнецов, В. С.–Фидельская, Р. П.: *Ж. Тех. Физ. СССР*, **38** (1968), 10, 1756.
140. (LEVITSKIY, S. M.–SIGALOVSKIY, D. YU.) Левицкий, С. М.–Сигаловский, Д. Ю.: *РИЭ СССР*, **14** (1969), 4, 692.
141. (MIKHEEV, N. I.–CHUYAN, R. K.–BRYUKHNOV, P. M.) Михеев, Н. И.–Чуян, Р. К.–Брюхнов, П. М.: *РИЭ СССР*, **12** (1967), 4, 642.
142. (MOROZ, E. M.–PISAREV, V. E.–SOLOVEV, N. S.) Мороз, Е. М.–Писарев, В. Е.–Соловьев, Н. С.: *Ж. Тех. Физ. СССР*, **36** (1966), 10, 1860.
143. (MOROZ, E. M.–SOLOVEV, N. S.) Мороз, Е. М.–Соловьев, Н. С.: *Ж. Тех. Физ. СССР*, **36** (1966), 9, 1601.
144. (OGORODNIKOV, S. N.) Огородников, С. Н.: *РИЭ СССР*, **12** (1967), 9, 1616.
145. (OGORODNIKOV, S. N.) Огородников, С. Н.: *РИЭ СССР*, **13** (1968), 10, 1907.
146. (OVCHAROV, V. T.) Овчаров, В. Т.: *РИЭ СССР*, **12** (1967), 12, 2156.
147. PAHLITZSCH, G.–KUPER, G.: *VDI-Zeit.*, **111** (1969), 2, 83.
148. RADLEY, D. E.–BIRTLES, A. B.: *Int. J. Electron.*, **21** (1966), 5, 465.
149. ROBERTS, A. S.: *Plasma Phys.* (Accels-Thermonucl. Res.), **8** (1966), 1, 53.
150. SEUNIK, H.: *Nachtech. Fachber.*, **35** (1968), 191. 7th *MOGA*.*
151. TWOMBLY, J. C.: *IEEE Trans.*, **ED–13** (1966), 934.
152. TYPKE, D.: *Optik Berlin*, **28** (1969), 5, 488.
153. (VOINOV, V. V.) Воинов, В. В.: *РИЭ СССР*, **13** (1968), 10, 1904.
154. WEBER, C.: *Philips Res. Rep. Suppl.*, **6** (1967), 84.

* See p. 484.

V. ELECTROSTATIC FOCUSING OF HIGH-INTENSITY ELECTRON BEAMS

MIKLÓS SZILÁGYI

In Chapter III we dealt with the production of high-intensity electron beams. Our next task is to investigate the problem of *focusing*, i.e. the maintenance of a given form and size of the cross section of a high-intensity long electron beam.

In this chapter focusing methods based on purely *electrostatic* fields will be treated in detail. These methods may be divided into two groups: (1) periodic electrostatic focusing; (2) centrifugal electrostatic focusing. We shall deal with these two groups, especially with the different methods of periodic electrostatic focusing. For this reason, periodic focusing will be briefly treated in general in the first part of this chapter.

A detailed analysis of magnetic focusing methods will be given in Chapter VI.

(A) THE PERIODIC FOCUSING

57. PERIODIC ELECTROSTATIC FOCUSING

If the maintenance of a given form and size of the cross section of a long high-intensity electron beam is required, it is convenient to use a periodic alignment of electron lenses so that each lens just compensates the effect of space-charge in a given region. In this way an electron beam with considerable length can be formed, for a great number of lenses can be placed in sequence.

The idea of using periodic alignments of electrostatic lenses for this dates back to 1939 [44], and the method has reached a high state of development since then. Now periodic focusing is the most widespread method of maintenance of high-intensity electron beams. The focusing device may be electrostatic or magnetic or a combination of electrostatic and magnetic fields. It can be used for maintenance of cylindrical, sheet or hollow electron beams or any other types of beams alike.

Periodic *electrostatic* focusing is advantageous in many respects. The elimination of magnetic fields leads to reduction of weight of the focusing device. Problems connected with the use of magnetic materials (inhomogeneities, temperature dependence, etc.) do not appear. The focusing electrodes do not require external adjustment. They are mounted in the vacuum system and it is possible to use them for other purposes; for example, as slow-wave structure in a microwave tube. The ions generated in the electron beam are quickly pumped up by the strong electrostatic fields. It leads to a longer durability of the cathode and to the reduction of the noise level.

A disadvantage of the periodic electrostatic focusing is that the maintenance of an electron beam with a given value of the perveance requires a smaller value for the period of the field than in case of periodic magnetic focusing. This leads to technological difficulties—electric discharge may occur between the electrodes—and as we shall see, the mathematical analysis will also be more complicated for this reason. It should be noted that both electrostatic and magnetic periodic focusing require that geometrical dimensions, centring of the electrodes, the length of the field period and the required transition region between the electron gun and the input of the periodic system should strictly follow the prescriptions.

We should like also to remark that it is necessary for the complete compensation of the effect of space-charge that the distribution of the space-charge density in the electron beam should be such that the repulsion force F_e acting on the electrons due to space-charge diminish towards the axis, according to the same law as the focusing force. As we have seen from expression 50.5, if the space-charge distribution is uniform across the whole beam, as is assumed in the paraxial approximation, the force F_e is proportional to the distance r from the axis of a cylindrical solid beam. The dependence of the radial component E_r of the electrostatic focusing field on the distance r is the same (see 21.1) in the paraxial approximation. However, if we consider a more general case for which the paraxial approximation is not suitable, the field component E_r will be a more complicated function of r and the ideal focusing will require a space-charge distribution such that $F_e(r)$ will follow the same law as $E_r(r)$. This requires a special type of electron gun producing an electron beam with a given current-density distribution. The realisation of such a gun is a very complicated problem.

Up to now, great progress has been achieved in the field of periodic electrostatic focusing. Its practical application is gradually coming into general use. It is especially convenient for the maintenance of high-energy electron beams.

However, a *general* theory of the electrostatic focusing has not been developed yet. As we shall see, the treatment of each different type of electrostatic focusing is only valid approximately: the methods are based on a more or less great number of assumptions. Therefore, the design of the focusing devices can hardly do without semi-empirical methods. An exact general theory is badly needed. Especially important is the analysis of the behaviour of the beam in the transition region between the electron gun and the focusing device. Analog methods, for example, resistance network analog, and methods using digital computers for determination of electron trajectories are of great importance in the investigation of various special problems arising at the design of focusing devices.

The characteristic features of various types of electrostatic, magnetic and complementary focusing can be determined on the basis of Chapters V and VI. The possibilities of application depend on these features.

After this introduction we shall now try to give a detailed and systematical description of the theoretical basis of electrostatic focusing.

58. ILLUSTRATION OF THE PERIODIC FOCUSING ON THE BASIS
OF THE OPTICAL ANALOGY

Let us first consider the effect of a lens system consisting of a periodic sequence of identical thin converging electron lenses with focal lengths f and spacings l between the lenses on an electron beam *without space-charge* considered only for illustration [87] (figure V.1). As usual, we call a lens 'thin' if its focal length is much longer than the axial extent of the field of the lens. We shall also assume that the distance l is greater than the extent

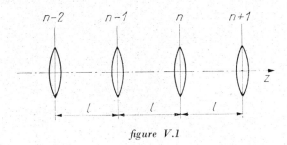

figure V.1

of the lens field. The lenses may be *electrostatic, magnetic* (or complementary) *thin* electron *lenses*. In this case the knowledge of the focal length f and spacing l is sufficient for the description of the whole system. The principal planes of any lens coincide with each other and with the medium plane of the lens. Thus, we can assume that the electron trajectories consist of straight lines, the slopes of which are suddenly changed by the lenses.

Let us now examine the electron trajectories in such a system. The electrons are moving in the direction of the z axis. In this section our treatment is independent of the symmetry properties of the beam and the lenses; it is valid for sheet beams as well as for cylindrical beams. One can find that the electron motion is bounded only if the following condition is fulfilled [87]

$$0 \leq \frac{l}{f} \leq 4 \qquad\qquad 58.1$$

If $l/f > 4$, the solution is unbounded. Actually, as the lens strength is increased, its focusing effect initially increases. If, however, the focal length is diminished further, the electron can cross the axis between the lenses and reach some distance on the other side; the next lens forces the electron back across to a still greater distance and so on. This leads to very intensive fluctuations, the amplitude of which increases with the distance. The same situation occurs if the spacing l is increased. The result is that the focusing becomes unstable.

It follows from these facts that if we have k finite number of lenses, the output slope of the electron beam behind the last lens (as $l = $ constant, the output coordinate is equal to $z = kl$) can be varied almost arbitrarily by the variation of the focal length f of the lenses. In spite of the fact that all the lenses are converging, we may get a strongly diverging beam at the output of the system.

When real thick lenses are used, the situation is more complicated. We have either to know the positions of the principal planes or determine the exact trajectories. The trajectories in this case are complicated curves. An increase in the field strengths of thick lenses leads to the above effect on the whole system. But beside this an additional effect arises: when the field strength of a thick lens is increased, its focal length initially decreases, then increases and further decreases again. This is a consequence of the fact that the electrons can cross the axis repeatedly in the field of the thick lens. A more detailed analysis of the periodic sequence of thick lenses can be found in [78–80].

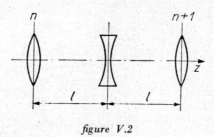

figure V.2

Let us now consider another case of great practical importance, again not taking space-charge into consideration for the moment. This is focusing by a periodic series of *alternating diverging and converging thin lenses* with focal lengths $|f|$ and spacings l between the lenses (figure V.2).

An example of such a system is a series of quadrupole lenses; each lens is rotated through an angle of 90 degrees with respect to its neighbour [30]. So, we have two periodic series of alternating diverging and converging lenses: one series in the x, z plane and another series in the normal y, z plane. Naturally, the lens diverging in x, z plane is converging in y, z plane and *vice versa*.

Let us examine the electron trajectories in this system. One may think at first that the diverging and converging lenses of equal strength compensate for each other. This is not the case, however. As is well known [65], electrons remain in the field of an electrostatic diverging lens for a shorter time than in that of a converging lens of equal strength. So, the resultant effect will be positive: the electrons will be focused by the system.

There is another reason for the appearance of the positive resultant effect in this case. As the slope r' is proportional to the distance r from the axis and the electron passes through the diverging lens closer to the axis than through the converging lens after having been bent by the diverging lens outwards, the effect of the converging lens is stronger than that of the diverging lens. For example, let us assume that an electron enters the field of the first converging lens parallel to the axis. It comes to the diverging

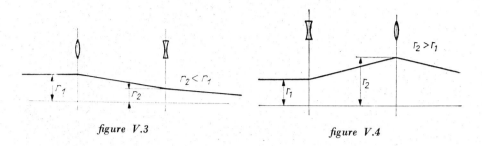

figure V.3   figure V.4

lens at a distance $r_2 < r_1$ and having a slope $r_1' = -r_1/f$. After the diverging lens the slope of the electron will be equal to

$$r_2' = -\frac{r_1}{f} + \frac{r_2}{f} < 0$$

etc. (figure V.3). If the lenses follow each other in reverse order (figure V.4), the electron enters the field of the diverging lens parallel to the axis. Then it comes to the converging lens at a distance $r_2 > r_1$ and with a slope $r_1' = r_1/f$. After passing the converging lens its slope is equal to

$$r_2' = \frac{r_1}{f} - \frac{r_2}{f} < 0$$

etc. The resultant effect is always positive.

We know from geometrical optics (see [65], formula 8.86) that the resultant focal length F of an optical system consisting of two lenses is determined by the following expression

$$\frac{1}{F} = \frac{1}{F_1} + \frac{1}{F_2} - \frac{q}{F_1 F_2} \qquad 58.2$$

where F_1 and F_2 are the focal lengths of the two lenses, respectively; q is the absolute value of the distance between the image-side principal plane of the first lens and the object-side principal plane of the second lens. For the case of $F_1 = -F_2$ we have from this expression

$$\frac{1}{F} = \frac{q}{F_2^2} > 0$$

independently of the order of succession of the lenses. Thus, we have proved that the resultant effect is always positive.

The solution is bounded in this case if the following condition is fulfilled [74]

$$0 \leq \frac{l}{f} \leq 2 \qquad 58.3$$

If $l/f > 2$, the electron can reach large distances from the axis and the solution becomes unstable.

Thus, the situation is similar in the case of alternating diverging and converging lenses to the case of a periodic sequence of converging lenses: we have alternate regions of focusing and defocusing at the output of the system as the strength of the lenses is varied.

A more comprehensive theory of periodic focusing without space-charge is given in the book by Sturrock [96] where special attention is paid to the problem of stability. The stability of the periodic focusing without space charge is also treated by [31]. A series of quadrupole lenses has been considered by [130] for the case when the adjacent quadrupoles are rotated with respect to each other by angles 180 deg/n ($n = 3, 4, 5, \ldots$).

(B) FOCUSING OF ELECTRON BEAMS BY AXIALLY SYMMETRIC PERIODIC ELECTROSTATIC FIELDS

59. FOCUSING BY A SEQUENCE OF AXIALLY SYMMETRIC THIN LENSES

Let us now consider a periodic sequence of identical thin converging lenses with focal lengths f and spacings l between the adjacent lenses, taking space-charge of the electron beam into account [87] (see figure V.1). The lenses may be *electrostatic or magnetic lenses* or combinations of electrostatic and magnetic thin lenses.

A laminar electron beam arrives into the system from the left-hand side, parallel to the z axis. The initial beam radius is equal to r_0. The edge electron trajectory of the beam will be examined in the followings (figure V.5).

In the thin lens approximation it can be assumed that the beam motion in the section between any two lenses is determined only by space-charge: there is a spreading of a drifting electron beam as it has been treated in Chapter IV. The lenses change suddenly the slopes of the trajectories of the beam.

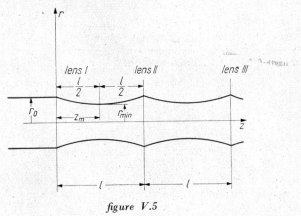

figure V.5

The slope r_0' so formed immediately after the lens gives the value of the initial slope for the motion in the following section.

Parameters l and f characterising the system can be chosen so that the configuration of the beam will be identical in all sections and symmetrical within the sections with respect to the centre of the section. It follows from the symmetry property of the beam spreading that if the minimum cross section of the beam is located just in the centre of a section, the same beam configuration will occur in all the other sections. At given values of the beam perveance P and lens spacing l the value of the focal length f cannot be chosen arbitrarily if we wish to obtain such a simple beam configuration. Naturally, the value of f depends also on the initial beam radius r_0.

Coordinate z is measured from the centre of the first lens. Thus, r_0' is the slope of the edge electron trajectory after this lens and its value will be negative. If the coordinate z_m of the minimum beam cross section is just in the centre of the first section, symmetry will cause the beam radius at the following lens to be equal to r_0 again. This is realised if the condition

$$l = 2z_m \qquad\qquad 59.1$$

is satisfied. Let us introduce the dimensionless coordinate R and Z, according to 53.2 and 53.3, respectively. As we have seen in Chapter IV, on increasing $-R_0'$ the value of Z_m first increases but later decreases. At given values of l, P and r_0 the proper value of the initial slope R_0' of the edge electron trajectory at which condition 59.1 is satisfied can be determined from figure IV.14.

We have seen in figure IV.14 that

$$(Z_m)_{\max} = 1.08$$

thus

$$(2Z_m)_{\max} = L_{\max} = 2.16 \qquad (Z = L \text{ when } z = l)$$

The corresponding value of R_0' is equal to $R_0' = -0.92$. If $L < L_{\max}$, two proper values of $-R_0'$ can be found in figure IV.14. According to 53.7 and 53.30, the lesser value of $-R_0'$ corresponds to a larger perveance, weaker lens and larger minimum beam radius $r_{\min}/r_0$ than the greater value of $-R_0'$. Thus, the lesser value of $-R_0'$ is more suitable because a lower rate of rippling occurs in the beam.

The focal length f of the lenses should be chosen so that the condition

$$\frac{r_0}{f} = -2r_0' \qquad\qquad 59.2$$

should be satisfied, according to 53.29. Here r_0' can be determined from R_0' if P is known by means of 53.28. The right-hand side of 59.2 is multiplied by 2 because the value of the slope is equal to $+|r_0'|$ when the beam arrives at the lens and it should be changed to $-|r_0'|$ by the lens (see figure V.5). The difference is $2|r_0'|$. The negative sign appears because we have $r_0' < 0$ behind the lens.

Naturally, the focal length of the first lens should be chosen in a different way. Its value depends on the slope at which the beam enters the system. If the beam enters the system parallel to z axis (figure V.5) the convergence $1/f$ of the first lens should be the half of the convergence of all the other lenses.

It is easy to see that

$$r' = \frac{dr}{dz} = r_0 \frac{dR}{dz} = r_0 \frac{dR}{dZ} \frac{dZ}{dz} = r_0 \frac{Z}{z} R' = r_0 R' \frac{L}{l} \qquad 59.3$$

as $Z/z = $ constant. It follows from 59.3 and 59.2 that

$$\frac{1}{f} = - 2R_0' \frac{L}{l} \qquad 59.4$$

where

$$L = 174\sqrt{P} \, \frac{l}{r_0} \qquad 59.5$$

Thus, we have

$$\frac{1}{f} = - 348\sqrt{P} \, \frac{R_0'}{r_0} = - \frac{2r_0'}{r_0} \qquad 59.6$$

It should be mentioned once again that the maximum possible value of L is 2.16. So

$$\frac{l_{\max}}{r_0} = \frac{2.16}{174\sqrt{P}} = \frac{1.24 \times 10^{-2}}{\sqrt{P}}$$

For example, in case of $P = 10^{-6}$ A/V$^{3/2}$ we have $l_{\max} = 12.4 r_0$.

Thus, first we have to calculate the value of L on the basis of 59.5 with given values of l, P and r_0. (The value of l can be chosen arbitrarily, while P and r_0 are determined by the parameters of the electron gun.) Then, using the correlation

$$L = 2Z_m$$

the suitable value of R_0' is to be determined by means of figure IV.14. The required value of the focal length can be obtained from 59.4 or 59.6. The value of $r_{\min}$ is determined by 53.7.

So, if the first lens is placed just in the plane of the minimum cross section of the beam leaving the electron gun (figure V.6), the focal length of the first lens should be doubled with respect to that of the other lenses. In this case

$$r_0 = r_{\min (\text{gun})}$$

The beam shape in the case of the lenses being absent is shown in the figure by dashed lines.

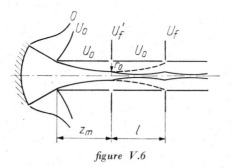

figure V.6

We have seen in Chapter IV that

$$Z_m = 2F(-R'_0)$$

where $F(x)$ is the function defined by 53.22. Hence we have

$$L = 2Z_m = 4F(-R'_0)$$

So, table IV.2 can also be used for the determination of R'_0.

As we have seen, at small values of $-R'_0$ we can use the approximation

$$F(-R'_0) \approx -R'_0$$

Thus, we have $-R'_0 \approx L/4$. In this case expressions 59.4 and 59.6 can be written in the following way

$$\frac{1}{f} = \frac{L^2}{2l} = \frac{174^2 P \dfrac{l^2}{r_0^2}}{2l} = 1.515 \times 10^4 P \frac{l}{r_0^2} \qquad [\mathrm{m}^{-1}] \qquad 59.7$$

This method of analysis is advantageous because it is valid for any type of axially symmetric thin electron lenses. The perveance of the beam determines only the required value of the focal length of the lenses but does not determine the other properties of the lenses. In this way we could separate the gun and the lenses, i.e. the beam and the lenses from each other and considerably simplify the analysis. Naturally, this treatment is possible only in the case of thin lenses. If thick lenses are used, electron trajectories in the field of the lenses must be determined, and what is more, space-charge is to be taken into account in the calculation.

Another possible solution is the connection of the electron gun with the lens system. In this case the value of z_m in expression 59.1 is equal to the value of z_m of the electron gun (figure V.7). Thus, in this case l cannot be chosen arbitrarily but is given by the parameters of the gun in a similar way to P, r_0 and r_{min}. Naturally, $r_0 > r_{min}$ in this case. The only task is to place thin lenses with focal lengths $f = F/2$ successively at distances $l = 2z_m$ from each other, where F is the resultant focal length of the beam leaving the gun, as determined by expression 45.20. Then the initial beam slope will correspond to this value of F after every lens and the beam configuration will be identical in all sections.

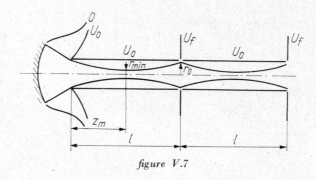

figure V.7

Substituting $r_0 = r_{min}$ and $z = z_m$ into expressions 53.2 and 53.3, we can control our solution. Considering the plane of the minimum cross section as the initial plane of the beam, we can determine the value of r_0/r_{min} from figure IV.12 and the value of $-R_0'$ from table IV.2 and expression 53.7. According to 53.30, the following value will correspond to this case

$$\frac{1}{F} = -R_0' \frac{174\sqrt{P}}{r_0}$$

Let us consider an *example*. The perveance of an electron gun is equal to $P = 3.3 \times 10^{-7}$ A/V$^{3/2}$, the radius of the cathode is $R_k = 25$ mm, the radius of the anode is $R_a = 10$ mm, i.e. $R_k/R_a = 2.5$. We have from 45.22 that

$$\vartheta_0 = \left(\frac{G^2 P}{7.33 \times 10^{-6}} \right)^{1/2} = 0.263 \approx 15 \text{ deg}$$

Hence $r = \vartheta_0 R_k = 6.57$ mm and $r_0 = \vartheta_0 R_a = 2.63$ mm. We have from figure III.16 that $r_{min}/r_k = 0.06$, i.e. $r_{min} = 0.39$ mm. From figure III.17: $z_m/R_k = 0.97$ and $F/R_k = 0.77$, i.e. $z_m = 24.2$ mm and $1/F = 0.052$ mm. It follows from 53.2 and 53.3, respectively, that

$$R = \frac{r}{r_{min}} \quad \text{and} \quad Z = 174\sqrt{P}\,\frac{z_m}{r_{min}} = 6.15$$

We obtain from figure IV.12 that $R = 6.7$, i.e. $r_0 = 2.64$ mm which value coincides with that calculated for the electron gun. We have from 53.7 and table IV.2 that $-R_0' = 1.38$, i.e. $1/F = 0.052$/mm, as it has been found above.

The result can be controlled also by means of the first method. In this case $l = 2z_m$ is to be substituted. We have for our example $L = 1.84$, i.e. $Z_m = L/2 = 0.92$. The corresponding two values of $-R_0'$ are 0.56 and 1.39. The second value is used, so

$$\frac{r_{min}}{r_0} = \exp(-1.39^2) = 0.145$$

whence $r_{min} = 0.38$ mm and $1/f = 0.106$ and $1/F = 0.053$ as it has been calculated above. (The focal length of the first lens is F, that of all the other lenses is equal to f.)

An electrostatic electron lens is called *single lens* if the potential on both sides of the lens is uniform and has the same value. Such lenses are represented in figures V.6 and V.7. The focal length of a thin single lens is determined by the following expression ([65], formula 4.67)

$$\frac{1}{f} = \frac{3}{16} \int_{z_1}^{z_2} \left(\frac{\Phi'}{\Phi}\right)^2 dz \qquad\qquad 59.8$$

where z_1 and z_2 are the coordinates bounding the field; the prime represents differentiation with respect to z. For small values of L expression 59.7 is valid. Taking 59.8 into account, we obtain from that expression

$$P = 1.237 \times 10^{-5} r_0^2 \left[\frac{1}{l} \int_{z_1}^{z_2} \left(\frac{\Phi'}{\Phi}\right)^2 dz\right] \quad [A/V^{3/2}] \qquad\qquad 59.9$$

Here the expression in brackets is the average value of the square of Φ'/Φ over the distance l, where Φ is the potential on the axis. According to [87], expression

$$\left[\left(\frac{\Phi'}{\Phi}\right)^2\right]_{average} = 2.54 \times 10^5 \frac{P}{S_0} \quad [m^{-2}] \qquad\qquad 59.10$$

derived from 59.9 is to be considered in any case of periodic electrostatic focusing, even if the electric field cannot be assumed as constituting a series of thin lenses. In this expression $S_0 = \pi r_0^2$ is the initial cross section of the beam.

60. FOCUSING OF CYLINDRICAL ELECTRON BEAMS BY PERIODIC ELECTROSTATIC FIELDS

The extension of the field of a lens used in a periodic sequence is in practice comparable with the spacing l between the lenses. So, if there is any uniform potential region between the adjacent lenses, its extension is always less than the spacing between the lenses. Thus, the conception of thin lenses is a rather rough approximation of the periodic focusing.

A periodic electrostatic focusing field may be produced practically by a series of electrodes held at alternately higher and lower potentials (figure V.8). The potential distribution of such a system is continuous, so we cannot refer to the localisation of discrete lenses. The 'lens' is extended over the whole length of the electron beam. In order to determine the beam configuration, it is necessary now to solve the equations of motion. It should be mentioned that the stability of an electron beam is higher in such a continuous field than in a system of separated lenses because focusing forces

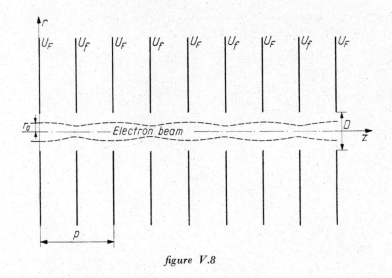

figure V.8

act over a longer region and so large fluctuations cannot be accumulated so easily.

Obviously, any field distribution may be divided into converging and diverging regions. Thus, we have physically the case treated in § 58. We have seen there that the resultant effect of a series of diverging and converging lenses is always positive (focusing effect) as the electrons are in a weaker diverging field (closer to the axis) than in the field of the converging lenses. This resultant focusing effect should be chosen so that it should just compensate the beam spreading due to space-charge. If this requirement is fulfilled we have the case of *optimum focusing*, which should be sufficiently stable: an electron shifted out of the beam should be forced back towards the beam by the focusing field. The matter in question is an *average* focusing effect; thus, an equilibrium state may only be achieved with regard to the whole beam. A given beam configuration therefore cannot be obtained quite exactly even theoretically; it can be approached only. If a periodic focusing field is used, the beam boundary is always rippling; it fluctuates about the given value. The minimum ripple is achieved in case of optimum focusing.

Let us consider now a cylindrical solid electron beam moving in the electrostatic field of an axially symmetric periodic focusing system. The z axis of the cylindrical coordinate system r, α, z is coincident with the axis of the focusing system. We shall assume first that the radius of the beam is much smaller than the characteristic dimensions of the focusing system, and the radial components of the electron velocities are small in comparison with the longitudinal ones in the whole beam. Then one can assume that at a given value of z the velocities of all the electrons of the beam are determined by the axial potential $\Phi(z)$. The *edge electron trajectory* of the beam is determined by the *paraxial equation* 21.14 for the axially symmetric case.

There is no magnetic field now. Taking space-charge into account, the paraxial equation can be written as follows

$$\frac{d^2r}{dz^2} + \frac{\Phi'}{2\Phi}\frac{dr}{dz} + \frac{\Phi''}{4\Phi}r = \frac{I}{4\sqrt{2\pi\varepsilon_0}\sqrt{\eta}\Phi^{3/2}}\frac{1}{r} \qquad 60.1$$

where the primes represent differentiation with respect to z.

The calculations become simpler frequently by elimination of the first derivative of the dependent variable from paraxial equation 60.1. As it is well known, it is necessary to introduce the following new variable for this

$$q = r\exp\left(\frac{1}{2}\int\chi(z)dz\right) \qquad 60.2$$

where $\chi(z)$ is the coefficient at r' in the equation. In our case

$$\chi = \frac{\Phi'}{2\Phi}$$

Thus, we have

$$q = r\exp\left(\frac{1}{2}\int\frac{d\Phi}{2\Phi}\right) = r\Phi^{1/4} \qquad 60.3$$

The values of r, r' and r'' can be written so with the new variable

$$r = q\Phi^{-1/4} \qquad 60.4$$

$$r' = -\frac{1}{4}\Phi^{-5/4}\Phi'q + q'\Phi^{-1/4} \qquad 60.5$$

and

$$r'' = -\frac{1}{4}\Phi^{-5/4}(\Phi''q + \Phi'q') + \frac{1}{4}\frac{5}{4}\Phi^{-9/4}(\Phi')^2q +$$

$$+ \Phi^{-1/4}q'' - \frac{1}{4}\Phi^{-5/4}\Phi'q' \qquad 60.6$$

Substituting these quantities into the paraxial equation 60.1 we obtain the following result

$$q'' + \frac{3}{16}\left(\frac{\Phi'}{\Phi}\right)^2 q - \frac{I}{4\sqrt{2\pi\varepsilon_0}\sqrt{\eta}\Phi}\frac{1}{q} = 0 \qquad 60.7$$

In most cases this equation can be solved only by numerical methods, but in some special cases it is easier to integrate this equation than equation 60.1.

In case of periodic electrostatic focusing of axially symmetric electron beams it is convenient to rewrite the paraxial equation with the following dimensionless new variables

$$x = \frac{2\pi}{p}z \qquad 60.8$$

and

$$y = \frac{r}{r_0} \qquad \qquad 60.9$$

where p is the period of the electric field and r_0 is the initial value of the radius of the beam. The intensity of the electron beam will be characterised by the following parameter [27]

$$A = \frac{p^2 P_0}{16\sqrt{2\pi^3 \varepsilon_0}\sqrt{\eta} r_0^2} = 385 \frac{p^2 P_0}{r_0^2} \qquad \qquad 60.10$$

where $P_0 = I/U_0^{3/2}$ is the perveance of the beam leaving the electron gun. Here U_0 is the potential at the entrance plane $z = 0$.

It should be mentioned that the dimensionless constant parameter A is proportional to the square of the ratio of two remarkable frequencies. Actually, the square of the *plasma frequency* ω_p of the electrons is defined by the following expression

$$\omega_p^2 = -\eta \frac{\bar{\varrho}}{\varepsilon_0} = \frac{\eta}{\varepsilon_0} \frac{I}{\pi r_0^2 (2\eta U_0)^{1/2}} = \text{constant} \qquad \qquad 60.11$$

where $\bar{\varrho}$ is the average space-charge density at the plane $z = 0$.

We may introduce also the frequency

$$\omega = \frac{2\pi}{p} v_0 = \frac{2\pi}{p} (2\eta U_0)^{1/2} = \text{constant} \qquad \qquad 60.12$$

where v_0 is the initial velocity of the electrons. It is easy to see then that

$$A = \frac{1}{2} \left(\frac{\omega_p}{\omega} \right)^2 \qquad \qquad 60.13$$

Let us express the potential on the axis by the following dimensionless quantity

$$V(x) = \frac{\Phi(x)}{U_0}$$

Then the paraxial equation 60.1 can be written as follows

$$\frac{d^2 y}{dx^2} + \frac{1}{2V} \frac{dV}{dx} \frac{dy}{dx} + \frac{1}{4V} \frac{d^2 V}{dx^2} y - \frac{A}{V^{3/2}} \frac{1}{y} = 0 \qquad \qquad 60.14$$

Equation 60.7 with this notation has the following form

$$\frac{d^2 \sigma}{dx^2} + \frac{3}{16} \left(\frac{1}{V} \frac{dV}{dx} \right)^2 \sigma - \frac{A}{V\sigma} = 0 \qquad \qquad 60.15$$

where a new variable

$$\sigma = \frac{q}{r_0 U_0^{1/4}} = y V^{1/4} \qquad \qquad 60.16$$

has been introduced.

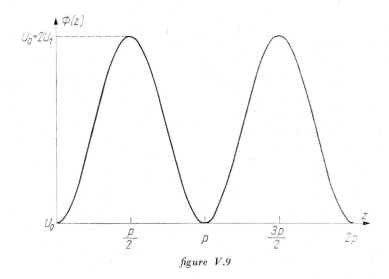

figure V.9

Equations 60.14 and 60.15 can be used for any type of periodic electro-static focusing of axially symmetric electron beams. The only mathematical assumption made up now is the paraxial approximation.

Let us suppose that an electron beam accelerated to potential U_0 arrives at the entrance of the system parallel to the z axis.

Then we have the following initial conditions

$$r(0) = r_0 \quad \text{and} \quad r'(0) = 0 \qquad\qquad 60.17$$

The electrostatic field with period p is produced by a series of electrodes placed at a distance $p/2$ from each other and held at periodically varying potentials U_F und U_f (see figure V.8, where the electrodes have been repre-sented schematically). The axial potential distribution of this field can be approximated by the following expression [27]

$$\Phi(z) = U_0 + U_1\left(1 - \cos\frac{2\pi}{p}z\right) \qquad\qquad 60.18$$

(figure V.9) where U_1 is the half-amplitude of the variable component of the potential on the axis which depends on the potentials U_f and U_F and also on the geometrical dimensions of the focusing system. The value of U_0 depends on the same parameters. It is convenient to express the potential distribution in this way as it simplifies the initial conditions: in the plane $z = 0$ we have $\Phi_0 = U_0$ and $\Phi_0' = 0$. Taking into account 60.8, the potential distribution 60.18 can be written as follows

$$V(x) = 1 + \Omega(1 - \cos x) \qquad\qquad 60.19$$

where

$$\Omega = \frac{U_1}{U_0} \qquad\qquad 60.20$$

20*

is the focusing parameter. The potential 60.18 on the axis is produced by the electric field of the electrodes only. Space-charge is only taken into account in the last term of the paraxial equation, its effect on the potential depression is neglected. As we have mentioned in Chapter IV, this effect is negligible at practical values of the beam perveance.

Any periodic potential distribution can be represented by a *Fourier* series. The potential distribution 60.18 contains only the first two terms of this series. It determines a special focusing system consisting of curved electrodes (the electrodes shown in figure V.8 are simple diaphragms). Substituting 60.18 into expression 5.54 we obtain the potential at an arbitrary point (not only in the vicinity of the axis) [21]

$$\varphi(r, z) = \sum_{\nu=0}^{\infty} \frac{(-1)^{\nu}}{(\nu!)^2} \left(\frac{r}{2}\right)^{2\nu} \Phi^{(2\nu)}(z) =$$

$$= U_0 + U_1 - U_1 \left[1 + \sum_{\nu=1}^{\infty} \frac{1}{(\nu!)^2} \left(\frac{\pi r}{p}\right)^{2\nu}\right] \cos \frac{2\pi}{p} z =$$

$$= U_0 + U_1 - U_1 \left[1 + \left(\frac{\pi r}{p}\right)^2 + \frac{1}{4} \left(\frac{\pi r}{p}\right)^4 + \right.$$

$$\left. + \frac{1}{36} \left(\frac{\pi r}{p}\right)^6 + \frac{1}{576} \left(\frac{\pi r}{p}\right)^8 + \frac{1}{14\,400} \left(\frac{\pi r}{p}\right)^{10} + \ldots\right] \cos \frac{2\pi}{p} z =$$

$$= U_0 + U_1 - U_1 I_0 \left(\frac{2\pi}{p} r\right) \cos \frac{2\pi}{p} z \qquad\qquad 60.21$$

where I_0 is the modified *Bessel* function of the first kind and zero order. The shape of the equipotential surfaces can easily be obtained from this expression. The equipotential curve $\varphi(r, z) = U_0$ is determined by the following equation derived from 60.21

$$\cos \frac{2\pi}{p} z = \frac{1}{I_0 \left(\frac{2\pi}{p} r\right)} \qquad\qquad 60.22$$

The equipotential curve $U_0 + 2U_1$ is determined by the following equation

$$\cos \frac{2\pi}{p} z = - \frac{1}{I_0 \left(\frac{2\pi}{p} r\right)} \qquad\qquad 60.23$$

Before the *determination of the electrode shapes* we shall first obtain the dependence of the potentials U_F and U_f on the parameters U_0, U_1, D and p. (Three of them may be chosen arbitrarily but so that they should satisfy other requirements. The value of U_1 is determined by the condition of optimum focusing, as we shall see later.) Substituting the values of

$$r = \frac{D}{2} \quad \text{and} \quad z = 2k\frac{p}{2} \quad \text{or} \quad z = (2k + 1)\frac{p}{2}$$

(k is an integer) into expression 60.21, we obtain the potentials on the electrodes

$$U_F = U_0 + U_1\left[1 - I_0\left(\frac{\pi D}{p}\right)\right] \qquad 60.24$$

and

$$U_f = U_0 + U_1\left[1 + I_0\left(\frac{\pi D}{p}\right)\right] \qquad 60.25$$

It is easy now to determine the electrode shapes. For this we shall substitute the values of U_F and U_f into 60.21. The equation of the equipotential U_F will have the following form

$$\cos\frac{2\pi}{p}z = \frac{I_0\left(\frac{\pi D}{p}\right)}{I_0\left(\frac{2\pi}{p}r\right)} \qquad 60.26$$

The equation of the equipotential U_f is as follows

$$\cos\frac{2\pi}{p}z = -\frac{I_0\left(\frac{\pi D}{p}\right)}{I_0\left(\frac{2\pi}{p}r\right)} \qquad 60.27$$

The electrode shapes and the equipotential curves U_0 and $(U_0 + 2U_1)$ are shown in figure V.10 for the case of $D = 0.5p$. Naturally, this electrode system is not practicable because it is very difficult to produce such curved electrodes with the required accuracy. Electrodes with simple designs are used in practice. The potential distribution of real electrode systems can be determined by analog methods or by calculations [37, 128, 129].

Expression 60.18 may be used, however, as an approximate formula for the potential distribution of a system consisting of *plane diaphragms* [103]. In this case the values of U_F and U_f should be calculated from the formula [54]

$$\Phi_c = \Phi_0 + \frac{D}{2\pi}(E_1 - E_2) \qquad 60.28$$

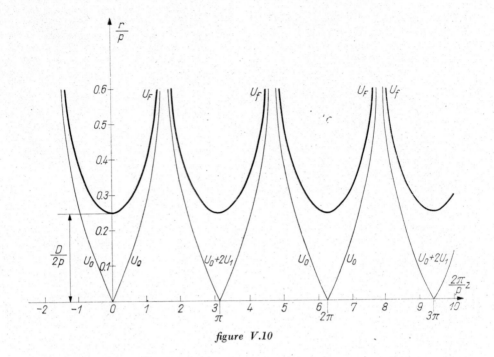

figure V.10

determining the potential at the centre of the round hole of a diaphragm held at potential Φ_0 if the diameter of the diaphragm is equal to D and there are uniform electric fields of strengths E_1 and E_2 on the left and right sides of the diaphragm, respectively. Assuming $p \gg D$, i.e. that the adjacent electrodes are plane surfaces without holes, and only the electrode in consideration has a hole, we have in this case

$$U_0 = U_F + \frac{2D}{\pi} \frac{U_f - U_F}{p} \qquad\qquad 60.29$$

and

$$U_0 + 2U_1 = U_f + \frac{2D}{\pi} \frac{U_F - U_f}{p} \qquad\qquad 60.30$$

Obtaining the following system of equations for the determination of U_F and U_f

$$U_F \left(1 - \frac{2D}{\pi p}\right) + U_f \frac{2D}{\pi p} = U_0$$

$$U_F \frac{2D}{\pi p} + U_f \left(1 - \frac{2D}{\pi p}\right) = U_0 + 2U_1 \qquad\qquad 60.31$$

we have the following solution

$$U_F = U_0 - \frac{4\frac{D}{p}}{\pi - 4\frac{D}{p}} U_1 \qquad 60.32$$

and

$$U_f = U_0 + 2 \frac{\pi - 2\frac{D}{p}}{\pi - 4\frac{D}{p}} U_1 \qquad 60.33$$

These formulae are valid if

$$\frac{D}{p} < \frac{\pi}{4}$$

and the less the value of D/p, the less is the deviation between these formulae and formulae 60.24 and 60.25.

We assume in paraxial approximation that the potential can be expressed in the vicinity of the electron beam in the form of

$$\varphi(r, z) \approx \Phi(z) - \frac{r^2}{4} \Phi''(z)$$

The paraxial approximation can be used only if this formula is valid, i.e. the terms containing higher powers of r are negligible. It follows from 60.21 that it is so if

$$\frac{\pi r_0}{p} \ll 1 \qquad 60.34$$

Thus, expression 60.34 is the condition of validity of the paraxial approximation.

On the other hand, as we shall see later, the rippling of the beam diminishes as the value of the parameter A is decreased. This means that at a given value of the perveance the value of the ratio p/r_0 should be chosen to be as small as possible. Moreover, the whole method is based on the assumption that the value of A is of second order of smallness [27]. Thus, we have two contradictory requirements. Condition 60.34 may be fulfilled so that the value of A remains sufficiently small only in the case when the value of perveance is not too great. This paraxial analysis is limited by this fact. We have $P_{0max} \approx 4 \times 10^{-6}$ $A/V^{3/2}$.

Let us substitute now the potential distribution 60.19 into equation 60.15. We obtain

$$\frac{d^2\sigma}{dx^2} + \frac{3}{16} \left[\frac{\Omega \sin x}{1 + \Omega(1 - \cos x)} \right]^2 \sigma - \frac{A}{1 + \Omega(1 - \cos x)} \frac{1}{1 + \Omega(1 - \cos x)} = 0 \qquad 60.35$$

We have the following initial conditions in the plane $x = 0$

$$V_0 = 1 \quad \text{and} \quad \left(\frac{dV}{dx}\right)_0 = \Omega \sin x \bigg|_{x=0} = 0$$

Thus, using 60.16 and 60.17, one can write

$$\sigma_0 = 1 \quad \text{and} \quad \frac{d\sigma}{dx}\bigg|_0 = 0 \qquad\qquad 60.36$$

Let us try to find such values of Ω at which we shall have a minimum rippling of the beam at a given value of the parameter A *(optimum focusing)*. For this, first we shall linearise equation 60.35 with respect to Ω and then neglect all the terms of the equation of third or higher order of smallness (Ω is assumed to be of first order). As it is seen from expression 60.10, the value of the parameter A is small enough if the perveance is not too large. For example: in case of $P_0 = 3.16 \times 10^{-8}$ A/V$^{3/2}$ and $p/r_0 = 25$ we have $A = 0.00766$. The value of Ω will be chosen so that it will be of a higher order of magnitude, in comparison with A. Thus, A can be assumed of second order of smallness. Choosing the values of A and Ω in such a way seems to be rather arbitrary, but it may be accepted in an approximate method on the basis of physical considerations and it has been shown by our calculations [103], this assumption is quite acceptable. Thus, equation 60.35 is transformed into the following form

$$\frac{d^2\sigma}{dx^2} + \frac{3}{32}\,\Omega^2\,(1 - \cos 2x)\sigma - \frac{A}{\sigma} = 0 \qquad\qquad 60.37$$

If we can find a value of Ω close to the optimum value of the focusing parameter, the rippling of the beam will be small. If the value of Ω is also small, then the solution can be found on the basis of 60.16, 60.19 and 60.36 in the form of

$$\sigma = 1 + \eta \qquad\qquad 60.38$$

where $\eta \ll 1$. Substituting 60.38 into 60.37 and linearising the equation with respect to η, we obtain

$$\frac{d^2\eta}{dx^2} + \frac{3}{32}\,\Omega^2(1 - \cos 2x)(1 + \eta) - A(1 - \eta) = 0 \qquad\qquad 60.39$$

This equation can be written in the following way

$$\frac{d^2\eta}{dx^2} + (a\cos 2x + b)\eta = -(a\cos 2x + c) \qquad\qquad 60.40$$

where

$$a = -\frac{3}{32}\,\Omega^2 \qquad\qquad 60.41$$

$$b = A + \frac{3}{32}\,\Omega^2 \qquad\qquad 60.42$$

and

$$c = -A + \frac{3}{32} \Omega^2 \qquad\qquad 60.43$$

Thus, we have an inhomogeneous *Mathieu* equation. This equation can be solved by the method of variation of constants if the solution of the homogeneous *Mathieu* equation is known [23, 59].

Let $\eta_1(x)$ and $\eta_2(x)$ be solutions of the homogeneous *Mathieu* equation

$$\frac{d^2\eta}{dx^2} + (a \cos 2x + b)\eta = 0 \qquad\qquad 60.44$$

As it is well known from the theory of the *Mathieu* equations [72], this equation may have stable or unstable solutions. The greater the absolute value of the ratio of $2b/a$, the better the stability and as we shall see, $|\,2b/a\,| \approx 4$, so the solution is quite stable.

Using the method of variation of constants, we can find the general solution of the inhomogeneous equation in the following form, where the primes represent differentiation with respect to x

$$\eta(x) = c_1\eta_1(x) + c_2\eta_2(x) - \eta_1(x) \int_0^x \frac{\eta_2(x)f(x)}{\eta_1\eta_2' - \eta_2\eta_1'}\, dx\ +$$

$$+\ \eta_2(x) \int_0^x \frac{\eta_1(x)f(x)}{\eta_1\eta_2' - \eta_2\eta_1'}\, dx \qquad\qquad 60.45$$

where

$$f(x) = -(a \cos 2x + c) \qquad\qquad 60.46$$

is the right-hand side of the inhomogeneous equation. For the determination of the constants c_1 and c_2 let us satisfy the initial conditions in the point $x = 0$. According to 60.36 we have the following initial conditions

$$\eta(0) = 0 \quad \text{and} \quad \frac{d\eta}{dx}\bigg|_0 = 0 \qquad\qquad 60.47$$

We obtain

$$\eta(0) = c_1\eta_1(0) + c_2\eta_2(0) = 0 \qquad\qquad 60.48$$

and

$$\eta'(0) = c_1\eta_1'(0) + c_2\eta_2'(0) = 0 \qquad\qquad 60.49$$

Thus, c_1 and c_2 can differ from zero only if the quantity

$$W = \eta_1(0)\eta_2'(0) - \eta_2(0)\eta_1'(0) \qquad\qquad 60.50$$

is equal to zero. But W is just the *Wronskian* determinant of the homogeneous *Mathieu* equation which is of constant value because it does not contain the first derivative of the dependent variable.

Thus we have

$$c_1 = c_2 = 0 \tag{60.51}$$

and

$$\eta(x) = \frac{1}{W}\left[\eta_2(x)\int_0^x \eta_1(x)f(x)dx - \eta_1(x)\int_0^x \eta_2(x)f(x)dx\right] \tag{60.52}$$

where

$$\eta_1(x) = \text{ce}\,(x) \quad \text{and} \quad \eta_2(x) = \text{se}\,(x)$$

are the periodic *Mathieu* functions.

It is not necessary to solve equation 60.40 if we consider only the case of *minimum rippling* of the beam. Let us return to equation 60.14 and try to find the solution of this equation in the form of

$$y(x) \approx 1 + y_1(x) + y_2(x) \tag{60.53}$$

where y_1 is a quantity of first order of smallness and y_2 is of second order. The initial conditions require that

$$y_1(0) = y_2(0) = y_1'(0) = y_2'(0) = 0 \tag{60.54}$$

Substituting 60.19 and 60.53 into 60.14, we obtain the following linearised equation

$$2[1 + \Omega(1 - \cos x)](y_1'' + y_2'') + \Omega \sin x\,(y_1' + y_2') + \frac{\Omega}{2}\cos x\,(1 + y_1 +$$

$$+ y_2) - 2A\left[1 - \frac{\Omega}{2}(1 - \cos x)\right](1 - y_1 - y_2) = 0 \tag{60.55}$$

Let us separate the terms of first and second order of smallness from each other and neglect the terms of higher order of smallness. We then obtain

$$\left\{2y_1'' + \frac{1}{2}\Omega\cos x\right\} + \left\{2y_2'' + 2\Omega y_1''\,(1 - \cos x) +\right.$$

$$\left. + \Omega y_1'\sin x + \frac{1}{2}\Omega y_1\cos x - 2A\right\} = 0 \tag{60.56}$$

As a first approximation, we shall consider only the terms of first order of smallness. Equating the terms in the first brackets of equation 60.56 to zero, we obtain

$$y_1'' = -\frac{\Omega}{4}\cos x \tag{60.57}$$

Integrating this equation twice and taking into account the initial conditions 60.54, we obtain

$$y_1(x) = -\frac{\Omega}{4}(1 - \cos x) \tag{60.58}$$

Let us calculate now the derivative y_1' and substitute it together with 60.57 and 60.58 into 60.56. The result is

$$y_2'' - \frac{\Omega^2}{4} \cos x \, (1 - \cos x) - \frac{\Omega^2}{8} \sin^2 x -$$

$$- \frac{\Omega^2}{16} \cos x \, (1 - \cos x) - A = y_2'' - \frac{5}{16} \Omega^2 \cos x +$$

$$+ \frac{7}{32} \Omega^2 \cos 2x + \frac{3}{32} \Omega^2 - A = 0 \qquad\qquad 60.59$$

Now integrating equation 60.59 twice, taking into account the initial conditions 60.54, we obtain the following result

$$y_2(x) = \frac{33}{128} \Omega^2 - \frac{5}{16} \Omega^2 \cos x + \frac{7}{128} \Omega^2 \cos 2x +$$

$$+ \left(A - \frac{3}{32} \Omega^2 \right) \frac{x^2}{2} \qquad\qquad 60.60$$

In case of *optimum focusing* the trajectory of an edge electron should not deviate considerably from the equilibrium state $y = 1$. Therefore, expression 60.60 should not contain terms with positive powers of x. The following condition is the consequence of this fact

$$\Omega_{\mathrm{opt}} = \pm \left(\frac{32}{3} A \right)^{1/2} \qquad\qquad 60.61$$

This very important formula determines the dependence of the space-charge parameter and the focusing parameter for the case when the approximation 60.53 is valid. This expression determines the values of the electrode potentials in case of an optimum focusing. The values of the electrode potentials U_f and U_F can be calculated by means of 60.61, together with 60.24 and 60.25 or 60.32 and 60.33. The sign in 60.61 is determined by the sign of U_1. It follows from 60.10 and 60.61 that the value of the perveance corresponding to an optimum value of Ω is equal to

$$P_0 = 2.43 \times 10^{-4} \Omega^2 \left(\frac{r_0}{p} \right)^2 \qquad [\mathrm{A/V^{3/2}}] \qquad\qquad 60.62$$

As it is seen from this formula, the greater is the perveance, the greater must be the potential U_1 and the ratio of r_0/p. This is obvious from the physical point of view.

We have assumed that $r_0 \ll p$ and $\Omega \ll 1$ and this will lead to a limitation of the value of the perveance. As a limiting case we may consider $\Omega = 0.5$ and $r_0/p = 0.25$. The maximum value of the perveance is given by the following result then

$$P_{0 \, \max} \approx 3.8 \times 10^{-6} \qquad [\mathrm{A/V^{3/2}}] \qquad\qquad 60.63$$

The beam configuration can be calculated by means of 60.53, 60.58, 60.60 and 60.61 for this case. The result is

$$y(x) = \frac{r}{r_0} = 1 - \frac{\Omega_{\text{opt}}}{4}(1 - \cos x) + \Omega_{\text{opt}}^2 \left(\frac{33}{128} - \right.$$

$$\left. - \frac{5}{16} \cos x + \frac{7}{128} \cos 2x \right) \qquad\qquad 60.64$$

It must be emphasised that 60.64 is valid only if 60.61 is fulfilled. If it is not so, equation 60.40 is to be solved. If even the linearisation used in equation 60.40 is not justified, equation 60.14 must be solved [103].

It follows from 60.64 that the beam configuration in first-order approximation is given by

$$\frac{r}{r_0} = 1 - \frac{\Omega_{\text{opt}}}{4}(1 - \cos x) \qquad\qquad 60.65$$

which means that in the case of the strict appliance of condition 60.61 and the initial conditions *the period of the beam rippling is* approximately *equal to that of the focusing system*. If $\Omega > 0$, the diameter of the beam is always less than the initial diameter; if $\Omega < 0$, it is always greater. The explanation is that in the case of $\Omega > 0$, the beam where arrives first at a converging region its diameter decreases, and then to a diverging region where spreading occurs, but before its diameter again equals its initial value the beam once again arrives at a converging region. We have an opposite situation in case of $\Omega < 0$. Thus, the diameter of the beam has a maximum value where the value of the potential is the minimal and *vice versa*. The greater the value of the parameter A, the stronger is the beam rippling. At a given value of A the rippling is stronger if $\Omega_{\text{opt}} < 0$. The reason for this is that in expression 60.64 the signs of the most considerable terms will coincide in this case and so the perturbation is larger.

Thus, using this method we have obtained the beam configuration and the value of the required focusing potential *approximately*. *The real configuration of the electron beam* in paraxial approximation can be obtained by numerical solution of equation 60.14. This equation has the following form if the potential distribution is given by 60.19

$$y'' + \frac{\Omega \sin x}{2[1 + \Omega(1 - \cos x)]} y' + \frac{\Omega \cos x}{4[1 + \Omega(1 - \cos x)]} y -$$

$$- \frac{A}{[1 + \Omega(1 - \cos x)]^{3/2}} \frac{1}{y} = 0 \qquad\qquad 60.66$$

Fixing the values of the parameter A, this equation has been solved by the author [103] for many values of Ω at the given initial conditions. We have found that equation 60.66 has stable solutions only in two definite intervals of the values of the parameter Ω. From both intervals ($\Omega < 0$ and $\Omega > 0$, respectively) one value of Ω may be chosen, each, at which the minimum beam rippling is achieved. The absolute values of the positive Ω_{opt+} and the negative Ω_{opt-} are not equal to each other and neither of them strictly satisfies the condition 60.61, but they do not differ greatly from the value of Ω_{opt} calculated from 60.61. We have found that

$$\Omega_{opt+} > |\Omega_{opt}| > -\Omega_{opt-} \qquad\qquad 60.67$$

The focusing parameter Ω has not been limited only to small values in our calculations. The values of Ω_{opt} calculated in this way have been plotted versus parameter A in figure V.11, where the dashed curve corresponds to expression 60.61.

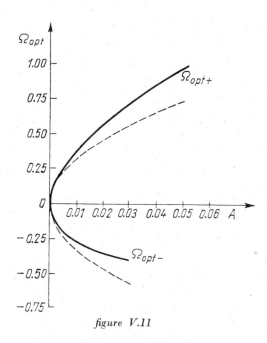

figure V.11

At these optimum values of the focusing parameter the beam rippling is greater than that calculated from 60.64 in case of Ω_{opt+} and almost equal to that value in case of Ω_{opt-}. The amplitudes δ of the beam rippling at different values of the parameter A are given in table V.1. The following quantities are listed in the table

(a) Ω_{opt} calculated from 60.61;
(b) Ω_{opt+} on the basis of numerical calculations;
(c) Ω_{opt-} on the basis of numerical calculations;
(d) δ_{+} the amplitude of the rippling at optimum focusing, in case of $\Omega_{opt} > 0$, calculated from 60.61 and 60.64;

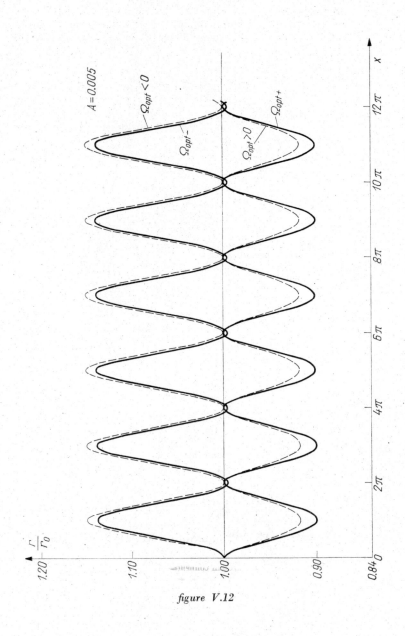

figure V.12

(e) $\delta_{+\,num}$ the amplitude of the rippling corresponding to Ω_{opt+} calculated numerically;

(f) δ_- the amplitude of the rippling at optimum focusing, in case of $\Omega_{opt} < 0$, calculated from 60.61 and 60.64;

(g) $\delta_{-\,num}$ the amplitude of the rippling corresponding to Ω_{opt-} and calculated numerically.

TABLE V.1

A	0.001	0.005	0.01	0.02	0.03	0.05
Ω_{opt}	0.1033	0.2309	0.3266	0.4619	0.5657	0.7303
Ω_{opt+}	0.1086	0.2572	0.3788	0.563	0.7196	0.978
Ω_{opt-}	−0.0980	−0.2040	−0.2724	−0.3533	−0.4027	—
δ_+	−0.045	−0.082	−0.096	−0.098	−0.083	−0.032
δ_{+num}	−0.05	−0.10	−0.13	−0.17	−0.20	−0.23
δ_-	0.059	0.148	0.230	0.364	0.483	—
δ_{-num}	0.06	0.14	0.21	0.35	0.49	—

The beam configuration calculated from 60.64 for the case of $A = 5 \times 10^{-3}$ and the corresponding value of $\Omega_{opt} = \pm 0.2309$ is given in figure V.12 (dashed curves). The continuous curves in the same figure represent the beam configurations calculated numerically from equation 60.66 in case of optimum focusing ($\Omega_{opt+} = 0.2572$ and $\Omega_{opt-} = -0.2040$).

61. THE BEAM CONFIGURATION IN THE CASE OF NON-OPTIMUM CONDITIONS

The beam configuration can also be determined when the value of the focusing parameter is different from the optimum one or the beam does not arrive parallel at the input of the focusing system [103, 109]. These are in practice very important cases the investigation of which gives us information on the phenomena arising at the variations of the electrode potentials or the entrance conditions.

(a) The non-optimum value of the focusing parameter

If we consider only ± 15–20% maximum deviations of the values of Ω from Ω_{opt}, the beam may be regarded to be laminar and paraxial and the paraxial equation is valid. The beam configuration can then be obtained by the numerical solution of equation 60.66 with the initial conditions 60.17.

We have solved this equation by means of the *Runge–Kutta* method [103] at suitably chosen values of the parameters A and Ω, in the interval of the independent variable $0 \leq z \leq 11p$. At each value of A the edge-electron trajectory of the beam has been determined for various positive and negative values of Ω. We have computed 188 trajectories in this way. Three typical trajectories are shown in figure V.13 ($A = 5 \times 10^{-3}$; $\Omega < 0$). The dashed

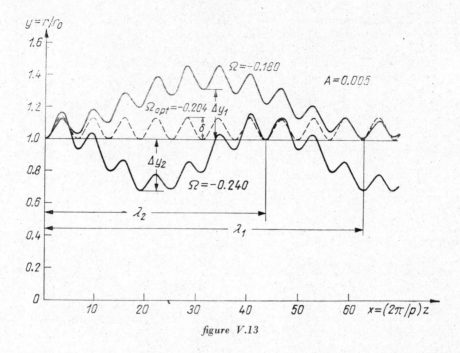

figure V.13

curve represents the edge-electron trajectory with minimum rippling corresponding to the optimum value Ω_{opt} of the focusing parameter. A small deviation of Ω from Ω_{opt} results in the fact that the beam rippling with amplitude δ and period p will be superposed on an additional greater fluctuation with amplitude Δy and period λ (see the continuous curves in figure V.13).

The results of our calculations have shown that the edge-electron trajectory of the beam in this case may be approximated by the following expression

$$y = 1 + \frac{\Delta y}{2}\left(1 - \cos\frac{p}{\lambda}x\right) + \frac{\delta}{2}(1 - \cos x) \qquad 61.1$$

We have found that $\lambda/p \gg 1$ and its value diminishes if the value of A is increased. At a fixed value of A the value of the wavelength λ is not constant but if the absolute value of Ω is increased the value of λ decreases (see figure V.13). In case of equal absolute values of Ω the value of λ is greater if $\Omega > 0$.

The qualitative and quantitative interpretation of these results obtained by means of numerical computations can be given by the following physical considerations [109]. In case of optimum focusing the space-charge spreading is just compensated by the focusing forces. Speaking of *average* effects, the small rippling with period p can be neglected. If the value of the focusing parameter is different from the optimum one, or if the entrance conditions have changed, the balance of forces is disturbed and the electrons are moved away from their equilibrium paths. This perturbation causes a change of the space-charge density. This, in turn, results a change in the balance of forces: electrostatic restoring forces appear which are tending to draw the electrons back towards their positions of equilibrium. As a result of these forces the electrons will oscillate around their equilibrium paths. A similar phenomenon can be observed in a plasma the charge neutrality of which has been disturbed.

The frequency of transversal oscillations in a plasma of infinite extent is equal to the plasma frequency defined by expression 60.11. Substituting there the radius r of the beam and its potential Φ for r_0 and U_0, respectively, we obtain

$$\omega_p^2 = \frac{\sqrt{\eta}I}{\sqrt{2\pi\varepsilon_0}\sqrt{\Phi}r^2} \qquad 61.2$$

The wavelength λ_p of the transversal oscillations is defined by

$$\lambda_p = \frac{2\pi v}{\omega_p} \qquad 61.3$$

where

$$v \approx (2\eta\Phi)^{1/2} \qquad 61.4$$

is the longitudinal component of the velocity of the electrons. Substituting 60.9, 61.2 and 61.4 into 61.3, we obtain

$$\lambda_p^2 = \frac{8\sqrt{2\pi^3\varepsilon_0}\sqrt{\eta}r_0^2\Phi^{3/2}y^2}{I} \qquad 61.5$$

In this expression Φ and y are functions of the independent variable x. In order to obtain the wavelength of the fluctuation considered here, these functions are to be replaced by their average values. The average values $\bar{\Phi}$ and $\bar{y}$ can be expressed from expressions 60.18 and 61.1, respectively, in the following way

$$\bar{\Phi} = U_0(1 + \Omega) \qquad 61.6$$

and

$$\bar{y} = 1 + \frac{\Delta y + \delta}{2} \qquad 61.7$$

Let us substitute these values into 61.5 for Φ and y, respectively, and take 60.10 into account. We obtain the following approximate formula for the wavelength λ [105]

$$\frac{\lambda}{p} \approx \frac{1}{(2A)^{1/2}}(1 + \Omega)^{3/4}\left(1 + \frac{\Delta y + \delta}{2}\right) \qquad 61.8$$

By means of this formula all the facts listed above can be derived. It directly follows from 61.8 and the smallness of the parameter A that $\lambda/p \gg 1$ and its value diminishes when the value of A is increased. It can also be easily

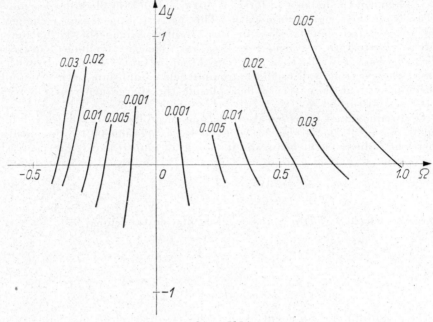

figure V.14

seen that in case of equal absolute values of Ω the value of λ is greater if $\Omega > 0$ than if $\Omega < 0$. If the absolute value of Ω is decreased the value of Δy increases (see later). It follows from 61.8 that in this case λ will increase, too. The rate of this increase is especially high if $\Omega < 0$.

Expression 61.8 has been derived on the basis of a rather rough physical analogy but similar fluctuations have been found in case of electrostatically focused sheet beams by [120]. A further inaccuracy occurs as a consequence of the approximate averaging of the quantities Φ and y. In spite of these facts, expression 61.8 corresponds with a deviation of several percents to the quantitative results gained from the numerical computation of the electron trajectories. This formula is especially accurate at small values of the parameter A and in case of $\Omega > 0$.

The value of the amplitude Δy determines the change of the beam radius when the focusing is not optimal. As we have already mentioned, the value of Δy increases when the absolute value of Ω is decreased. The beam radius increases ($\Delta y > 0$) if $|\Omega| < |\Omega_{opt}|$ and the beam radius decreases ($\Delta y < 0$) if $|\Omega| > |\Omega_{opt}|$. Naturally, $\Delta y = 0$ if $\Omega = \Omega_{opt}$. These facts correspond to the physical consideration given above.

We should like to remark that there is a weak dependence of the amplitude Δy on the independent variable x. This dependence should be taken into consideration if expression 61.1 is applied to a very long electron beam.

The dependence of the amplitude Δy of the fluctuation with wavelength λ on the focusing parameter Ω is shown in figure V.14. There are several curves in the figure. These curves are independent of each other and correspond to various values of the parameter A, which are given on the corresponding curves. It can easily be seen from the figure which value of Ω_{opt} corresponds to a given value of A. Besides, the 'depth' of the focusing, i.e. the interval of the focusing parameter Ω within which the beam rippling does not exceed a given value of Δy_{max} can also be determined from the figure.

If the value of Ω differs from Ω_{opt} greatly, the beam configuration changes in a considerable extent. Greater and greater fluctuations occur; at a further deviation of Ω from Ω_{opt} the electron trajectories will cross each other and our assumptions will not be valid. The conclusions given above cannot be extended for this case. Such trajectories have been calculated by [21].

It should be mentioned that in case of very strong increase of the focusing parameter Ω the transversal forces become so strong that space-charge may even be neglected. This case is practically important because in this way focusing is possible even at very large space-charge fluctuations. We have nearly the case of periodic focusing without space-charge (see § 58). But the value of the focusing parameter cannot be increased arbitrarily: at a certain value of Ω the focusing becomes unstable.

(b) The non-parallel entrance of the electron beam into the focusing system

If the focusing parameter has an optimum value but the initial conditions of the beam motion have changed (the beam is diverging or converging at the entrance plane), the second initial condition 60.17 will not be zero. We have also examined this case, by numerical solutions of equation 60.66 [109]. As an example, the edge-electron trajectories for the case of $A = 0.005$ and $\Omega = \Omega_{opt} = -0.204$ are shown with the following initial conditions

$$y(0) = 1 \quad \text{and} \quad \frac{dy}{dx}\bigg|_{x=0} = y_0' = \pm\, 0.05$$

(continuous curves in figure V.15). For comparison, we have also shown in the figure the optimum trajectory corresponding to the case when the electron beam enters the system parallel to the axis, i.e. $y_0' = 0$ (dashed curve).

We have found that an additional fluctuation with amplitude Δy^* and period λ^* arises in this case, too. The edge-electron trajectory of the beam is given by the following expression [105]

$$y = 1 + \Delta y^* \sin\frac{p}{\lambda^*}\, x + \frac{\delta}{2}\,(1 - \cos x) \tag{61.9}$$

The value of the amplitude Δy^* increases when y_0' is increased; its sign coincides with the sign of y_0'.

21*

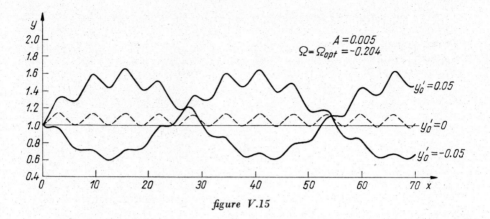

figure V.15

The wavelength λ^* can be calculated from 61.8 where $\Delta y = 0$ is to be substituted because in this case we have

$$\bar{y} = 1 + \frac{\delta}{2}$$

At a fixed value of Ω_{opt} the value of λ^* is nearly constant for different values of the initial angle y_0'.

Let us introduce the stiffness K of the focusing, according to [120]. The value of the stiffness characterises the stability of the focusing against the perturbations of the initial conditions

$$K = \frac{y_0'}{\Delta y^*} \qquad\qquad 61.10$$

The greater is the value of the stiffness, the lesser is the amplitude of the fluctuation caused by a given y_0' variation of the initial slope. Neglecting the value of δ we obtain from 61.8, 61.9 and 61.10

$$K = \frac{1}{\lambda^*/p} = (2A)^{1/2}(1 + \Omega_{opt})^{-3/4} \qquad\qquad 61.11$$

It follows from 61.11 that at a fixed value of the parameter A the beam stiffness is greater for negative values of Ω_{opt} than for positive ones.

The beam configuration can be determined easily from expressions 61.9 and 61.8. The value of Δy^* is determined by the following expression derived from 61.10 and 61.11

$$\Delta y^* = \frac{y_0'}{K} = \frac{y_0'}{(2A)^{1/2}}(1 + \Omega_{opt})^{3/4} \qquad\qquad 61.12$$

62. FOCUSING OF THICK CYLINDRICAL SOLID BEAMS

If the perveance of the electron beam is so large that the period of the focusing system is comparable with the radius of the beam, the paraxial approximation is not valid (see § 60). A method of analysis has been proposed by P. K. Tien [113] for this case.

The periodic potential distribution produced by an axially symmetric focusing system can be expressed by a *Fourier* series, and the analysis of arbitrary focusing systems with potential distribution given in form of a general *Fourier* series has been carried out by the author [148]. For simplicity, we shall give here the potential distribution approximated by the first two terms of this series as it has been used by Tien

$$U(r, z) = U_0 + U_1(r) \cos \frac{2\pi}{p} z \qquad 62.1$$

where U_0 is the uniform component of the potential; $U_1(r)$ is the amplitude of the variable component of the potential which is a function of the radius r and depends on the geometrical dimensions of the focusing system as well as on the potentials at the electrodes. We assume that

$$U_1 \ll U_0$$

The period of the focusing system is equal to p. We shall try to find the edge-electron trajectory in the form of

$$r(z) = r_0 + r_1(z) \qquad 62.2$$

where $r_0 = $ constant, r_1 is a periodic function of z and for a well-focused electron beam we have

$$r_1 \ll r_0$$

Let us expand $U_1(r)$ in *Taylor* series at $r = r_0$. We obtain

$$U_1(r) = U_1(r_0) + r_1 \frac{dU_1}{dr}\bigg|_{r=r_0} + \frac{r_1^2}{2} \frac{d^2U_1}{dr^2}\bigg|_{r=r_0} + \cdots \qquad 62.3$$

As a result of r_1 being very small, terms higher than the second power of r_1 can be neglected. The value of the radial component of the electric field can be expressed then in the vicinity of r_0 by the following expression

$$E_r(r, z) = -\frac{\partial U(r, z)}{\partial r} = -\frac{dU_1(r)}{dr} \cos \frac{2\pi}{p} z =$$

$$= -\left[\frac{dU_1}{dr}\bigg|_{r=r_0} + r_1 \frac{d^2U_1}{dr^2}\bigg|_{r=r_0}\right] \cos \frac{2\pi}{p} z \qquad 62.4$$

In addition, an average space-charge force of

$$F_e = \frac{eI}{2\pi\varepsilon_0 r_0 v_z} \qquad 62.5$$

acts on the boundary electrons, as it follows from 52.1. Here v_z is the longitudinal component of the velocity of the electrons. As a first approximation, we may assume that

$$v_z = v_0 = (2\eta U_0)^{1/2} = \text{constant}$$

Thus, the equation of motion of the boundary electron can be written as follows

$$\frac{d^2 r_1}{dt^2} = \eta \left[\frac{dU_1}{dr} \bigg|_{r=r_0} + r_1 \frac{d^2 U_1}{dr^2} \bigg|_{r=r_0} \right] \cos \frac{2\pi}{p} z +$$

$$+ \frac{\eta I}{2\pi\varepsilon_0 r_0 (2\eta U_0)^{1/2}} \qquad\qquad 62.6$$

Using the relation $v_0 = dz/dt$, we can replace the differentiation with respect to time by differentiation with respect to coordinate z. We obtain

$$\frac{d^2 r_1}{dz^2} - \frac{\dfrac{d^2 U_1}{dr^2} \bigg|_{r=r_0}}{2U_0} r_1 \cos \frac{2\pi}{p} z = \frac{\dfrac{dU_1}{dr} \bigg|_{r=r_0}}{2U_0} \cos \frac{2\pi}{p} z +$$

$$+ \frac{I/U_0^{3/2}}{4\pi\varepsilon_0 r_0 (2\eta)^{1/2}} \qquad\qquad 62.7$$

We should like to emphasise that the following physical simplifications have been used here, beside the assumptions accepted in this book:

1. We assume that the trajectory of a boundary electron has a small deviation only from a given constant value of r_0. This constant value does not correspond to a real electron trajectory, for we have seen in § 60 that in the case of periodic focusing all the trajectories are rippling. The greater the value of r_0, the stronger is the rippling of the electron trajectories; but the deviation related to the value of r_0 can be assumed to be small in all cases. (It may be remarked that the parameters of the field can also be expressed by a series expansion around a possible electron trajectory [81].)

2. As a consequence of the previous assumption, the space-charge force is assumed to be of constant value.

It is to be mentioned that equation 62.7 does not contain the axial potential. This method may be used also for analysis of focusing systems which are not axially symmetric; for example: bifilar helix (see § 64).

Thus, we have obtained an inhomogeneous *Mathieu* equation, without any specific mathematical transformation. The general solution of the inhomogeneous equation can be expressed as the sum of the general solution of the corresponding homogeneous *Mathieu* equation and a particular integral of the inhomogeneous equation. It can be easily proved that the coefficients at the *Mathieu* functions will be equal to zero if we have the following initial conditions: $(dr_1/dz)\,|_{z=0} = 0$ and the value of the initial beam radius is equal to $r_0 + r_1(0)$.

In this case the solution of equation 62.7 consists only of the particular integral. Naturally, it is valid only in the stable region of the *Mathieu* functions. (See the stability diagram shown in figure V.16.) The homogeneous equation corresponding to equation 62.7 coincides with the *Mathieu* equation

$$\frac{d^2y}{dx^2} + (a - 2q \cos 2x)y = 0 \qquad\qquad 62.8$$

if

$$y = r_1, \qquad x = \frac{\pi z}{p}, \qquad a = 0$$

and

$$q = \left(\frac{p}{2\pi}\right)^2 \frac{\dfrac{d^2 U_1}{dr^2}\Big|_{r=r_0}}{U_0}$$

The solution is stable at every practical value of q. It will be obvious in the followings that $q \ll 1$.

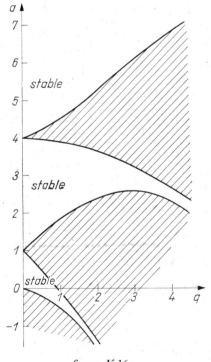

figure V.16

If the general solution of the *Mathieu* equation is to be taken into consideration, the analysis will be much more complicated. The results of the calculations have shown that in this case it is more difficult to realise an effective focusing: oscillations with larger amplitude and wavelength treated in § 61 will appear. The strict fulfilment of the initial conditions is therefore a very important requirement.

As a first-order approximation, the second terms of both sides of equation 62.7 can be omitted because they are much smaller than the first terms of the left-hand side and right-hand side of this equation [113].

After the omission of these terms the approximate form of equation 62.7 can be written as follows

$$\frac{d^2 r_1}{dz^2} = \frac{\left.\dfrac{dU_1}{dr}\right|_{r=r_0}}{2U_0} \cos \frac{2\pi}{P} z \qquad 62.9$$

Let $r_0 + r_1(0)$ be the radius of the parallel incident beam at the plane $z = 0$. We have then the following initial conditions

$$r_1 = r_1(0) = r_{10} \quad \text{and} \quad \left.\frac{dr_1}{dz}\right|_{z=0} = 0 \qquad 62.10$$

Equation 62.9 has the following solution

$$r_1 = -\left(\frac{P}{2\pi}\right)^2 \frac{\left.\dfrac{dU_1}{dr}\right|_{r=r_0}}{2U_0} \cos \frac{2\pi}{P} z \qquad 62.11$$

This solution is valid if the initial beam radius is chosen so that

$$r_{10} = -\left(\frac{P}{2\pi}\right)^2 \frac{\left.\dfrac{dU_1}{dr}\right|_{r=r_0}}{2U_0} \qquad 62.12$$

As we can see, *the rippling of the beam is determined mainly by the periodic focusing field and not by space-charge.* The focusing field required for the maintenance of an electron beam with given charge density is to be so strong that in practice the electron trajectories do not deviate from those in the absence of space-charge, which means that the focusing is stable enough against the perturbations of space-charge.

The beam configuration calculated by means of 62.11 and the longitudinal section of the focusing system are shown in figure V.17.

Using 62.11, we shall consider now the neglected terms of equation 62.7

$$\frac{1}{2}\left(\frac{P}{2\pi}\right)^2 \frac{\left.\dfrac{dU_1}{dr}\right|_{r=r_0}}{2U_0} \frac{\left.\dfrac{d^2U_1}{dr^2}\right|_{r=r_0}}{2U_0}\left(1 + \cos \frac{4\pi}{P} z\right) =$$

$$= \frac{I}{4\pi\varepsilon_0 r_0 (2\eta)^{1/2} U_0^{3/2}} \qquad 62.13$$

In the case of optimum focusing, the space-charge forces are compensated *on average* by the external focusing forces. Consequently, the constant terms of equation 62.13 should balance each other independently of the value of the coordinate z. Equating the constant terms we obtain

$$\frac{dU_1}{dr}\bigg|_{r=r_0} \frac{d^2U_1}{dr^2}\bigg|_{r=r_0} = \left(\frac{2\pi}{p}\right)^2 \frac{(2U_0)^{1/2}I}{\pi\varepsilon_0\sqrt{\eta}\,r_0} \qquad 62.14$$

The value of the focusing potential U_f is determined by this expression because its left-hand side is proportional to U_f^2. The remaining term of equation 62.13 determines an additional component of the beam rippling, the amplitude of which is a quantity of second order of smallness.

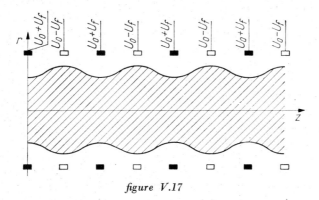

figure V.17

Up to now, we have assumed that the velocity of the electrons is of constant v_0 value. It is a rather rough approximation. If we take into account that the velocity varies with the variation of the potential, we obtain for the axial electron velocity at a distance r_0 from the axis the following expression on the basis of 62.1 and the condition $U_1 \ll U_0$ (the transversal components of the velocity will be neglected as before)

$$v_z = \left\{2\eta\left[U_0 + U_1(r_0)\cos\frac{2\pi}{p}z\right]\right\}^{1/2} \approx$$

$$\approx v_0\left[1 + \frac{U_1(r_0)}{2U_0}\cos\frac{2\pi}{p}z\right] \qquad 62.15$$

As v_z is function of the coordinate z now $[v_z = v_z(z)]$ we shall need the following relation

$$\frac{d^2r_1}{dt^2} = \frac{d}{dt}\left(\frac{dr_1}{dt}\right) = v_z\frac{d}{dz}\left(v_z\frac{dr_1}{dz}\right) = v_z^2\frac{d^2r_1}{dz^2} + v_z\frac{dv_z}{dz}\frac{dr_1}{dz} \qquad 62.16$$

Equation 62.6 has the following form

$$\frac{d^2 r_1}{dz^2} + \frac{1}{v_z}\frac{dv_z}{dz}\frac{dr_1}{dz} - \frac{\eta}{v_z^2} r_1 \left.\frac{d^2 U_1}{dr^2}\right|_{r=r_0} \cos\frac{2\pi}{p} z =$$

$$= \frac{\eta}{v_z^2}\left.\frac{dU_1}{dr}\right|_{r=r_0} \cos\frac{2\pi}{p} z + \frac{\eta}{v_z^2}\frac{I}{2\pi\varepsilon_0 r_0 (2\eta U_0)^{1/2}} \qquad 62.17$$

This equation differs from equation 62.7 only in the appearance of the term

$$\frac{1}{v_z}\frac{dv_z}{dz}\frac{dr_1}{dz}$$

Naturally, v_0 is everywhere replaced by v_z with the exception of the space-charge term where the average axial electron velocity v_0 may be used because the error caused by this assumption in such a small term is not significant. Thus, v_0 and v_z being of the same order of magnitude, the same terms can be neglected in equation 62.17 as in equation 62.7. Besides, one can see from 62.11 and 62.15 that

$$\frac{1}{v_z}\frac{dv_z}{dz}\frac{dr_1}{dz} \approx \frac{1}{v_0} v_0 \frac{2\pi}{p}\frac{U_1(r_0)}{2U_0}\frac{p}{2\pi}\frac{\left.\dfrac{dU_1}{dr}\right|_{r=r_0}}{2U_0} =$$

$$= \frac{U_1(r_0)}{2U_0}\frac{\left.\dfrac{dU_1}{dr}\right|_{r=r_0}}{2U_0} \qquad 62.18$$

This term is of the same order of smallness as the neglected terms, and so it can also be neglected. If we assume in the remaining terms that $v_z = v_0$, equation 62.9 is again obtained. The solution of this equation being 62.11. The only difference is that the value of the focusing potential U_f will differ from its previous value. Actually, if we substitute 62.11 into equation 62.17, the result is

$$\frac{\left.\dfrac{dU_1}{dr}\right|_{r=r_0}}{2U_0} \cos\frac{2\pi}{p} z - \frac{1}{v_0}\left[1 - \frac{U_1(r_0)}{2U_0}\cos\frac{2\pi}{p} z\right] \times$$

$$\times v_0 \frac{2\pi}{p}\frac{U_1(r_0)}{2U_0}\sin^2\frac{2\pi}{p} z \times \frac{p}{2\pi}\frac{\left.\dfrac{dU_1}{dr}\right|_{r=r_0}}{2U_0} +$$

$$+ \frac{\eta}{v_0^2}\left[1 - \frac{U_1(r_0)}{U_0}\cos\frac{2\pi}{p} z\right]\left(\frac{p}{2\pi}\right)^2 \frac{\left.\dfrac{dU_1}{dr}\dfrac{d^2 U_1}{dr^2}\right|_{r=r_0}}{2U_0}\cos^2\frac{2\pi}{p} z =$$

$$= \frac{\eta}{v_0^2}\left[1 - \frac{U_1(r_0)}{U_0}\cos\frac{2\pi}{p}z\right]\frac{dU_1}{dr}\bigg|_{r=r_0}\cos\frac{2\pi}{p}z +$$

$$+ \frac{\eta}{v_0^2}\left[1 - \frac{U_1(r_0)}{U_0}\cos\frac{2\pi}{p}z\right]\frac{I}{2\pi\varepsilon_0 r_0(2\eta U_0)^{1/2}} \qquad 62.19$$

Equating the constant terms in this expression, we obtain

$$\left[\frac{d^2U_1}{dr^2}\bigg|_{r=r_0}\left(\frac{p}{2\pi}\right)^2 + U_1(r_0)\right]\frac{dU_1}{dr}\bigg|_{r=r_0} = \frac{\sqrt{2}I\sqrt{U_0}}{\pi\varepsilon_0 r_0\sqrt{\eta}} \qquad 62.20$$

Substituting the actual function $U_1(r)$ into equation 62.20 we can determine the value U_f of the focusing potential. Comparing this equation with 62.14, one can see that the difference is in the term of $U_1(r_0)$. Thus, the consideration of the variation of the electron velocity, i.e. of the axial component of the field results an additional focusing effect. The coefficient of U_f^2 increases; this means that at a given value of the perveance the required value of the focusing potential decreases. This result is independent of the sign of $U_1(r_0)$.

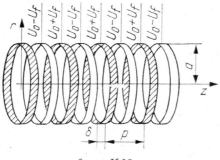

figure V.18

As an *example* let us consider a focusing system consisting of a series of annular rings held at periodically varying potentials $(U_0 + U_f)$ and $(U_0 - U_f)$ (figure V.18). The potential distribution inside the system is given by the following approximate formula [122]

$$U(r,z) \approx U_0 + \frac{4U_f}{\pi}\left[\frac{\sin\frac{\pi}{2}\left(1 - \frac{2\delta}{p}\right)}{\frac{\pi}{2}\left(1 - \frac{2\delta}{p}\right)}\right]\frac{I_0\left(\frac{2\pi}{p}r\right)}{I_0\left(\frac{2\pi}{p}a\right)}\cos\frac{2\pi}{p}z \qquad 62.21$$

where a and δ are the radius and the width of the rings, respectively, I_0 is the modified *Bessel* function of the first-kind and zero-order.

Introducing the following notation

$$F\left(\frac{\delta}{p}\right) = \frac{4}{\pi} \frac{\sin\dfrac{\pi}{2}\left(1 - \dfrac{2\delta}{p}\right)}{\dfrac{\pi}{2}\left(1 - \dfrac{2\delta}{p}\right)} \qquad 62.22$$

As we can see, F depends only on the ratio of δ/p and is independent of z. F is an increasing monotonic function of the ratio of δ/p.

The potential distribution of the system of annular rings may be written then in the following way

$$U(r, z) \approx U_0 + F U_f \frac{I_0\left(\dfrac{2\pi r}{p}\right)}{I_0\left(\dfrac{2\pi a}{p}\right)} \cos \frac{2\pi}{p} z \qquad 62.23$$

It should be mentioned that expression 62.23 contains only the first two terms of a *Fourier* series, all the other terms having been omitted. As a consequence of this, the potentials at the rings derived from the expression $(U_0 \pm F U_f)$ are slightly different from the real values of these potentials $(U_0 \pm U_f)$. Nevertheless, the potential distribution is in practice well approximated by expression 62.23. According to 62.1 we have for the system of annular rings

$$U_1(r) = F U_f \frac{I_0\left(\dfrac{2\pi r}{p}\right)}{I_0\left(\dfrac{2\pi a}{p}\right)} \qquad 62.24$$

Let us calculate the first and second derivatives of this function at $r = r_0$

$$\left.\frac{dU_1}{dr}\right|_{r=r_0} = F U_f \frac{\dfrac{2\pi}{p} I_0'\left(\dfrac{2\pi r_0}{p}\right)}{I_0\left(\dfrac{2\pi a}{p}\right)} = \frac{2\pi}{p} F U_f \frac{I_1\left(\dfrac{2\pi r_0}{p}\right)}{I_0\left(\dfrac{2\pi a}{p}\right)} \qquad 62.25$$

and

$$\left.\frac{d^2 U_1}{dr^2}\right|_{r=r_0} = \left(\frac{2\pi}{p}\right)^2 F U_f \frac{I_0''\left(\dfrac{2\pi r_0}{p}\right)}{I_0\left(\dfrac{2\pi a}{p}\right)} =$$

$$= \left(\frac{2\pi}{p}\right)^2 F U_f \frac{I_0\left(\frac{2\pi r_0}{p}\right) - \frac{p}{2\pi r_0} I_1\left(\frac{2\pi r_0}{p}\right)}{I_0\left(\frac{2\pi a}{p}\right)} \quad 62.26$$

It follows from expressions 62.24, 62.25 and 62.26 and from the properties of the *Bessel* functions that in the case of

$$\frac{U_1(r_0)}{U_0} \ll 1 \quad\quad 62.27$$

we also have

$$\frac{p}{2\pi U_0} \frac{dU_1}{dr}\bigg|_{r=r_0} \ll 1 \quad\quad 62.28$$

and

$$\frac{1}{U_0}\left(\frac{p}{2\pi}\right)^2 \frac{d^2U_1}{dr^2}\bigg|_{r=r_0} \ll 1 \quad\quad 62.29$$

As 62.27 is one of the basic assumptions accepted in this method, relations 62.28 and 62.29 are also valid in any case.

The left-hand side of equation 62.20 is determined for our example by expressions 62.25 and 62.26. Naturally, these expressions will be replaced by other ones if another kind of focusing system is used. The left-hand side of equation 62.20, however, is always proportional to U_f^2. Thus, the required value of the focusing potential can be determined with the knowledge of the function of $U_1(r)$.

So, we can determine now the value of the focusing potential required if the system of annular rings is used. Using 62.24, 62.25 and 62.26, we obtain for 62.20 the following expression

$$(FU_f)^2 \frac{I_0''\left(\frac{2\pi r_0}{p}\right) + I_0\left(\frac{2\pi r_0}{p}\right)}{I_0^2\left(\frac{2\pi a}{p}\right)} I_0'\left(\frac{2\pi r_0}{p}\right) = \frac{p}{2\pi} \frac{\sqrt{2I}\sqrt{U_0}}{\pi\varepsilon_0 r_0\sqrt{\eta}} \quad 62.30$$

Hence we have for the focusing potential

$$(FU_f)^2 = 1.21 \times 10^5 I \sqrt{U_0} \frac{I_0^2\left(\frac{2\pi a}{p}\right)}{\frac{4\pi r_0}{p} I_0\left(\frac{2\pi r_0}{p}\right) I_1\left(\frac{2\pi r_0}{p}\right) - I_1^2\left(\frac{2\pi r_0}{p}\right)} \quad 62.31$$

We obtain the boundary electron trajectory from 62.2 and 62.11

$$r(z) = r_0 - \frac{FU_f}{2U_0} \frac{p}{2\pi} \frac{I_1\left(\frac{2\pi r_0}{p}\right)}{I_0\left(\frac{2\pi a}{p}\right)} \cos \frac{2\pi}{p} z \qquad 62.32$$

In *paraxial approximation* we have

$$\frac{2\pi r_0}{p} \ll 1$$

and it is sufficient to consider the potential distribution 62.1 only along the axis where

$$U_1(r) = U_1(0)$$

Thus, we have

$$\Phi(z) = U_0 + U_1(0) \cos \frac{2\pi}{p} z \qquad 62.33$$

Using 5.54, we obtain then

$$U(r, z) \approx \Phi(z) - \frac{r^2}{4} \Phi''(z) = U_0 + U_1(0)\left[1 + \left(\frac{2\pi}{p}\right)^2 \frac{r^2}{4}\right] \times$$

$$\times \cos \frac{2\pi}{p} z \approx U_0 + U_1(0) \cos \frac{2\pi}{p} z \qquad 62.34$$

$$\frac{\partial U}{\partial r} \approx \left(\frac{2\pi}{p}\right)^2 \frac{r}{2} U_1(0) \cos \frac{2\pi}{p} z \qquad 62.35$$

and

$$\frac{\partial^2 U}{\partial r^2} \approx \left(\frac{2\pi}{p}\right)^2 \frac{U_1(0)}{2} \cos \frac{2\pi}{p} z \qquad 62.36$$

The variables have been separated. According to 62.1, we can write

$$U_1(r_0) \approx U_1(0) \qquad 62.37$$

$$\frac{dU_1}{dr}\bigg|_{r=r_0} \approx \left(\frac{2\pi}{p}\right)^2 \frac{r_0}{2} U_1(0) \qquad 62.38$$

and

$$\frac{d^2U_1}{dr^2}\bigg|_{r=r_0} \approx \left(\frac{2\pi}{p}\right)^2 \frac{U_1(0)}{2} \qquad 62.39$$

Substituting 62.37, 62.38 and 62.39 into 62.20, we obtain

$$\left[\frac{U_1(0)}{2} + U_1(0)\right]\left(\frac{2\pi}{p}\right)^2 \frac{r_0}{2} U_1(0) = \frac{\sqrt{2}\,I\sqrt{U_0}}{\pi\varepsilon_0\,r_0\sqrt{\eta}} \qquad 62.40$$

We can see now how important the consideration of the variation of the electron velocity is: the quantity in the brackets has increased threefold. We obtain from 62.40

$$\left[\frac{U_1(0)}{U_0}\right]^2 = \frac{\sqrt{2}\,p^2}{3\pi^3\,\varepsilon_0\sqrt{\eta}\,r_0^2} \frac{I}{U_0^{3/2}} \qquad 62.41$$

Let us substitute now 62.38 into 62.11 and then into 62.2. We obtain the boundary electron trajectory for the case when 62.41 is fulfilled

$$\frac{r}{r_0} = 1 - \frac{1}{4}\frac{U_1(0)}{U_0}\cos\frac{2\pi}{p}\cdot z \qquad 62.42$$

With the aid of 60.10 one can easily see that 62.41 coincides with 60.61.

In the paraxial case we obtain for the system of annular rings from 62.31 and 62.32 or from 62.24, 62.41 and 62.42 that

$$(FU_f)^2 = \frac{1.21\times10^5\,I\sqrt{U_0}\,I_0^2\left(\frac{2\pi a}{p}\right)}{\frac{3}{4}\left(\frac{2\pi r_0}{p}\right)^2} \qquad 62.43$$

and

$$r(z) = r_0\left[1 - \frac{FU_f}{4U_0}\frac{\cos\frac{2\pi}{p}z}{I_0\left(\frac{2\pi a}{p}\right)}\right] \qquad 62.44$$

Let us now examine the influence of the variation of the geometrical parameters of the beam and the focusing system.

a) If the values of the parameters p and a are fixed, the required value of the focusing potential U_f decreases with the increase of r_0. The focusing effect of the strong field near the focusing system is more efficient than that of the weak field in the vicinity of the axis.

b) If the values of r_0 and p are fixed, the value of U_f increases with the increase of the parameter a. It is obvious because in this case the relative distance of the boundary electron from the axis decreases.

c) If the values of a and r_0 are fixed we have a more complicated case. Let us start from large values of p. The decrease of the value of p is practically equivalent to the increase of the number of focusing lenses and the value of U_f decreases (paraxial case). Let us decrease further the value of p. It will cause an abrupt decrease of the focusing field strength in the beam region;

a stronger aberration occurs, and the focusing potential U_f must be increased, though the required variable component $U_1(r)$ of the potential diminishes. This effect is illustrated by figure V.19 where FU_f versus $2\pi a/p$ is given for two fixed values of $U_1(r_0)$, in case of $r_0/a=0.8$. The dependence is calculated on the basis of 62.24.

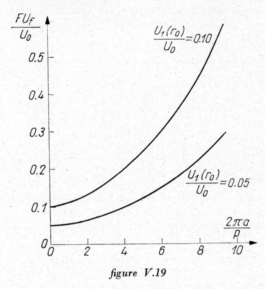

figure V.19

As we can see in the figure, when the value of $2\pi a/p$ is increased, the value of FU_f corresponding to the smaller $U_1(r_0)$ may be much greater than that corresponding to a larger value of $U_1(r_0)$ and to a smaller value of $2\pi a/p$.

The value of FU_f can be calculated from 62.31 as a function of the geometrical parameters if I and U_0 are given. If r_0/p is a constant, U_f abruptly increases when a/p or a/r_0 is increased. In case of $a/p = $ constant, the value of U_f decreases when r_0/p or r_0/a is increased.

A plot of FU_f versus a/p is given in figure V.20 for the case $r_0/a = $ constant $= 0.8$, $I = 1$ mA, $U_0 = 1$ kV. As we can see in the figure, in the paraxial case the increase of the value of a/p leads to the decrease of the required value of FU_f. At larger values of a/p the dependence is inverse. The dependence of FU_f on the value of r_0/p is similar. All these facts also follow from the physical picture outlined above.

As we can see in figure V.20, at given values of the perveance and of the ratio r_0/a a certain value of a/p can be considered optimal because a minimum value of the focusing potential corresponds to this value of a/p. In our example: $(2\pi a/p)_{opt} = 3.4$ and $(FU_f)_{min} = 56.2$ volts. This means also that if the focusing potential is given, the maximum possible value of the beam perveance P_{max} is determined by the value of $(a/p)_{opt}$. As $(a/p)_{opt}$ does not belong to the paraxial region, it is obvious that a focusing system constructed on the basis of Tien's method is suitable for electron beams with higher intensity as if only the paraxial case were considered.

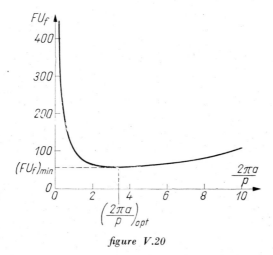

figure V.20

The focusing is complete if the repulsion force acting on the electrons diminishes towards the axis according to the same law as the focusing force diminishes. This takes place if the condition 62.20 is fulfilled not only at the boundary of the beam but at any value of $r < r_0$, i.e.

$$I(r) = \int\int_S j(r)\,dS = 2\pi \int_0^r j(r)\,r\,dr = \frac{\pi\varepsilon_0 r\sqrt{\eta}}{\sqrt{2}\sqrt{U_0}}\frac{dU_1}{dr} \times$$

$$\times \left[U_1(r) + \left(\frac{p}{2\pi}\right)^2 \frac{d^2 U_1}{dr^2}\right] \qquad 62.45$$

Here $I(r)$ is the current inside that part of the beam with radius r. We obtain from 62.45 the current-density distribution across the beam required for the optimum focusing

$$j(r) = \frac{\pi\varepsilon_0\sqrt{\eta}}{\sqrt{2}\sqrt{U_0}\,2\pi r}\frac{d}{dr}\left[rU_1(r)\,U_1'(r) + \left(\frac{p}{2\pi}\right)^2 rU_1'(r)\,U_1''(r)\right] =$$

$$= \frac{4.12\times10^{-6}}{\sqrt{U_0}\,\pi}\left[U_1\,U_1'' + U_1'^2 + \left(\frac{p}{2\pi}\right)^2 (U_1'\,U_1''' + U_1''^2) +\right.$$

$$\left. + \frac{1}{r}\,U_1\,U_1' + \frac{1}{r}\left(\frac{p}{2\pi}\right)^2 U_1'\,U_1''\right] \qquad 62.46$$

The primes represent differentiation with respect to r in this formula. Substituting 62.24, 62.25 and 62.26 together with

$$U_1''' = FU_f\left(\frac{2\pi}{p}\right)^3 \frac{I_0'''\left(\frac{2\pi r}{p}\right)}{I_0\left(\frac{2\pi a}{p}\right)} \qquad 62.47$$

into 62.46, we obtain the following result for the system of annular rings

$$j(r) = \frac{8.24 \times 10^{-6}(FU_f)^2 \left(\dfrac{2\pi r_0}{p}\right)^2}{\pi r_0^2 \sqrt{U_0} I_0^2 \left(\dfrac{2\pi a}{p}\right)} \left[I_0^2\left(\frac{r}{r_0}\frac{2\pi r_0}{p}\right) + \right.$$

$$+ I_1^2\left(\frac{r}{r_0}\frac{2\pi r_0}{p}\right) + \frac{I_1^2\left(\dfrac{r}{r_0}\dfrac{2\pi r_0}{p}\right)}{\left(\dfrac{r}{r_0}\right)^2\left(\dfrac{2\pi r_0}{p}\right)^2} -$$

$$\left. - \frac{I_0\left(\dfrac{r}{r_0}\dfrac{2\pi r_0}{p}\right) I_1\left(\dfrac{r}{r_0}\dfrac{2\pi r_0}{p}\right)}{\dfrac{r}{r_0}\dfrac{2\pi r_0}{p}} \right] \qquad 62.48$$

The graph $j(r)/J$ versus r/r_0 has been plotted in figure V.21 for the case of $2\pi r_0/p = 3.2$. Here J is the quantity ahead of the brackets, so the expression in brackets is plotted in the figure (curve 1).

If $j_0 = I/\pi r_0^2 = $ constant, i.e. the current density is assumed to be constant across the whole beam, we obtain from 62.31 that

$$\frac{j_0}{J} = \frac{2\left(\dfrac{2\pi r_0}{p}\right) I_0\left(\dfrac{2\pi r_0}{p}\right) I_1\left(\dfrac{2\pi r_0}{p}\right) - I_1^2\left(\dfrac{2\pi r_0}{p}\right)}{\left(\dfrac{2\pi r_0}{p}\right)^2} \qquad 62.49$$

For our example we have $j_0/J = 14.8$. This value is given in figure V.21 by a dashed line (2).

We can see in figure V.21 that the current-density distribution required for a complete focusing decreases strongly towards the axis. As has been mentioned in Chapter IV, the transversal current-density distribution in solid cylindrical electron beams usually can be assumed Gaussian, i.e. increases towards the axis. The current-density distribution has been assumed constant in most of our previous calculations. The distribution determined by 62.46 may only be achieved by means of very complicated special types of electron guns. A possible simple practical solution of this problem has been suggested by [4]. The idea is based on the production of a hollow electron beam. If such a beam is focused by a usual periodic electrostatic system designed for the focusing of solid cylindrical beams, there is no electrode inside the hollow beam. Therefore, as we have seen in Chapter IV, there is no space-charge force in the charge-free region inside the beam. The only force in this region is that produced by the focusing system. This force acts on the electrons in the direction towards the axis until a solid electron

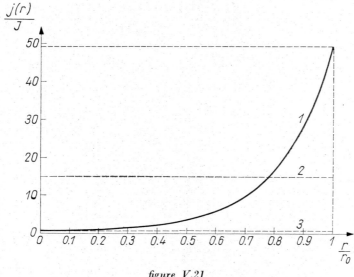

figure V.21

beam with current-density distribution 62.46 is formed. In such a beam the space-charge forces are just in equilibrium with the external focusing forces.

If the current-density distribution $j(r)$ is different from the one required, perturbations occur in the beam. If the requirement 62.20 is fulfilled, the current-density distribution does not influence the boundary electron trajectory.

We have from 62.46, 62.37, 62.38 and 62.39 for the paraxial case

$$j(r) = \frac{8.24 \times 10^{-6}}{\pi \sqrt{U_0}} \left(\frac{2\pi}{p}\right)^2 \frac{3}{4} [U_1(0)]^2 = \text{constant} \qquad 62.50$$

In the paraxial case we obtain for the system of annular rings from 62.50, 62.24 and 62.48

$$\frac{j}{J} = \text{constant} = \frac{3}{4} \qquad\qquad 62.51$$

If the approximation $j_0 = I/\pi r_0^2 = \text{constant}$ is used, we obtain from 62.43 that

$$\frac{j_0}{J} = \frac{I}{\pi r_0^2} \frac{\pi r_0^2 \dfrac{3}{4} \left(\dfrac{2\pi r_0}{p}\right)^2}{8.24 \times 10^{-6} \left(\dfrac{2\pi r_0}{p}\right)^2 1.21 \times 10^5 I} = \frac{3}{4}$$

Thus, in paraxial case we have $j = j_0 = \text{constant}$. This value is plotted in figure V.21 (dashed line 3).

22*

The required non-uniformity of the current density increases with the increase of the value of $2\pi r_0/p$. It can be easily understood by the use of the optical analogy. The main point of the spherical aberration of an electron-optical system is that the focusing force increases too rapidly with the radius. Therefore, it is necessary that space-charge force should increase at the same rate. Thus, the essential point is to compensate the spherical aberration of the focusing system by space-charge with special distribution $j(r)$. In the paraxial case the spherical aberration is negligible which makes it possible to assume $j = $ constant. The value of j_0/J rapidly increases with an increase in the value of $2\pi r_0/p$. The reason being the decrease in J. When $2\pi r_0/p$ is increased, the value of $(FU_f)^2$ abruptly diminishes and therefore J diminishes.

The above method of determination of the required current-density distribution $j(r)$ is of general validity. The space-charge term in 62.20 has been derived from the basis of the assumption $\varrho = $ constant. If we take into account that $j = j(r)$, i.e. the current density is a function of the radius, this assumption is not valid and the solution of the *Poisson's* equation will be

$$F_e = \frac{e}{\varepsilon_0 r v_z} \int_0^r j(r) r dr$$

instead of

$$F_e = \frac{eI}{2\pi\varepsilon_0 r v_z}$$

Comparing these two expressions, we obtain

$$\frac{I(r)}{2\pi} = \int_0^r j(r) r dr$$

Thus, equation 62.45 is really valid.

Although Tien's method is based on rather rough approximations, it is still very important as it can be used for electron beams with considerable perveance values. As we have seen, the required period of the focusing system is to be comparable with the radius of the beam. The advantage of this fact is that minor space-charge fluctuations are rapidly compensated by the strongly varying periodic field. As we have already mentioned, Tien's method is applicable also for focusing systems which are not axially symmetric.

In case of very high-perveance electron beams, however, this method is not suitable because the variable component of the potential becomes comparable with its uniform component. Besides, the axial potential distribution varies very strongly and therefore many terms of the *Fourier* series should be taken into account. For this case a method similar to that used in the design of a *Pierce* gun has been proposed [95]. The main point of this method is the consideration of space-charge flow between a series of grids having alternatively high and low potentials. Assuming the flow to be infinitely extended in the transverse direction, we determine the potential distribution along the direction of the flow. Then the given electron beam with finite transverse cross section is to be considered. The electric field produced by the abandoned space-charge flow in the charge-free region outside the beam must be represented by the electric field of suitably chosen electrodes. The electron beam focused by this way has a theoretically uniform cross section. The required electrode shapes can be determined by analog methods or by the use of approximate analytical techniques [68, 75, 76, 94]. This method is suitable for the analysis of the periodic focusing of solid cylindrical, hollow, and sheet-electron beams. Its advantages are obvious; a serious disadvantage is that the practical realisation of electrodes with strictly determined shapes is a very complicated technological problem. Therefore, the electrode shapes are usually simplified in order to satisfy technological aspects [11]. In practice, a current transmission of 96% has been achieved by means of such a system [10] at a value of the perveance equal to $3.2 \times 10^{-6} \, A/V^{3/2}$.

The theory of the periodic electrostatic focusing is dealt with also by [7, 56]. A simple qualitative treatment has been given by [101]. A special method has been proposed by [46] for the calculation of electron trajectories in electrostatic fields, taking space-charge into account.

The practical realisation of periodic electrostatic focusing systems may be series of diaphragms [55, 85, 86], annular rings [45], cylinders [39], or diaphragms and cylinders alternately [9, 68, 93, 131]. Two special systems have been used by [15].

An electrostatically focused backward-wave oscillator is described in [125]. Electrostatic focusing of klystrons is treated in [49, 50, 89, 90, 100]. The influence of periodic electrostatic focusing on the operation of micro-wave tubes has been investigated [92]. It has been shown that the use of electrostatic focusing does not cause many difficulties.

A relativistic treatment of periodic electrostatic focusing is given by [73]. The influence of thermal velocities has also been taken into consideration [6]. There is an intensive development of this field at the present time [38, 58, 71, 111, 134, 137–140, 143, 144]. We have recently proposed a new analog method for the determination of the focusing parameters and electron trajectories in periodic electrostatic focusing systems [148]. An experimental investigation of electrostatically focused electron beams has been carried out by the author [147], using a photographic method.

Reviews of the various types of electrostatic focusing can be found in [3, 34, 47, 48, 77, 127, 135].

63. FOCUSING OF HOLLOW ELECTRON BEAMS BY AXIALLY SYMMETRIC PERIODIC ELECTROSTATIC FIELDS

As we have seen in § 62, the required current-density distribution of an electrostatically focused solid cylindrical electron beam is determined by very complicated functions if the beam diameter is large.

In solid beams the space-charge forces are just compensated by the focusing forces. As these forces are relatively small, the stability of the beam is also small, in spite of the fact that the rate of increase of the restoring force acting on an electron displaced from its equilibrium path is large (since the focusing forces increase abruptly in radial direction outside the beam, while space-charge forces abruptly decrease). The reason is that the magnitudes of these forces are small and so this type of beam is very sensitive to perturbations. It is desirable that space-charge forces should be small in comparison with the focusing forces.

For this reason solid beams are not very practical in some cases and, in microwave tubes they have another disadvantage, too. In practice only a thin layer of the beam is interacting with the high-frequency field. It is very convenient then to use *hollow beams* instead of solid ones. In hollow beams all the electrons are concentrated in a thin cylindrical tube. The production of hollow beams has been treated in § 43. In this section the maintenance of hollow beams will be dealt with.

It follows from expression 49.31 that the space-charge force in a hollow electron beam moving between two cylinders is equal to

$$F_c = \frac{(2\eta)^{1/2} Im}{4\pi\varepsilon_0 \sqrt{U_0}} \frac{1}{r} \frac{r^2 - r_e^2}{b^2 - a^2} \qquad 63.1$$

at an arbitrary distance r from the axis. Here a and b are the inner and outer radius of the beam, respectively; r_e is the so-called 'equilibrium radius' where the space-charge force is equal to zero. At $r > r_e$ the space-charge force is directed outwards in radial direction. If $r < r_e$, this force is directed towards the axis.

The focusing system must be such as to balance the space-charge forces. The focusing forces must act inwards in the region outside of the beam and outwards in the inner region. As these forces act in opposite directions, the focusing is not so much sensitive to perturbations of space-charge density. One of the best realisations of such a system is the biperiodic electrostatic system consisting of an inner and an outer periodic system (figure V.22) [25, 62]. The potential distribution produced by this system can be approximated by the following expression

$$U(r, z) = U_0 + U_1(r) \cos \frac{2\pi}{p_1} z + U_2(r) \cos \frac{2\pi}{p_2} z \qquad 63.2$$

where U_0 is the uniform component of the potential; $U_1(r)$ is the amplitude of the variable component of the potential produced by the inner periodic system; $U_2(r)$ is the amplitude of the variable component of the potential produced by the outer periodic system; p_1 and p_2 are the periods of the inner and outer system, respectively.

We may assume the beam moving between two cylinders held at the same potential U_0 as a first approximation. The space-charge forces can then be expressed by 63.1.

Let us use the method given in the previous section for this case. If the focusing is accomplished, any electron trajectory can be expressed in the

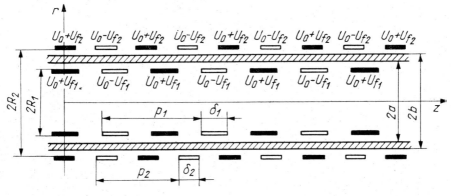

figure V.22

following way

$$r(z) = r_0 + r_1(z) + r_2(z)$$ 63.3

where $r_0 = $ constant, $r_1 \ll r_0$ and $r_2 \ll r_0$. In this case r_0 is not the boundary electron trajectory, but the uniform component of the trajectory of an arbitrary electron of the beam. The variable component $r_1(z)$ arises due to the inner periodic system, while the component $r_2(z)$ arises due to the outer periodic system. As we have already seen, in practice space-charge does not affect the trajectory.

Let use expand the functions $U_1(r)$ and $U_2(r)$ in *Taylor* series in the vicinity of r_0 and drop terms of higher order than $(r_1 + r_2)^2$. We obtain

$$U_1(r) \approx U_1(r_0) + (r_1 + r_2) U_1'(r_0) + \frac{(r_1 + r_2)^2}{2} U_1''(r_0)$$ 63.4

and

$$U_2(r) \approx U_2(r_0) + (r_1 + r_2) U_2'(r_0) + \frac{(r_1 + r_2)^2}{2} U_2''(r_0)$$ 63.5

The primes represent differentiation with respect to r.

The equation of motion of the electron is

$$\frac{d^2r}{dt^2} = \eta \frac{\partial U}{\partial r} + \frac{1}{m} F_e$$ 63.6

We shall use the relation

$$\frac{d^2r}{dt^2} = \frac{d^2r}{dz^2} \dot{z}^2 + \frac{dr}{dz} \ddot{z}$$ 63.7

where, according to 63.2

$$\dot{z} = v_z \approx v_0 \left[1 + \frac{U_1(r_0)}{2 U_0} \cos \frac{2\pi}{p_1} z + \frac{U_2(r_0)}{2 U_0} \cos \frac{2\pi}{p_2} z \right]$$ 63.8

and

$$\ddot{z} = \eta \frac{\partial U}{\partial z} = -\eta \left\{ \frac{2\pi}{P_1} U_1(r) \sin \frac{2\pi}{P_1} z + \frac{2\pi}{P_2} U_2(r) \sin \frac{2\pi}{P_2} z \right\} \approx$$

$$\approx -\eta \left\{ \frac{2\pi}{P_1} [U_1(r_0) + (r_1 + r_2) U_1'(r_0)] \sin \frac{2\pi}{P_1} z + \right.$$

$$\left. + \frac{2\pi}{P_2} [U_2(r_0) + (r_1 + r_2) U_2'(r_0)] \sin \frac{2\pi}{P_2} z \right\} \qquad 63.9$$

We obtain from 63.2, 63.4 and 63.5 that

$$\frac{\partial U}{\partial r} = \frac{dU_1}{dr} \cos \frac{2\pi}{P_1} z + \frac{dU_2}{dr} \cos \frac{2\pi}{P_2} z =$$

$$= [U_1'(r_0) + (r_1 + r_2) U_1''(r_0)] \cos \frac{2\pi}{P_1} z +$$

$$+ [U_2'(r_0) + (r_1 + r_2) U_2''(r_0)] \cos \frac{2\pi}{P_2} z \qquad 63.10$$

Using 63.7 and 63.3, we can rewrite equation 63.6 in the following form

$$\frac{d^2 r_1}{dz^2} + \frac{d^2 r_2}{dz^2} + \left(\frac{dr_1}{dz} + \frac{dr_2}{dz} \right) \frac{\ddot{z}}{\dot{z}^2} = \frac{\eta}{\dot{z}^2} \frac{\partial U}{\partial r} + \frac{1}{\dot{z}^2} \frac{F_e(r_0)}{m} \qquad 63.11$$

Substituting the above expressions into this equation, neglecting the terms of higher order of smallness and carrying out the calculations as in the previous section, we obtain the following approximate results similar to that expressed by 62.11

$$r_1 = - \left(\frac{P_1}{2\pi} \right)^2 \frac{U_1'(r_0)}{2 U_0} \cos \frac{2\pi}{P_1} z \qquad 63.12$$

and

$$r_2 = - \left(\frac{P_2}{2\pi} \right)^2 \frac{U_2'(r_0)}{2 U_0} \cos \frac{2\pi}{P_2} z \qquad 63.13$$

These results are valid if the initial conditions at the plane $z = 0$ are

$$\frac{dr}{dz} = 0 \quad \text{and} \quad r(0) = r_0 - \left(\frac{P_1}{2\pi} \right)^2 \frac{U_1'(r_0)}{2 U_0} - \left(\frac{P_2}{2\pi} \right)^2 \frac{U_2'(r_0)}{2 U_0} \qquad 63.14$$

In case of $p_1 = p_2$ the quantities U_1' and U_2' are of opposite sign and therefore $r(0) \approx r_0$.

Let us now substitute 63.12 and 63.13 for r_1 and r_2, respectively, into equation 63.11. Taking into account expressions 63.8, 63.9, 63.10 and 63.1, we obtain the following result

$$\frac{U_1'(r_0)}{2U_0}\cos\frac{2\pi}{p_1}z + \frac{U_2'(r_0)}{2U_0}\cos\frac{2\pi}{p_2}z -$$

$$- \left[\frac{p_1}{2\pi}\frac{U_1'(r_0)}{2U_0}\sin\frac{2\pi}{p_1}z + \frac{p_2}{2\pi}\frac{U_2'(r_0)}{2U_0}\sin\frac{2\pi}{p_2}z\right]\frac{\eta}{v_0^2}\left[1 -\right.$$

$$- \frac{U_1(r_0)}{U_0}\cos\frac{2\pi}{p_1}z - \frac{U_2(r_0)}{U_0}\cos\frac{2\pi}{p_2}z\right]\left\{\left\langle U_1(r_0) -\right.\right.$$

$$- U_1'(r_0)\left[\left(\frac{p_1}{2\pi}\right)^2\frac{U_1'(r_0)}{2U_0}\cos\frac{2\pi}{p_1}z +\right.$$

$$+ \left(\frac{p_2}{2\pi}\right)^2\frac{U_2'(r_0)}{2U_0}\cos\frac{2\pi}{p_2}z\right]\left.\right\rangle\frac{2\pi}{p_1}\sin\frac{2\pi}{p_1}z +$$

$$+ \left\langle U_2(r_0) - U_2'(r_0)\left[\left(\frac{p_1}{2\pi}\right)^2\frac{U_1'(r_0)}{2U_0}\cos\frac{2\pi}{p_1}z +\right.\right.$$

$$+ \left(\frac{p_2}{2\pi}\right)^2\frac{U_2'(r_0)}{2U_0}\cos\frac{2\pi}{p_2}z\right]\left.\right\rangle\frac{2\pi}{p_2}\sin\frac{2\pi}{p_2}z\right\} =$$

$$= \frac{\eta}{v_0^2}\left[1 - \frac{U_1(r_0)}{U_0}\cos\frac{2\pi}{p_1}z - \frac{U_2(r_0)}{U_0}\cos\frac{2\pi}{p_2}z\right]\left\{\left\langle U_1'(r_0) -\right.\right.$$

$$- U_1''(r_0)\left[\left(\frac{p_1}{2\pi}\right)^2\frac{U_1'(r_0)}{2U_0}\cos\frac{2\pi}{p_1}z +\right.$$

$$+ \left(\frac{p_2}{2\pi}\right)^2\frac{U_2'(r_0)}{2U_0}\cos\frac{2\pi}{p_2}z\right]\left.\right\rangle\cos\frac{2\pi}{p_1}z +$$

$$+ \left\langle U_2'(r_0) - U_2''(r_0)\left[\left(\frac{p_1}{2\pi}\right)^2\frac{U_1'(r_0)}{2U_0}\cos\frac{2\pi}{p_1}z +\right.\right.$$

$$+ \left(\frac{p_2}{2\pi}\right)^2\frac{U_2'(r_0)}{2U_0}\cos\frac{2\pi}{p_2}z\right]\left.\right\rangle\cos\frac{2\pi}{p_2}z\right\} +$$

$$+ \frac{1}{v_0^2}\left[1 - \frac{U_1(r_0)}{U_0}\cos\frac{2\pi}{p_1}z - \frac{U_2(r_0)}{U_0}\cos\frac{2\pi}{p_2}z\right]\times$$

$$\times \frac{(2\eta)^{1/2}I(r_0^2 - r_e^2)}{4\pi\varepsilon_0\sqrt{U_0}r_0(b^2 - a^2)} \tag{63.15}$$

Equating the constant terms, we obtain

$$U_1(r_0)\ U_1'(r_0) + U_2(r_0)\ U_2'(r_0) + \left(\frac{p_1}{2\pi}\right)^2 U_1'(r_0)U_1''(r_0) +$$

$$+ \left(\frac{p_2}{2\pi}\right)^2 U_2'(r_0)U_2''(r_0) = \frac{\sqrt{2I}\sqrt{U_0}}{\pi\varepsilon_0\sqrt{\eta}r_0}\ \frac{r_0^2 - r_e^2}{b^2 - a^2} \qquad 63.16$$

In this equation all the terms of higher order of smallness have been neglected.

If the periods of the inner and outer periodic systems are equal to each
other ($p_1 = p_2 = p$), some additional terms appear in the left-hand side of
equation 63.16. In this case the equation determining the values of the
focusing potentials can be written as follows

$$\left[U_1(r_0) + \left(\frac{p_1}{2\pi}\right)^2 U_1''(r_0)\right]U_1'(r_0) + \left[U_2(r_0) + \right.$$

$$+ \left(\frac{p_2}{2\pi}\right)^2 U_2''(r_0)\right]U_2'(r_0) + \left[U_1(r_0) + \left(\frac{p}{2\pi}\right)^2 U_1''(r_0)\right]U_2'(r_0) +$$

$$+ \left[U_2(r_0) + \left(\frac{p}{2\pi}\right)^2 U_2''(r_0)\right]U_1'(r_0) = \frac{\sqrt{2I}\sqrt{U_0}}{\pi\varepsilon_0\sqrt{\eta}r_0}\ \frac{r_0^2 - r_e^2}{b^2 - a^2} \qquad 63.17$$

In this equation the third and fourth terms of the left-hand side arise only
if $p_1 = p_2 = p$. In case of $p_1 \neq p_2$ these terms should be omitted.

Equation 63.17 corresponds to equation 62.20 in the case of the solid
cylindrical beam. Equation 63.17, however, in itself is not sufficient for the
determination of the electrode potentials. Let us consider for example the
case of $p_1 \neq p_2$. Introducing the notation $f(r_0)$, equation 63.17 can be rewritten for this case as follows

$$f(r_0) = f_1(r_0) + f_2(r_0) + f_\varrho(r_0) = 0 \qquad 63.18$$

where

$$f_1(r_0) = \left[U_1(r_0) + \left(\frac{p_1}{2\pi}\right)^2 U_1''(r_0)\right]U_1'(r_0) \qquad 63.19$$

$$f_2(r_0) = \left[U_2(r_0) + \left(\frac{p_2}{2\pi}\right)^2 U_2''(r_0)\right]U_2'(r_0) \qquad 63.20$$

and

$$f_\varrho(r_0) = -\frac{\sqrt{2I}\sqrt{U_0}}{\pi\varepsilon_0\sqrt{\eta}r_0}\ \frac{r_0^2 - r_e^2}{b^2 - a^2} \qquad 63.21$$

The equation $f(r_0) = 0$ expresses the equilibrium of the forces acting on the electrons of the beam. The average force produced by the inner system is proportional to f_1; that produced by the outer system is proportional to f_2 and the space-charge force is proportional to f_ϱ.

Let us rewrite 63.18 for the equilibrium radius ($r_0 = r_e$). Here we have $f_\varrho(r_e) = 0$ and so

$$f_1(r_e) + f_2(r_e) = 0 \qquad\qquad 63.22$$

It means that the focusing forces are in equilibrium with each other.

Let us now consider an arbitrary radius r_0 in the electron beam which is close to the equilibrium radius. Then we can write

$$r_0 = r_e + \hat{r} \qquad\qquad 63.23$$

where $\hat{r} = $ constant and $\hat{r} \ll r_e$. We can write approximately that

$$f_1(r_0) \approx f_1(r_e) + \hat{r} f_1'(r_e) + \frac{\hat{r}^2}{2} f_1''(r_e) \qquad\qquad 63.24$$

$$f_2(r_0) \approx f_2(r_e) + \hat{r} f_2'(r_e) + \frac{\hat{r}^2}{2} f_2''(r_e) \qquad\qquad 63.25$$

and

$$f_\varrho(r_0) \approx \hat{r} f_\varrho'(r_e) + \frac{\hat{r}^2}{2} f_\varrho''(r_e) \qquad\qquad 63.26$$

where the primes represent differentiation with respect to r_0. For very small values of $\hat{r}$ we have then, taking 63.22 into account, the following form of equation 63.18 for a radius r_0

$$f_1'(r_e) + f_2'(r_e) + f_\varrho'(r_e) = 0 \qquad\qquad 63.27$$

Equations 63.22 and 63.27 together determine the dependence between the parameters of the beam and of the focusing system. The focusing is optimal if the deviations of the boundary radii a and b from the equilibrium radius r_e remain small, i.e.

$$(b - r_e) \ll r_e \quad \text{and} \quad (r_e - a) \ll r_e$$

In this case fulfilment of the conditions 63.22 and 63.27 is sufficient for the formation of an equilibrium of forces across the whole beam and so a minimum beam rippling can be achieved. In case of a larger beam thickness the terms of the *Taylor* series containing $\hat{r}^2$ are to be taken into account, too. It means that equation

$$f_1''(r_e) + f_2''(r_e) + f_\varrho''(r_e) = 0 \qquad\qquad 63.28$$

must be fulfilled, beside equations 63.22 and 63.27. Equations 63.27 and 63.28 can be derived from 63.18 without any conditions. We wanted to prove that the fulfilment of equation 63.28 is necessary only for thick beams.

There is no requirement in connection with the current-density distribution of a hollow beam focused by periodic electrostatic fields: the current density may be assumed uniform across the whole beam. The relations between the parameters of the beam and of the focusing system must be fulfilled, however. This means that at given values for the parameters of the electron beam not only the focusing potentials are strictly determined but also some relations between the geometrical parameters of the focusing system most be satisfied. Naturally, the design of such a system is more complicated: these relations appear in the form of transcendental equations.

A special case of the biperiodic system is if $p_1 = p_2 = p$ and $| F_1 U_{f1} | = = | F_2 U_{f2} |$. The simplicity of such a system makes it very practical. There are two possible solutions

$$F_1 U_{f1} = F_2 U_{f2} \quad \text{or} \quad F_1 U_{f1} = - F_2 U_{f2}$$

The electron trajectories are different in the two cases (in the second case the value of the equilibrium radius r_e is not constant but it has a small rippling), but the focusing effects are the same in first-order approximation.

A possible solution of the periodic electrostatic focusing of hollow electron beams is to replace one of the periodic systems by a metal cylinder. The uniform potential of this cylinder is not equal to the average potential of the periodic system. In this case the focusing field produced by the periodic system and the space-charge field are balanced by a uniform radial field. The periodic system may be placed outside [62, 64, 91] or inside [52, 53] the beam. The advantage of such a system is its simplicity and relative insensitivity to the variations of the initial conditions. The required value of the variable component of the focusing potential is by some 40% higher than in case of the biperiodic system [63].

Another possibility is to rotate the electron beam by means of a spiratron gun (see § 69) or a special magnetic field. The external periodic system is sufficient in this case, too. Its field is in equilibrium with the centrifugal force produced by the rotation of the beam. Space-charge forces only have an additional role in all these systems, and the stability of the beam is consequently very good.

(C) PERIODIC FOCUSING BY BIFILAR HELICES

64. FOCUSING OF SOLID ELECTRON BEAMS
BY BIFILAR HELICES

The most simple practical solution of periodic electrostatic focusing is the application of bifilar helices. The advantages of bifilar helices are their extreme simplicity, and lack of sensitivity to inaccuracies in centring the system. Though in microwave-tube applications such systems can be used only at low powers. This system is not axially symmetric, therefore its mathematical treatment is more complicated. The focusing system consists of two helical wires (figure V.23) held at potentials $U_0 + U_f$ and $U_0 - U_f$, respectively. Here U_0 is approximately equal to the anode potential

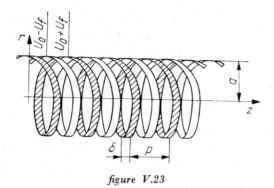

figure V.23

of the electron gun, U_f is the focusing potential the value of which is to be determined in the following treatment.

The potential distribution inside a bifilar tape helix with uniform pitch can be approximated by the following expression [60, 122]

$$U(r, \alpha, z) \approx U_0 + FU_f \; \frac{I_1\left(\dfrac{2\pi}{p} r\right)}{I_1\left(\dfrac{2\pi}{p} a\right)} \; \cos\left(\frac{2\pi}{p} z - \alpha\right) \qquad 64.1$$

Here a is the radius of the helices, I_1 is the modified *Bessel* function of the first kind and first order. The value of the parameter F is determined by the geometrical dimensions of the system, according to expression 62.22. The helices are wound in the direction of the increase of the angle α.

Introducing the notation

$$U_1(r) = F \, U_f \; \frac{I_1\left(\dfrac{2\pi}{p} r\right)}{I_1\left(\dfrac{2\pi}{p} a\right)} \qquad 64.2$$

we can write the potential distribution similarly to 62.1

$$U(r, \alpha, z) \approx U_0 + U_1(r) \cos\left(\frac{2\pi}{p} z - \alpha\right) \qquad 64.3$$

Let us calculate the derivatives of the function 64.3 at $r = r_0$. We obtain

$$\frac{dU_1}{dr}\bigg|_{r=r_0} = \frac{2\pi}{p} FU_f \; \frac{I_0\left(\dfrac{2\pi r_0}{p}\right) - \dfrac{p}{2\pi r_0} I_1\left(\dfrac{2\pi r_0}{p}\right)}{I_1\left(\dfrac{2\pi a}{p}\right)} \qquad 64.4$$

and

$$\frac{d^2 U_1}{dr^2}\bigg|_{r=r_0} = \left(\frac{2\pi}{p}\right)^2 FU_f \frac{\left[1 + \frac{2}{r_0^2}\left(\frac{p}{2\pi}\right)^2\right] I_1\left(\frac{2\pi}{p} r_0\right) - \frac{p}{2\pi r_0} I_0\left(\frac{2\pi}{p} r_0\right)}{I_1\left(\frac{2\pi a}{p}\right)}$$

64.5

We shall use the method given in § 62 for the analysis of this system [24, 113].

The equations of the electron motion in an electric field with azimuthal component are as follows

$$\frac{d^2 r_1}{dt^2} - r_0\left(\frac{d\alpha}{dt}\right)^2 = \eta \frac{\partial U(r, \alpha, z)}{\partial r} + \frac{\eta I}{2\pi \varepsilon_0 r_0 v_0}$$

64.6

$$r_0^2 \frac{d^2\alpha}{dt^2} + 2r_0 \frac{dr_1}{dt}\frac{d\alpha}{dt} = \eta \frac{\partial U(r, \alpha, z)}{\partial \alpha}$$

64.7

and

$$\frac{d^2 z}{dt^2} = \eta \frac{\partial U(r, \alpha, z)}{\partial z}$$

64.8

In these equations condition

$$r(z, \alpha) = r_0 + r_1(z, \alpha)$$

has been used, where $r_1 \ll r_0$ and $r_0 = $ constant. If one neglects the term $r_0(d\alpha/dt)^2$ in 64.6 and the term $2r_0(dr_1/dt)(d\alpha/dt)$ in 64.7 [113], equation 64.6 will coincide with equation 62.6. The only difference will be that in equation 64.6 cos $(2\pi z/p - \alpha)$ arises instead of cos $(2\pi z/p)$. However, in first-order approximation we can replace α by α_0 here and in the following (α_0 is the azimuth of the considered boundary electron in the initial plane $z = 0$) because it may be expected that the azimuth of the electron will have only small periodic variations around that value in the course of the motion in this system, similarly as the radius of the beam oscillates around a constant value of r_0. The solution of equation 64.6 will then be similar to 62.11

$$r_1 \approx - \left(\frac{p}{2\pi}\right)^2 \frac{\frac{dU_1}{dr}\bigg|_{r=r_0}}{2U_0} \cos\left(\frac{2\pi}{p} z - \alpha_0\right)$$

64.9

We obtain from equation 64.7 that

$$\frac{d^2\alpha}{dt^2} \approx \frac{\eta U_1(r_0)}{r_0^2} \sin\left(\frac{2\pi}{p} z - \alpha_0\right)$$

64.10

Integrating twofold, and taking

$$\frac{dz}{dt} \approx v_0 = (2\eta U_0)^{1/2}$$

into account, we obtain

$$\alpha \approx \alpha_0 - \frac{U_1(r_0)}{2r_0^2 U_0} \left(\frac{p}{2\pi}\right)^2 \sin\left(\frac{2\pi}{p} z - \alpha_0\right) \qquad 64.11$$

As it can be seen from 64.11, $(\alpha - \alpha_0)$ is really a small quantity. It can also be proved easily that the terms neglected in equations 64.6 and 64.7 are of higher order of smallness than the considered terms.

In this case the transformation of the differentiation with respect to time into differentiation with respect to coordinates is more complicated because r is a function of not only z but also of α. We have

$$\frac{dr}{dt} = \dot{\alpha} \frac{\partial r}{\partial \alpha} + \dot{z} \frac{\partial r}{\partial z} \qquad 64.12$$

and

$$\frac{d^2 r}{dt^2} = \dot{z}^2 \frac{\partial^2 r}{\partial z^2} + \dot{\alpha}^2 \frac{\partial^2 r}{\partial \alpha^2} + 2\dot{\alpha}\dot{z} \frac{\partial^2 r}{\partial \alpha \partial z} + \ddot{\alpha} \frac{\partial r}{\partial \alpha} + \ddot{z} \frac{\partial r}{\partial z} \qquad 64.13$$

as

$$\frac{\partial r}{\partial t} = 0$$

Here

$$\dot{z} \approx v_0 \left[1 + \frac{U_1(r_0)}{2U_0} \cos\left(\frac{2\pi}{p} z - \alpha_0\right)\right] \qquad 64.14$$

The value of $\ddot{z}$ is determined by 64.8. Taking into account that $\dot{\alpha} \ll \dot{z}$, we can find the values of $\dot{\alpha}$ and $\ddot{\alpha}$ from 64.10 and the derivatives of r from 64.9. We shall expand the function of $U_1(r)$ into *Taylor* series in the vicinity of r_0, according to 62.3, and drop the terms of higher order of smallness than r_1^2. Carrying out all these operations, we can rewrite equation 64.6 in the following form

$$\frac{dU_1}{dr}\bigg|_{r=r_0} \frac{v_0^2}{2U_0} \left[1 + \frac{U_1(r_0)}{U_0} \cos\left(\frac{2\pi}{p} z - \alpha_0\right)\right] \times$$

$$\times \cos\left(\frac{2\pi}{p} z - \alpha_0\right) + \left(\frac{p}{2\pi}\right)^2 \frac{1}{2U_0} \frac{dU_1}{dr}\bigg|_{r=r_0} \times$$

$$\times \cos\left(\frac{2\pi}{p} z - \alpha_0\right) \left(\frac{p}{2\pi}\right)^2 \left[\frac{U_1(r_0)}{2U_0}\right]^2 \frac{v_0^2}{r_0^4} \cos^2\left(\frac{2\pi}{p} z - \alpha_0\right) +$$

$$+ \left(\frac{p}{2\pi}\right)^2 \frac{2v_0^2}{r_0^2} \frac{U_1(r_0)\dfrac{dU_1}{dr}\bigg|_{r=r_0}}{4U_0^2} \left[1 + \frac{U_1(r_0)}{2U_0} \cos\left(\frac{2\pi}{p} z - \alpha_0\right)\right] \times$$

$$\times \cos^2\left(\frac{2\pi}{p}z - \alpha_0\right) - \frac{\eta}{2U_0}\frac{dU_1}{dr}\bigg|_{r=r_0} U_1(r_0)\sin^2\left(\frac{2\pi}{p}z - \alpha_0\right) -$$

$$- \left(\frac{p}{2\pi}\right)^2 \frac{v_0^2}{r_0^2}\frac{U_1(r_0)}{4U_0^2}\frac{dU_1}{dr}\bigg|_{r=r_0}\sin^2\left(\frac{2\pi}{p}z - \alpha_0\right) -$$

$$- r_0\left(\frac{p}{2\pi}\right)^2 \frac{U_1^2(r_0)}{4U_0^2}\frac{v_0^2}{r_0^4}\cos^2\left(\frac{2\pi}{p}z - \alpha_0\right) = \frac{\eta I}{2\pi\varepsilon_0 r_0 v_0} +$$

$$+ \eta\left[\frac{dU_1}{dr}\bigg|_{r=r_0} - \frac{d^2U_1}{dr^2}\bigg|_{r=r_0}\left(\frac{p}{2\pi}\right)^2\frac{dU_1}{dr}\bigg|_{r=r_0} \times\right.$$

$$\left.\times \frac{1}{2U_0}\cos\left(\frac{2\pi}{p}z - \alpha_0\right)\right]\cos\left(\frac{2\pi}{p}z - \alpha_0\right) \qquad 64.15$$

Equating the constant terms of this equation, we obtain the following equality

$$\left(\frac{p}{2\pi}\right)^2\frac{dU_1}{dr}\bigg|_{r=r_0}\frac{d^2U_1}{dr^2}\bigg|_{r=r_0} + U_1(r_0)\frac{dU_1}{dr}\bigg|_{r=r_0} +$$

$$+ \left(\frac{p}{2\pi r_0}\right)^2 U_1(r_0)\frac{dU_1}{dr}\bigg|_{r=r_0} - \frac{1}{r_0}\left(\frac{p}{2\pi r_0}\right)^2 U_1^2(r_0) = \frac{\sqrt{2}I\sqrt{U_0}}{\pi\varepsilon_9 r_0\sqrt{\eta}} \qquad 64.16$$

This expression differs from 62.20 in the third and fourth terms of its left-hand side. These terms appear as a consequence of the azimuthal component of the focusing field and the centrifugal force produced by the rotation of the electrons, respectively. All the three components of the electric field have focusing effect. This effect is balanced by space-charge force and the centrifugal force. Thus, the stability is better than in the axially symmetric case.

Using 64.2, 64.4 and 64.5, one can obtain the value of the focusing potential U_f from 64.16

$$(FU_f)^2 = \frac{1.21 \times 10^5 I\sqrt{U_0}I_1^2\left(\frac{2\pi a}{p}\right)}{A + B} \qquad 64.17$$

where

$$A = \left(\frac{4}{\frac{2\pi r_0}{p}} + 2\frac{2\pi r_0}{p}\right)I_0\left(\frac{2\pi r_0}{p}\right)I_1\left(\frac{2\pi r_0}{p}\right)$$

and

$$B = -I_0^2\left(\frac{2\pi r_0}{p}\right) - \left[2 + \frac{4}{\left(\frac{2\pi r_0}{p}\right)^2}\right]I_1^2\left(\frac{2\pi r_0}{p}\right)$$

We obtain the trajectory from 64.4 and 64.9

$$r = r_0 - \frac{p}{2\pi}\frac{FU_f}{2U_0}\frac{I_0\left(\frac{2\pi r_0}{p}\right) - \frac{1}{\frac{2\pi r_0}{p}}I_1\left(\frac{2\pi r_0}{p}\right)}{I_1\left(\frac{2\pi a}{p}\right)} \times$$

$$\times \cos\left(\frac{2\pi}{p}z - \alpha_0\right) \tag{64.18}$$

It should be mentioned that the parameter $2\pi a/p$ has in practice important geometrical meaning. A winding of the tape helix can be derived by putting the tape along the diagonal of a rectangle with sides equal to $2\pi a$ and p, respectively, and then covering a cylinder of radius a with this rectangle. We have then

$$\frac{2\pi a}{p} = \cot\psi \tag{64.19}$$

where ψ is the angle between the tape and the circumference of the cylinder.

When designing a focusing system, the values of the angle ψ and of the ratio r_0/a are usually given. It is therefore convenient to rewrite expressions 64.17 and 64.18, taking 64.19 into consideration, to obtain

$$(FU_f)^2 = \frac{1.21\times 10^5 I\sqrt{U_0}I_1^2(\cot\psi)}{C+D} \tag{64.20}$$

where

$$C = \left(2\frac{r_0}{a}\cot\psi + \frac{4}{\frac{r_0}{a}\cot\psi}\right)I_0\left(\frac{r_0}{a}\cot\psi\right)I_1\left(\frac{r_0}{a}\cot\psi\right)$$

$$D = -I_0^2\left(\frac{r_0}{a}\cot\psi\right) - \left[2 + \frac{4}{\left(\frac{r_0}{a}\cot\psi\right)^2}\right]I_1^2\left(\frac{r_0}{a}\cot\psi\right)$$

and

$$\frac{r(z)}{r_0} = 1 - \frac{FU_f}{2U_0}\frac{1}{\frac{r_0}{a}\cot\psi} \times$$

$$\times \frac{I_0\left(\frac{r_0}{a}\cot\psi\right) - \frac{1}{\frac{r_0}{a}\cot\psi}I_1\left(\frac{r_0}{a}\cot\psi\right)}{I_1(\cot\psi)}\cos\left(\frac{2\pi}{p}z - \alpha_0\right) \tag{64.21}$$

Gy. Nagy—M. Szilágyi: Introduction

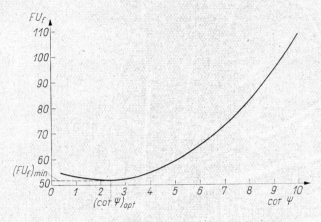

figure V. 24

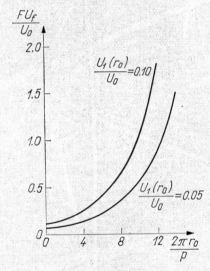

figure V. 25

At given values of I, U_0 and r_0/a the dependence of FU_f versus $\cot \psi$ can be calculated from 64.20. The result of this calculation is given in figure V.24 for the case of $I = 1$ mA, $U_0 = 1000$ volts, $r_0/a = 0.8$. This dependence is similar to that in the axially symmetric case (see figure V.20). At small values of $\cot \psi$ the value of FU_f decreases with the increase of $\cot \psi$. At greater values of $\cot \psi$ the value of FU_f must be increased as $\cot \psi$ is increased. The reason is the same as in the axially symmetric case: when the value of r_0/p is increased, the value of FU_f corresponding to the smaller $U_1(r_0)$ may be greater than that corresponding to a larger $U_1(r_0)$ and to a smaller value of r_0/p. This effect is illustrated by figure V.25 where FU_f is plotted against $2\pi r_0/p$ for two fixed values of $U_1(r_0)$, in case where $r_0/a = 0.8$ [24].

In this case we have $(\cot \psi)_{opt} = 2.4$ and $(FU_f)_{min} = 52$ volts.

If the value of FU_f is given, the maximum possible value of the beam perveance is determined by the value of $(\cot \psi)_{opt}$.

Let us determine now the current-density distribution $j(r)$ required for the fulfilment of the condition 64.17 at any value of $r < r_0$. Similarly to 62.45, this takes place if

$$I(r) = 2\pi \int_0^r j(r)r dr = \frac{\pi \varepsilon_0 \sqrt{\eta}(FU_f)^2}{\sqrt{2}\sqrt{U_0}I_1^2\left(\frac{2\pi a}{p}\right)}\left[\xi I_1'(\xi)I_1''(\xi) + \right.$$

$$\left. + \xi I_1(\xi)I_1'(\xi) + \frac{1}{\xi} I_1(\xi)I_1'(\xi) - \frac{1}{\xi^2} I_1^2(\xi)\right] \tag{64.22}$$

Hence we obtain

$$j(r) = \frac{4.12 \times 10^{-6}(FU_f)^2\left(\dfrac{r_0}{a}\cot\psi\right)^2}{\sqrt{U_0}I_1^2(\cot\psi)\pi r_0^2}\left[I_1'^2 + I_1''^2 + \right.$$

$$+ I_1 I_1'' + I_1' I_1''' + \frac{1}{\xi}(I_1' I_1'' + I_1 I_1') + \frac{1}{\xi^2}(I_1'^2 +$$

$$\left. + I_1 I_1'') - \frac{3}{\xi^3} I_1 I_1' + \frac{2}{\xi^4} I_1'^2\right] \tag{64.23}$$

where

$$\xi = \frac{2\pi r}{p} = \frac{r}{a}\cot\psi$$

and the primes represent differentiation with respect to ξ.

The dependence of $j(r)/J$ on r/r_0 has been plotted on the basis of 64.23 in figure V.26 for the case of $\cot \psi = 4$ and $r_0/a = 0.8$ [113]. J is the constant quantity ahead of the brackets, so in the figure the expression in brackets is plotted. It is interesting as a comparison that in the approximation $j_0 = I/\pi r_0^2$ we have $j_0/J = 22$. This value is given in the figure by a dashed line.

We can see in figure V.26 that the distribution $j(r)$ is similar to that in case of the system of annular rings. All the conclusions drawn in connection with the current-density distribution in § 62 are valid here, too. In paraxial approximation, similarly to the axially symmetric case, the current density is constant across the whole beam.

According to [61], the current-density distribution $j(r)$ as determined by 64.23 is not required so strictly if higher accelerating voltages are used.

23*

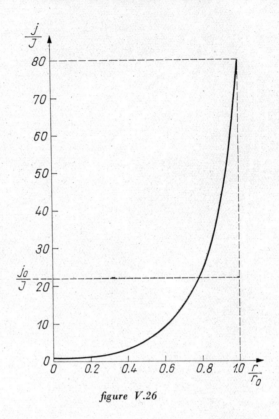

figure V.26

The first practical application of the periodic focusing by bifilar helices has been accomplished by [114]. This method of focusing is very advantageous in travelling-wave tubes as the simple focusing system may be used as a slow-wave circuit simultaneously. Such a travelling-wave tube is the *estiatron* [16–19, 35, 36]. Its microwave and electron-optical features are very good in spite of the fact that no care has been taken for the required current-density distribution $j(r)$.

65. FOCUSING OF HOLLOW ELECTRON BEAMS
BY BIFILAR HELICES

As in the case of solid beams, the periodic system of bifilar helices is suitable for focusing of hollow beams, as well. In this case the beam moves between two bifilar helices *(biperiodic focusing)*. The average potentials at both systems are the same. The difference between this method and that based on the use of two systems of annular rings is the same as the difference between the focusing of a solid beam by bifilar helices and by a system of annular rings. The electric field is not axially symmetric. Therefore, the centrifugal force produced by the rotation of the electrons and the azi-muthal component of the focusing field play their role, too. There is no other difference between this case and the periodic electrostatic focusing of hollow electron beams as treated in § 63.

As a result of the theoretical analysis [25, 26], the relations plotted in figure V.27 take place between the parameters of the beam and the focusing bifilar helices in case of thin hollow beams.

In figure V.27 the ratio of the beam perveance to the square of the focus-ing potential related to the accelerating voltage is plotted against the equi-librium radius r_e for the case of equal periods of the inner and outer bifilar helices. It has been also assumed that $U_{f1} = U_{f2} = U_f$ and the beam thick-ness is so small that the relation between the parameters is determined by expressions 63.22 and 63.27. In these expressions f_e remains unaltered but f_1 and f_2 will have other values corresponding to the new geometrical di-mensions. In this case the function plotted in the figure depends on three arbitrary parameters: for all the curves $R_2/b = 1.25$; the values of the ratios

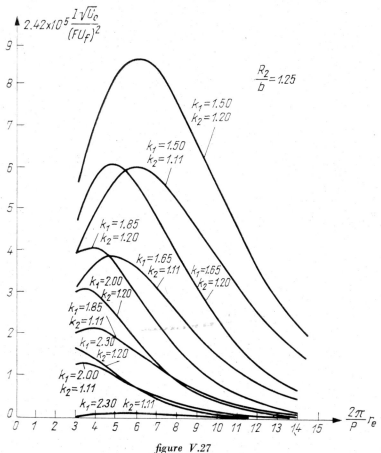

figure V.27

$k_1 = R_2/R_1$ and $k_2 = b/a$ are given at the corresponding curves. Ten curves have been plotted: the value of k_2 is equal to 1.11 and 1.20 while the values of k_1 are 1.50, 1.65, 1.85, 2.00 and 2.30. The notation is given in figure V.22.

It can be seen in figure V.27 that the required value of the focusing potential decreases at the increase of k_2 and at the decrease of k_1. It means that the more completely the space between the focusing helices is filled by the electron beam, the lesser focusing field is required at a given value of the perveance or the greater is the possible beam perveance at a given value of the focusing potential. At given values of the parameters k_1 and k_2 there is a certain optimum value of r_e at which a minimum focusing potential is required.

A more detailed analysis of this method of focusing of hollow electron beams can be based on the solution of the equations of motion. It has been stated [61] that the periodic electrostatic focusing may serve as a transformer of the cross section of the hollow electron beam: the cross section of the beam can be varied by the variation of the focusing parameters.

The stability of the biperiodic focusing is very good because the effect of space-charge is negligible in comparison with the focusing forces acting in opposite directions.

A current transmission of 97% has been achieved in a travelling-wave tube with biperiodic focusing of a hollow beam with perveance 1.7×10^{-6} A/V$^{3/2}$ [26].

It is to be mentioned that one of the bifilar helices may be replaced by a metal tube in this case, too.

(D) FOCUSING OF ELECTRON BEAMS BY PLANE-SYMMETRIC PERIODIC ELECTROSTATIC FIELDS

Periodic electrostatic focusing of plane-symmetric high-intensity sheet-electron beams will be treated in this part. As we have seen in Chapter IV, there are some differences between space-charge effects in sheet- and cylindrical electron beams. Therefore, the focusing of sheet beams by plane-symmetric periodic fields must be treated separately.

We shall assume that the beam width in the direction of coordinate x is much greater than its thickness in the direction of coordinate y (see figure IV.16). At the same time, the length of the beam is much greater than its width. Therefore, space-charge forces act only in the direction of coordinate y. All the formulae derived in Chapter IV in this approximation can be used then here.

The notation and the situation of the coordinate system are the same as in Chapter IV.

66. FOCUSING BY A SEQUENCE OF PLANE-SYMMETRIC THIN LENSES

Let us now consider the case of focusing a dense sheet beam by a periodic sequence of identical thin converging lenses with focal lengths f and equal spacings l between the adjacent lenses [106]. In this case plane-symmetric cylindrical lenses are to be used instead of axially symmetric ones. The lenses may be *electrostatic or magnetic thin cylindrical lenses*. We shall follow the treatment given in § 59 for the axially symmetric case. Thus, it will be assumed that the beam motion in the sections between any two lenses is determined only by space-charge, according to Chapter IV. The lenses cause sudden changes in the slopes of the trajectories of the beam. Another requirement is that the configuration of the electron beam should be identical in all sections and symmetrical within the sections with respect to the centre of the section. (See figure V.5.) As we have seen in § 59, in order to fulfill this requirement, the following condition must be satisfied

$$\frac{y_0}{f} = -2y_0' \qquad\qquad 66.1$$

where the value of y_0' is determined by the condition

$$l = 2z_m \qquad\qquad 66.2$$

Using the dimensionless variables Y and Z_s introduced in Chapter IV, we can rewrite expression 66.2 on the basis of 54.8 as follows

$$L_s = 2(Z_s)_m = -Y_0' \qquad\qquad 66.3$$

where we have, according to 54.3, that

$$L_s = Z_s(l) = 154 \left(\frac{P}{Wy_0}\right)^{1/2} l = \frac{l}{ky_0} \qquad\qquad 66.4$$

According to 54.10 we have

$$Y' = \frac{dY}{dZ_s} = \frac{1}{154} \left(\frac{W}{Py_0}\right)^{1/2} \frac{dy}{dz} = ky' \qquad\qquad 66.5$$

where

$$k = \frac{1}{154} \left(\frac{W}{Py_0}\right)^{1/2} \qquad\qquad 66.6$$

We can rewrite 66.3 as follows

$$\frac{l}{y_0} = -k^2 y_0' \qquad\qquad 66.7$$

Thus, we can write condition 66.1 in the following final form

$$\frac{1}{f} = \frac{2l}{k^2 y_0^2} = \frac{2L_s}{ky_0} = \frac{2L_s^2}{l} = 4.74 \times 10^4 \frac{Pl}{Wy_0} \qquad\qquad 66.8$$

Obviously, if the beam enters the system parallel to the z axis, condition

$$\frac{1}{f_1} = \frac{1}{2} \frac{1}{f} \qquad\qquad 66.9$$

proved in § 59 will be valid here, too (f_1 is the focal length of the first lens).

Expression 66.8 determines the focal lengths f of the thin ciyndrical lenses required for periodic focusing of a sheet-el $\frac{c}{8}$ tron beam witlh perveance P, width W and initial thickness $2y_0$, if the value l of the period is given.

If the variations of the beam boundary should not be too large, evidently the value of L_s must be decreased. This may be achieved by the decrease of the spacing l, that is by putting a greater number of lenses into the sequence. According to expression 54.13, in case of $(Z_s)_m \geq 1$, the beam boundary crosses the axis. As it is usually not desirable, we can assume the value of $(L_s)_{max} = 2$ as a limit from the point of view of practical application. According to 66.8, this gives the condition

$$\left(\frac{l}{f}\right)_{max} = 8 \qquad\qquad 66.10$$

which determines the practically applicable maximum values of the convergence and spacing of the lenses. Obviously, it must also be taken into account that both the focal length and the lens spacing must be considerably larger than the extension of the lens field (thin lens approximation).

Let us consider an example: $P = 10^{-6} \, A/V^{3/2}$, $y_0 = 1$ mm and $l = W$. Then, according to 66.8, we have $f = 21.1$ mm. It follows from 66.10 that in this case $l_{max} = 16.9$ cm so that it is practically convenient to place the lenses at a distance of several centimeters from each other.

As we have shown in § 59, the first lens of the periodic sequence can be placed at the plane of minimum cross section of the beam leaving the electron gun or the lens system can be connected with the gun. In the latter case the parameters of the focusing system are determined by the parameters of the electron gun. A more detailed treatment of this problem is given in § 59.

The focal length of a thin electrostatic single cylindrical lens is given by the following expression ([87], formula 6.67)

$$\frac{1}{f} = \frac{7}{16} \int_{z_1}^{z_2} \left(\frac{\Phi'}{\Phi}\right)^2 dz \qquad\qquad 66.11$$

where z_1 and z_2 are the coordinates bounding the field; the prime represents differentiation with respect to z. We obtain from 66.8 and 66.11 that

$$P = \frac{7 \times 10^{-4} W y_0}{16 \times 4.74 l} \int_{z_1}^{z_2} \left(\frac{\Phi'}{\Phi}\right)^2 dz =$$

$$= 9.24 \times 10^{-6} W y_0 \left[\frac{1}{l} \int_{z_1}^{z_2} \left(\frac{\Phi'}{\Phi}\right)^2 dz\right] \qquad [AV^{-3/2}] \qquad 66.12$$

Hence we have

$$\left[\left(\frac{\Phi'}{\Phi}\right)^2\right]_{average} = \frac{P}{9.24 \times 10^{-6} W y_0} = 2.16 \times 10^5 \frac{P}{S_0} \qquad [m^{-2}] \quad 66.13$$

where $S_0 = 2Wy_0$ is the initial cross section of the beam. Comparing expressions 66.13 and 59.10, one can find that the periodic focusing of a sheet beam requires a somewhat weaker field than that of a cylindrical beam.

67. FOCUSING OF SHEET-ELECTRON BEAMS BY PERIODIC ELECTROSTATIC FIELDS

Let us now consider a plane-symmetric periodic electrostatic focusing field with continuous potential distribution. Let the x, z plane of the Cartesian coordinate system be the medium plane of the sheet-electron beam and the focusing system (see figure IV.16). The beam moves in the direction of the z axis.

We shall initially consider the *paraxial approximation*. The paraxial equation for plane-symmetric electrostatic fields will be written by the use of dimensionless variables

$$\eta = \frac{y}{y_0} \qquad \qquad 67.1$$

and

$$\zeta = \frac{2\pi}{p} z \qquad \qquad 67.2$$

where p is the period of the electric field. The intensity of the electron beam will be characterised by the parameter

$$A_s = \left(\frac{\omega_p}{\omega} \right)^2 \qquad \qquad 67.3$$

where

$$\omega_p^2 = -\eta \frac{\bar{\varrho}}{\varepsilon_0} = \frac{\eta}{\varepsilon_0} \frac{I}{2\sqrt{2}\sqrt{\eta}Wy_0\sqrt{U_0}} = \text{constant} \qquad 67.4$$

and

$$\omega = \frac{2\pi}{p} v_0 = \frac{2\pi}{p} (2\eta U_0)^{1/2} = \text{constant} \qquad 67.5$$

Here ω_p is the plasma frequency of the electrons, $\bar{\varrho}$ is the average space-charge density at the plane $z = 0$ and v_0 is the initial velocity of the electrons. Using 67.4 and 67.5, one can rewrite expression 67.3 in the following way

$$A_s = \frac{p^2 P_0}{16\sqrt{2}\pi^2 \varepsilon_0 \sqrt{\eta} Wy_0} = 1.2 \times 10^3 \frac{p^2 P_0}{Wy_0} \qquad 67.6$$

where

$$P_0 = \frac{I}{U_0^{3/2}}$$

is the initial value of the perveance of the beam. We shall consider the value of A_s of second order of smallness (see § 60).

The potential on the axis will be expressed by the dimensionless function

$$V(\zeta) = \frac{\Phi(z)}{U_0} \qquad 67.7$$

Then the paraxial equation 22.13 can be written as follows

$$\frac{d^2\eta}{d\zeta^2} + \frac{1}{2V}\frac{dV}{d\zeta}\frac{d\eta}{d\zeta} + \frac{1}{2V}\frac{d^2V}{d\zeta^2}\eta - \frac{A_s}{V^{3/2}} = 0 \qquad 67.8$$

This linear second-order inhomogeneous differential equation determines the *boundary electron trajectory* of the laminar sheet beam in paraxial approximation.

In the simplest case, when at the plane $z = 0$, the beam thickness is equal to $2y_0$ and its slope is $y_0' = 0$, we have the following initial conditions

$$\eta_0 = 1 \quad \text{and} \quad \eta_0' = 0 \qquad 67.9$$

In order to eliminate the term containing the first derivative of the dependent variable from equation 67.8 we shall use again the transformation

$$\sigma = \eta V^{1/4} \qquad 67.10$$

Equation 67.8 will have then the following form

$$\frac{d^2\sigma}{d\zeta^2} + \left[\frac{1}{4V}\frac{d^2V}{d\zeta^2} + \frac{3}{16}\left(\frac{1}{V}\frac{dV}{d\zeta}\right)^2\right]\sigma = \frac{A_s}{V^{5/4}} \qquad 67.11$$

In most practical cases, however, this equation cannot be integrated in terms of tabulated functions as well as equation 67.8. Therefore, only the case of *optimum focusing* will be treated in detail.

Let us consider now the periodic electrostatic focusing of a sheet-electron beam in paraxial approximation. Let us suppose that the sheet beam accelerated to potential U_0 arrives into the focusing system parallel to the z axis so that initial conditions 67.9 are valid. The electrostatic field with period p is produced by a series of electrodes held at periodically varying potentials U_F and U_f (see figure V.8). Similarly to the axially symmetric case, the potential distribution along the axis is approximated by expression

$$\Phi(z) = U_0 + U_1\left(1 - \cos\frac{2\pi}{p}z\right) \qquad 67.12$$

where U_1 is the half-amplitude of the variable component of the axial potential which depends on the potentials U_F and U_f and also on period p and on the geometrical dimensions of the electrodes.

Let us determine the electrode shapes corresponding to potential distribution 67.12. We shall use expression

$$\varphi(y, z) = \frac{1}{2}\left[\Phi(z + iy) + \Phi(z - iy)\right] \qquad 67.13$$

([87], formula 1.10) determining the value of the potential at an arbitrary point if the potential distribution is known along the axis. Substituting 67.12 into 67.13 we obtain

$$\varphi(y, z) = \frac{1}{2} \left\{ 2U_0 + U_1 \left[2 - \cos \frac{2\pi}{p} (z + iy) - \right. \right.$$

$$\left. \left. - \cos \frac{2\pi}{p} (z - iy) \right] \right\} = U_0 + U_1 \left(1 - \cos \frac{2\pi}{p} z \cosh \frac{2\pi}{p} y \right) \qquad 67.14$$

Hence we obtain the equation of the equipotential curve $\varphi(y, z) = U_0$ as follows

$$\cos \frac{2\pi}{p} z = \frac{1}{\cosh \dfrac{2\pi}{p} y} \qquad 67.15$$

The equipotential curve $\varphi(y, z) = U_0 + 2 U_1$ is determined by the following equation

$$\cos \frac{2\pi}{p} z = - \frac{1}{\cosh \dfrac{2\pi}{p} y} \qquad 67.16$$

Let us now express the electrode potentials U_F and U_f by U_0, U_1, p and T (T is the aperture of the electrode slit). We shall substitute firstly

$$\varphi = U_F, \qquad y = \frac{T}{2} \qquad \text{and} \qquad z = 2k \frac{p}{2}$$

into 67.14, then

$$\varphi = U_f, \qquad y = \frac{T}{2} \qquad \text{and} \qquad z = (2k + 1) \frac{p}{2} \qquad (k = 0, 1, 2 \ldots).$$

We obtain

$$U_F = U_0 + U_1 \left(1 - \cosh \frac{\pi T}{p} \right) \qquad 67.17$$

and

$$U_f = U_0 + U_1 \left(1 + \cosh \frac{\pi T}{p} \right) \qquad 67.18$$

Substituting now 67.17 and 67.18, respectively, into equation 67.14, we obtain the electrode shapes [104]. The equation of the equipotential U_F will have the following form

$$\cos \frac{2\pi}{p} z = - \frac{\cosh \dfrac{\pi T}{p}}{\cosh \dfrac{2\pi}{p} y} \qquad 67.19$$

Similarly, the equation of the electrode held at potential U_f is as follows

$$\cos \frac{2\pi}{p} z = - \frac{\cosh \dfrac{\pi T}{p}}{\cosh \dfrac{2\pi}{p} y} \tag{67.20}$$

The electrode shapes and the equipotential curves U_0 and $(U_0 + 2\,U_1)$ have been plotted in figure V.28 for the case of $T = 0.5p$. Naturally, more simple electrode shapes are used in practice. The potential distribution of real electrode systems can be determined by conformal mapping or by analog methods.

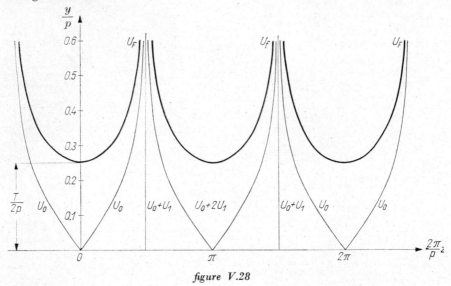

figure V.28

If the focusing system consists of plane slit diaphragms, the potential at the centre of the slit Φ_c can be calculated from the following expression [54]

$$\Phi_c = \Phi_0 + \frac{T}{4}(E_1 - E_2) \tag{67.21}$$

where Φ_0 is the potential of the diaphragm, T is the width of the slit and there are uniform electric fields of strengths E_1 and E_2 on the left and right sides of the diaphragm, respectively. If $p \gg T$, we can assume that only the electrode in consideration has a slit, while the adjacent electrodes are plane surfaces without slits. Then we have

$$U_0 = U_F + \frac{T}{p}(U_f - U_F) \tag{67.22}$$

and

$$U_0 + 2U_1 = U_f + \frac{T}{p}(U_F - U_f) \qquad 67.23$$

Thus, we obtain the following system of equations for the determination of U_F and U_f

$$
\left.
\begin{aligned}
U_F\left(1 - \frac{T}{p}\right) + U_f\frac{T}{p} &= U_0 \\[2mm]
U_F\frac{T}{p} + U_f\left(1 - \frac{T}{p}\right) &= U_0 + 2U_1
\end{aligned}
\right\} \qquad 67.24
$$

The solution of this system is

$$U_F = U_0 - U_1\frac{2\dfrac{T}{p}}{1 - 2\dfrac{T}{p}} \qquad 67.25$$

and

$$U_f = U_0 + 2U_1\frac{1 - \dfrac{T}{p}}{1 - 2\dfrac{T}{p}} \qquad 67.26$$

The potentials of the slit diaphragms are determined by these formulae if U_0 and U_1 are given and the axial potential distribution is approximated by 67.12. These formulae are valid if $T/p < 1/2$ and the lesser is the value of T/p, the lesser is the deviation between these formulae and 67.17 and 67.18.

Let us consider now the case of optimum focusing, that is minimum beam rippling. We shall try to find the solution of equation 67.8 in the form of

$$\eta(\zeta) = 1 + \eta_1(\zeta) + \eta_2(\zeta) \qquad 67.27$$

where η_1 is a quantity of first order of smallness, η_2 is a quantity of second order of smallness. The initial conditions require that

$$\eta_1(0) = \eta_2(0) = \eta_1'(0) = \eta_2'(0) = 0 \qquad 67.28$$

where the primes represent differentiation with respect to ζ.

The axial potential distribution is determined by 67.7 and 67.12 as follows

$$V(\zeta) = 1 + \Omega(1 - \cos\zeta) \qquad 67.29$$

Here $\Omega = U_1/U_0$ is a quantity of first order of smallness.

It is to be mentioned that the paraxial approximation is valid only if $y_0/p \ll 1$. On the other hand, the smallness of the parameter A_s requires that the perveance P_0 or the ratio of p/y_0 should be as small as possible. These two requirements are contradictory. As a consequence of this fact, this method of analysis is valid only at not too large values of the perveance.

Substituting 67.27 and 67.29 into 67.8, we obtain the following equation after linearisation

$$2[1 + \Omega(1 - \cos \zeta)](\eta_1'' + \eta_2'') + \Omega \sin \zeta(\eta_1' + \eta_2') +$$
$$+ \Omega \cos \zeta(1 + \eta_1 + \eta_2) - 2A_s\left[1 - \frac{\Omega}{2}(1 - \cos \zeta)\right] = 0 \qquad 67.30$$

Let us separate the terms of first order of smallness and the terms of second order of smallness from each other and neglect the terms of higher order of smallness. We obtain the following equation (see 60.56)

$$\{2\eta_1'' + \Omega \cos \xi\} + \{2\eta_1''\Omega(1 - \cos \zeta) + 2\eta_2'' +$$
$$+ \Omega \eta_1' \sin \zeta + \Omega \eta_1 \cos \zeta - 2A_s\} = 0 \qquad 67.31$$

As a first-order approximation, we shall consider only terms of first order of smallness, i.e. we shall have to solve equation

$$\eta_1'' = -\frac{\Omega}{2} \cos \zeta \qquad 67.32$$

instead of equation 67.31 with initial conditions 67.28. The result is

$$\eta_1(\zeta) = -\frac{\Omega}{2}(1 - \cos \zeta) \qquad 67.33$$

Substituting it again into 67.31 we obtain

$$\eta_2'' - \frac{\Omega^2}{2} \cos \zeta (1 - \cos \zeta) - \frac{\Omega^2}{4} \sin^2 \zeta -$$
$$- \frac{\Omega^2}{4} \cos \zeta (1 - \cos \zeta) - A_s = \eta_2'' + \left(\frac{\Omega^2}{4} - A_s\right) -$$
$$- \frac{3}{4} \Omega^2 \cos \zeta + \frac{\Omega^2}{2} \cos 2\zeta = 0 \qquad 67.34$$

Integrating this equation twofold and taking the initial conditions into account, we obtain

$$\eta_2(\zeta) = \frac{5}{8} \Omega^2 - \frac{3}{4}\Omega^2 \cos \zeta + \frac{\Omega^2}{8} \cos 2\zeta + \left(A_s - \frac{\Omega^2}{4}\right)\frac{\zeta^2}{2} \qquad 67.35$$

In case of optimum focusing the boundary electron trajectory should not deviate considerably from the equilibrium state $\eta = 1$. Therefore, expression 67.35 should not contain terms with positive powers of ζ. It follows from this fact that

$$\Omega_{opt} = \pm 2\sqrt{A_s} \qquad 67.36$$

This expression determines the values of Ω at which a minimum beam rippling occurs at given value of the space-charge parameter A_s. Expression 67.36 determines the electrode potentials required for optimum focusing. These values of U_F and U_f can be calculated from 67.17 and 67.18 or 67.25 and 67.26 after the determination of the value of Ω_{opt} from 67.36. The sign is defined by the sign of U_1. It follows from 67.6 and 67.36 that the value of the perveance corresponding to an optimum value of Ω is equal to

$$P_0 = 2.08 \times 10^{-4} \Omega^2 \frac{W y_0}{p^2} \qquad [\text{A/V}^{3/2}] \qquad \qquad 67.37$$

As it can be seen from this formula, the maximum value of the perveance is much greater than in the axially symmetric case. Actually, in case of $\Omega = 0.5$ and $y_0/p = 0.25$ we have

$$P_0 = 1.3 \times 10^{-5} \frac{W}{p} \qquad [\text{A/V}^{3/2}]$$

As the value of W may be a large multiple of p, the value of the perveance may be very large.

It can be seen also from expression 67.37 that at the increase of the values of P_0 or $p^2/W y_0$ the value of the focusing potential U_1 must be increased, similarly as in the axially symmetric case.

The beam configuration can be obtained from 67.27, 67.33, 67.35 and 67.36 as follows

$$\eta(\zeta) = \frac{y}{y_0} = 1 - \frac{\Omega_{opt}}{2}(1 - \cos\zeta) +$$
$$+ \Omega_{opt}^2 \left(\frac{5}{8} - \frac{3}{4}\cos\zeta + \frac{1}{8}\cos 2\zeta \right) \qquad \qquad 67.38$$

It is to be emphasised once again that 67.38 is valid only if condition 67.36 is satisfied. If it is not so, equation 67.8 with potential distribution 67.29 is to be solved. Then we have the following equation

$$\frac{d^2\eta}{d\zeta^2} + \frac{\Omega \sin\zeta}{2[1 + \Omega(1 - \cos\zeta)]}\frac{d\eta}{d\zeta} +$$
$$+ \frac{\Omega \cos\zeta}{2[1 + \Omega(1 - \cos\zeta)]}\eta - \frac{A_s}{[1 + \Omega(1 - \cos\zeta)]^{3/2}} = 0 \qquad 67.39$$

It follows from 67.38 that the beam configuration in first-order approximation is given by

$$\frac{y}{y_0} = 1 - \frac{\Omega_{opt}}{2}\left(1 - \cos\frac{2\pi}{p}z\right) \qquad \qquad 67.40$$

Thus, in case of the strict fulfilment of the initial conditions and condition 67.36 the period of the beam rippling is equal to that of the focusing system in first-order approximation. As in the axially symmetric case, if $\Omega_{\text{opt}} > 0$ the beam diameter is always smaller than the initial diameter; if $\Omega_{\text{opt}} < 0$ it is always greater than the initial diameter. Obviously, the greater is the value of the parameter A_s (and, consequently, the value of Ω_{opt}) the greater is the amplitude of the beam rippling. At a given value of A_s the rippling is stronger if $\Omega_{\text{opt}} < 0$.

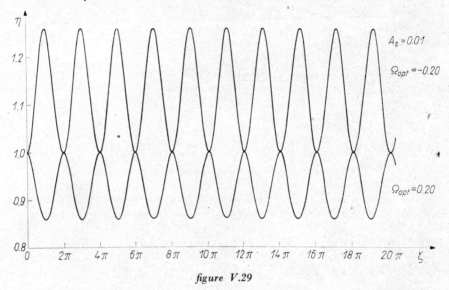

figure V.29

The beam configurations calculated from 67.38 for the case of $A_s = 10^{-2}$ and the corresponding values of $\Omega_{\text{opt}} = \pm 0.20$ are given in figure V.29.

Let us *compare* now *the axially symmetric* and *the plane-symmetric cases* [104]. We shall introduce the initial cross section S_0 of the beam. Its value is equal to πr_0^2 in the axially symmetric case and to $2 W y_0$ in the plane-symmetric case. Let us consider an axially symmetric and a plane-symmetric electron beam with equal values of P_0 and S_0 and assume that the periods of both focusing systems are equal to p. We obtain from 60.10 that

$$A = \frac{1}{16\sqrt{2}\,\pi^2 \varepsilon_0 \sqrt{\eta}} \frac{p^2 P_0}{S_0} \qquad\qquad 67.41$$

and from 67.6 that

$$A_s = \frac{1}{8\sqrt{2}\,\pi^2 \varepsilon_0 \sqrt{\eta}} \frac{p^2 P_0}{S_0} \qquad\qquad 67.42$$

Comparing 67.41 and 67.42 we obtain the relation between the two space-charge parameters

$$\frac{A_s}{A} = 2 \qquad\qquad 67.43$$

Let us denote the optimum value of the focusing parameter with Ω in axially symmetric case and with Ω_s in the plane-symmetric case. Similarly, the amplitude of the beam rippling calculated in the first-order approximation will be denoted by δ in the axially symmetric case and with δ_s in the plane-symmetric case. Using 67.43, we then obtain from 60.61 and 67.36 that:

$$\frac{\Omega_s}{\Omega} = \frac{2}{\sqrt{\dfrac{32}{3}}} \sqrt{\frac{A_s}{A}} = 2\sqrt{\frac{3}{16}} = \frac{\sqrt{3}}{2} = 0.866 \qquad 67.44$$

It follows from 60.65, 67.40 and 67.44 that

$$\frac{\delta_s}{\delta} = \frac{\dfrac{\Omega_s}{2}}{\dfrac{\Omega}{4}} = 2\frac{\Omega_s}{\Omega} = \sqrt{3} = 1.732 \qquad 67.45$$

As one can see from expressions 67.43, 67.44 and 67.45, in case of identical parameters the value of the space-charge parameter is doubled in the plane-symmetric case in comparison with the axially symmetric case. Somewhat less focusing field is required for the plane-symmetric case but the beam rippling is stronger.

If the value of Ω is slightly different from the optimum value Ω_{opt} determined by 67.36, the beam rippling treated above will be superposed on an additional fluctuation with greater wavelength (see § 61). The wavelength λ of this greater fluctuation is equal to the wavelength

$$\lambda_p = 2\pi \frac{v_0}{\omega_p} \qquad 67.46$$

calculated from the plasma frequency [120]. According to 67.3, 67.5 and 67.46, this wavelength is equal to

$$\lambda_p = \frac{p\omega}{\omega_p} = \frac{p}{\sqrt{A_s}} \qquad 67.47$$

According to [120], the amplitude $\Delta\eta$ of this fluctuation is determined by expression

$$\Delta\eta = 1 - \frac{P_{real}}{P_0} \qquad 67.48$$

where P_{real} is the real value of the perveance at the plane $z = 0$, P_0 is the theoretical value of the perveance connected with the value of Ω_{opt} by expressions 67.6 and 67.36. On the basis of the same expressions one can express the dependence of P_{real} on Ω which leads to the following formula

$$\Delta\eta = 1 - \left(\frac{\Omega}{\Omega_{opt}}\right)^2 \qquad 67.49$$

It is to be mentioned that expression 67.48 is valid only if

$$P_{\text{real}} > \frac{P_0}{2}$$

If the value of the focusing parameter is just equal to Ω_{opt} but the beam enters the focusing system with a certain initial slope $\eta_0' \neq 0$, the additional fluctuation with wavelength λ_p will appear again. If the smaller rippling with period p is neglected, the following approximate formula will determine the edge-electron trajectory

$$\eta = 1 + \Delta\eta \sin \frac{2\pi}{\lambda_p} z \qquad\qquad 67.50$$

It follows from this expression that

$$\Delta\eta = \frac{\eta_0' \lambda_p}{p} \qquad\qquad 67.51$$

According to 61.10 the beam stiffness K can be expressed by

$$K = \frac{\eta_0'}{\Delta\eta} \qquad\qquad 67.52$$

The lesser is the amplitude of the fluctuation caused by a given η_0' variation of the initial slope of the beam, the greater is the value of the stiffness. It follows from 67.47, 67.51 and 67.52 that in this case

$$K = \frac{p}{\lambda_p} = \sqrt{A_s} \qquad\qquad 67.53$$

68. FOCUSING OF THICK SHEET BEAMS

If the period of the focusing system is comparable with the beam thickness, the paraxial approximation is not valid. We shall use the method given in § 62 for the case of sheet-electron beams [107].

The potential distribution produced by the periodic focusing system can be approximated by the first two terms of a *Fourier* series

$$U(y, z) = U_0 + U_1(y) \cos \frac{2\pi}{p} z \qquad\qquad 68.1$$

The analysis of plane-symmetric focusing systems with potential distribution given in the form of a general *Fourier* series has been carried out as well [148].

Using expression 67.13, we obtain from 68.1 that

$$U(y, z) = \frac{1}{2} \left\{ 2U_0 + U_1(0) \left[\cos \frac{2\pi}{p} (z + iy) + \right. \right.$$

$$\left. + \cos \frac{2\pi}{p} (z - iy) \right\} = U_0 + U_1(0) \cosh \frac{2\pi}{p} y \cos \frac{2\pi}{p} z \qquad 68.2$$

whence

$$U_1(y) = U_1(0) \cosh \frac{2\pi}{p} y \qquad 68.3$$

is the amplitude of the variable component of the potential depending on the geometrical dimensions of the focusing system and on the electrode voltages. U_0 is the uniform component of the potential, p is the period of the focusing system. We assume that

$$\frac{U_1(0)}{U_0} \ll 1 \qquad 68.4$$

In the followings the notation

$$U_1(0) = U_1$$

will be used.

We shall try to find the boundary electron trajectory in the form of

$$y(z) = y_0 + y_1(z) \qquad 68.5$$

If the focusing is successful, $y_1(z)$ is a periodic function and its amplitude is much smaller than y_0.

Expanding $U_1(y)$ in *Taylor* series at $y = y_0$, neglecting the terms with higher than second powers of y_1 and taking the axial variation of the electron velocity into account, we can write the equation of the *boundary* electron trajectories. The average force caused by space-charge is given by the following expression

$$F_e = \frac{eI}{2\varepsilon_0 W v_z} \qquad 68.6$$

Here W is the beam width. This expression is based on 51.3 and 51.12. The equation of boundary electron trajectories will have the following form

$$\frac{d^2 y_1}{dz^2} + \frac{1}{v_z} \frac{dv_z}{dz} \frac{dy_1}{dz} - \frac{\eta}{v_z^2} U_1 \left[\left(\frac{2\pi}{p} \right)^2 y_1 \cosh \frac{2\pi}{p} y_0 + \right.$$

$$\left. + \left(\frac{2\pi}{p} \right)^3 \frac{y_1^2}{p} \sinh \frac{2\pi}{p} y_0 \right] \cos \frac{2\pi}{p} z =$$

$$= \frac{\eta}{v_z^2} U_1 \frac{2\pi}{p} \sinh \frac{2\pi}{p} y_0 \cos \frac{2\pi}{p} z + \frac{\eta I}{2\varepsilon_0 W v_z^2 (2\eta U_0)^{1/2}} \qquad 68.7$$

The approximate solution of equation 68.7 will be carried out similarly to that in axially symmetric case (see § 62). We obtain the following approximate expression for the boundary electron trajectory

$$y(z) = y_0 - \frac{p}{2\pi} \frac{U_1}{2U_0} \sinh \frac{2\pi}{p} y_0 \cos \frac{2\pi}{p} z \qquad 68.8$$

Let us now substitute 68.8 into the equation of electron trajectories and equate its constant terms. We obtain then the relation determining the value of the focusing potential U_f

$$\left(\frac{U_1}{U_0}\right)^2 = \frac{pI}{\pi\varepsilon_0 W(2\eta)^{1/2} U_0^{3/2}} \frac{1}{\sinh \frac{4\pi}{p} y_0} \qquad 68.9$$

Let us consider the periodic focusing system consisting of a series of electrodes held at alternating potentials $(U_0 + U_f)$ and $(U_0 - U_f)$ as an example (figure V.30). The electrodes are shown in the figure schematically. Potential distribution 68.1 strictly corresponds to the electrode system given in figure V.28. In this case we have

$$U_1 = \frac{U_f}{\cosh \frac{\pi T}{p}} \qquad 68.10$$

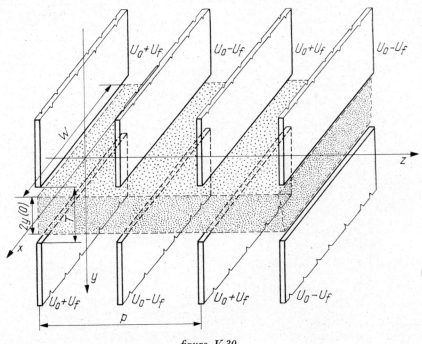

figure V.30

where T is the aperture of the electrode slits. Substituting 68.10 into expressions 68.8 and 68.9, we obtain the boundary electron trajectory and the required value of the focusing potential for this case

$$y(z) = y_0 - \frac{p}{4\pi} \frac{U_f}{U_0} \frac{\sinh \dfrac{2\pi}{p} y_0}{\cosh \dfrac{\pi T}{p}} \cos \frac{2\pi}{p} z \qquad 68.11$$

and

$$\left(\frac{U_f}{U_0}\right)^2 = \frac{pI}{\pi \varepsilon_0 (2\eta)^{1/2} W U_0^{3/2}} \frac{\cosh^2 \dfrac{\pi T}{p}}{\sinh \dfrac{4\pi}{p} y_0} \qquad 68.12$$

If the ratio of U_f/U_0 is given, the value of the perveance corresponding to the optimum focusing follows from 68.12

$$P = \frac{I}{U_0^{3/2}} = \pi \varepsilon_0 (2\eta)^{1/2} \frac{W}{p} \left(\frac{U_f}{U_0}\right)^2 \frac{\sinh \dfrac{4\pi}{p} y_0}{\cosh^2 \dfrac{\pi T}{p}} \qquad 68.13$$

Let us examine the dependence of the perveance on the value of y_0/p at a fixed value of W/y_0 [107]. We shall introduce the following notation

$$\frac{2y_0}{T} = \gamma < 1 \qquad 68.14$$

and

$$2\pi \frac{y_0}{p} = \xi \qquad 68.15$$

Substituting the values of the physical constants, we can rewrite expression 68.13 in the following way

$$P = 2.63 \times 10^{-6} \left(\frac{U_f}{U_0}\right)^2 \frac{W}{y_0} f(\xi, \gamma) \quad [\text{A/V}^{3/2}] \qquad 68.16$$

where

$$f(\xi, \gamma) = \xi \frac{\sinh 2\xi}{\cosh^2 \dfrac{\xi}{\gamma}} \qquad 68.17$$

Function $f(\xi, \gamma)$ has the following asymptotes:
(a) $\xi \ll 1$ (paraxial case)

$$f(\xi, \gamma) \approx 2\xi^2 \qquad 68.18$$

if the value of γ is not too small.

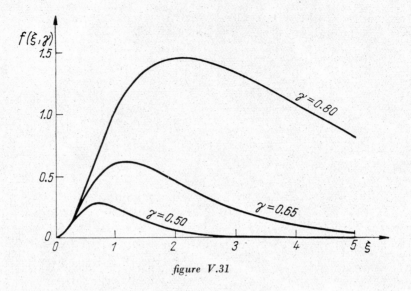

figure V.31

(b) In case of $\xi \gg 1$ we have

$$f(\xi, \gamma) \approx 2\xi \exp\left[-2\xi \frac{1-\gamma}{\gamma}\right] \qquad 68.19$$

Thus, the value of the perveance first increases but then abruptly decreases with the increase of ξ. The perveance has its maximum value at a certain value of ξ_{opt}. It follows from expression 68.17 that the value of ξ_{opt} is determined by the following transcendental equation

$$\left(\frac{1}{\gamma} \tanh \frac{\xi_{opt}}{\gamma} - \frac{1}{2\xi_{opt}}\right) \tanh 2\xi_{opt} = 1 \qquad 68.20$$

Function $f(\xi)$ has been plotted in figure V.31 for three different values of γ. The value of $f(\xi)$ strongly increases with the increase of the value of γ; consequently, the perveance increases as well. At the same time, the position of the maximum of this function is displaced towards greater values of ξ. At practical values of the parameter γ ($\gamma \approx 1$) the maximum value of the perveance gets out of the paraxial region. Thus, the method of analysis given in this section is suitable for electron beams of higher intensity than the paraxial approximation.

In *paraxial approximation* we have $\xi \ll 1$ and $U_1(y) = U_1$. In this case expression 68.9 determining the value of the required focusing potential can be written as follows

$$\left(\frac{U_1}{U_0}\right)^2 = \frac{\sqrt{2}Ip^2}{8\pi^2\varepsilon_0\sqrt{\eta}Wy_0 U_0^{3/2}} \qquad 68.21$$

If this requirement is fulfilled, the boundary electron trajectory can be expressed, according to 68.8, in the following way

$$\frac{y}{y_0} = 1 - \frac{U_1}{2U_0} \cos \frac{2\pi}{p} z \qquad\qquad 68.22$$

Using 67.6 we can prove that 68.21 coincides with 67.36.

The repulsion force acting on the electrons should diminish towards the axis according to the same law as the focusing force diminishes. It is necessary for this that condition 68.9 should be fulfilled not only at the boundary of the beam but at any value of $y < y_0$. Thus, the following condition must be fulfilled [104]

$$I(y) = \iint_S j(y)dS = \int_{-W/2}^{W/2} \int_{-y}^{y} j(y)dydx = 2W \int_0^y j(y)dy =$$

$$= \frac{\pi \varepsilon_0 W (2\eta)^{1/2} U_0^{3/2}}{p} \left(\frac{U_1}{U_0}\right)^2 \sinh \frac{4\pi}{p} y \qquad\qquad 68.23$$

Here $I(y)$ is the current inside the beam portion with thickness $2y$. As the current density is a function of y now, expression 68.6 derived on the basis of the approximation $j =$ constant is to be replaced, similarly to the axially symmetric case treated in § 62, by the following expression of the space-charge force

$$F_e = \frac{e}{\varepsilon_0 v_z} \int_0^y j(y)dy \qquad\qquad 68.24$$

Comparing 68.6 and 68.24 we obtain formally

$$\frac{I(y)}{2W} = \int_0^y j(y)dy$$

Let us express now the current-density distribution required for the optimum focusing from 68.23

$$j(y) = \frac{1}{2W} \frac{dI}{dy} = \frac{2\pi^2 \varepsilon_0 (2\eta)^{1/2} U_0^{3/2}}{p^2} \left(\frac{U_1}{U_0}\right)^2 \cosh \frac{4\pi}{p} y \qquad\qquad 68.25$$

Substituting 68.10 into expression 68.25, we obtain the formula of the current density for our example

$$j(y) = \frac{2\pi^2 \varepsilon_0 (2\eta)^{1/2} U_0^{3/2}}{p^2} \left(\frac{U_f}{U_0}\right)^2 \frac{\cosh \dfrac{4\pi}{p} y}{\cosh^2 \dfrac{\pi T}{p}} \qquad\qquad 68.26$$

It is to be mentioned that the production of the current-density distribution determined by 68.25 is a very difficult problem. Obviously, in paraxial
approximation the current density may be assumed constant across the
whole beam.

The paraxial treatment of the periodic electrostatic focusing of sheet-
electron beams has been given by [1, 120].

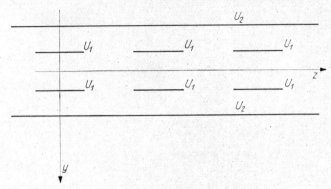

figure V.32

The optimum value of the focusing parameter and the approximate electron trajectories in some special focusing systems have been determined
by W. E. Waters [119]. He has analysed in detail the system shown schematically in figure V.32. This system is advantageous from the point of view
of the microwave-tube applications [120]. This plane-symmetric focusing
system consists of a parallel pair of tape ladder lines and two parallel plates.
The ladder lines are held at an equal potential U_1 while the potential of the
plates being U_2 which is a smaller potential than U_1.

A travelling-wave tube based on an electrostatically focused sheet electron
beam has been proposed by [2]. The focusing system consists of plane electrodes with periodically varying potentials. This system corresponds to that
consisting of a sequence of equal cylinders in axially symmetric case.

New developments in this field have been reported by [110, 133, 141,
146, 150].

We should like to mention that any analysis of sheet-electron beams is
approximately valid for hollow beams as well, if the beam thickness and the
period of the focusing system are small enough in comparison with the diameter of the beam. In this case, rotating the longitudinal section of the
plane system around an axis we obtain a hollow system. The smaller the
diameter of the beam and the larger the beam thickness and the period of
the focusing system, the greater is the difference between the two systems.
Such a calculation of the periodic focusing of hollow electron beams can be
made more accurate by various perturbation methods. The focusing system
consisting of an inner continuous conductor and an outer periodic system
and not having any symmetry planes as well as the plane-symmetric focus-

ing system corresponding to the biperiodic system shown in figure V.22 have been analysed by [62]. The results obtained for these plane systems have been extended to hollow beams as well.

(E) FOCUSING OF CURVILINEAR SHEET-ELECTRON BEAMS USING ELECTROSTATIC FIELDS

Focusing systems in which the motion of the electron beam is not symmetrical with respect to a rectilinear axis but has in itself a curvilinear axis, are widely used in electron optics [42, 97, 102]. In this part of the book these will be treated in such a way, that by maintaining long high-intensity sheet-electron beams the axis of the beam becomes curvilinear. This axis may be a plane curve or a curve in space, depending on the concrete system. The common feature of these systems is that their focusing forces are balanced by space-charge and centrifugal forces. Thus, space-charge plays only an additional role beside the centrifugal force. This leads to a very good stability against space-charge perturbations; therefore, the maintenance of high-perveance electron beams becomes possible.

A more general treatment of curvilinear electron beams can be found in [67, 81, 98, 118]. We shall give only the description of some special methods.

69. THE CENTRIFUGAL ELECTROSTATIC FOCUSING

The main point of the centrifugal electrostatic focusing is that the electrons of the beam are forced to move along helical trajectories by electrostatic forces [32]. Thus, the axial trajectory of the beam is a curve in space (figure V.33).

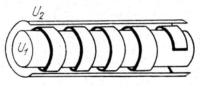

figure V.33

The electron gun is to be placed so that the electrons leaving the gun should gain momentum of rotation. Thus, the electrons will have axial and azimuthal components of their initial velocity

$$\dot{r}_0 = 0, \qquad \dot{z}_0 \neq 0 \qquad \text{and} \qquad r_0\dot{\alpha}_0 \neq 0$$

The electrons come to the electric field of a cylindrical condenser from the electron gun. The internal cylinder of the condenser has a radius R_1 and is held at potential U_1. The coaxial external cylinder with radius R_2 is held at potential U_2. Potential U_1 is greater than potential U_2. The electrons will move in this system along stable helical trajectories if the following condition is fulfilled: the centrifugal force produced by the rotation of the electrons must be equal and oppositely directed to the electric force acting on the electrons by the cylindrical condenser. In first-order approximation space-charge forces may be neglected because they play only an additional role, in spite of the fact that definitely high-perveance electron beams are concerned.

This condition can be written as follows

$$mr_0\dot{\alpha}_0^2 = -(-eE_{r_0}) = -e\frac{dU}{dr}\Big|_{r=r_0} \qquad 69.1$$

where r_0 is the radius of the equilibrium trajectory, $\dot{\alpha}_0$ is the angular velocity which is constant on the equilibrium trajectory, E_{r_0} is the value of the radial electric field strength of the cylindrical condenser along the equilibrium trajectory. The potential distribution of the cylindrical condenser is determined by expression 49.37 whence we have

$$\frac{dU}{dr} = \frac{U_2 - U_1}{\log\dfrac{R_2}{R_1}}\frac{1}{r} \qquad 69.2$$

$dU/dr < 0$ as $R_2 > R_1$ and $U_1 > U_2$. Thus, there are positive quantities in both sides of equation 69.1. We obtain from 69.1 and 69.2 that

$$mr_0\dot{\alpha}_0^2 = \frac{e}{r_0}\frac{U_1 - U_2}{\log\dfrac{R_2}{R_1}} \qquad 69.3$$

The radius of the stable trajectory is determined by this equation as a function of the value of $\dot{\alpha}_0$ given by the initial conditions. As there is no force in axial direction, the axial component of the electron velocity remains constant

$$\dot{z} = \dot{z}_0 \qquad 69.4$$

Thus, the electron moves along a helical trajectory with radius r_0.

We shall prove now that this is a stable trajectory. Because of the existence of equation 69.4 it is sufficient to examine the projection of the trajectory to the plane normal to the z axis. As is well known, the value of the angular momentum p_α is constant in a central field

$$p_\alpha = r^2\dot{\alpha} = r_0^2\dot{\alpha}_0 = \text{constant} \qquad 69.5$$

Using 69.2 and 69.5 we can write the equation of motion 18.1 as follows

$$\ddot{r} - r\dot{\alpha}^2 = \ddot{r} - \frac{p_\alpha^2}{r^3} = \eta\frac{U_2 - U_1}{\log\dfrac{R_2}{R_1}}\frac{1}{r} \qquad 69.6$$

Let us denote

$$B = \eta\frac{U_2 - U_1}{\log\dfrac{R_2}{R_1}} \qquad 69.7$$

Equation 69.6 can be written then in the following simple form

$$\ddot{r} - \frac{p_\alpha^2}{r^3} = \frac{B}{r} \qquad\qquad 69.8$$

Let us suppose that the electron has left the equilibrium trajectory with radius r_0 for any reason. The radius r corresponding to the situation of the electron in the given moment can be written as follows

$$r = r_0 + \varDelta r = r_0\left(1 + \frac{\varDelta r}{r_0}\right) \qquad\qquad 69.9$$

If the equilibrium trajectory is actually stable, we must have $\varDelta r \ll r_0$. Then we may assume that

$$\frac{1}{r} \approx \frac{1}{r_0}\left(1 - \frac{\varDelta r}{r_0}\right) \qquad\qquad 69.10$$

and

$$\frac{1}{r^3} \approx \frac{1}{r_0^3}\left(1 - 3\frac{\varDelta r}{r_0}\right) \qquad\qquad 69.11$$

Using 69.9, 69.10 and 69.11 we can rewrite equation 69.8 as follows

$$\frac{d^2(\varDelta r)}{dt^2} - \frac{p_\alpha^2}{r_0^3}\left(1 - 3\frac{\varDelta r}{r_0}\right) - \frac{B}{r_0}\left(1 - \frac{\varDelta r}{r_0}\right) = 0 \qquad\qquad 69.12$$

Equation 69.3 is valid for the equilibrium trajectory. This equation can be written with the new notation in the following way

$$\frac{p_\alpha^2}{r_0^3} = -\frac{B}{r_0} \qquad\qquad 69.13$$

Taking this equation into account, equation 69.12 becomes much simpler

$$\frac{d^2(\varDelta r)}{dt^2} + 2\frac{p_\alpha^2}{r_0^4}\varDelta r = 0 \qquad\qquad 69.14$$

We obtain from 69.5 that

$$\frac{p_\alpha^2}{r_0^4} = \dot{\alpha}_0^2 \qquad\qquad 69.15$$

Equation 69.14 has the following solution

$$\varDelta r = \text{constant} \times \sin\left[\sqrt{2}\dot{\alpha}_0(t - t_0)\right] \qquad\qquad 69.16$$

Thus, the deviation $\varDelta r$ from the equilibrium trajectory is described by a periodic function. It means that the equilibrium trajectory is really stable.

The electron which has left this trajectory will return to the equilibrium trajectory after passing through an angle of

$$\alpha - \alpha_0 = \frac{n\pi}{\sqrt{2}} = 127°17'$$ 69.17

(Focusing by Hughes and Rojansky.)

The stability of the equilibrium trajectory can be clearly illustrated by means of equation 69.13. If the radius of the electron trajectory increases, the value of the left-hand side of this equation decreases, i.e. the electric force acting on the electron towards the axis will be prevalent and the electron will return to the equilibrium trajectory. If the the radius decreases, the centrifugal force will be prevalent and the electron will return again to the equilibrium trajectory.

As all the electrons move along helical trajectories, in practice this results in a continuous hollow beam being formed in the cylindrical condenser, which moves in the direction of the z axis. (In figure V.33 a curvilinear sheet beam is shown for the sake of illustration.) The centrifugal electrostatic focusing is used therefore for the maintenance of hollow electron beams and is treated in this part of the book only for homogeneity of the treatment.

A rigorous analysis of the centrifugal electrostatic focusing should take into consideration also the force 49.29 produced by space-charge of the hollow electron beam. This force appears in the right-hand side of equation 69.3. The parameters of the focusing must be chosen so that the radius of the equilibrium trajectory r_0 should coincide with the equilibrium radius r_e of the electron beam (see 49.28). If $r > r_e$ the electrons are forced by space-charge to move outwards from the axis; if $r < r_e$ the space-charge force acts on the electrons in the direction towards the axis. As we have seen above, the focusing is stable and the electrons cannot move away far from the equilibrium trajectory. But the proof of stability has been carried out only for the case without space-charge. It is obvious, however, that space-charge cannot change to any great extent the stability of the system where there are small values for the beam perveance. The greater the potential difference $(U_1 - U_2)$ between the electrodes of the cylindrical condenser and the smaller the value of the ratio R_2/R_1, then the more negligible is the role of space-charge.

Thus, if the perveance of the beam is increased, the value of the potential difference $(U_1 - U_2)$ should also increase. The increase of the potential difference is limited by practical considerations—stable power source, discharge, etc. A serious result cannot be achieved by the reduction of the ratio of R_2/R_1. Thus, the stability of the system will become worse with the increase of the perveance; further, the focusing becomes unstable and at a certain value of the perveance even the condition of equilibrium trajectory cannot be fulfilled. This is the limit of the possible value of the perveance.

The maximum value of the current which can be transmitted by the system is determined on the basis of the following expression [32]

$$\frac{dE_r}{dr} + \frac{3}{r} E_r > 0 \qquad \qquad 69.18$$

In this expression E_r is the total radial electric field containing the electric fields of both space-charge and the cylindrical condenser.

The analysis has shown that the maintenance of beams of considerable currents is possible by this method.

The value of the maximum beam current is given by

$$I_{max} = \frac{33 \times 10^{-6}(U_1 - U_2)\sqrt{U_z}}{\log \dfrac{b}{R_1} - \dfrac{1}{2} - \dfrac{a^2}{b^2 - a^2} \log \dfrac{b}{a} + \dfrac{b^2}{b^2 - a^2} \log \dfrac{R_2}{R_1}} \quad [A] \qquad 69.19$$

where U_z is the potential determining the axial component of the electron velocity

$$\dot{z}_0^2 = 2\eta U_z \qquad \qquad 69.20$$

b and a are the outer and inner radii of the beam, respectively. If the beam thickness

$$2\delta r = b - a$$

is small in comparison with the radius r_0 of the stable trajectory, expression 69.19 may be written [48] in the form of

$$\frac{I_{max}}{U_z^{3/2}} = 265 \times 10^{-6} \frac{\delta r}{r_0} \cot^2 \beta \quad [A/V^{3/2}] \qquad 69.21$$

where

$$\tan \beta = \frac{\dot{z}_0}{r_0 \dot{\alpha}_0} \qquad \qquad 69.22$$

(β is the angle of departure of the electrons). It follows from expressions 69.21 and 69.22 that

$$P_{max} = \left(\frac{I}{U^{3/2}}\right)_{max} = 265 \times 10^{-6} \frac{\delta r}{r_0} \sin \beta \cos^2 \beta \qquad 69.23$$

where U is the potential of the beam connected with the resultant velocity of the electrons by expression

$$v^2 = 2\eta U \qquad \qquad 69.24$$

As the function

$$f(\beta) = \sin \beta \cos^2 \beta$$

has a maximum value at $\beta_m = 0.615$ and this maximum value is equal to

$$f_{max}(\beta_m) = 0.385$$

the maximum possible value of the perveance is determined by the following expression

$$(P_{\max})_{\max} = 102 \times 10^{-6} \frac{\delta r}{r_0} \quad [\text{A}/\text{V}^{3/2}] \qquad 69.25$$

Obviously, this value may be achieved only in a special case because the value of the angle β at given potentials and geometrical dimensions is determined by expressions 69.3 and 69.22 and therefore cannot be chosen arbitrarily.

It is to be mentioned that the condition of equilibrium 69.3 may be fulfilled rigorously only at a given radius, namely for electrons moving along the beam axis, even if space-charge is negligible. Electrons moving closer to the boundary of the beam perform stable oscillations according to 69.16.

A more exact analysis [5] has shown that in case of negligible space-charge the outer boundary of the hollow electron beam changes more strongly than its inner boundary. If space-charge is taken into account, one can find a certain optimal value of the space-charge density of the beam at given values of the parameters, at which the oscillations of both boundaries of the beam are of minimum value. This optimum value of the space-charge density is not equal to zero!

The equations of motion of both inner and outer boundary electrons have been solved by [69, 70]. Beside space-charge, the variation of the electric potential due to the replacement of one of the cylindrical electrodes by a slow-wave structure of more complicated geometry in microwave tubes has been taken into consideration. The optimum space-charge density distribution and potential distribution corresponding to minimum beam rippling have been determined, too. As a result of the consideration of all these factors, the maximum possible value of the beam current has been calculated. The maximum current is determined by a formula similar to 69.19 but much more complicated.

A backward-wave tube based on the centrifugal electrostatic focusing has been given the name of *spiratron* [12–14, 33].

The centrifugal electrostatic focusing has the following advantages:

(1) The construction of the focusing system is very simple; it does not require an accurate centering.

(2) The beam current can be regulated by the variation of the potential difference on the electrodes of the cylindrical condenser; the axial electron velocity may remain constant meanwhile.

(3) It provides a possibility for stable focusing of high-current electron beams.

(4) There is no ion bombing of the cathode. The ions produced in the system are pumped towards the outer cylinder.

The disadvantage of the centrifugal electrostatic focusing is the very complicated method of entrance of the electron beam into the focusing system. Besides, the cylindrical condenser may cause some additional difficulties in microwave tubes.

The greatest problem is that the electrons must gain a momentum of rotation of a given value before entering the field of the cylindrical condenser.

A very ingenious solution of this problem has been proposed by Chernov [32] (figure V.34). The electron gun consists of an annular cathode *1* and two focusing electrodes *2* surrounding the cathode from outside and inside. The ends of all the electrodes are cut helically. The end of the outer electrode *3* of the cylindrical condenser is helically cut, too, from the side of the electron gun. The inner electrode *4* of the cylindrical condenser is continued up to the gun. Thus, the electrons leaving the cathode gain their required azimuthal initial velocity component due to the special form of the electrodes. In this way the hollow electron beam is formed between the electrodes of the cylindrical condenser.

This spiratron-type electron gun may also be used for the production of rotating electron beams in periodic focusing systems.

The slow-wave structure is a helix on the place of the outer cylinder in the spiratron. The microwave features of the spiratron are very good. A linear spiratron has been reported by [142]. A study has been made by [136] of the scalloping of electron beams of finite cross section in spiratrons allowing for space-charge, thermal velocities and nonuniformities of the static potential produced by the helical apertures.

A variant of the spiratron is a backward wave oscillator named *helitron* [117, 121]. The helix is placed in lieu of the inner cylinder in this tube. The proper entrance conditions are provided by an electron gun placed at a suitably chosen angle to the axis of the system.

Another variant of the centrifugal electrostatic focusing is the so-called *magnetless magnetron* [115, 116]. The only difference between this variant and the spiratron is that the electrons have no axial velocity component in the magnetless magnetron. The sheet-electron beam moves along azimuthal paths in the field of a cylindrical condenser. Thus, the axial trajectory is a circle. In this microwave tube the electron beam is in interaction with the azimuthal component of the high-frequency electromagnetic field. This tube is only of theoretical interest because it is restricted to small power levels and can be tuned only by the variation of its geometrical dimensions.

There are some other focusing systems based also on the motion of the electron beam in the field of a cylindrical condenser [43, 51, 83, 88].

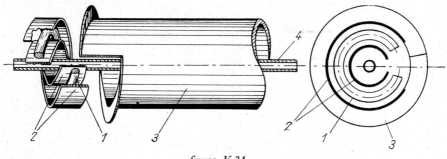

figure V.34

70. PERIODIC ELECTROSTATIC FOCUSING BY SYSTEMS
WITH CURVILINEAR AXIS

The two-dimensional focusing systems consisting of periodically placed electrodes and having curvilinear axis of the electron beam are combinations of the periodic and the centrifugal focusing systems. The axial trajectory is a plane curve in such a system. It means that the medium plane of the beam is a single-curved surface.

(a) The slalom focusing

The first system based on this principle is the so-called slalom focusing system [28, 29]. In the slalom system a sheet electron beam is made to weave through an array of periodically placed rod or wire electrodes held at positive potential in a similar manner to the ski-runners in a slalom competition. The electrodes are placed midway between two negative plates as shown in figure V.35.

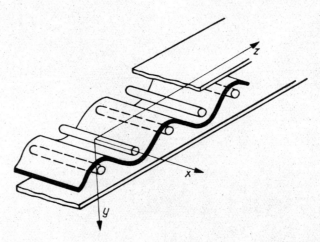

figure V.35

The potential distribution produced by an array of infinitely long (in the direction of the coordinate x) line charges placed parallel to each other at equal distances a periodically can be expressed by

$$U(y, z) = U_0 \left[1 - \frac{1}{2} \log \left(\sinh^2 \frac{\pi y}{a} + \sin^2 \frac{\pi z}{a} \right) \right] \qquad 70.1$$

The system is two-dimensional, i.e the potential distribution does not depend on coordinate x and it can be represented in the y, z plane (figure V.36) [29]. The values of the potentials corresponding to the equipo-

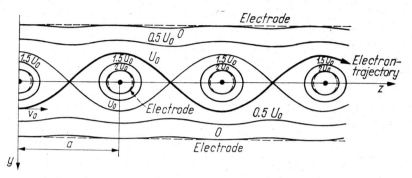

figure V.36

tential curves are given in the figure. In expression 70.1 a is the distance between the line charges and U_0 is the value of the potential at the cross-over point midway between any two line charges

$$U_0 = U\left(0, (2n+1)\frac{a}{2}\right) \quad \text{where } n = 0, 1, 2, \ldots$$

We shall demonstrate that if an electron has just the required initial velocity and position and initial slope, it will exactly follow the equipotential curve $U = U_0$. The equation of this equipotential curve can be obtained from 70.1

$$\sinh^2 \frac{\pi y}{a} + \sin^2 \frac{\pi z}{a} = 1 \tag{70.2}$$

or

$$\sinh \frac{\pi y}{a} = \pm \cos \frac{\pi z}{a} \tag{70.3}$$

This is the equation of two equipotential lines weaving through the array of line charges (figure V.36).

The electrostatic field of the system acts on an electron moving along one of these equipotentials by the force with absolute value of

$$|\mathbf{F}| = e\,|\mathbf{E}| = e\left[\left(\frac{\partial U}{\partial y}\right)^2 + \left(\frac{\partial U}{\partial z}\right)^2\right]^{1/2} \tag{70.4}$$

(We shall consider the electron moving along the equipotential line corresponding to the positive sign in equation 70.3.) Using 70.1 and 70.2 one can rewrite expression 70.4 in the following way

$$|\mathbf{F}| = \frac{\sqrt{2}\pi e U_0}{a}\left|\cos \frac{\pi z}{a}\right| \tag{70.5}$$

The absolute value of the centrifugal force acting on the electron is equal to

$$\left| \frac{mv^2}{r} \right| = mv^2 \left| \frac{\dfrac{d^2y}{dz^2}}{\left[1 + \left(\dfrac{dy}{dz} \right)^2 \right]^{3/2}} \right| \qquad 70.6$$

where r is the radius of curvature of the trajectory. It follows from 70.3 that we have along the considered equipotential line

$$\frac{dy}{dz} = - \frac{\sin \dfrac{\pi z}{a}}{\cosh \dfrac{\pi y}{a}} \qquad 70.7$$

and

$$\frac{d^2y}{dz^2} = - \frac{\pi}{a} \frac{\cos \dfrac{\pi z}{a} \cosh \dfrac{\pi y}{a} + \sinh \dfrac{\pi y}{a} \dfrac{\sin \dfrac{\pi z}{a}}{\cosh \dfrac{\pi y}{a}} \sin \dfrac{\pi z}{a}}{\cosh^2 \dfrac{\pi y}{a}} \qquad 70.8$$

We can write on the basis of 70.6, 70.7 and 70.8 that

$$\left| \frac{mv^2}{r} \right| = \frac{\pi mv^2}{a} \frac{\cos \dfrac{\pi z}{a} \cosh^2 \dfrac{\pi y}{a} + \sin^2 \dfrac{\pi z}{a} \sinh \dfrac{\pi y}{a}}{\left(\cosh^2 \dfrac{\pi y}{a} + \sin^2 \dfrac{\pi z}{a} \right)^{3/2}} \qquad 70.9$$

Using 70.2 and 70.3 we obtain the final expression from 70.9

$$\left| \frac{mv^2}{r} \right| = \frac{\pi mv^2}{\sqrt{2}a} \left| \cos \frac{\pi z}{a} \right| \qquad 70.10$$

Comparing 70.5 with 70.10 one can see that if the condition

$$v = v_0 = (2\eta U_0)^{1/2} \qquad 70.11$$

is fulfilled, we have

$$|F| = \left| \frac{mv^2}{r} \right| \qquad 70.12$$

It can be seen from figure V.36 that the directions of the electrostatic force and the centrifugal force acting on the electrons along the equipotential lines $U = U_0$ are opposite in every point of the equipotential lines. This, together with equality 70.12, means that these equipotential lines really may be electron trajectories. For this it is necessary that the output of the electron gun should be placed on the equipotential line, its potential should be equal to U_0 and the direction of the motion of the electrons leaving the gun should coincide with the direction of the equipotential line. As in the crossover points midway between any two line charges the field strength is equal to zero, at these 'saddle' points the electron trajectories must cross the z axis at an angle of 45° (see p. 356 of [65]). The most convenient solution is to put the electron gun so that its output be situated just in a crossover point and the axis of the electron beam leaving the gun have an angle of 45° with the z axis.

As we can see in figure V.36, in the vicinity of the line charges the equipotential curves are nearly circular. Therefore, replacing the line charges with electrodes of the form of circular cylinders held at positive potential will cause little change in the potential distribution. Similarly, the equipotential lines flatten out as they get farther away from the line charges. Thus, potential distribution 70.1 can be generated by cylindrical electrodes held at positive potential and a pair of flat plates placed at ground potential (the electrodes are shown in figure V.36 by dashed lines).

A more detailed analysis has shown that the slalom system is remarkably suitable for the maintenance of high-intensity sheet-electron beams. The axial trajectory of the beam will strictly follow the equipotential line, as it has been shown above, because there is no space-charge force in the medium plane of the beam. Naturally, in other parts of the beam space-charge force will be superposed on the focusing and centrifugal forces. According to the theoretical analysis, the maintenance of very high-perveance electron beams is possible as space-charge plays only an additional role in this system, too. In a beam testing experiment a transmission of 97% has been measured with a perveance of 2×10^{-6} A/V$^{3/2}$ and system length equal to $27a$. Even with a perveance of 12.7×10^{-6} A/V$^{3/2}$ the transmission was still 48%.

The disadvantage of the slalom system is, as the analysis carried out by numerical solution of the equations of motion has shown, that the focusing is stable only if the magnitude and direction of the initial velocity of the electrons do not deviate considerably from the values determined by the equipotentials. Besides, the electron beam must be launched from a crossover point. It is interesting to remark that it has been found experimentally that the optimum angle for launching the electron beam is not 45° but 35° with respect to the z axis.

The slalom system has been used in a microwave oscillator tube. The system of cylindrical electrodes has also constituted a slow-wave structure. The electrons interlace the slow-wave circuit and so their interaction with the high-frequency electromagnetic field is very efficient.

(b) The 'double-ladder' focusing

The 'double-ladder' focusing system is similar to the slalom system [57]. The difference is that instead of the array of the cylindrical electrodes two arrays of long parallel tape electrodes are placed between the two parallel

flat plates in such a way that each electrode faces a gap between the electrodes
of the opposite array (figure V.37). The tape electrodes are held at
an equal positive potential U_1, while the potential of the flat plates is U_2.
The potential U_1 is greater than the potential U_2. The axis of the sheet-
electron beam is of a similar form to that of the slalom orbit but it does not
weave through the electrodes; the beam moves entirely between the tape
electrodes.

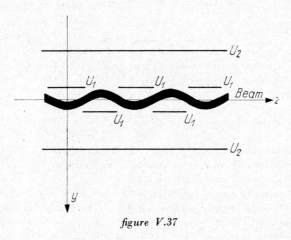

figure V.37

The fulfilment of the initial conditions is a strict requirement in this case,
too. The maximum beam transmission obtained with this system was
70% at a perveance of 0.5×10^{-6} A/V$^{3/2}$ and beam potential of 750 volts.
In this case the value of the focusing potential U_2 was equal to 300 volts
and the entrance angle of the beam was 21°.

This focusing principle has been used in the *ophitron* tube [40, 82].

(c) The focusing system proposed by P. A. Sturrock

An improved variation of the slalom focusing system is the system proposed
by P. A. Sturrock [99]. Its electrodes do not differ from those of the slalom
system but the potential distribution, and hence the motion of the electron
beam, are quite different. One of the flat plates is held at ground potential,
the potential of the other flat plate is equal to U_0. The cylindrical electrodes
are held at a potential of $3U_0$. Thus, the focusing system and the axis of the
focused sheet electron beam are not symmetric with respect to the x, z
plane. This absence of symmetry in the potential distribution is the difference between this system and the slalom focusing. The electron beam weaves
through the array of cylindrical electrodes in such a way that it is closer
to the U_0-potential plate in the course of the whole motion (figure V.38).
The beam thickness varies so that the beam is thinnest in the vicinity of
the cylindrical electrodes. The electrons of the beam spend most time

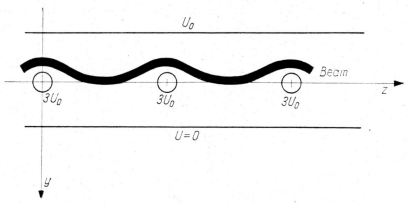

figure V.38

between the central electrodes. Therefore, this system is quite suitable for the use in microwave tubes. In this case the cylindrical electrodes constitute also a slow-wave structure.

Another advantage of this system is that it is theoretically free from instabilities. The bands of instability appearing at the practical realisation of the system have proved to be narrow enough. Furthermore, as opposed to other deflection-focusing systems, the deformation of the planar system for focusing of hollow beams does not lead to the appearance of further bands of instability.

Deflection-focusing systems with more complicated electrode configurations have been proposed by [66, 84, 126, 149]. Electron beams focused by three-dimensional periodic fields have been treated by [41].

(F) PERIODIC FOCUSING BY QUADRUPOLE FIELDS

It is well known that the focusing effect of transversal fields, where the direction of the lines of force is nearly perpendicular to the direction of motion of the electron beam, is stronger than that of the longitudinal fields. The most widespread transversal electron optical system is the *quadrupole lens*, the detailed treatment of which can be found, for example, in [65]. The focusing effect of a series of periodically placed electrostatic quadrupole lenses has been investigated by [20], without taking space-charge into consideration.

The application of quadrupole fields for the maintenance of high-intensity electron beams is advantageous, too. We shall consider a series of quadrupole lenses rotated 90 degrees each, with respect to the neighbouring one, around the z axis (figure V.39 [27]). So, we have two periodic series of alternating diverging and converging lenses in perpendicular planes x, z and y, z, respectively. The lens diverging in the x, z plane is converging in the y, z plane and vice versa. (See § 58.) These series have equal period p. The resulting converging effect in both planes may be used for compensation of the diverging effect due to space-charge of a long high-intensity electron beam moving in the direction of the coordinate z by suitable choice of the lens parameters. The cross section of a cylindrical electron beam becomes elliptical in such a focusing system. Therefore, the analysis of the focusing is a complicated problem which can be solved only by numerical or approximate analytical methods. We shall give two analytical methods in the following.

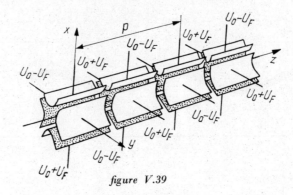

figure V.39

71. FOCUSING BY A SEQUENCE OF THIN QUADRUPOLE LENSES

The thin-lens approximation used in §§ 59 and 66 for axially symmetric and plane-symmetric lenses, respectively, can be applied for quadrupole lenses, too. The lenses may be *electrostatic or magnetic thin quadrupole lenses or their combinations* [108].

Let us consider the periodic sequence of thin quadrupole lenses as shown in figure V.40, in which the sections of the lenses and the electron beam by the planes x, z and y, z respectively, are shown. Here f_1 and f_2 are the absolute values of the focal lengths of any two neighbouring lenses. The positive sign indicates a converging lens, the negative sign corresponds to a diverging lens. l_1 and l_2 are the drift spacings separating two neighbouring lens pairs. We shall consider the case when the effective length L of the quadrupole lenses is small in comparison with the drift spacings separating the lenses and with the focal lengths of the lenses. Then we may assume that the

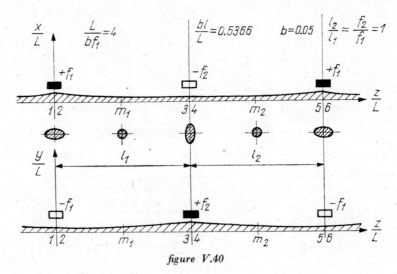

figure V.40

action of the thin lenses is concentrated at their medium planes and their only effect is that the slopes of the electron trajectories are changed suddenly. On the other hand, the only forces acting on the electrons in the drift regions are those of space-charge. Therefore, in the drift regions we have the spreading of a drifting elliptical-cross-section electron beam as it has been treated in § 56.

For the examination of the space-charge spreading of an elliptical-cross-section electron beam it is sufficient to consider two edge-electron trajectories moving in the medium planes x, z and y, z, respectively. These trajectories are determined by expressions 56.13 and 56.14. If we introduce numeral indexes referring to respective points at the ends of drift regions, immediately before and after the lenses, as shown in figure V.40, we can obtain the following expressions from 56.13 and 56.14 for the first two sections

$$Z(l_1) = b\frac{l_1}{L} = 2u_2 \exp\left(-u_2'^2\right) \left[F(u_3') - F(u_2')\right] \qquad 71.1$$

$$Z(l_2) = b\frac{l_2}{L} = 2u_4 \exp\left(-u_4'^2\right) \left[F(u_5') - F(u_4')\right] \qquad 71.2$$

(L is the effective length of the quadrupole lenses.)

$$u_3' = \pm\left(\log\frac{u_3}{u_2} + u_2'^2\right)^{1/2} \qquad 71.3$$

$$u_5' = \pm\left(\log\frac{u_5}{u_4} + u_4'^2\right)^{1/2} \qquad 71.4$$

$$v_3 = v_2 + v_2' \, Z(l_1) \qquad 71.5$$

$$v_3' = v_2' \qquad 71.6$$

$$v_5 = v_4 + v_4' \, Z(l_2) \qquad 71.7$$

and

$$v_5' = v_4' \qquad 71.8$$

where

$$F(x) = \int_0^x \exp\left(w^2\right)dw \qquad 71.9$$

is the function determined by 53.12 and tabulated in table IV.2 (denoted by f in table IV.2). The primes represent differentiation with respect to Z (see 56.6). The value of the space-charge parameter b is, according to 56.3, equal to

$$b = \left(\frac{I}{2\sqrt{2}\,\pi\varepsilon_0\sqrt{\eta}\,U_0^{3/2}}\right)^{1/2} \qquad 71.10$$

The influence of the lenses on the slope of electron trajectories can be expressed in the following way

$$u_1 = u_2 \qquad\qquad\qquad 71.11$$

$$u_3 = u_4 \qquad\qquad\qquad 71.12$$

$$v_1 = v_2 \qquad\qquad\qquad 71.13$$

$$v_3 = v_4 \qquad\qquad\qquad 71.14$$

$$u_2' = u_1' - \frac{L}{b f_1} v_1 \qquad\qquad\qquad 71.15$$

$$u_4' = u_3' + \frac{L}{b f_2} v_3 \qquad\qquad\qquad 71.16$$

$$v_2' = v_1' - \frac{L}{b f_1} u_1 \qquad\qquad\qquad 71.17$$

and

$$v_4' = v_3' + \frac{L}{b f_2} u_3 \qquad\qquad\qquad 71.18$$

The requirement of periodic beam configuration leads to four additional expressions

$$u_1 = u_5 \qquad\qquad\qquad 71.19$$

$$v_1 = v_5 \qquad\qquad\qquad 71.20$$

$$u_1' = u_5' \qquad\qquad\qquad 71.21$$

and

$$v_1' = v_5' \qquad\qquad\qquad 71.22$$

Thus, we have obtained 20 equations: 71.1–71.8 and 71.11–71.22. Eliminating all the terms regarding intermediate points, we obtain from these equations the following relations for the parameters characterising the electron beam and the focusing system, i.e. beam perveance, entrance conditions, focal lengths and drift spacings [108]

$$\frac{b l_1}{L} = 2 u_1 \exp\left[-\left(u_1' - \frac{L}{b f_1} v_1\right)^2\right]\left[F\left(\frac{L}{b f_1} v_1 - u_1'\right) + F(u_3')\right] \quad 71.23$$

$$\frac{b l_2}{L} = 2 u_1 \exp\left(-u_1'^2\right)\left[F(u_1') - F(u_4')\right] \qquad\qquad 71.24$$

$$\frac{b l_1}{L} = \frac{\dfrac{b f_2}{L}(u_4' - u_3') - v_1}{v_1' - \dfrac{L}{b f_1} u_1} \qquad\qquad\qquad 71.25$$

and

$$v_1' = \frac{L}{bf_1} \frac{u_1}{1 + \dfrac{l_2}{l_1}} > 0 \qquad\qquad 71.26$$

where

$$u_3' = \pm \left[\log \frac{f_2}{f_1} + \left(\frac{L}{bf_1} v_1 - u_1' \right)^2 \right]^{1/2} \qquad\qquad 71.27$$

and

$$u_4' = \pm \left(\log \frac{f_2}{f_1} + u_1'^2 \right)^{1/2} \qquad\qquad 71.28$$

In expressions 71.23–71.26 there are only quantities u and v with index '1' if 71.27 and 71.28 are taken into account. According to 56.9–56.12, these quantities uniquely determine the initial values of

$$x_1, y_1, \left. \frac{dx}{dz} \right|_1 \quad \text{and} \quad \left. \frac{dy}{dz} \right|_1$$

corresponding to the entrance plane $z = 0$, immediately before the first lens. If the system of equations 71.23–71.26 is satisfied by the proper choosing of these initial values, an electron beam of periodic configuration can be formed.

From the practical point of view the entirely *symmetric case* ($f_1 = f_2 = f$ and $l_1 = l_2 = l$) is of special interest. In this case equations 71.23–71.26 become much simpler

$$\frac{bl}{L} = 4u_1 \exp\left(-u_1'^2\right) F(u_1') \qquad\qquad 71.29$$

$$\frac{l}{f} = 4 \frac{v_1}{u_1} \qquad\qquad 71.30$$

$$u_1' = \frac{L}{2bf} v_1 \qquad\qquad 71.31$$

and

$$v_1' = \frac{L}{2bf} u_1 \qquad\qquad 71.32$$

In this case the electron beam has a circular cross section at its middle planes, denoted by index m, between the lenses. (See figure V.40.) The beam radius and the slopes of the edge trajectories in these planes are given by

$$r_m = L u_1 \exp(-u_1'^2) \qquad\qquad 71.33$$

and

$$\left. \frac{dx}{dz} \right|_m = - \left. \frac{dy}{dz} \right|_m = \pm b v_1' \qquad\qquad 71.34$$

Using this fact, the entrance conditions may be satisfied even for the case if the electron beam produced by the gun is axially symmetric. For this it is only necessary to place an additional thin quadrupole lens at a distance $l/2$ before the first lens.

The following requirements must be satisfied by the design of a focusing system by means of the method presented here:

(i) It is required by the thin-lens approximation that

$$\frac{f_1}{L} \gg 1, \quad \frac{f_2}{L} \gg 1, \quad \frac{l_1}{L} \gg 1 \quad \text{and} \quad \frac{l_2}{L} \gg 1$$

(ii) It is required by the paraxial approximation that at any point along the whole beam the values of

$$x, y, \quad \frac{dx}{dz} \quad \text{and} \quad \frac{dy}{dz}$$

must be small; besides, the values of x and y must be positive.

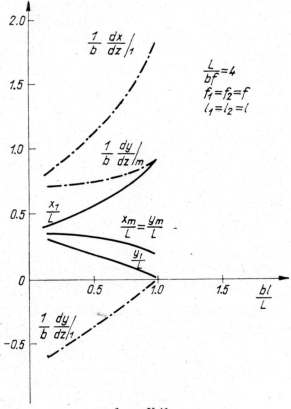

figure V.41

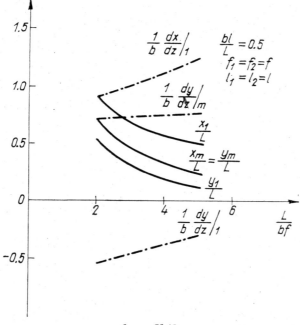

figure V.42

The beam perveance is limited by these requirements as well: the method is practically applicable at values of the perveance up to $(1 \div 2) \times 10^{-6}$ $A/V^{3/2}$.

Design curves have been plotted in figures V.41 and V.42 for the symmetrical case ($l_1 = l_2 = l$ and $f_1 = f_2 = f$). The required initial values for the production of periodic beam configuration and the values corresponding to the middle planes are shown in the figures versus parameters $L/b\,f$ and $b\,l/L$.

The stability of this system has been analysed by [145].

72. FOCUSING OF ELECTRON BEAMS BY PERIODIC ELECTROSTATIC QUADRUPOLE FIELDS

In case of focusing systems with continuous potential distribution the thin lens approximation is not suitable. The analysis of the electron trajectories of an elliptical-cross-section electron beam moving in a quadrupole field is a very complicated problem. However, the aim of this analysis is to determine such relations between the parameters of the electron beam and the focusing system, the fulfilment of which would lead to minor variations of the shape and sizes of the electron beam — optimum focusing. Thus we may assume as a rough approximation that the electron beam is a circular cylinder with constant radius r_0 [27]. In this case the value of the force F_e acting on the boundary electrons due to space-charge is constant in the paraxial approximation and, according to 52.1, is equal to

$$F_e = \frac{e\,I}{2\pi\varepsilon_0\,r_0\,(2\eta\,U_0)^{1/2}} \qquad 72.1$$

The potential distribution of a quadrupole lens with hyperbolic electrodes (figure V.43) is given by [65] (formula 8.57) as follows

$$\varphi(x, y, z) = U_0 + U_F \frac{f(z)}{a^2}(x^2 - y^2) \qquad 72.2$$

where a is the smallest distance of the electrodes from the z axis, U_0 is the uniform potential along the axis, U_F is the additional potential on the electrodes and $f(z)$ is the function regarding the end effects of the lenses.

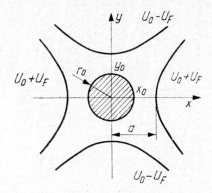

figure V.43

Expression 72.2 may be used also for the description of the potential distribution of the periodic focusing system shown in figure V.39 by the proper choosing of the function $f(z)$. It is easy to see that the function

$$f(z) = \cos\frac{2\pi}{p}z \qquad 72.3$$

approximately corresponds to this system. (A power series containing the lengths of the lenses and the gaps between them as parameters would describe the potential distribution of the system exactly.) Substituting 72.3 into expression 72.2 we obtain

$$\varphi(x, y, z) = U_0 + U_F \frac{x^2 - y^2}{a^2}\cos\frac{2\pi}{p}z \qquad 72.4$$

Let us consider the electron starting from the point with coordinates $x = x_0$, $y = 0$, $z = 0$ at the boundary of the beam exactly parallel to the z axis (its initial velocity is equal to $v_0 = \dot{z}_0$). As the x, z plane is the plane of symmetry of the system, the electron will move in this plane all the time and it is sufficient to determine the function of $x = x(z)$ for the complete description of the electron trajectory. Similarly, the trajectory of an electron starting from the point with coordinates $x = 0$, $y = y_0$, $z = 0$ parallel to the z axis is fully determined by the function of $y = y(z)$. Thus, our task is to determine these two functions. We should like to emphasise once more that $x(z)$ and $y(z)$ are not projections of the same trajectory but they describe two different electron trajectories characterising the whole beam. The initial radius of the beam is assumed to be $r_0 = x_0 = y_0$ (see figure V.43).

Let us write now the equations of motion of the two boundary electrons separately

$$\frac{d^2x}{dt^2} = \eta \frac{\partial \varphi}{\partial x} + \frac{F_e}{m}$$

and

$$\frac{d^2y}{dt^2} = \eta \frac{\partial \varphi}{\partial y} + \frac{F_e}{m}$$

where in the first equation $r_0 = x_0$ should be substituted in expression 72.1 determining the value of F_e, in the second equation $r_0 = y_0$. The derivatives of the potential can be calculated from 72.4. Then, in accordance with 23.7 and 23.8, the equations can be written as follows

$$\frac{d^2x}{dt^2} = \left(\frac{2\eta U_F}{a^2} \cos \frac{2\pi}{p} z \right) x + \frac{I\eta}{2\pi \varepsilon_0 x_0 \, (2\eta U_0)^{1/2}} \qquad 72.5$$

and

$$\frac{d^2y}{dt^2} = -\left(\frac{2\eta U_F}{a^2} \cos \frac{2\pi}{p} z \right) y + \frac{I\eta}{2\pi \varepsilon_0 y_0 \, (2\eta U_0)^{1/2}} \qquad 72.6$$

As in the paraxial approximation the velocity of the electrons is constant and equal to

$$v_0 = (2\eta U_0)^{1/2} = \frac{dz}{dt} \qquad 72.7$$

it is easy to replace the differentiation with respect to time by differentiation with respect to coordinate z. Besides, we shall introduce the dimensionless new variables

$$\xi = \frac{x}{x_0}, \quad \eta = \frac{y}{y_0} \quad \text{and} \quad \zeta = \frac{2\pi}{p} z \qquad 72.8$$

and the space-charge parameter A defined by 60.10. The equations will then have the following form

$$\frac{d^2\xi}{d\zeta^2} = \left[\left(\frac{p}{2\pi a}\right)^2 \frac{U_F}{U_0} \cos \zeta\right] \xi + A \qquad 72.9$$

and

$$\frac{d^2\eta}{d\zeta^2} = -\left[\left(\frac{p}{2\pi a}\right)^2 \frac{U_F}{U_0} \cos \zeta\right] \eta + A \qquad 72.10$$

Let us introduce the notation

$$\Omega_{kv} = \left(\frac{p}{2\pi a}\right)^2 \frac{U_F}{U_0} \qquad 72.11$$

and represent the differentiation with respect to ζ by primes. The equations will be written then by the following way

$$\xi'' - (\Omega_{kv} \cos \zeta)\xi - A = 0 \qquad 72.12$$

and

$$\eta'' + (\Omega_{kv} \cos \zeta)\,\eta - A = 0 \qquad 72.13$$

Let us try to find the solution of these equations in the form of

$$\xi(\zeta) = 1 + \xi_1(\zeta) + \xi_2(\zeta) \qquad 72.14$$

and

$$\eta(\zeta) = 1 + \eta_1(\zeta) + \eta_2(\zeta) \qquad 72.15$$

where ξ_1 and η_1 are quantities of first order of smallness, ξ_2 and η_2 are quantities of second order of smallness. As in the axially symmetric case, Ω_{kv} is a quantity of first order of smallness, A is a quantity of second order of smallness. We have the following initial conditions

$$\xi_1(0) = \xi_2(0) = \eta_1(0) = \eta_2(0) = \xi_1'(0) = \xi_2'(0) = \eta_1'(0) = \eta_2'(0) = 0 \quad 72.16$$

Let us substitute 72.14 into equation 72.12 and 72.15 into equation 72.13. In the equations obtained in this way we shall separate the terms of first order of smallness and the terms of second order of smallness from each other and neglect the terms of higher order of smallness. We obtain the following result

$$\left[\xi_1'' - \Omega_{kv} \cos \zeta\right] + \left[\xi_2'' - \Omega_{kv} \xi_1 \cos \zeta - A\right] = 0 \qquad 72.17$$

and

$$\left[\eta_1'' + \Omega_{kv} \cos \zeta\right] + \left[\eta_2'' + \Omega_{kv} \eta_1 \cos \zeta - A\right] = 0 \qquad 72.18$$

We shall first consider only the terms of first order of smallness. Integrating the corresponding equations twice and taking the initial conditions into account we obtain

$$\xi_1(\zeta) = \Omega_{kv}(1 - \cos \zeta) \qquad 72.19$$

and

$$\eta_1(\zeta) = -\Omega_{kv}(1 - \cos \zeta) \qquad 72.20$$

Substituting these results back into equations 72.17 and 72.18 we obtain

$$\xi_2'' - \Omega_{kv}^2 \cos \zeta(1 - \cos \zeta) - A = 0 \qquad 72.21$$

and

$$\eta_2'' - \Omega_{kv}^2 \cos \zeta(1 - \cos \zeta) - A = 0 \qquad 72.22$$

These two equations are identical. Integrating them twice and taking the initial conditions into account we obtain

$$\xi_2(\zeta) = \eta_2(\zeta) = \frac{7}{8} \Omega_{kv}^2 - \Omega_{kv}^2 \cos \zeta + \frac{\Omega_{kv}^2}{8} \cos 2\zeta +$$

$$+ \left(A - \frac{\Omega_{kv}^2}{2}\right) \frac{\zeta^2}{2} \qquad 72.23$$

As in case of optimum focusing the expression describing the trajectory must not contain terms with positive powers of ζ: the following condition must be satisfied

$$(\Omega_{kv})_{\text{opt}} = + (2A)^{1/2} \qquad 72.24$$

This expression, together with 72.11, determines the value of the focusing potential U_F required for the optimum focusing of an electron beam with space-charge parameter A. The positive sign has been chosen before the square root because, according to 72.11, $\Omega_{kv} > 0$.

The electron trajectories of an optimally focused electron beam are determined on the basis of 72.14, 72.15, 72.19, 72.20, 72.23 and 72.24 by the following two expressions

$$\xi(\zeta) = \frac{x}{x_0} = 1 + \Omega_{kv}(1 - \cos \zeta) + \Omega_{kv}^2 \left(\frac{7}{8} - \cos \zeta + \frac{1}{8} \cos 2\zeta\right) \qquad 72.25$$

and

$$\eta(\zeta) = \frac{y}{y_0} = 1 - \Omega_{kv}(1 - \cos \zeta) + \Omega_{kv}^2 \left(\frac{7}{8} - \cos \zeta + \frac{1}{8} \cos 2\zeta\right) \qquad 72.26$$

Naturally, expressions 72.25 and 72.26 are valid only if 72.24 is satisfied. It is seen from the form of these expressions that $\xi \geq 1$ and $\eta \leq 1$, i.e. the cross section of the beam is elliptical. The functions $\xi(\zeta)$ and $\eta(\zeta)$ calculated from 72.25 and 72.26 are plotted in figure V.44 for the case of $A = 5 \times 10^{-3}$ and the corresponding value of $(\Omega_{kv})_{\text{opt}} = 0.1$.

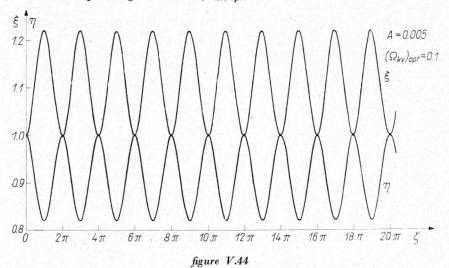

figure V.44

Thus, if the condition 72.24 is satisfied, it is possible to maintain the form and sizes of the electron beam nearly constant. The value of the required focusing potential follows from 72.11 and 72.24

$$\frac{U_F}{U_0} = \left(\frac{2\pi a}{p}\right)^2 (2A)^{1/2} \qquad\qquad 72.27$$

It is seen from expressions 60.24, 60.25 and 60.61 that in the axially symmetric case the corresponding value is greater. It is obviously a consequence of the stronger focusing effect of the transversal fields. The amplitude δ of the beam rippling calculated in the first-order approximation, however, is greater in the case of quadrupole fields than in the axially symmetric case. We have from 60.61, 60.65, 72.24 and 72.25 that

$$\frac{\delta_{kv}}{\delta} = \frac{(\Omega_{kv})_{\text{opt}}}{\dfrac{\Omega_{\text{opt}}}{4}} = \frac{(2A)^{1/2}}{\left(\dfrac{32}{3\times16}A\right)^{1/2}} = \sqrt{3} \qquad\qquad 72.28$$

The numerical solution of equations 72.12 and 72.13 has shown that condition 72.24 determines the real optimum value of the focusing parameter with an error of a few percent [27].

The assumption that the electron beam enters the system strictly parallel to the z axis is most important. If it is not so, the beam configuration strongly varies during the motion, and the space-charge force cannot be assumed constant. Therefore, for this case this treatment is not valid. The quadrupole-field focusing is very sensitive to variations of the entrance conditions (see § 71).

If condition 72.24 is not satisfied and a value of the parameter Ω_{kv} much greater than that determined by 72.24 is chosen, the effect of space-charge may be neglected and we have the case treated in § 58 with the only difference that now thin lenses are not in consideration. In the case of very large values of the parameter Ω_{kv} the electron beam cannot be assumed laminar and the trajectories can cross the axis. The calculations have shown that a stable focusing may be achieved only if

$$\Omega_{kv} < 0.44 \qquad\qquad 72.29$$

Periodic sequences of quadrupole lenses are used mainly in particle accelerators [22, 112, 123, 124, 132] but they are applicable also in microwave tubes [8].

REFERENCES FOR CHAPTER V

1. ADLER, R.–KROMHOUT, O. M.–CLAVIER, P. A.: *Proc. Instn Radio Engrs.*, **43** (1955), 3 339.
2. ADLER, R.–KROMHOUT, O. M.–CLAVIER, P. A.: *Proc. Instn Radio Engrs.*, **44** (1956), 1, 82.
3. (ALYAMOVSKIY, I. V.) Алямовский, И. В.: Электронные пучки и электронные пушки *(Electron Beams and Electron Guns)*. Советское Радио; Москва, 1966.
4. AYERS, W. R.–EVANS, K. R.: IRE Electron Devices Meeting, Washington, 1959.
5. (BAKHRAKH, L. E.) Бахрах, Л. Е.: *РИЭ СССР*, 4 (1959), 12, 2097.
6. (BAKHRAKH, L. E.–MEDOKS, V. G.) Бахрах, Л. Е.–Медокс, В. Г.: *РИЭ СССР*, **10** (1965), 8, 1461.
7. BARNES, C. W.: *Tech. Rept.* **33**, Electronics Research Lab., Stanford Univ., 1954.
8. BASS, J. C.–WOLSON, M. G. F.: *J. Electron. Control*, **11** (1961), 2, 125.
9. BELOHOUBEK, E. F.: *RCA Rev.*, **21** (1960), 3, 377.
10. BELOHOUBEK, E. F.–SIEKANOWICZ, W.–VACCARO, F. E.: IRE Electron Devices Meeting, Washington, 1959.
11. BELOHOUBEK, E. F.–SIEKANOWICZ, W.–VACCARO, F. E.: *IEEE Trans.*, **ED–11** (1964), 3, 102.
12. (BERNASHEVSKIY, G. A.–NOVSKOVA, T. A.) Бернашевский, Г. А.–Новскова, Т. А.: *РИЭ СССР*, **3** (1958), 9, 1218.
13. (BERNASHEVSKIY, G. A.–NOVSKOVA, T. A.) Бернашевский, Г. А.–Новскова, Т. А.: *РИЭ СССР*, **4** (1959), 9, 1499.
14. (BERNASHEVSKIY, G. A.–VORONOV, P. S.–NOVSKOVA, T. A.) Бернашевский, Г. А.–Воронов, П. С.–Новскова, Т. А.: *Сб. Труд. Ин-та Радиотех. Электрон. АН СССР*, 1 (1956), 265.
15. BIRDSALL, C. K.–HAAS, L.–MÜLLER, R.: *Nachtech. Fachber.*, **22** (1961), 232.
16. BLATTNER, D. J.–VACCARO, F. E.: *IRE Nat. Convention Rec.*, **6** (1958), 3, 101.
17. BLATTNER, D. J.–VACCARO, F. E.: *Electr. Inds.*, **18** (1959), 1, 58.
18. BLATTNER, D. J.–VACCARO, F. E.: *Electronics*, **32** (1959), 1, 46.
19. BLATTNER, D. J. et al.: *RCA Rev.*, **20** (1959), 3, 426.
20. BLEWETT, J. P.: *Phys. Rev.*, **88** (1952), 5, 1197.
21. BORGHI, R. P.–DUNN, D. A.: *J. appl. Phys.*, **34** (1963), 3, 692.
22. BURNOT, G.–LAFOUCRIERE, J.: *Nucl. Instrum. Meth.*, **32** (1965), 2, 287.
23. CHANG, K.: *Proc. Instn Radio Engrs.*, **43** (1955), 1, 62.
24. CHANG, K.: *Proc. Instn Radio Engrs.*, **45** (1957), 1, 66.
25. CHANG, K.: *Proc. Instn Radio Engrs.*, **45** (1957), 11, 1522

26. CHANG, K.: *RCA Rev.*, **19** (1958). 1, 86.
27. CLOGSTON, A. M.–HEFFNER, H.: *J. appl. Phys.*, **25** (1954), 4, 436.
28. COOK, J. S.–KOMPFNER, R.–YOCOM, W.: *Proc. Instn Radio Engrs.*, **45** (1957), 11, 1517.
29. COOK, J. S.–LOUISELL, W.–YOCOM, W.: *J. appl. Phys.*, **29** (1958), 3, 583.
30. COURANT, E. D.–LIVINGSTON, M. S.–SNYDER, H. S.: *Phys. Rev.*, **88** (1952), 5, 1190.
31. COURANT, E. D.–SNYDER, H. S.: *Annl. Phys.*, **3** (1958), 1.
32. (CHERNOV, Z. S.) Чернов, З. С.: *РИЭ СССР*, **1** (1956), 11, 1428.
33. (CHERNOV, Z. S.) Чернов, З. С.: *Сб. Труд. Ин-та Радиотех. Электрон. АН СССР*, **1** (1956), 7.
34. (CHERNOV, Z. S.) Чернов, З. С.: *РИЭ СССР*, **3** (1958), 10, 1227.
35. CUCCIA, C. L.: *Electr. Inds.*, **20** (1961), 11, 96.
36. CUCCIA, C. L.–JOHNSON, W.: IRE Proc. Nat. Electronics Conf., **15** (1959), 404.
37. (CYRLIN, L. E.) Цырлин, Л. Е.: *Ж. Тех. Физ. СССР*, **36** (1966), 5, 843.
38. (DANOVICH, I. A.) Данович, И. А.: *РИЭ СССР*, **10** (1965), 3, 435
39. (DANOVICH, I. A.) Данович, И. А.: *Изв. Высш. Учеб. Завед. Радиофиз. СССР*, **9** (1966), 2, 351.
40. DYOTT, R. B. et al.: *Nachtech. Fachber.* **22** (1961), 114.
41. (GOLDENBERG, L. L.–PETELIN, M. N.) Гольденберг, Л. Л.–Петелин, М. Н.: *РИЭ СССР*, **9** (1964), 9, 1675.
42. (GRINBERG, G. A.) Гринберг, Г. А.: Избранные вопросы математической теории электрических и магнитных явлений *(Selected Problems of the Mathematical Theory of Electric and Magnetic Phenomena)*. Изд. Академии наук СССР; Москва, 1948.
43. GUENARD, P.–DOEHLER, O.: *Proc. Instn Radio Engrs.*, **44** (1956), 2, 261.
44. HAHN, W. C.–METCALF, G. F.: *Proc. Instn Radio Engrs.*, **27** (1939), 106.
45. HARPER, R.–HERGENROTHER, R. C.–UNGER, R. M.: *Microwave J.*, **5** (1962), 9, 181.
46. HECHTEL, J. R.: *Telefunken-Röhre*, **31** (1953), 233.
47. HECHTEL, J. R.: *Microwave J.*, **3** (1960), 11, 41; 3, 12, 81.
48. HECHTEL, J. R.: *Nachtech. Fachber.*, **22** (1961), 463.
49. HECHTEL, J. R.–MIZUHARA, A.: Microwaves, Proc. 4th Intern. Conf., p. 31, Eindhoven 1962.
50. HECHTEL, J. R.–MIZUHARA, A.: Microwave Tubes, Proc. 5th Intern. Conf., p. 230, Paris, 1964.
51. HEFFNER, H.–WATKINS, D. A.: *Proc. Instn Radio Engrs.*, **43** (1955), 8, 1007.
52. HENNE, W.: *Arch. elekt. Übertr.*, **16** (1962), 2, 83.
53. HENNE, W.: *Telefunken-Röhre*, **41** (1962), 51.
54. HENNEBERG, W.: *Z. Phys.*, **94** (1935), 22.
55. HERGENROTHER, R. C.–BOWERS, W. A.: IRE Electron Devices Meeting, Washington, 1959.
56. HO KUO CHU: *Scientia sin.*, **7** (1958), 12, 1247.
57. HOGG, H. A. C.: *Proc. IEE*, **B–105** (1958), 12, 1016.
58. HUIZENGA, W.–SCHUURMAN, W.: *Plasma Phys. (Accel.-Thermonucl. Res.)*, **6** (1964), 5, 493.
59. (IGRITSKIY, A. L.) Игрицкий, А. Л.: *РИЭ СССР*, **5** (1960), 2, 255.
60. (IGRITSKIY, A. L.) Игрицкий, А. Л.: *РИЭ СССР*, **6** (1961), 4, 613.
61. (IGRITSKIY, A. L.) Игрицкий, А. Л.: *РИЭ СССР*, **6** (1961), 6, 964.
62. JOHNSON, C. C.: *Trans. IRE*, **ED–5** (1958), 4. 233.
63. JOHNSON, C. C.: *IRE. Wescon. Convention Record*, 4 (1960), 3, 103.
64. JOHNSON, C. C.: *Trans. IRE*, **ED–7** (1960), 4, 274.
65. (KELMAN, V. M.–YAVOR, S. YA.) Кельман, В. М.–Явор, С. Я.: Электронная оптика *(Electron Optics)*. Изд. Академии наук СССР; Москва–Ленинград, 1963.
66. KIRSTEIN, P. T.: *Proc. Instn Radio Engrs.*, **46** (1958), 10, 1716.
67. KIRSTEIN, P. T.: *J. appl. Phys.*, **30** (1959), 7, 967.
68. (KOTSERZHINSKIY, V. A.) Коцержинский, Б. А.: *РИЭ СССР*, **10** (1965), 8, 1549.
69. (KOROSTELEV, G. N.) Коростелев, Г. Н.: *Изв. Высш. Учеб. Завед. Радиотех. СССР*, **3** (1960), 5, 445.
70. (KOROSTELEV, G. N.) Коростелев, Г. Н.: *РИЭ СССР*, **8** (1963), 1, 116.
71. KOZIAK, R.: *Sb. pr. elektrovuového ob.*, 4 (1964), 76, Praha.
72. MACLAHLAN, N. W.: *Theory and Applications of Mathieu Functions*. New York, 1947.
73. (MESHKOV, I. N.–CHIRIKOV, B. V.) Мешков, И. Н.–Чириков, Б. В.: *Ж. Тех. Физ. СССР*, **35** (1965), 12, 2202.

74. MILLER, S. E.: *Bell Syst. tech. Journ.*, **43** (1964), 4, Pt. 2, 1741.
75. (MOLOKOVSKIY, S. I.) Молоковский, С. И.: *РИЭ СССР*, **7** (1962), 6, 1048.
76. MOLOKOVSKIY, S. I.: *J. Inst. Telecomm. Engrs.* (India), **9** (1963), 4, 328.
77. (MOLOKOVSKIY, S. I.–SUSHKOV, A. D.) Молоковский, С. И.–Сушков, А. Д.: Электронно-оптические системы приборов сверхвысоких частот *(Electron-Optical Systems for Microwave Devices)*. Энергия; Москва, 1965.
78. MORIKAWA, M. I.: *J. appl. Phys.*, **33** (1962), 1, 87.
79. MORIKAWA, M. I.: *Z. angew. math. Phys.*, **13** (1962), 2, 167.
80. MORIKAWA, M. I.: *Z. angew. math. Phys.*, **13** (1962), 3, 279.
81. NAGY, GY. A.: C. Sc. Thesis. Budapest, 1965.
82. NEWLAND, F. J.: Microwaves, Proc. 4th Intern. Conf., p. 620, Eindhoven, 1962.
83. NUNN, W. M.–ROWE, J. E.: *Proc. Instn Radio Engrs.*, **50** (1962), 1, 89.
84. NUNN, W. M.–TAN, T. Y.: *IEEE Trans.*, **ED–11** (1964), 11, 524.
85. PALLUEL, P.: *Annls. Radioélectr.*, **11** (1956), 44, 145.
86. PALLUEL, P.–GOLDBERGER, A. K.: *Proc. Instn Radio Engrs.*, **44** (1956), 333.
87. PIERCE, J. R.: *Theory and Design of Electron Beams*, Chapter XI; Van Nostrand; New York, 1954.
88. PÖSCHL, K.–VEITH, W.: *Nachtech. Fachber.*, **22** (1961), 230.
89. PROMMER, A. J.: *Electr. Inds. N.Y.*, **23** (1964), 6, 152.
90. ROCKWELL, R. G.: *IRE Wescon Convention Record*, **4** (1960), 3, 109.
91. SAUSENG, O.: Investigations of electrostatic focusing of electron beams (Dissertation). Technische Hochschule; Wien, 1956.
92. (SHEVCHIK, V. N.–TRUBETSKOV, D. I.) Шевчик, В. Н.–Трубецков, Д. И.: *РИЭ СССР*, **5** (1960), 10, 1734.
93. SIEKANOWICZ, W. W.: *Proc. Instn Radio Engrs.*, **48** (1960), 11, 1888.
94. SIEKANOWICZ, W. W.: *RCA Rev.*, **23**, (1962), 1, 47.
95. SIEKANOWICZ, W. W.–VACCARO, F. E.: *Proc. Instn Radio Engrs.*, **47** (1959), 3, 451.
96. STURROCK, P. A.: *Static and Dynamic Electron Optics*, Cambridge University Press; Cambridge, 1955.
97. STURROCK, P. A.: *Phil. Trans.*, **A245** (1952), 155.
98. STURROCK, P. A.: *J. Electron. Control*, **7** (1959), 2, 153.
99. STURROCK, P. A.: *J. Electron. Control*, **8** (1960), 4, 267.
100. SUTHERLAND, A. D. et al.: *Nachtech. Fachber.*, **22** (1961), 510.
101. (SAMORODOV, YU. D.) Самородов, Ю. Д.: Труды Конференции по электронике СВЧ *(Proceedings of the Microwave Electronics Conference)*. Госэнергоиздат; Москва, 1959.
102. SZILÁGYI, M.: MTA Műszaki Tudományok Osztályának Közleményei *(Proc. Technical Section of the Hungarian Academy of Sciences)*, **29** (1961), 1–4, 269.
103. SZILÁGYI, M.: Microwave Tubes, Proc. 5th Intern. Conf., p. 339. Paris, 1964.
104. SZILÁGYI, M.: *Tungsram Technische Mitteilungen*, **No. 14** (1964), 614.
105. SZILÁGYI, M.: *Investigation of Two-Dimensional Electron-Optical Systems with Medium Planes and Some Problems of Periodic Focusing of High-Intensity Electron Beams.* Electrotechnical Institute of Leningrad; Leningrad, 1965.
106. SZILÁGYI, M.: *Acta phys. hung.*, **18** (1965), 2, 87.
107. SZILÁGYI, M.: *Acta phys. hung.*, **18** (1965), 4, 335.
108. SZILÁGYI, M.: *6th MOGA,** 70.
109. (SZILÁGYI, M.) Силадьи, М.: *РИЭ СССР*, **11** (1966), 5, 870.
110. (SZILÁGYI, M.–YAVOR, S. YA.) Силадьи, М.–Явор, С. Я.: *Ж. Тех. Физ. СССР*, **35** (1965), 3, 402.
111. (SOKOLOV, I. P.) Соколов, И. П.: *РИЭ СССР*, **10** (1965), 5, 960.
112. (STEPANOV, K. N.–SHARSHANOV, A. A.) Степанов, К. Н.–Шаршанов, А. А.: *Ж. Тех. Физ. СССР*, **27** (1957), 1863.
113. TIEN, P. K.: *J. appl. Phys.*, **25** (1954), 10, 1281.
114. TIEN, P. K.: *Proc. Instn Radio Engrs.*, **42** (1954), 7, 1137.
115. VERSNEL, A.: *Vide*, **12** (1957), 67, 59.
116. VERSNEL, A.–JONKER, J. L. H.: *Philips Res. Rep.*, **9** (1954), 458.
117. WADA, G.–PANTELL, R.: *IRE, Wescon Convention Record*, **3** (1959), 92.
118. WATERS, W. E.: *J. appl. Phys.*, **29** (1958), 1, 100.

* See p. 484.

119. WATERS, W. E.: *Diamond Ordnance Fuze Laboratories, Tech. Rev.*, **2** (1959), 1.
120. WATERS, W. E.: *J. appl. Phys.*, **31** (1960), 10, 1814.
121. WATKINS, D. A.–WADA, G.: *Proc. Instn Radio Engrs.*, **46** (1958), 10, 1700.
122. WEBER, E.: *Electromagnetic Fields, I*, Wiley; New York, 1950.
123. (ZEIDLITS, P. M. et al.) Зейдлиц, П. М.: *Атомн. Энерг.*, **8** (1960), 127.

Recent Developments

124. (ABRAMYAN, E. A.–VECHESLAVOV, V. V.–KONONOV, V. I.) Абрамян, Е. А.–Вечеславов, В. В.–Кононов, В. И.: *Ж. Тех. Физ. СССР*, **38** (1968), 10, 1762.
125. ALEKSEYENKO, A. M.: *Nachtech. Fachber.*, **35**, 93. *7th MOGA.**
126. (BORODIN, A. A.–PCHELNIKOV, YU. N.) Бородин, А. А.–Пчелников, Ю. Н.: *РИЭ СССР*, **13** (1968), 4, 719.
127. BREWER, G. R.: *Focusing of High-Density Electron Beams.* Focusing of Charged Particles, Vol. 2, Chapter 3.3, p. 73. Academic Press; New York, 1967.
128. (CYRLIN, L. E.) Цырлин, Л. Е.: *Ж. Тех. Физ. СССР*, **38** (1968), 3, 442.
129. FROBIN, W.: *Optik Berlin*, **27** (1968), 4, 203.
130. FUNSTEN, H. O.: *Nuclear Instrum. Meth.*, **44** (1966), 2, 301.
131. (GLAZOV, A. A.–NOVIKOV, D. L.) Глазов, А. А.–Новиков, Д. Л.: *Ж. Тех. Физ. СССР*, **38** (1968), 5, 922.
132. GOUIRAN, R.: *Annls. Phys.*, **3** (1968), 2, 67.
133. (GURFEYN, R. E.–MOLOKOVSKIY, S. I.–TREGUBOV, V. F.) Гурфейн, Р. Е.–Молоковский, С. И.–Трегубов, В. Ф.: *Изв. Высш. Учеб. Завед. Радиоэлектр. СССР*, **12** (1969), 9, 1068.
134. HARTNAGEL, H. L.: *Nachtech. Fachber.*, **35**, 200. *7th MOGA.**
135. KIRSTEIN, P. T.–KINO, G. S.–WATERS, W. E.: *Space-Charge Flow* (Physical and quantum electronics series, pp. 509). McGraw-Hill Book Company; New York–San Francisco–Toronto–London–Sydney, 1967.
136. (KOROSTELEV, G. N.) Коростелев, Г. Н.: *Изв. Высш. Учеб. Завед. Радиотех. СССР*, **9** (1966), 1, 34.
137. (KOTSERZHINSKIY, B. A.) Коцержинский, Б. А.: *Изв. Высш. Учеб. Завед. Радиоэлектрон. СССР*, **11** (1968), 4, 388.
138. (KOTSERZHINSKIY, B. A.) Коцержинский, Б. А.: *Изв. Высш. Учеб. Завед. Радиоэлектрон. СССР*, **12** (1969), 9, 1057.
139. (KOTSERZHINSKIY, B. A.–SHEVCHENKO, V. I.) Коцержинский, Б. А.–Шевченко, В. И.: *Изв. Высш. Учеб. Завед. Радиоэлектрон. СССР*, **12** (1969), 1, 11.
140. (MESHKOV, O. F.) Мешков, О. Ф.: *РИЭ СССР*, **11** (1966), 12, 2176.
141. (MOLOKOVSKIY, S. I.–TREGUBOV, V. F.) Молоковский, С. И.—Трегубов, В. Ф.: *Изв. Высш. Завед. Радиоэлектрон. СССР*, **12** (1969), 9, 1063.
142. (NAIDOB-ZHELEZOV, K. G.–PLATONOVA, A. L.) Наидоб-Железов, К. Г.–Платонова, А. Л.: *РИЭ СССР*, **11** (1966), 7, 1322.
143. PRIESTLAND, P. B.–HARTNAGEL, H. L.: *IEEE Trans.*, **ED–15** (1968), 11, 915.
144. PRIESTLAND, P. B.–HARTNAGEL, H. L.: *IEEE Trans.*, **ED–16** (1969), 9, 803.
145. (SHPAK, YE. V.–YAVOR, S. YA.) Шпак, Е. В.–Явор, С. Я.: *РИЭ СССР*, **13** (1968), 1, 82.
146. (SYROVOY, V. A.) Сыровой, В. А.: *Ж. Прикл. Мех. Тех. Физ. СССР*, **4** (1967), 3.
147. SZILÁGYI, M.–FEJES, I.: *Tungsram Technische Mitteilungen*, No. **23** (1973).
148. SZILÁGYI, M.–KŐHALMI, Zs.–SZEKERES, B.: *8th MOGA,** 14.
149. TAN, T. Y.–W. M. NUNN, Jr.: *IEEE Trans.*, **ED–13** (1966), 10, 706.
150. UDELSON, B. J.: *Int. J. Electron.*, **21** (1966), 3, 241.

* See p. 484.

VI. FOCUSING BY MAGNETIC AND ELECTRIC-MAGNETIC FIELDS

GYULA ANDRÁS NAGY

Any arbitrary focusing problem can be solved using magnetic field focusing: practical experience has demonstrated that beams of any arbitrary current density or power can be focused by magnetic means. It can be utilised for very high-frequency and microwave tubes, and even for electron tubes operating in the millimetre-wave range. The above are true for every focusing method, and when choosing the method to be employed, the investigations producing the characteristic properties which yield the scope most suitable for the given employment possibilities are to be relied upon. The magnetic focusing methods have been thoroughly elaborated both theoretically and in practice, as proved by the numerous theoretical papers published in the literature, and the informative publications of the electron tube manufacturers.

On account of the given size of the present book, detailed problems are not treated, and only the basic principles and the basic relations are discussed. The design and realisation of the structural elements are still less dealt with, although it should certainly be noted that both the structural elements and their implementation are simple.

Magnetic focusing possesses numerous advantageous properties. Some of these will be mentioned.

With magnetic focusing, paraxiality derived from the structural solutions, where the permanent magnet or coil producing the magnetic field is the outermost element of the given device, and in comparison with the beam diameter, its internal diameter is large, is assured in almost all cases. Consequently, the dimensioning formulae are in harmony with practice.

In case of long beams, the actually existing paraxiality brings about a high degree of stability and reliable existence, since the deviation of the calculated and real trajectory is negligibly small in the region of paraxiality.

The magnetic field-exciting elements and other elements of the device are independent of each other in magnetic focusing, therefore their design involves no restrictions which are difficult (or impossible) to meet. As an example we mention the travelling wave tube, where the period of the slow-wave structure and the period of the focusing field can be chosen independently of each other, and the most advantageous setting required for performance of the main problem can be realised for both.

The disadvantage of the magnetic focusing systems follows from the above: the large-dimension magnetic device results in greater net weight (maximum doubled). This disadvantage may be disregarded in case of a fixed equipment (as in the majority of cases). On the other hand, the magnetic equipment, also ensuring protection of the tube, which can be separately operated and adjusted, possesses an unsurpassable advantage: its position can be subsequently and arbitrarily adjusted. In addition to technological facilitating, this also results in good operation of the tube.

Magnetic focusing is free of the disadvantageous properties of electric focusing. As examples let us mention: vacuum-technological materials of exceptional quality can only be used in the vacuum; the form and spacing of the electrodes cannot be chosen arbitrarily in systems with higher voltages, due to electric breakdown, various disturbing discharges, and leakage currents; the external disturbing fields and the polarization of dielectrics such as support rods and bulbs cause distortion of the focusing field; extreme difficulty in attaining the required degree of accuracy when mounting the components in vacuum, e.g. heat treatment is indispensable; uniaxial fitting of the gun and the focusing system must be most accurately performed (initial conditions, stability), since this cannot be corrected afterwards. The undesirable properties listed in the foregoing all arise in practice i.e. they are technological difficulties; original concomitants of the structural arrangement, and as a result, the overwhelming majority of focusing systems are now of the magnetic type.

The most widely used focusing methods are the homogeneous magnetic, the *Brillouin*, the periodic magnetic and quadrupole focusing. In the following we shall deal in detail with these four methods. Other focusing methods will also figure, but in most cases they will only be mentioned. In the completely omitted cases among which only the crossed field-focusing method is of practical significance, reference is made to the literature.

In view of the fact that this chapter deals with a part of the focusing methods based on simultaneously acting electric and magnetic fields, we mention here that *today the most general problems of space-charge optics are solvable, even on curvilinear central trajectories in space, or in simultaneously acting arbitrary electric-magnetic fields, taking into consideration space-charge, current density and thermal velocities, for both low- and high-velocity motions, including calculability of imaging, chromatic and mass aberrations* [12].

Any focusing method is investigated only in plane-symmetric, axially symmetric and quadrupole cases, in harmony with the basic equations given in Chapter I.

(A) FOCUSING BY HOMOGENEOUS MAGNETIC FIELD

The most simple method for focusing of electron beams is *focusing by homogeneous magnetic field*. In case of this method of focusing the beam is started in a homogeneous magnetic field of z direction, and induction is chosen so that the maximum diameter of the beam does not exceed the value required. Naturally, the magnetic field is excited over the whole length of the beam and not only at the starting point of the beam. This focusing method is known also as *focusing by strong magnetic field*. The literature generally identifies the starting point of the beam with the cathode surface, and speaks of partial or other shielding of the cathode. It is important, however, that at the initial point of the beam, instead of homogeneous induction, the induction should differ therefrom, and a homogeneous field should be present only in a subsequent section of the trajectory [50, 92]. According to the terminology mentioned *(see note at the end of the paragraph)*, the case discussed here includes also the cases of fully shielded and unshielded cathodes.

73. AXIALLY SYMMETRIC BEAM

The movement of the electrons is considered in a field in which the potential on the axis is constant, the induction has only one component, in the direction of the axis (z direction), and this is independent of the position (homogeneous induction field). Summarising the conditions

$$\Phi = \text{constant} \; ; \quad B = \text{constant} \qquad\qquad 73.1$$

Considering the conditions 73.1, equation 21.14 becomes the following

$$r'' + \frac{1}{\Phi}\left(\frac{1}{4\varepsilon_0}\varrho_0 + \frac{\eta}{8}B^2 - \frac{\eta C^2}{2}\frac{1}{r^4}\right)r = 0 \qquad\qquad 73.2$$

The equilibrium radius R_e of the trajectory described by equation 73.2 is

$$r'' = 0 \qquad\qquad 73.3$$

since the resultant force on this radius equals zero.

For determination of ϱ_0 appearing in equation 73.2, we start off from the following approximations

$$\dot{z}^2 = 2\eta\varphi \qquad\qquad 73.4$$

$$\mathbf{j} = \varrho \dot{z} \mathbf{e}_z \qquad\qquad 73.5$$

since current eventually flows only in the direction of axis z. Denoting the absolute value of $\mathbf{j}$ in equation 73.5 with j_z, ϱ can be expressed by equation 73.4

$$\varrho = \frac{j_z}{(2\eta\varphi)^{1/2}} \qquad\qquad 73.6$$

In order to identify ϱ in equation 73.6 with ϱ_0 in series expansion 5.43, we must assume that ϱ is not dependent upon r

$$\varrho(r, z) = \varrho_0(z) \qquad\qquad 73.7$$

$$\varrho_{2\nu} = 0 , \quad \nu = 1, 2, \ldots \qquad\qquad 73.8$$

Hence, equation 73.6 with approximation $\varphi \cong \Phi$ becomes

$$\varrho_0 = \frac{j_z}{(2\eta\Phi)^{1/2}} \qquad\qquad 73.9$$

Integrating the current density (with 34.4) we introduce the current flowing in the beam, instead of current density

$$I = - j_z r^2 \pi \qquad\qquad 73.10$$

Expressing j_z from 73.10 and substituting into 73.9

$$\varrho_0 = - \frac{I}{\sqrt{2\pi}\sqrt{\eta}\sqrt{\Phi}} \frac{1}{r^2} \qquad\qquad 73.11$$

Via function $r(z)$, ϱ_0 in equation 73.11 is a function of z. Equation 73.11 is now substituted into 73.2

$$r'' + \frac{1}{\Phi} \left(- \frac{I}{4\sqrt{2\pi}\varepsilon_0\sqrt{\eta}\sqrt{\Phi}} \frac{1}{r^2} + \frac{\eta}{8} B^2 - \frac{\eta C^2}{2} \frac{1}{r^4} \right) r = 0 \qquad 73.12$$

From equation 73.3 and equation 73.12, the following can be obtained for the equilibrium radius, R_e

$$- \frac{I}{4\sqrt{2\pi}\varepsilon_0\sqrt{\eta}\sqrt{\Phi}} \frac{1}{R_e^2} + \frac{\eta}{8} B^2 - \frac{\eta C^2}{2} \frac{1}{R_e^4} = 0 \qquad 73.13$$

from which the induction required for the specified equilibrium radius is

$$B^2 = \frac{1}{R_e^2} \left(\frac{\sqrt{2}I}{\pi\varepsilon_0\eta^{3/2}\Phi^{1/2}} + \frac{4C^2}{R_e^2} \right) \qquad\qquad 73.14$$

Equation 73.14 forms one of the dimensioning final formulae. The current I flowing in the beam, the beam voltage Φ and the beam radius R_e are, therefore, given. If it is required that the equilibrium radius of the beam be of R_e value, a homogeneous induction field calculable from equation 73.14 must be used.

Solution of the reversed problem can also be given. We introduce the notation

$$2K = \frac{\sqrt{2}I}{\pi \varepsilon_0 \eta^{3/2} \Phi^{1/2} B^2} \qquad 73.15$$

Now we express R_e from equation 73.13

$$R_e = \left[K + \left(K^2 + \frac{C^2}{B^2} \right)^{1/2} \right]^{1/2} \qquad 73.16$$

From equation 73.16 we are able to calculate the value of the equilibrium radius of the given beam in the given homogeneous field.

The edge electron of the beam oscillates about the equilibrium radius. The oscillation in a stronger magnetic field is, as will be seen, of lower amplitude. By linearising equation 73.2 an approximate solution is determined. The distance of the edge electron of the beam from the axis is assumed in the following form

$$r = R_e + r_d \qquad 73.17$$

and it is essential that $R_e \gg r_d$ (we confine ourselves to these cases). With approximations

$$r^{-1} \simeq \frac{1}{R_e^2}(R_e - r_d) \qquad 73.18$$

$$r^{-3} \simeq \frac{1}{R_e^4}(R_e - 3r_d) \qquad 73.19$$

equation 73.2 becomes

$$r_d'' + \left(\frac{I}{4\sqrt{2}\pi\varepsilon_0\sqrt{\eta}\Phi^{3/2}R_e^2} + \frac{\eta B^2}{8\Phi} + \frac{3\eta C^2}{2\Phi R_e^4} \right) r_d + \left[R_e'' - \right.$$

$$\left. - \frac{I}{4\sqrt{2}\pi\varepsilon_0\sqrt{\eta}\Phi^{3/2}R_e^2} R_e + \frac{\eta B^2}{8\Phi} R_e - \frac{\eta C^2}{2\Phi R_e^4} R_e \right] = 0 \qquad 73.20$$

In equation 73.20 the term in square brackets equals zero since R_e is constant and equation 73.13 remains valid.

Finally, solution of the equation derived by notation

$$\omega^2 = \frac{I}{4\sqrt{2}\pi\varepsilon_0\sqrt{\eta}\Phi^{3/2}R_e^2} + \frac{\eta B^2}{8\Phi} + \frac{3\eta C^2}{2\Phi R_e^4} \qquad 73.21$$

with initial conditions

$$r_d(z_0) = r_{d0}; \ r_d'(z_0) = r_{d0}' \qquad 73.22$$

is

$$r_d = r_{d0} \cos \left[\omega(z - z_0)\right] + \frac{r_0'}{\omega} \sin \left[\omega(z - z_0)\right] \qquad 73.23$$

from which, on the basis of 73.21, it will be seen that the amplitude decreases with the increase of B.

Equation 73.23 is the other dimensioning final formula. With the help of this equation we can determine the maximum value of the amplitude superposed on the equilibrium radius R_e, and therewith the maximum and minimum diameter of the beam.

Note

(*i*) In connection with the terminology used in the literature, mention must be made of the following [50, 92].

The fields acting earlier on the electron are chosen in such a way that in position z_0, in addition to the required induction value B_0, the value of constant C calculable from equation 21.6 shall be correct. If at a later stage investigation of motion occurring in the homogeneous field is required, the induction of the homogeneous field can be B_0 only, otherwise axis induction B would necessarily vary by leaps, and this is not possible. If, on the other hand, the axis induction reaches the induction value of the homogeneous region with continuous changes from value B_0, the axis induction with constant value differing from B_0 cannot be used in the equation of motion, and instead, the actual dependence on coordinate z must be taken into consideration. A correct description of this phenomenon is obtained according to the latter process. The preceding process can be used as a satisfactory approximation if the arbitrarily assumed leap of the induction is not excessive.

It should be added to the foregoing that electrons started from 'partially screened' cathodes must pass along a section of finite length in a field with varying axis potential, which is also in contradiction with the condition Φ = constant, used in the equations.

In accordance with this Note the modified forms of equations 73.14, 73.16, 73.21 are to be used, with the substitution of $B_0 = B$.

(*ii*) Part (*i*) of this Note determines also the initial conditions 73.22 for the first case containing the leap

$$r_{d0} = r_0 - R_e ; \qquad r_{d0}' = r_0' \qquad 73.24$$

as follows from equations 18.31 and 18.32.

(*iii*) Note (*i*) is valid in all cases of axially and plane-symmetric beams (e.g. beams focused by periodic field), and will no longer be mentioned.

74. PLANE-SYMMETRIC BEAM

Similarly to the case of axial symmetry

$$\Phi = \text{constant} ; \quad B = \text{constant} \qquad 74.1$$

i.e. the axis potential and the axis induction are constants. Using equation 74.1, the equation of motion 22.13 is

$$y'' + \frac{1}{2\Phi} \left(\frac{1}{\varepsilon_0} \varrho_0 + \eta B^2 - \eta C B \Phi \frac{1}{y} \right) y = 0 \qquad 74.2$$

The condition of equilibrium of forces is the following equation

$$y'' = 0 \qquad 74.3$$

from which distance Y_e, the distance of the equilibrium of forces can be calculated. The space-charge term ϱ_0 (see series expansion 7.35) figuring in 74.2 can be calculated similarly to the axially symmetric case (extending integration 34.4 to the rectangular beam cross section with height $2y$ and width W)

$$\varrho_0 = - \frac{I}{2\sqrt{2}\sqrt{\eta} W \sqrt{\Phi}} \frac{1}{y} \qquad 74.4$$

Substituting equation 74.4 into 74.2, equation

$$y'' + \frac{1}{2\Phi} \left(- \frac{I}{2\sqrt{2}\varepsilon_0\sqrt{\eta} W \sqrt{\Phi}} \frac{1}{y} \, \eta B^2 \, \eta C B \Phi \frac{1}{y} \right) y = 0 \qquad 74.5$$

yields the equation determining the equilibrium distance

$$- \frac{I}{2\sqrt{2}\varepsilon_0\sqrt{\eta} W \sqrt{\Phi}} \frac{1}{Y_e} + \eta B^2 - \eta C B \Phi \frac{1}{Y_e} = 0 \qquad 74.6$$

in the previously given manner.

Equation 74.6 gives the induction required for the specified equilibrium distance

$$B = \frac{1}{Y_e} \left[\frac{C\Phi}{2} + \left(\frac{C^2\Phi^2}{4} + \frac{Y_e I}{2\sqrt{2}\varepsilon_0 \eta^{3/2} W \sqrt{\Phi}} \right)^{1/2} \right] \qquad 74.7$$

Equation 74.7 is one of the dimensioning final formulae.
The equilibrium distance can be calculated from equation 74.6

$$Y_e = \frac{I}{2\sqrt{2}\varepsilon_0 \eta^{3/2} W B \sqrt{\Phi}} + \frac{C\Phi}{B} \qquad 74.8$$

Finally, the general solution of the inhomogeneous linear differential equation 74.5 with initial conditions 19.19, 19.20 is

$$y = \left(y_0 - \frac{P}{\omega^2} \right) \cos\left[\omega(z - z_0)\right] + \frac{y_0'}{\omega} \sin\left[\omega(z - z_0)\right] + \frac{P}{\omega^2} \qquad 74.9$$

In equation 74.9

$$\omega^2 = \frac{\eta B^2}{2\Phi} \qquad 74.10$$

$$P = \frac{I}{4\sqrt{2}\varepsilon_0\sqrt{\eta} W \Phi^{3/2}} + \frac{\eta C B}{2} \qquad 74.11$$

By the second dimensioning formula 74.9, the maximum and minimum diameters of the beam can be determined.

Note

(*i*) The Note given with regard to the axially symmetric case is also valid here, and the substitution $B_0 = B$ must be made in equations 74.7, 74.8 and 74.11.

(*ii*) As a consequence of the existence of exact solution of equation 74.5, the equation analogous with 73.24 does not appear, since the original initial conditions have been used.

(B) BRILLOUIN FOCUSING

A frequently used but somewhat more cumbersome method for focusing of electron beams is the *Brillouin focusing method*. In case of this method the beam bounded by an edge trajectory with a horizontal tangent is led to a homogeneous magnetic field of *z* direction, which increases by leaps from zero field strength before the point of entrance to the required constant field strength. The beam passes without spreading in this field, if the induction of the homogeneous field is appropriate. The focusing magnetic field *(Brillouin field)* is stated to be more difficult to realise than the previous homogeneous magnetic field, since its realisation is theoretically impossible and in practice it is more difficult. Moreover, *Brillouin* focusing is a special case of the homogeneous field focusing, and will be discussed separately [62, 82] on account of its importance and in order to gain knowledge surpassing that gained with regard to homogeneous field focusing.

Over and above, the ideal *Brillouin* focusing, the effect of two factors which occur in practical cases, will be treated.

In the first case it is assumed that the induction distribution required for *Brillouin* focusing has been realised. However, setting of the electron gun, or more generally the previous trajectory of the beam, satisfying the initial conditions required for focusing, has not been realised. Investigation of this problem is of significant practical importance, since *Brillouin* focusing is used fairly frequently. In view of the fact that *Brillouin* focusing forms a special case of homogeneous field focusing as discussed in the preceding section, this problem may be considered as solved, with the solution given there pertaining to the general initial conditions.

In the second case, we are dealing with investigation of an interesting problem. The abruptly changing induction field necessary for *Brillouin* focusing cannot be realised in practice. (It is theoretically non-existent due to equation 1.4.) Focusing occurs also in the induction field increasing continuously. Functional relations fairly arbitrary with regard to the induction are permissible in the transition region, ensuring adaptability to practical course [59, 63, 108].

75. AXIALLY SYMMETRIC BEAM

Motion of the electrons is investigated in a field wherein the following conditions are valid

$$\Phi = \text{constant}, \qquad 0 \leq z \qquad\qquad 75.1$$

$$B = 0, \qquad\qquad z \leq 0 \qquad\qquad 75.2$$

$$B = \text{constant}, \qquad 0 < z \qquad\qquad 75.3$$

$$A = \frac{1}{2} Br \qquad\qquad\qquad 75.4$$

The induction field determined by equations 75.2, 75.3 is shown in figure VI.1.

Initial conditions are

$$r(0) = R_0 ; \qquad \dot{\alpha}(0) = 0 \qquad\qquad 75.5$$

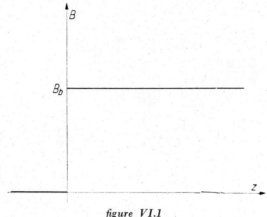

figure VI.1

and taking these into consideration, equations 18.10, 18.12, 18.22 and 18.23 become

$$C = 0 \qquad 75.6$$

$$\ddot{r} - r\dot{\alpha}^2 = \eta \frac{\partial \varphi}{\partial r} - \eta \dot{\alpha} Br \qquad 75.7$$

$$\dot{\alpha} = \frac{\eta}{2} B \qquad 75.8$$

$$\ddot{z} = 0 \qquad 75.9$$

Our aim is that after their entry, the edge electrons of the beam (in the meridian plane) should move parallel to axis z, and therefore the conditions

$$\dot{r} = 0 ; \qquad \ddot{r} = 0 \qquad 75.10$$

should be valid. The second term of condition 75.10 is applied to equation 75.7 and simultaneously equation 75.8 is substituted. After rearrangement

$$\frac{\partial \varphi}{\partial r} = \frac{\eta}{4} B^2 r \qquad 75.11$$

to give

$$\int_{\Phi}^{\varphi} d\varphi = \frac{\eta}{4} B^2 \int_{0}^{r} r \, dr \qquad 75.12$$

After integration

$$\varphi = \Phi + \frac{\eta}{8} B^2 r^2 \qquad 75.13$$

In our case, since

$$\frac{\partial \varphi}{\partial z} = 0 \qquad\qquad 75.14$$

equation 5.11 assumes the following form

$$\frac{\partial^2 \varphi}{\partial r^2} + \frac{1}{r}\frac{\partial \varphi}{\partial r} = -\frac{1}{\varepsilon_0}\varrho \qquad\qquad 75.15$$

The derivatives necessary for 75.15 are determined from equation 75.13

$$\frac{1}{r}\frac{\partial \varphi}{\partial r} = \frac{\eta}{4}B^2 ; \qquad \frac{\partial^2 \varphi}{\partial r^2} = \frac{\eta}{4}B^2 \qquad\qquad 75.16$$

Substituting equation 75.16 into 75.15, and expressing ϱ we obtain

$$\varrho = -\frac{1}{2}\varepsilon_0\eta B^2 \qquad\qquad 75.17$$

We now write the energy equation, taking into account that $\dot{r} = 0$

$$r^2\dot{\alpha}^2 + \dot{z}^2 = 2\eta\varphi \qquad\qquad 75.18$$

Using equations 75.8 and 74.13

$$r^2\frac{\eta^2}{4}B^2 + \dot{z}^2 = 2\eta\Phi + \frac{\eta^2}{4}B^2 r^2 \qquad\qquad 75.19$$

wherefrom

$$\dot{z}^2 = 2\eta\Phi \qquad\qquad 75.20$$

Only the axial component of the current density is taken into account

$$j_z = \varrho\dot{z} \qquad\qquad 75.21$$

Equations 75.17 and 75.20 are substituted into 75.21

$$j_z = -\frac{1}{2}\varepsilon_0\eta B^2 (2\eta\Phi)^{1/2} \qquad\qquad 75.22$$

The beam current is determined by integration of the current density (from 34.4)

$$I = -j_z\pi R_0^2 \qquad\qquad 75.23$$

Expressing j_z from equation 75.23 and substituting into 75.22

$$-\frac{I}{\pi R_0^2} = -\frac{1}{2}\varepsilon_0\eta B^2 (2\eta\Phi)^{1/2} \qquad\qquad 75.24$$

B^2 is expressed from equation 75.24

$$B^2 = \frac{\sqrt{2}I}{\pi\varepsilon_0\eta^{3/2}R_0^2\Phi^{1/2}} \qquad\qquad 75.25$$

Equation 75.25 represents the final dimensioning formula. Thus, the current I flowing in the beam, the beam voltage Φ and the beam radius R_0 are given. If it is desired that the beam should not spread, a homogeneous induction field calculated from equation 75.25 should be used.

Solution of the reversed problem can also be given. Let us express R_0^2 from equation 75.25

$$R_0^2 = \frac{\sqrt{2}\,I}{\pi\varepsilon_0\eta^{3/2}\Phi^{1/2}B^2} \qquad\qquad 75.26$$

From equation 75.26 we can calculate the entrance condition at which the diameter of the given beam remains constant in the given homogeneous field.

Summarising the solutions of equations 75.7, 75.8, 75.9 (region $z > 0$)

$$r(t) = R_0 \qquad\qquad 75.27$$

$$\alpha(t) = \alpha_0 + \frac{1}{2}\,\eta Bt \qquad\qquad 75.28$$

$$z(t) = (2\eta\Phi)^{1/2}t \qquad\qquad 75.29$$

where conditions

$$\alpha(0) = \alpha_0 ; \qquad z(0) = 0 \qquad\qquad 75.30$$

are used.

Note

(i) Due to equation 75.8, angular velocity of the electrons is independent of r. The electron beam rotates as a solid cylinder.

(ii) *Brillouin* focusing may exist also in case of other induction distributions. Two things are important: the induction on the axis is constant beyond the position of entrance; at the point of entrance (and thereafter also) C equals zero.

Example

$$\Phi = 1000\ \text{V}; \quad I = 10^{-2}\ \text{A} ; \quad R_0 = 10^{-3}\ \text{m}$$

Calculated from equation 75.25

$$B = 147 \times 10^{-4}\ \text{V s/m}^2$$

76. PLANE-SYMMETRIC BEAM

Motion of the electrons is investigated, in a similar way to the axially symmetric case

$$\Phi = \text{constant}, \qquad 0 \leq z \qquad\qquad 76.1$$

$$B = 0, \qquad z \leq 0 \qquad\qquad 76.2$$

$$B = \text{constant}, \qquad 0 < z \qquad\qquad 76.3$$

$$A = -By \qquad\qquad 76.4$$

The induction field determined by equations 76.2 and 76.3 is shown in figure VI.1 (see § 75).

The initial conditions are

$$x(0) = 0 ; \qquad y(0) = Y_0 \qquad\qquad 76.5$$

with which the respective equations of motion according to § 19 are the following

$$C = 0 \qquad\qquad 76.6$$

$$\dot{x} = -\eta By \qquad\qquad 76.7$$

$$\ddot{y} = \eta \frac{\partial \varphi}{\partial y} + \eta B\dot{x} \qquad\qquad 76.8$$

$$\ddot{z} = 0 \qquad\qquad 76.9$$

The edge electrons in the meridian plane of the beam move parallel to the z axis, thus conditions

$$\dot{y} = 0 ; \qquad \ddot{y} = 0 \qquad\qquad 76.10$$

are valid. Now the second term of equation 76.10 is applied to equation 76.8. Equation 76.7 is substituted and integrated. After the integration we have

$$\varphi = \Phi + \frac{\eta}{2} B^2 y^2 \qquad\qquad 76.11$$

Due to

$$\frac{\partial \varphi}{\partial z} = 0 \qquad\qquad 76.12$$

equation 7.7 assumes the following form

$$\frac{\partial^2 \varphi}{\partial y^2} = -\frac{1}{\varepsilon_0} \varrho \qquad\qquad 76.13$$

The derivative necessary for equation 76.13 is determined from 76.11. Substituting and expressing ϱ

$$\varrho = -\varepsilon_0 \eta B^2 \qquad\qquad 76.14$$

Taking into account that $\dot{y} = 0$, the energy equation becomes

$$\dot{x}^2 + \dot{z}^2 = 2\eta\Phi \qquad\qquad 76.15$$

Using 76.7 and 76.11

$$\dot{z}^2 = 2\eta\Phi \qquad\qquad 76.16$$

Here, too, only the axial component of the current density is taken into account

$$j_z = \varrho\dot{z} \qquad\qquad 76.17$$

Equations 76.14 and 76.16 are substituted into 76.17

$$j_z = -\varepsilon_0 \eta B^2 (2\eta\Phi)^{1/2} \qquad\qquad 76.18$$

In the same manner as the foregoing, the beam current is determined by integration of the current density. Using the already known notations, we have

$$I = -j_z 2 Y_0 W \qquad\qquad 76.19$$

Using 76.19, from 76.18 we obtain

$$B^2 = \frac{I}{2\sqrt{2}\ \varepsilon_0 \eta^{3/2} Y_0 \Phi^{1/2} W} \qquad\qquad 76.20$$

Equation 76.20 forms the final dimensioning formula. Given are the beam current per unit length I/W, the beam voltage Φ and the half height Y_0 of the beam. If we require that the beam should not spread, the homogeneous induction field calculable from equation 76.20 is to be used.
For solution of the reversed problem, Y_0 is expressed from equation 76.20

$$Y_0 = \frac{I}{2\sqrt{2}\ \varepsilon_0 \eta^{3/2} W \Phi^{1/2} B^2} \qquad\qquad 76.21$$

From equation 76.21 we are able to calculate the entrance condition under which the given beam remains at constant height in the given homogeneous field.
Now we summarise the solutions of equations 76.7, 76.8, 76.9

$$x(t) = x_0 - \eta B Y_0 t \qquad\qquad 76.22$$
$$y(t) = Y_0 \qquad\qquad 76.23$$
$$z(t) = (2\eta\Phi)^{1/2} t \qquad\qquad 76.24$$

The conditions

$$x(0) = x_0 ; \qquad z(0) = 0 \qquad\qquad 76.25$$

are used for the solution.

Note

(*i*) Owing to equation 76.7, the velocity in the direction of x is dependent upon y. The x-direction velocity of the electrons more remote from the basic plane is greater: the trajectories at various heights y slide one upon the other.
(*ii*) Note (*i*) referring to the axially symmetric case is valid here too, according to the meaning.

Example

$$\Phi = 10\ 000 \text{ V}; \quad I = 1 \text{ A}; \quad W = 10^{-3} \text{ m}; \quad Y_0 = 5 \times 10^{-4} \text{ m}$$

Calculated from 76.20

$$B = 0.140 \text{ V s/m}^2$$

77. FOCUSING IN THE TRANSITION REGION
OF A NON-IDEAL BRILLOUIN FIELD

(a) Axially symmetric case

Owing to practical reasons discussed at the beginning of Section (B), motions of the electrons are investigated in a field wherein the following conditions are valid

$$\Phi = \text{constant} \qquad\qquad 77.1$$

$$B = \frac{B_b}{1 + z^2/a^2}, \qquad z \leq 0 \qquad\qquad 77.2$$

$$B = B_b, \qquad\qquad 0 \leq z \qquad\qquad 77.3$$

$$A = \frac{1}{2} Br \qquad\qquad 77.4$$

The induction field determined by equations 77.2 and 77.3 is shown in figure VI.2.

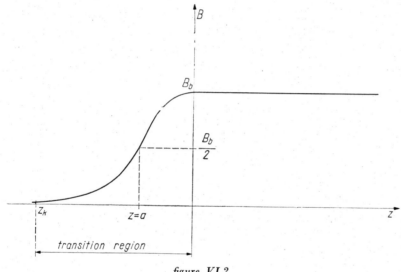

figure VI.2

The initial conditions are

$$r(0) = R_0 ; \quad r'(0) = 0 ; \quad \dot{\alpha}(t_0) = 0 \qquad\qquad 77.5$$

$$A(z_0) = 0 \qquad\qquad 77.6$$

Among the initial conditions, 77.6 can be satisfied (with approximation) only if z_0 has a great negative value.

With the above conditions, equation of motion 21.14, with the space-charge term 73.11, is

$$r'' + \frac{\eta B_b^2}{8\Phi} \frac{1}{(1 + z^2/a^2)^2} r - \frac{I}{4\sqrt{2}\,\pi\varepsilon_0\sqrt{\eta}\sqrt{\Phi^3}} \frac{1}{r} = 0 \qquad 77.7$$

A new dependent variable is introduced

$$r = R_0 R \qquad 77.8$$

With 77.8, equation 77.7 becomes

$$R'' + \frac{\eta B_b^2}{8\Phi} \frac{1}{(1 + z^2/a^2)^2} R - \frac{I}{4\sqrt{2}\,\pi\varepsilon_0\sqrt{\eta}\,R_0^2\sqrt{\Phi^3}} \frac{1}{R} = 0 \qquad 77.9$$

A new independent variable is introduced

$$z = ax \qquad 77.10$$

With 77.10, equation 77.9 becomes

$$R'' + \frac{\eta a^2}{8\Phi} \frac{B_b^2}{(1 + x^2)^2} R - \frac{a^2 I}{4\sqrt{2}\,\pi\varepsilon_0\sqrt{\eta}\,R_0^2\sqrt{\Phi^3}} \frac{1}{R} = 0 \qquad 77.11$$

Finally, with introduction of the abbreviations

$$\alpha^* = \frac{\eta a^2}{8\Phi} B_b^2; \quad \beta^* = \frac{a^2 I}{4\sqrt{2}\,\pi\varepsilon_0\sqrt{\eta}\,R_0^2\sqrt{\Phi^3}} \qquad 77.12$$

the following equation is obtained

$$R'' + \alpha^* \frac{1}{(1 + x^2)^2} R - \beta^* \frac{1}{R} = 0 \qquad 77.13$$

If for B_b^2 appearing in equation 77.13 the induction according to equation 75.25, i.e. the induction for *Brillouin* focusing is chosen, then $\alpha^* = \beta^*$. In this case equation 77.13 becomes

$$R'' + \alpha^* \frac{1}{(1 + x^2)^2} R - \alpha^* \frac{1}{R} = 0 \qquad 77.14$$

The solution of this equation is given in the paper [129]. A distorted-scale qualitative picture of the solution is shown in figure VI.3. In the figure, the position of the smallest beam radius is z_m, while R_m represents the smallest beam radius.

According to the solution, *the ratio of z_m/a is a value closely approaching zero, independently of the value of α^*, while the ratio of R_m/R_0 is a value approaching unity. The ratio of z_m/a shows that the minimum cross section of the beam appears at the end of the transition region, immediately adjacent to the position of the maximum induction. The ratio of R_m/R_0 demonstrates that the diameter of the beam does not vary to any appreciable extent in the transition region,* therefore the use of the paraxial space-charge term 73.11 is justified.

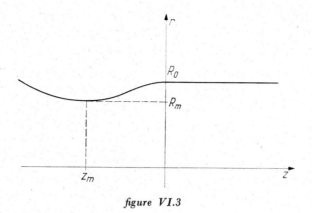

figure VI.3

(b) Plane-symmetric case

The relevant conditions are

$$\Phi = \text{constant} \qquad 77.15$$

$$B = \frac{B_b}{1 + z^2/a^2}, \qquad z \leq 0 \qquad 77.16$$

$$B = B_b, \qquad 0 \leq z \qquad 77.17$$

$$A = -By \qquad 77.18$$

Figure VI.2 illustrates the induction field. The initial conditions are

$$\dot{x}(t_0) = 0 ; \quad y(0) = Y_0 ; \quad y'(0) = 0 \qquad 77.19$$

$$A(z_0) = 0 \qquad 77.20$$

Equation 77.20 is approximately satisfied for a high negative value of z_0. Substituting the space-charge term 74.4 into equation of motion 22.13 we have

$$y'' + \frac{\eta}{2\Phi} \frac{B_b^2}{(1 + z^2/a^2)^2} y - \frac{I}{4\sqrt{2}\,\varepsilon_0\sqrt{\eta}\,W\Phi^{3/2}} = 0 \qquad 77.21$$

With the dependent and independent variables

$$y = Y_0 Y ; \qquad z = ax \qquad 77.22$$

and the abbreviations

$$\alpha_1 = \frac{\eta a^2}{2\Phi} B_b^2 ; \; \beta_1 = \frac{a^2 I}{4\sqrt{2}\,\varepsilon_0\sqrt{\eta}\,W Y_0 \Phi^{3/2}} \qquad 77.23$$

27*

the new form of equation 77.21 is

$$Y'' + \alpha_1 \frac{1}{(1 + x^2)^2} Y - \beta_1 = 0 \qquad 77.24$$

Choosing for B_b the induction required for *Brillouin* focusing calculable from 76.20, $\alpha_1 = \beta_1$ is yielded, giving

$$Y'' + \alpha_1 \frac{1}{(1 + x^2)^2} Y - \alpha_1 = 0 \qquad 77.25$$

Solution of the homogeneous equation pertaining to equation 77.25 [Chapter I: 96, 97] is

$$Y = c_1 (1 + x^2)^{1/2} \cos \left[(1 + \alpha_1)^{1/2} \arctan x \right] +$$
$$+ c_2 (1 + x^2)^{1/2} \sin \left[(1 + \alpha_1)^{1/2} \arctan x \right] \qquad 77.26$$

For the solution of the inhomogeneous equation 77.25 (*Lagrange's* method), the following two quadratures must be performed [Chapter I: 154]

$$c_1' = - \frac{\alpha_1}{(1 + \alpha_1)^{1/2}} (1 + x^2)^{1/2} \sin \left[(1 + \alpha_1)^{1/2} \arctan x \right] \qquad 77.27$$

$$c_2' = \frac{\alpha_1}{(1 + \alpha_1)^{1/2}} (1 + x^2)^{1/2} \cos \left[(1 + \alpha_1)^{1/2} \arctan x \right] \qquad 77.28$$

Substituting the solutions of equations 77.27 and 77.28 into equation 77.26, we obtain (with the aid of an addition) the general solution of equation 77.25, which solution gives access to the edge trajectory as a function of the auxiliary variable α_1 contained therein.

(C) FOCUSING BY PERIODIC MAGNETIC FIELD

The most frequently employed, and also the most complicated method of the maintenance of electron beams is *focusing by periodic magnetic field*. In case of this method of focusing the beam bounded by the edge trajectory having a horizontal tangent is led into a magnetic field whose axis induction is a given periodic function of z. The axis induction is zero before the point of entrance. The trajectory of the edge electron and therefore the beam is rippled in the field thus chosen. In practice we endeavour to obtain a minimum ripple and that the maximum distance of the beam edge from the plane x, z or from axis z should be below a predetermined value. In the first case the beam moves in a space section limited by two parallel planes, and in the second case in a space section limited by a cylindrical surface.

In accordance with the introductory part of this chapter, paraxiality is valid in the case of magnetic focusing. Therefore, in microwave applications the beam used must be considered a thick beam as referred to the minimum internal dimension of the slow-wave structure. The thick beam is in good interaction with the field travelling along the slow-wave structure, resulting in excellent high-frequency operation.

78. AXIALLY SYMMETRIC BEAM

In the following we shall investigate the beam-forming effect of the periodic magnetic field, in a field corresponding to the following conditions

$$\Phi = \text{constant} , \qquad\qquad 0 \leq z \qquad\qquad 78.1$$

$$B = 0 , \qquad\qquad z \leq 0 \qquad\qquad 78.2$$

$$B = \hat{B} \cos\left(\frac{2\pi}{L} z\right) , \qquad\qquad 0 < z \qquad\qquad 78.3$$

The induction field determined by equations 78.2 and 78.3 is shown in
figure VI.4.

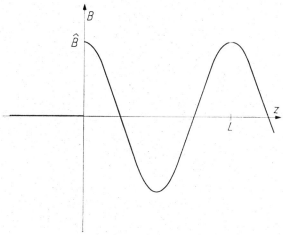

figure VI.4

The initial conditions are

$$r(0) = R_0 ; \quad r'(0) = 0 ; \quad \dot{\alpha}(0) = 0 \qquad\qquad 78.4$$

With consideration of the above conditions, equations 21.6 and 21.14
become

$$C = 0 \qquad\qquad 78.5$$

$$\Phi r'' + \left[\frac{1}{4\varepsilon_0} \varrho_0 + \frac{\mu \hat{B}^2}{8} \cos^2\left(\frac{2\pi}{L} z\right)\right] r = 0 \qquad\qquad 78.6$$

The expression of ϱ_0 appearing in equation 78.6 is chosen in accordance
with equation 73.11 and substituted

$$\Phi r'' + \frac{\mu \hat{B}^2}{8} \cos^2\left(\frac{2\pi}{L} z\right) r - \frac{I}{4\sqrt{2\pi\varepsilon_0}\sqrt{\eta}\sqrt{\Phi}} \frac{1}{r} = 0 \qquad\qquad 78.7$$

Equation 78.7 forms the basic equation for the focusing of axially symmetric electron beams by spatially periodic magnetic field, taking into consideration the discussed simplifications.

A new dependent variable is introduced

$$r = R_0 R \qquad\qquad 78.8$$

After transformation equation 78.7 yields

$$R'' + \frac{\eta \hat{B}^2}{8\Phi} \cos^2 \left(\frac{2\pi}{L} z \right) R - \frac{I}{4\sqrt{2\pi\varepsilon_0}\sqrt{\eta} R_0^2 \sqrt{\Phi^3}} \frac{1}{R} = 0 \qquad 78.9$$

Using the relation

$$\cos^2 \left(\frac{2\pi}{L} z \right) = \frac{1}{2} + \frac{1}{2} \cos \left(\frac{4\pi}{L} z \right) \qquad 78.10$$

equation 78.9 becomes

$$R'' + \frac{\eta \hat{B}^2}{16\Phi} \left[1 + \cos \left(\frac{4\pi}{L} z \right) \right] R - \frac{I}{4\sqrt{2\pi\varepsilon_0}\sqrt{\eta} R_0^2 \sqrt{\Phi^3}} \frac{1}{R} = 0 \qquad 78.11$$

We now introduce the new independent variable

$$x = \frac{2\pi}{L} z \qquad\qquad 78.12$$

Equation 78.11 becomes

$$R'' + \frac{L^2}{4\pi^2} \frac{\eta \hat{B}^2}{16\Phi} (1 + \cos 2x) R -$$

$$- \frac{L^2}{4\pi^2} \frac{I}{4\sqrt{2\pi\varepsilon_0}\sqrt{\eta} R_0^2 \sqrt{\Phi^3}} \frac{1}{R} = 0 \qquad 78.13$$

Using the abbreviations

$$\alpha^* = \frac{L^2}{4\pi^2} \frac{\eta \hat{B}^2}{16\Phi} \qquad 78.14$$

$$\beta^* = \frac{L^2}{4\pi^2} \frac{I}{4\sqrt{2\pi\varepsilon_0}\sqrt{\eta} R_0^2 \sqrt{\Phi^3}} \qquad 78.15$$

the differential equation

$$R'' + \alpha^* (1 + \cos 2x) R - \beta^* \frac{1}{R} = 0 \qquad 78.16$$

appears. The initial conditions referred to function $R(x)$ are

$$R(0) = 1 ; \qquad R'(0) = 0 \qquad 78.17$$

The solutions of the differential equation 78.16 have been investigated with the help of a computer as functions of parameters α^* and β^* and it has been found that among the solutions, the smallest deviation from the function

$$R_1(x) \equiv 1 \qquad\qquad 78.18$$

appeared, where

$$\alpha^* = \beta^* \qquad\qquad 78.19$$

From the focusing aspect this condition is natural, since in this case the edge of the beam has minimum ripple. Substituting equations 78.14 and 78.15 into 78.19 and expressing $\hat{B}^2$

$$\hat{B}^2 = \frac{2\sqrt{2}\,I}{\pi\varepsilon_0\eta^{3/2}R_0^2\,\Phi^{1/2}} \qquad\qquad 78.20$$

Equation 78.20 represents one of the dimensioning final formulae. Thus, current I flowing in the beam, beam voltage Φ and the initial beam radius R_0 are given values. If it is desired to reduce the beam ripple, the peak value of the axis induction is to be calculated from equation 78.20.

For the determination of the induction the period L is still unknown. In order to find the equation yielding the period L, equation 78.16 is to be linearised. A new dependent variable is introduced

$$y = R_0 R - R_0 \qquad\qquad 78.21$$

where $y \ll R_0$, which follows from equations 78.8 and 78.18

$$y'' + \alpha^*(1 + \cos 2x)(R_0 + y) - \beta^*\,\frac{R_0}{1 + \dfrac{y}{R_0}} = 0 \qquad\qquad 78.22$$

Using the series expansion

$$\frac{1}{1 + \dfrac{y}{R_0}} = 1 - \frac{y}{R_0} + \frac{y^2}{R_0^2} - \ldots \qquad\qquad 78.23$$

and disregarding the powers of y/R_0 higher than the first equation, 78.22 becomes (after rearrangement)

$$y'' + (\alpha^* + \beta^* + \alpha^* \cos 2x)y = R_0(\beta^* - \alpha^*) - \alpha^* R_0 \cos 2x \qquad\qquad 78.24$$

Introducing the notations taking into account the condition 78.19

$$a = \alpha^* + \beta^* = 2\alpha^* \qquad\qquad 78.25$$

$$2q = \alpha^* \qquad\qquad 78.26$$

the following equation is produced

$$y'' + (a + 2q \cos 2x)y = -2R_0 q \cos 2x \qquad\qquad 78.27$$

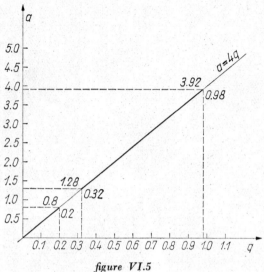

figure VI.5

After transformation, an inhomogeneous *Mathieu* differential equation appears, as the linearised form of the differential equation 78.16. The right-hand side of the equation may be disregarded, since the coefficient $2R_0q$ amounts to approximately one-thousandth part of the other coefficients. Disregarding the excitation term [4, 9], the solution of equation 78.27 is

$$y(x) = c_1 ce_{m+\vartheta}(z, -q) + c_2 se_{m+\vartheta}(x, -q) \qquad 78.28$$

where $m = 2n$ or $m = 2n + 1$.

It is obvious that only bounded solutions can be considered as solutions of the differential equation. Considering equations 78.14, 78.15, 78.19 and assuming the potential Φ as positive, the following appear

$$a > 0; \qquad q > 0 \qquad\qquad 78.29$$

$$a = 4q \qquad\qquad 78.30$$

Equation 78.28 forms a solution only if the parameters appearing therein are of appropriate value. Therefore, the values of the parameters a and q are chosen so that the solution be bounded. On account of equation 78.30 a and q cannot be chosen independently of each other. Plotting the straight line given by equation 78.30 into the stability diagram of the *Mathieu* functions (figure V.16) a multitude of intersection points with the character-istic curves appears. The straight sections between two intersection points within the stability region give the related values of a and q which may be chosen for the bounded solution. The two first stability regions determined in this manner are given in figure VI.5.

In practice q and therefore a are chosen in the first stability region. Using equations 78.15, 78.19, 78.26 we obtain

$$L^2 = 32\sqrt{2\pi^3}\varepsilon_0\sqrt{\eta}\,\frac{R_0^2\sqrt{\Phi^3}}{I}\,q \qquad\qquad 78.31$$

Equation 78.31 represents the second dimensioning final formula. Therefore, the current I flowing in the beam, the beam potential Φ and the initial beam radius R_0 are given, and similarly the value of q is determined from the stability diagram. If it is required that the edge electron trajectory of the beam should be bounded, the period of the axis induction must be calculated from equation 78.31.

It has been seen that there exists a relation between the parameters. With knowledge of q and with the help of equations 78.14, 78.25, 78.30, the following equations are obtained

$$0 < \frac{L^2\hat{B}^2}{\Phi} \le 14.3\times10^{-10} \qquad\qquad 78.32$$

$$22.9\times10^{-10} \le \frac{L^2\hat{B}^2}{\Phi} \le 70.2\times10^{-10} \qquad\qquad 78.33$$

The formulae 78.32 and 78.33 can be advantageously used for dimensioning, since they show the permissible limits when choosing L and $\hat{B}$.

Example

$\Phi = 1000$ V;
$I = 10^{-2}$ A ;
$R_0 = 10^{-3}$ m ;
$q = 6\times10^{-2}$

Calculated from 78.20 and 78.31

$\hat{B} = 208\times10^{-4}$ V s/m^2 ;
$L = 31.4\times10^{-2}$ m

79. PLANE-SYMMETRIC BEAM

As in the case of axial symmetry, we start from the following conditions

$$\Phi = \text{constant}\,, \qquad\qquad 0 \le z \qquad\qquad 79.1$$

$$B = 0\,, \qquad\qquad z \le 0 \qquad\qquad 79.2$$

$$B = \hat{B}\cos\frac{2\pi}{L}z\,, \qquad\qquad 0 < z \qquad\qquad 79.3$$

The induction field determined with the help of equations 79.2 and 79.3 is given in figure VI.4 (§ 78).

The initial conditions are

$$y(0) = Y_0 \; ; \quad y'(0) = 0 \; ; \quad \dot{x}(0) = 0 \qquad\qquad 79.4$$

Using the above, the equations of motion become the following (see § 22)

$$C = 0 \qquad\qquad 79.5$$

$$\Phi y'' + \left[\frac{1}{2\varepsilon_0} \varrho_0 + \frac{\eta \hat{B}^2}{2} \cos^2 \frac{2\pi}{L} z \right] y = 0 \qquad\qquad 79.6$$

The expression of ϱ_0 given in 74.4 is substituted into equation 79.6

$$\Phi y'' + \frac{\eta \hat{B}^2}{2} \cos^2 \left(\frac{2\pi}{L} z \right) y - \frac{I}{4\sqrt{2}\,\varepsilon_0 \sqrt{\eta}\, W \sqrt{\Phi}} = 0 \qquad\qquad 79.7$$

Equation 79.7 is the basic equation of plane-symmetric electron beam focusing by spatially periodic magnetic field.

Using equation 78.10, with the dependent and independent variables

$$y = y_0 Y \; ; \quad x = \frac{2\pi}{L} z \qquad\qquad 79.8$$

and the abbreviations

$$\alpha^* = \frac{L^2}{4\pi^2} \frac{\eta \hat{B}^2}{4\Phi} \qquad\qquad 79.9$$

$$\beta^* = \frac{L^2}{4\pi^2} \frac{I}{4\sqrt{2}\,\varepsilon_0 \sqrt{\eta}\, Y_0 W \sqrt{\Phi^3}} \qquad\qquad 79.10$$

the differential equation

$$Y'' + \alpha^* (1 + \cos 2x) Y - \beta^* = 0 \qquad\qquad 79.11$$

is obtained. The initial conditions for the function $Y(x)$ are

$$Y(0) = 1 \; ; \qquad Y'(0) = 0 \qquad\qquad 79.12$$

The solutions of the differential equation 79.11 as function of α^* and β^* have been investigated with the help of computers, and similarly to the axially symmetric case it has been found that the solutions deviating least from the function

$$Y_1(x) \equiv 1 \qquad\qquad 79.13$$

are those where

$$\alpha^* = \beta^* \qquad\qquad 79.14$$

With the help of equations 79.9 and 79.10 the peak value of the induction on the axis is obtained from equation 79.14

$$\hat{B}^2 = \frac{I}{\sqrt{2}\,\varepsilon_0 \eta^{3/2} Y_0 W \Phi^{1/2}} \qquad\qquad 79.15$$

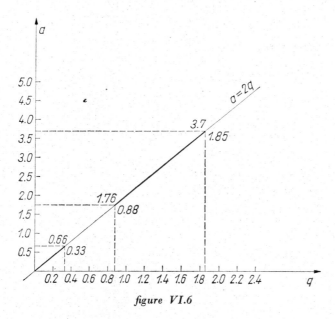

figure VI.6

Equation 79.15 is one of the final dimensioning formulae. The beam current for unit length I/W, the beam voltage Φ and the initial height Y_0 of the beam are given. The peak value of the axis induction pertaining to the minimum ripple of the beam is calculated from equation 79.15.

Similarly to the axially symmetric case, using the transformation $(u \ll Y_0)$

$$u = Y_0 Y - Y_0 \qquad\qquad 79.16$$

and the notations

$$a = \alpha^* \qquad\qquad 79.17$$

$$2q = \alpha^* \qquad\qquad 79.18$$

the still unknown period is obtained from *Mathieu's* differential equation

$$u'' + (a + 2q \cos 2x)u = -2Y_0 q \cos 2x \qquad\qquad 79.19$$

disregarding the negligible excitation term. The form of the solution of equation 79.19 is identical to that of equation 78.28. The bounded solutions are in the stability region, for positive a and q pertaining to positive potential Φ, as points of the straight line

$$a = 2q \qquad\qquad 79.20$$

derived from equation 79.14 as shown in figure VI.6.

By using equations 79.10, 79.14 and 79.18

$$L^2 = 32\sqrt{2}\,\pi^2 \varepsilon_0 \sqrt{\eta}\,\frac{WY_0\sqrt{\Phi^3}}{I}\,q \qquad\qquad 79.21$$

Equation 79.21 is the other dimensioning final formula, from which the period of the induction on the axis can be calculated.

From the relation between the parameters, if q is known, the following equations are obtained with the help of equations 79.9, 79.17 and 79.20

$$0 < \frac{L^2 \hat{B}^2}{\Phi} \leq 5.92 \times 10^{-10} \qquad \qquad 79.22$$

$$15.8 \times 10^{-10} \leq \frac{L^2 \hat{B}^2}{\Phi} \leq 33.2 \times 10^{-10} \qquad \qquad 79.23$$

Example

$\Phi = 10\,000$ V;
$I = 1$ A;
$W = 10^{-3}$ m;
$Y_0 = 5 \times 10^{-4}$ m;
$q = 0.11$

Calculated from 79.15 and 79.21
$\hat{B} = 0.147$ V s/m^2;
$L = 9.5 \times 10^{-3}$ m

(D) FOCUSING BY SIMULTANEOUSLY ACTING PERIODIC ELECTRIC AND PERIODIC MAGNETIC FIELDS

Numerous obstacles appear in the maintenance of beams of maximum power. In the case of periodic electric focusing the period is small and the focusing potential is high; in the case of periodic magnetic focusing the period is also small, slightly larger than that required for periodic electric focusing, and peak induction is large. These all present various difficulties such as electric breakdown, leakage conductance, technological problems due to small dimensions, overheating, large fringe fields, etc., the elimination of which can be achieved with the help of *focusing by simultaneously acting periodic electric and periodic magnetic fields*. When comparing the results yielded by the following discussions, with the corresponding results of periodic electric and magnetic focusing, *the following can be established: beams of higher power can be employed; for a beam of given power a lower focusing potential and a lower peak induction is required; the focusing stability regions are broader.*

The beam power can be increased also by using other focusing methods (see Section H).

80. AXIALLY SYMMETRIC BEAM

In view of the statements given above we will now investigate the focusing performed with the help of simultaneously acting periodic electric and periodic magnetic fields. The focusing field may be characterised by the following condition

$$\varkappa = \frac{L^2 I}{4\sqrt{2}\ \pi^3 \varepsilon_0 \eta^{1/2} U^{3/2} R_0^2} \qquad \qquad 80.1$$

which is identical to equation 85.3 and has been derived from the conditions of the parallel flow, moreover

$$\Phi = U(1 + \varkappa) = \text{constant}, \qquad z \leq 0 \qquad \qquad 80.2$$

$$\Phi = U(1 + \varkappa \cos npz), \qquad\qquad 0 < z \qquad\qquad 80.3$$

$$B = 0, \qquad\qquad\qquad z \leq 0 \qquad\qquad 80.4$$

$$B = \hat{B} \cos pz, \qquad\qquad\qquad 0 < z \qquad\qquad 80.5$$

therefore the period of the electric field is n-times that of the magnetic field (n being an integer). The initial conditions are

$$r(0) = R_0; \quad r'(0) = 0; \quad \dot\alpha(0) = 0 \qquad\qquad 80.6$$

In view of the initial conditions 80.6, $C = 0$. Substituting equation 73.11 transformed by 23.18 into equation 24.19 (the transformed equation of 21.14 where R' is absent), and using the notation r instead of R appearing in 24.19, we obtain

$$r'' + \left(\frac{3}{16} \frac{\Phi'^2}{\Phi^2} + \frac{\eta B^2}{8\Phi} - \frac{I}{4\sqrt{2}\,\pi\varepsilon_0\,\eta^{1/2}\Phi^{3/2}} \frac{1}{r^2} \right) r = 0 \qquad 80.7$$

The space-charge term appearing in equation 80.7 may be considered constant: on the one hand we seek solutions in which r varies to a small degree only, while on the other hand we may write U instead of Φ, since the axis potential fluctuates about U. In consideration of the foregoing, equation 80.7 becomes

$$r'' + \left(\frac{3}{16} \frac{\Phi'^2}{\Phi^2} + \frac{\eta B^2}{8\Phi} - \frac{I}{4\sqrt{2}\,\pi\varepsilon_0\eta^{1/2}U^{3/2}R_0^2} \right) r = 0 \qquad 80.8$$

In equation 80.8 the space-charge density assumed as constant is expressed with the help of R_0 pertaining to the point of entrance.

In view of the fact that $\varkappa < 1$, using the approximations (and known trigonometrical transformations)

$$\Phi^2 \cong U^2 \ (1 + 2\varkappa \cos npz) \qquad\qquad 80.9$$

$$\Phi^{-1} \cong U^{-1} \ (1 - \varkappa \cos npz) \qquad\qquad 80.10$$

$$\Phi^{-2} \cong U^{-2} \ (1 - 2\varkappa \cos npz) \qquad\qquad 80.11$$

the new form of equation 80.8 is

$$r'' + \left(\frac{3\varkappa^2 n^2 p^2}{32} - \frac{3\varkappa^3 n^2 p^2}{16} \cos npz - \frac{3\varkappa^2 n^2 p^2}{32} \cos npz + \right.$$

$$+ \frac{3\varkappa^3 n^3 p^2}{16} \cos 2npz \cos npz + \frac{\eta \hat{B}^2}{16U} - \frac{\eta \varkappa \hat{B}^2}{16U} \cos npz +$$

$$+ \frac{\eta \hat{B}^2}{16U} \cos 2pz - \frac{\eta \varkappa \hat{B}^2}{16U} \cos 2pz \cos npz -$$

$$\left. - \frac{I}{4\sqrt{2}\,\pi\varepsilon_0\eta^{1/2}U^{3/2}R_0^2} \right) r = 0 \qquad\qquad 80.12$$

In equation 80.12 we may disregard the terms in which $\varkappa^3$ or $\varkappa B^2 \cos npz$ appear. Now

$$r'' + \left(\frac{3\varkappa^2 n^2 p^2}{32} + \frac{\eta \hat{B}^2}{16U} - \frac{3\varkappa^2 n^2 p^2}{32} \cos 2npz + \right.$$

$$\left. + \frac{\eta \hat{B}^2}{16U} \cos 2pz - \frac{I}{4\sqrt{2}\pi\varepsilon_0 \eta^{1/2} U^{3/2} R_0^2} \right) r = 0 \qquad 80.13$$

A new independent variable is introduced

$$x = pz \qquad 80.14$$

and equation 80.13 becomes

$$r'' + \left(\frac{3\varkappa^2 n^2}{32} + \frac{\eta \hat{B}^2}{16p^2 U} - \frac{3\varkappa^2 n^2}{32} \cos 2nx + \right.$$

$$\left. + \frac{\eta \hat{B}^2}{16p^2 U} \cos 2x - \frac{I}{4\sqrt{2}\,\pi\varepsilon_0 \eta^{1/2} U^{3/2} p^2 R_0^2} \right) r = 0 \qquad 80.15$$

A new dependent variable is introduced

$$r = R_0 + R_0 y; \qquad y \ll 1 \qquad 80.16$$

Using equations 80.16, 80.15 yields the following equation

$$y'' + \left(\frac{3\varkappa^2 n^2}{32} + \frac{\eta \hat{B}^2}{16p^2 U} + \frac{\eta \hat{B}^2}{16p^2 U} \cos 2x - \frac{3\varkappa^2 n^2}{32} \cos nx - \right.$$

$$\left. - \frac{I}{4\sqrt{2}\,\pi\varepsilon_0 \eta^{1/2} U^{3/2} p^2 R_0^2} \right) y + \frac{3\varkappa^2 n^2}{32} + \frac{\eta \hat{B}^2}{16p^2 U} +$$

$$+ \frac{\eta \hat{B}^2}{16p^2 U} \cos 2x - \frac{3\varkappa^2 n^2}{32} \cos nx -$$

$$- \frac{I}{4\sqrt{2}\,\pi\varepsilon_0 \eta^{1/2} U^{3/2} p^2 R_0^2} = 0 \qquad 80.17$$

With the notations

$$\lambda_1 = \frac{3\varkappa^2 n^2}{32} + \frac{\eta \hat{B}^2}{16p^2 U} \qquad 80.18$$

$$\lambda_2 = \frac{\eta \hat{B}^2}{16p^2 U} \qquad 80.19$$

$$\lambda_3 = - \frac{3\varkappa^2 n^2}{32} \qquad 80.20$$

$$\lambda_4 = - \frac{I}{4\sqrt{2}\,\pi\varepsilon_0 \eta^{1/2} U^{3/2} p^2 R_0^2} \qquad 80.21$$

equation 80.17 becomes

$$y'' + (\lambda_1 + \lambda_2 \cos 2x + \lambda_3 \cos nx + \lambda_4)y + \lambda_1 +$$
$$+ \lambda_2 \cos 2x + \lambda_3 \cos nx + \lambda_4 = 0 \qquad 80.22$$

Equation 80.22 is an inhomogeneous *Hill's* equation. The general solution of the corresponding homogeneous equation [4, 9] is

$$y_h(x) = K_1 H_1^*(x) + K_2 H_2^*(x) \qquad 80.23$$

The expressions of the functions $H_1^*(x)$ and $H_2^*(x)$ are obtained in the following manner (the method of the solution is not dealt with separately)

$$\lambda_1 + \lambda_4 = \nu^2 + l_{20}\lambda_2 + l_{30}\lambda_3 + l_{22}\lambda_2^2 + l_{32}\lambda_3^2 + l_{20, 30}\lambda_2\lambda_3 + \ldots \quad 80.24$$

$$H_1^*(x) = \cos \nu x + f_{20}(x)\lambda_2 + f_{30}(x)\lambda_3 + f_{22}(x)\lambda_2^2 + f_{32}(x)\lambda_3^2 +$$
$$+ f_{20, 30}(x)\lambda_2\lambda_3 + \ldots \qquad 80.25$$

i.e. in case of $\lambda_2 = \lambda_3 = 0$ the first linearly independent solution turns into the function $\cos \nu x$. The constants l_{20}, l_{30} etc. (ν is also a constant) are then determined, and thereafter the functions $f_{20}(x)$, $f_{30}(x)$, etc. Following differentiation and substitution we have

$$- \nu^2 \cos \nu x + f_{20}''\lambda_2 + f_{30}''\lambda_3 + \nu^2 \cos \nu x + \nu^2 f_{20}\lambda_2 +$$
$$+ \nu^2 f_{30}\lambda_3 + l_{20} \cos \nu x\lambda_2 + l_{30} \cos \nu x\lambda_3 +$$
$$+ \cos 2x \cos \nu x\lambda_2 + \cos nx \cos \nu x\lambda_3 + \ldots = 0 \qquad 80.26$$

We have written the terms of equation 80.26 up to first order. From the coefficients of λ_2 and λ_3

$$f_{20}'' + \nu^2 f_{20} = - \cos \nu x l_{20} - \cos \nu x \cos 2x \qquad 80.27$$

$$f_{30}'' + \nu^2 f_{30} = - \cos \nu x l_{30} - \cos \nu x \cos nx \qquad 80.28$$

Investigation of equations 80.27 and 80.28 demonstrate that the constants λ_{20} and λ_{30} must be chosen with a value of zero, otherwise non-periodic solutions of the equations will appear (resonance). The solutions are

$$f_{20}(x) = C_1 \cos \nu x + C_2 \sin \nu x - \frac{1}{4\nu} \left[\frac{\cos 2(\nu + 1)x}{2(\nu + 1)} + \right.$$
$$+ \left. \frac{\cos 2(\nu - 1)x}{2(\nu - 1)} \right] \cos \nu x - \frac{1}{4\nu} \left[\frac{\sin 2(\nu + 1)x}{2(\nu + 1)} + \sin 2x + \right.$$
$$+ \left. \frac{\sin 2(\nu - 1)x}{2(\nu - 1)} \right] \sin \nu x , \quad (\nu \neq 1) \qquad 80.29$$

$$f_{30}(x) = K_1 \cos vx + K_2 \sin vx - \frac{1}{4v}\left[\frac{\cos(2v+n)x}{2v+n} + \right.$$

$$\left. + \frac{\cos(2v-n)x}{2v-n}\right]\cos vx - \frac{1}{4v}\left[\frac{\sin(2v+n)x}{2v+n} + \frac{2\sin nx}{n} + \right.$$

$$\left. + \frac{\sin(2v-n)x}{2v-n}\right]\sin vx, \quad \left(v \neq \frac{n}{2}\right) \qquad 80.30$$

From the foregoing, retaining the terms required for the first linearly independent solution

$$\lambda_1 + \lambda_4 \cong v^2 \qquad\qquad 80.31$$

$$H_1^*(x) \cong \cos vx\left[1 - \frac{\lambda_2}{4v}\frac{\cos 2(v+1)x}{2(v+1)} - \frac{\lambda_2}{4v}\frac{\cos 2(v-1)x}{2(v-1)} - \right.$$

$$\left. - \frac{\lambda_3}{4v}\frac{\cos(2v+n)x}{2v+n} - \frac{\lambda_3}{4v}\frac{\cos(2v-n)x}{2v-n}\right] \qquad 80.32$$

For the second linearly independent solution, the series 80.24 and the series expansion

$$H_2^*(x) = \sin vx + g_{20}(x)\lambda_2 + g_{30}(x)\lambda_3 + \cdots \qquad 80.33$$

are used. By a procedure corresponding to the foregoing, equations with structures identical to those of equations 80.27 and 80.28 are obtained, with the only difference that sin vx is written instead of cos vx. The solutions are

$$g_{20}(x) = C_1' \sin vx + C_2' \cos vx + \frac{1}{4v}\left[\frac{\cos 2(v+1)x}{2(v+1)} + \right.$$

$$\left. + \frac{\cos 2(v-1)x}{2(v-1)}\right]\sin vx - \frac{1}{4v}\left[\frac{\sin 2(v+1)x}{2(v+1)} - \right.$$

$$\left. - \sin 2x + \frac{\sin 2(v-1)x}{2(v-1)}\right]\cos vx, \quad (v \neq 1) \qquad 80.34$$

$$g_{30}(x) = K_1' \sin vx + K_2' \cos vx + \frac{1}{4v}\left[\frac{\cos(2v+n)x}{2v+n} + \right.$$

$$\left. + \frac{\cos(2v-n)x}{2v-n}\right]\sin vx - \frac{1}{4v}\left[\frac{\sin(2v+n)x}{2v+n} - \right.$$

$$\left. - \frac{2\sin nx}{n} + \frac{\sin(2v-n)x}{2v-n}\right]\cos vx, \quad \left(v \neq \frac{n}{2}\right) \qquad 80.35$$

The second linearly independent solution is

$$H_2^*(x) \simeq \sin \nu x \left[1 - \frac{\lambda_2}{4\nu} \frac{\cos 2(\nu + 1)x}{2(\nu + 1)} + \frac{\lambda_2}{4\nu} \frac{\cos 2(\nu - 1)x}{2(\nu - 1)} + \right.$$
$$\left. + \frac{\lambda_3}{4\nu} \frac{\cos (2\nu + n)x}{2\nu + n} + \frac{\lambda_3}{4\nu} \frac{\cos (2\nu - n)x}{2\nu - n} \right] \qquad 80.36$$

The general solution with approximation of the homogeneous equation is now available. One solution of the inhomogeneous equation may be obtained on the pattern of the process for the homogeneous equation, or from the generally valid equation 82.14. Now, instead of the lengthy derivation, we refer to the paper [170] and on the basis of this we write the solution pertaining to the initial conditions

$$y(0) = y_0 ; \quad y'(0) = y_0' \qquad 80.37$$

One of the solutions of the inhomogeneous equation is provided by

$$y_p(x) = \sum_{\mu=0}^{\infty} y_{p\mu} \cos 2\mu x \qquad 80.38$$

The general solution is

$$y(x) = \left(y_0 - \sum_{\mu=0}^{\infty} y_{p\mu} \right) \frac{H_1^*(x)}{H_1^*(0)} + y_0' \frac{H_2^*(x)}{H_2^{*'}(0)} + \sum_{\mu=0}^{\infty} y_{p\mu} \cos 2\mu x \qquad 80.39$$

As it can be established from equations 80.32 and 80.36, the first two terms of equation 80.39 characterise the long-period rippling of the trajectory while the third term gives a short-period rippling with perturbational character. The nearly parallel flow occurs when the coefficients of the first two terms are equal to zero

$$y_0 - \sum_{\mu=0}^{\infty} y_{p\mu} = 0 ; \quad y_0' = 0 \qquad 80.40$$

In equation 80.40, the second part is the already known natural condition, while from *the first part the dimensioning condition*

$$\frac{3\varkappa^2 n^2}{32} + \frac{\eta \hat{B}^2}{16 p^2 U} = \frac{I}{4\sqrt{2\pi\varepsilon_0}\eta^{1/2} U^{3/2} p^2 R_0^2} \qquad 80.41$$

follows, i.e. generalisation of condition 78.19. The condition 80.41 gives the dimensioning formula for focusing by electric field in case of $\hat{B} = 0$, while in case of $\varkappa = 0$ the dimensioning formula for magnetic field focusing is given. The left-hand side of equation 80.41 is identical to the left-hand side of equation 78.15, from which it follows that for a beam of given power, a lower focusing potential or lower peak induction is required. When multiplying equation 80.41 by p^2 it will be seen that at very small periods the electric field carries the decisive role in the condition for the parallel flow, and the effect of the magnetic field can increasingly be disregarded.

The work [170] demonstrates that broader stability regions pertain to the discussed focusing method.

81. PLANE-SYMMETRIC BEAM

In the plane-symmetric case the electric field can be described by equation 85.12 which follows from the condition of parallel flow; the period of the electric field, similarly to the axially symmetric case, is chosen as n-times the period of the magnetic field. The characteristic data of the field are therefore

$$\varkappa = \frac{L^2 I}{8\sqrt{2}\pi^2 \varepsilon_0 \eta^{1/2} U^{3/2} W Y_0} \qquad\qquad 81.1$$

$$\Phi = U(1 + \varkappa) = \text{constant}, \qquad z \leq 0 \qquad 81.2$$

$$\Phi = U(1 + \varkappa \cos npz), \qquad 0 < z \qquad 81.3$$

$$B = 0, \qquad z \leq 0 \qquad 81.4$$

$$B = \hat{B} \cos pz, \qquad 0 < z \qquad 81.5$$

The chosen initial conditions

$$y(0) = Y_0; \quad y'(0) = 0; \quad \dot{x}(0) = 0 \qquad 81.6$$

yield the value of $C = 0$.

Discussion of the plane-symmetric case is performed with the simplified differential equation, too. Equations 24.5, 24.6 and 74.4 are used, from which the following equation is derived by the already known method (writing y instead of Y)

$$y'' + \left(\frac{3}{16} \frac{\Phi'^2}{\Phi^2} + \frac{\Phi''}{4\Phi} + \frac{\eta B^2}{2\Phi} - \frac{I}{4\sqrt{2}\varepsilon_0 \eta^{1/2} W \Phi^{5/4}} \frac{1}{y} \right) y = 0 \qquad 81.7$$

For reasons similar to the axially symmetric case, the space-charge term is considered constant, and we express it with the help of Y_0, pertaining to the point of entrance, and U

$$y'' + \left(\frac{3}{16} \frac{\Phi'^2}{\Phi^2} + \frac{\Phi''}{4\Phi} + \frac{\eta B^2}{2\Phi} - \frac{I}{4\sqrt{2}\varepsilon_0 \sqrt{\eta} W U^{3/2} Y_0} \right) y = 0 \qquad 81.8$$

With the transformations 80.9, 80.10, 80.11 the new form of 81.8 is obtained

$$y'' + \left(\frac{3}{32} n^2 p^2 \varkappa^2 - \frac{3n^2 p^2 \varkappa^2}{16} \cos npz - \frac{3n^2 p^2 \varkappa^2}{32} \cos 2npz + \right.$$

$$+ \frac{3n^2 p^2 \varkappa^2}{16} \cos 2npz \cos npz - \frac{n^2 p^2 \varkappa}{4} \cos npz +$$

$$\left. + \frac{n^2 p^2 \varkappa^2}{8} + \frac{n^2 p^2 \varkappa^2}{8} \cos 2npz + \frac{\eta \hat{B}^2}{4U} + \frac{\eta \hat{B}^2}{4U} \cos 2pz - \right.$$

$$-\frac{\eta \varkappa \hat{B}^2}{4U}\cos npz - \frac{\eta \varkappa \hat{B}^2}{4U}\cos 2pz \cos npz -$$

$$\left. -\frac{I}{4\sqrt{2}\,\varepsilon_0 \sqrt{\eta}\,WU^{3/2}Y_0}\right)y = 0 \qquad 81.9$$

In addition to the coefficient of $\cos npz$, the coefficients of $\cos 2pz$ and $\cos 2npz$ may be disregarded. Disregarding some other terms due to the reasons given in the foregoing, the following equation is obtained

$$y'' + \left(\frac{7n^2 p^2 \varkappa^2}{32} + \frac{\eta \hat{B}^2}{4U} + \frac{n^2 p^2 \varkappa}{4}\cos npz - \right.$$

$$\left. -\frac{I}{4\sqrt{2}\,\varepsilon_0 \sqrt{\eta}\,WU^{3/2}Y_0}\right)y = 0 \qquad 81.10$$

With the independent variable

$$x = \frac{np}{2}z \qquad 81.11$$

the equation

$$y'' + \left(\frac{7\varkappa^2}{8} + \frac{\eta \hat{B}^2}{n^2 p^2 U} + \varkappa \cos 2x - \frac{I}{\sqrt{2}\,\varepsilon_0 \sqrt{\eta}\,n^2 p^2 WU^{3/2}Y_0}\right)y = 0 \quad 81.12$$

is given.

With the transformation (v is the new function)

$$y = Y_0 + Y_0 v \qquad (v \ll 1) \qquad 81.13$$

equation

$$v'' + \left(\frac{7\varkappa^2}{8} + \frac{\eta \hat{B}^2}{n^2 p^2 U} + \varkappa \cos 2x - \frac{I}{\sqrt{2}\,\varepsilon_0 \sqrt{\eta}\,n^2 p^2 WU^{3/2}Y_0}\right)v +$$

$$+\frac{7\varkappa^2}{8} + \frac{\eta \hat{B}^2}{n^2 p^2 U} + \varkappa \cos 2x - \frac{I}{\sqrt{2}\,\varepsilon_0 \sqrt{\eta}\,n^2 p^2 WU^{3/2}Y_0} = 0 \qquad 81.14$$

is given.

The abbreviations

$$a = \frac{7\varkappa^2}{8} + \frac{\eta \hat{B}^2}{n^2 p^2 U} - \frac{I}{\sqrt{2}\,\varepsilon_0 \sqrt{\eta}\,n^2 p^2 WU^{3/2}Y_0} \qquad 81.15$$

$$2q = -\varkappa \qquad 81.16$$

yield the inhomogeneous *Mathieu's* equation

$$v'' + (a - 2q \cos 2x)v = -a + 2q \cos 2x \qquad 81.17$$

28*

Investigation of equation 81.17 is performed on the pattern of the axially symmetric case. Due to lack of space we shall not repeat the process, instead we refer to the work [170]. However, we will give the condition of nearly parallel flow, the dimensioning equation

$$\frac{I}{4\sqrt{2}\,\varepsilon_0\eta^{1/2}p^2WU^{3/2}Y_0} = \frac{\varkappa^2n^2}{4} + \frac{\eta\hat{B}^2}{4p^2U} \qquad 81.18$$

which is a generalisation of equation 79.14. All the conclusions which were arrived at in the axially symmetric case can be obtained here also (focusing of higher powers; smaller field intensities; broader stability regions).

(E) FOCUSING BY INCREASING MAGNETIC FIELD

Electron tubes operating in the very short (millimetre) wave range require especially high current densities. Similar is the position in case of high-power tubes and various electron-technological equipment. *The cathodes now in use are not capable of delivering current densities of such values, and therefore the diameter or the height of the beam is to be reduced by a suitable field.* In the following we shall treat two cases of compression performed by a purely magnetic field. These cases characterise the subject, and by suitable choosing of the parameters employed, numerous actual cases can be approximated.

The increasing magnetic field figures in various experimental devices of nuclear power generation, and is known as magnetic trap or magnetic bottle (magnetic bottles are used in order to prevent departure of charged particles from determined space sections).

82. AXIALLY SYMMETRIC BEAM

The increasing magnetic field is described with the help of a function having three parameters and thus suitable for approximation of numerous types of increasing magnetic fields.

For simplification, the constant C in 21.6 is chosen as zero which is achieved by magnetic shielding of the space section before the starting point of the electron beam. Another way is also possible to reach zero value of constant C by another formation of the beam.

Our conditions are therefore

$$\Phi = \text{constant} \qquad 82.1$$

$$B = \left[B_0^2 + \hat{B}^2\left(1 - \cos\frac{2\pi}{L}z\right)\right]^{1/2}, \quad 0 \le z \le \frac{L}{2} \qquad 82.2$$

$$r(0) = R_0 ; \quad r'(0) = 0 ; \quad \dot{\alpha}(0) = 0 \qquad 82.3$$

With the space-charge term 73.11 and the above conditions, equation 21.14 becomes

$$r'' + \left(\frac{\eta B_0^2}{8\Phi} + \frac{\eta\hat{B}^2}{8\Phi} + \frac{\eta\hat{B}^2}{8\Phi}\cos\frac{2\pi}{L}z - \frac{I}{4\sqrt{2}\pi\varepsilon_0\sqrt{\eta}\,\Phi^{3/2}}\frac{1}{r^2}\right)r = 0 \qquad 82.4$$

With the new variables

$$x = \frac{\pi}{L} z \qquad\qquad 82.5$$

and

$$y = \frac{r - R_0}{R_0} \quad (y \ll 1) \qquad\qquad 82.6$$

equation 82.4 becomes

$$
\begin{aligned}
y'' + \Bigg(& \frac{\eta B_0^2 L^2}{8\pi^2 \Phi} + \frac{\eta \hat{B}^2 L^2}{8\pi^2 \Phi} + \frac{IL^2}{4\sqrt{2\pi^3}\varepsilon_0\sqrt{\eta}\Phi^{3/2}R_0^2} - \\
& - \frac{\eta \hat{B}^2 L^2}{8\pi^2 \Phi} \cos 2x \Bigg) y = \frac{IL^2}{4\sqrt{2\pi^3}\varepsilon_0\sqrt{\eta}\Phi^{3/2}R_0^2} - \\
& - \frac{\eta B_0^2 L^2}{8\pi^2 \Phi} - \frac{\eta \hat{B}^2 L^2}{8\pi^2 \Phi} + \frac{\eta \hat{B}^2 L^2}{8\pi^2 \Phi} \cos 2x \qquad 82.7
\end{aligned}
$$

The notations

$$a = \frac{\eta B_0^2 L^2}{8\pi^2 \Phi} + \frac{\eta \hat{B}^2 L^2}{8\pi^2 \Phi} + \frac{IL^2}{4\sqrt{2\pi^3}\varepsilon_0\sqrt{\eta}\Phi^{3/2}R_0^2} \qquad 82.8$$

$$2q = \frac{\eta \hat{B}^2 L^2}{8\pi^2 \Phi} \qquad\qquad 82.9$$

$$k_1 = \frac{IL^2}{4\sqrt{2\pi^3}\varepsilon_0\sqrt{\eta}\Phi^{3/2}R_0^2} - \frac{\eta B_0^2 L^2}{8\pi^2 \Phi} - \frac{\eta \hat{B}^2 L^2}{8\pi^2 \Phi} \qquad 82.10$$

yield the equation

$$y'' + (a - 2q \cos 2x)y = k_1 + 2q \cos 2x \qquad 82.11$$

which will readily be recognised as an inhomogeneous *Mathieu*'s equation.

In case of beam compression no such requirement exists according to which the solution must be bounded in the entire region of x. The only requirement is that it should be bounded in the compression region. Under these conditions any arbitrary *Mathieu* function may be used. Using the notation y_h for the solution of the homogeneous equation

$$y_h = Ay_1 + By_2 \qquad\qquad 82.12$$

is the form given for the general solution of the homogeneous equation. A solution of the inhomogeneous equation may be obtained by the *Lagrange* method. With the notation

$$y_1 y_2' - y_2 y_1' = W(y_1, y_2) \neq 0 \qquad \text{(constant)} \qquad 82.13$$

the known formula [4] is

$$y_p = \frac{1}{W(y_1, y_2)} \left\{ -y_1 \int_{x_0}^{x} y_2 f \, dx + y_2 \int_{x_0}^{x} y_1 f \, dx \right\} \qquad 82.14$$

In equation 82.14 $f = f(x)$ is the inhomogeneity, and y_p a (particular) solution of the inhomogeneous equation. In our case

$$f(x) = k_1 + 2q \cos 2x \qquad 82.15$$

In accordance with [9], from the integrals appearing

$$\int_{x_0}^{x} y_1 \cos 2x \, dx = \frac{a}{2q} \int_{x_0}^{x} y_1 \, dx + \frac{1}{2q} y_1' - \frac{1}{2q} y_1'(0) \qquad 82.16$$

and similarly for y_2. Using the foregoing, the general solution of equation 82.11 (the sum of the general solution of the homogeneous equation and a particular solution of the inhomogeneous equation) is

$$y(x) = Ay_1(x) + By_2(x) - \frac{y_2'(x) - y_2'(0)}{W(y_1, y_2)} y_1(x) +$$

$$+ \frac{y_1'(x) - y_1'(0)}{W(y_1, y_2)} y_2(x) - \frac{a + k_1}{W(y_1, y_2)} y_1(x) \int_{x_0}^{x} y_2(t) dt +$$

$$+ \frac{a + k_1}{W(y_1, y_2)} y_2(x) \int_{x_0}^{x} y_1(t) dt \qquad 82.17$$

Dimensioning is performed as follows. With knowledge of the characteristic data (Φ, I, R_0) of the beam, and data $(B_0, \hat{B}, L)$ of the magnetic field, the parameters a and $2q$ can be determined from equations 82.8 and 82.9. These determine the *Mathieu* functions figuring in the solution. The value of constant k_1 can be calculated from equation 82.10. With knowledge of the foregoing the (transformed) functional curve of the trajectory can be calculated from equation 82.17.

83. PLANE-SYMMETRIC BEAM

Similarly to the axially symmetric case, the magnetic field is given by a three-parameter function, and the value of C in 22.6 is chosen as zero. The group of relevant conditions consists of

$$\Phi = \text{constant} \qquad 83.1$$

$$B = \left[B_0^2 + \hat{B}^2 \left(1 - \cos \frac{2\pi}{L} z \right) \right]^{1/2}, \quad 0 \leq z \leq \frac{L}{2} \qquad 83.2$$

$$y(0) = Y_0 \; ; \quad y'(0) = 0 \; ; \quad \dot{x}(0) = 0 \qquad \text{83.3}$$

With the above conditions and space-charge 74.4, equation 22.13 becomes

$$y'' + \left(\frac{\eta B_0^2}{2\Phi} + \frac{\eta \hat{B}^2}{2\Phi} - \frac{\eta \hat{B}^2}{2\Phi} \cos \frac{2\pi}{L} z \right) y - \frac{I}{4\sqrt{2}\,\varepsilon_0\sqrt{\eta}\,W\Phi^{3/2}} = 0 \qquad \text{83.4}$$

We now introduce the new variables

$$x = \frac{\pi}{L} z \qquad \text{83.5}$$

and

$$v = \frac{1}{Y_0} y \qquad \text{83.6}$$

with which equation 83.4 becomes

$$v'' + \left(\frac{\eta \hat{B}_0^2 L^2}{2\pi^2\Phi} + \frac{\eta B^2 L^2}{2\pi^2\Phi} - \right.$$

$$\left. - \frac{\eta \hat{B}^2 L^2}{2\pi^2\Phi} \cos 2x \right) v = \frac{IL^2}{4\sqrt{2\pi^2}\,\varepsilon_0\sqrt{\eta}\,W Y_0 \Phi^{3/2}} \qquad \text{83.7}$$

Now we introduce the notations

$$a = \frac{\eta B_0^2 L^2}{2\pi^2\Phi} + \frac{\eta \hat{B}^2 L^2}{2\pi^2\Phi} \qquad \text{83.8}$$

$$2q = \frac{\eta \hat{B}^2 L^2}{2\pi^2\Phi} \qquad \text{83.9}$$

$$k_2 = \frac{IL^2}{4\sqrt{2\pi^3}\,\varepsilon_0\sqrt{\eta}\,W Y_0 \Phi^{3/2}} \qquad \text{83.10}$$

The new form is

$$v'' + (a - 2q \cos 2x) v = k_2 \qquad \text{83.11}$$

Equation 83.11 is an inhomogeneous *Mathieu*'s equation.

Taking into account the statements made with regard to the axially symmetric case, the general solution of equation 83.11 may be directly written

$$y(x) = A' y_1(x) + B' y_2(x) - \frac{k_2}{W(y_1, y_2)} y_1(x) \int_{x_0}^{x} y_2(t)\,dt +$$

$$+ \frac{k_2}{W(y_1, y_2)} y_2(x) \int_{x_0}^{x} y_1(t)\,dt \qquad \text{83.12}$$

Dimensioning is performed similarly to the axially symmetric case.

(F) COMPLEMENTARY FOCUSING

84. THE BASIC PRINCIPLE

In the preceding parts of this book (with the exception of Section D) focusing has been performed with the help of either electric or magnetic fields. We have investigated the conditions under which the beam could be bounded by planes or cylinders, or if this is not possible, the ripple should be of minimum value.

When focusing was performed using electric field, the magnetic field was chosen as zero, and we investigated the beams produced in the most simple cases. When focusing was performed by a magnetic field, the electric field was chosen as zero (the potential is constant), and again we investigated the beams produced in the most simple cases.

In the more general case of simultaneous magnetic and electric field action we may also consider focusing.

Complementary focusing involves only such complementary fields, under the effect of which the beams produced may be bounded by planes or cylinders. In case of complementary focusing, either the simultaneously acting electric or the magnetic field may be chosen entirely arbitrarily, while the other can be calculated from the focusing conditions [208].

Thus in consequence of the foregoing, we seek a relation between the complementary electric and magnetic fields, under which the beam dimensions do not vary. This fairly general focusing principle is investigated on the basis of equations 21.14 and 22.13.

85. CALCULATION OF COMPLEMENTARY FIELDS

(a) Axially symmetric beam

When the beam radius is constant the beam dimensions do not vary. However, in this case r' and r'' are equal to zero. In case of a beam of constant radius the space-charge ϱ_0 can be calculated from equation 73.11 with the substitution of $r = R_0$. Taking this into consideration, equation 21.14 becomes

$$\frac{1}{4}\Phi''R_0 - \frac{I}{4\sqrt{2\pi\varepsilon_0}\sqrt{\eta R_0}\sqrt{\Phi}} + \frac{\eta}{8}B^2R_0 - \frac{\eta}{2}C^2\frac{1}{R_0^3} = 0 \qquad 85.1$$

Let Φ (and Φ'' which can be calculated) be given. The axis induction necessary for a beam of constant diameter is

$$B^2 = \frac{4C^2}{R_0^4} - \frac{2\Phi''}{\eta} + \frac{\sqrt{2}\,I}{\pi\varepsilon_0\eta^{3/2}R_0^2\Phi^{1/2}} \qquad 85.2$$

Equation 85.2 gives the induction necessary for *Brillouin* focusing, if for example the valid conditions $C = 0$, $\Phi'' = 0$ are enforced.

In case of simultaneously acting periodic electric and periodic magnetic fields, with the notation

$$\varkappa = \frac{L^2 I}{4\sqrt{2\pi^3 \varepsilon_0 \eta^{1/2}}\, U^{3/2} R_0^2} \qquad 85.3$$

the related values of the potential on the axis and the induction on the axis for the edge trajectory entering on radius R_0 with condition $C = 0$, are given via the equation

$$\Phi'' + \frac{\eta}{2}\, B^2 = \frac{I}{\sqrt{2\pi\varepsilon_0 \eta^{1/2} U^{1/2} R_0^2}} \qquad 85.4$$

obtained from equation 21.14, with ϱ_0 calculated from 73.11, as

$$\Phi = U\left(1 + \varkappa \cos \frac{2\pi}{L} z\right) \qquad 85.5$$

$$B^2 = \frac{2\sqrt{2} I}{\pi\varepsilon_0 \eta^{3/2} U^{1/2} R_0^2}\, \cos^2 \frac{\pi}{L} z \qquad 85.6$$

All the notations given in the equations are already known, or are ascertainable from defining equations. One item of interest, however, must be pointed out: the period of the electric field is double the period of the magnetic field.

Let B be given. In this case Φ can be calculated from the following differential equation

$$\Phi'' + A^* \frac{1}{\sqrt{\Phi}} = B^* \qquad 85.7$$

where

$$A^* = -\frac{I}{\sqrt{2\pi\varepsilon_0}\sqrt{\eta} R_0^2} \qquad 85.8$$

$$B^* = \eta\left(\frac{2C^2}{R_0^4} - \frac{B^2}{2}\right) \qquad 85.9$$

(b) Plane-symmetric beam

The beam dimensions remain unchanged here also, if the half-height of the beam is constant. In this case y' and y'' are equal to zero. In case of a constant half-heigth beam, the space-charge ϱ_0 can be given by using 74.4. Accordingly, equation 22.13 becomes

$$\frac{1}{2}\, \Phi'' Y_0 - \frac{I}{4\sqrt{2}\varepsilon_0\sqrt{\eta} W\sqrt{\Phi}} + \frac{\eta}{2}\, B^2 Y_0 - \frac{\eta}{2}\, CB = 0 \qquad 85.10$$

First let Φ (and Φ'' calculable therefrom) be given. The axis induction necessary for the constant half-height beam is

$$B = \frac{C}{2Y_0} \pm \left[\frac{C^2}{4Y_0} - \frac{\Phi''}{\eta} + \frac{I}{2\sqrt{2}\varepsilon_0\eta^{3/2}Y_0 W\Phi^{1/2}} \right]^{1/2} \qquad 85.11$$

Equation 85.11 yields the induction necessary for *Brillouin* focusing if the valid conditions $C = 0$, $\Phi'' = 0$ are enforced.

Similarly to the case of axial symmetry, the following are yielded by equations 22.13 and 74.4 (here also C is equal to zero)

$$\varkappa = \frac{L^2 I}{8\sqrt{2}\pi^2\varepsilon_0\eta^{1/2}U^{3/2}W Y_0} \qquad 85.12$$

$$\Phi'' + \eta B^2 = \frac{I}{2\sqrt{2}\varepsilon_0\eta^{1/2}U^{1/2}W Y_0} \qquad 85.13$$

$$\Phi = U\left(1 + \varkappa \cos\frac{2\pi}{L}z\right) \qquad 85.14$$

$$B^2 = \frac{I}{\sqrt{2}\varepsilon_0\eta^{3/2}U^{1/2}W Y_0}\cos^2\frac{\pi}{L}z \qquad 85.15$$

Here also the period of the electric field is double the period of the magnetic field.

Now let B be given. In this case Φ can be calculated from the following differential equation

$$\Phi'' + A'\frac{1}{\sqrt{\Phi}} = B' \qquad 85.16$$

where

$$A' = - \frac{I}{2\sqrt{2}\varepsilon_0\sqrt{\eta}W Y_0} \qquad 85.17$$

$$B' = \frac{\eta B}{Y_0}(C - BY_0) \qquad 85.18$$

(G) GENERAL PARAXIAL BEAMS WITH STRAIGHT AXIS

86. THE BASIC PRINCIPLE

Equations 21.6, 21.13, 21.14 and 22.6, 22.12, 22.13 are the general equations of axially symmetric and plane-symmetric electron beams, respectively, with knowledge of the constants 21.6 and 22.6, the equations 21.14 and 22.13 can be treated independently, since in these equations the functions $\alpha(z)$ [or, respectively, $x(z)$] do not figure.

As customary, it is assumed that among the functions figuring in the equations, $\Phi(z)$, $\varrho_0(z)$, $B(z)$ which figure as coefficients in the differential equations referring to the unknown functions $r(z)$, $y(z)$ are known.

As a departure from the usual practice, in general cases either $\Phi(z)$, $\varrho_0(z)$ or $B(z)$ may also be considered as unknown functions, and any of the four single variable functions may be determined from equations 21.14 or 23.13, with knowledge of the other three.

With this conception, the main tasks are the following:

a) the electron trajectory is to be determined if the axis potential, the axis induction and the space-charge are prescribed (basic problem);

b) the axis potential is to be determined when the trajectory, the axis induction and the space-charge are prescribed;

c) the axis induction is to be determined when the trajectory, axis potential and space-charge are prescribed;

d) the space-charge is to be determined when the trajectory, axis potential and axis induction are prescribed.

It is not essential that the relations 73.11, 74.4 will exist between the space-charge ϱ_0, the axis potential Φ and the trajectory $r(z)$ or $y(z)$, since these relations are approximations only.

87. CALCULATION OF THE AXIS INDUCTION
AND OF THE SPACE-CHARGE

Among the main problems, the solution of *a)* and *b)* is reached by solving a differential equation.

The solution of *c)* and *d)* represents the solution of algebraic equations, and can be given in explicit form.

Formulae referring to the axially symmetric case

$$B^2 = \frac{4C^2}{r^4} - \frac{8\Phi r''}{\eta r} - \frac{4\Phi' r'}{\eta r} - \frac{2\Phi''}{\eta} - \frac{2\varrho_0}{\varepsilon_0 \eta} \qquad 87.1$$

$$\varrho_0 = \varepsilon_0 \left(\frac{2\eta C^2}{r^4} - \frac{4\Phi r''}{r} - \frac{2\Phi' r'}{r} - \Phi'' - \frac{\eta B^2}{2} \right) \qquad 87.2$$

Formulae referring to the plane-symmetric case

$$B = \frac{C}{4y} \pm \left[\frac{C^2}{16y^2} - \frac{1}{2\eta} \left(\frac{2\Phi y''}{y} + \frac{\Phi' y'}{y} + \Phi'' + \frac{\varrho_0}{\varepsilon_0} \right) \right]^{1/2} \qquad 87.3$$

$$\varrho_0 = \varepsilon_0 \left(\frac{\eta C B}{y} - 2\eta B^2 - \frac{2\Phi y''}{y} - \frac{\Phi' y'}{y} - \Phi'' \right) \qquad 87.4$$

Note

(*i*) With the substitutions of $C = 0$, $\Phi = $ constant, $r = $ constant and $y = $ constant, the formulae 75.17 and 76.14 can be obtained from equations 87.2 and 87.4. Formula 76.14

gives one half of the charge density calculated from the present formula, and this is understandable since the charge, taken into consideration there, is distributed in twice the
volume.

(*ii*) The conception according to which any of the functions figuring in the basic equation
may be considered as unknown, enables solution of one of the important problems in
practice. This problem occurs principally in the case of microwave tubes, and consists of
the fact that trajectory elements—distance from the axis or from the basic plane; tangent
to the trajectory—arising when leaving a preceding system are unsuitable when entering a
system next in sequence. In such cases matching or bypass sections are employed between
the two systems, with the help of which the trajectory elements are transformed as
necessary.

*The field required in the matching or bypass sections can be calculated directly from the
foregoing equations.*

(H) FOCUSING BY QUADRUPOLE FIELD

*The most widely used method for focusing of high-power beams is focusing by quadrupole
field.* This fact is suggested already by its origin, since first [235, 236] it was used in particle
accelerators. The efficiency of the focusing method will be readily comprehended. The force
acting on the electrons in the quadrupole field is approximately perpendicular to the
electron trajectory, and this results in the greatest possible change in the direction of the
trajectory.

Focusing by quadrupole field will be investigated only in the case of cylindrical beams. The
properties of plane-symmetric beams in quadrupole field will not be investigated on account
of the large-scale deviations of geometric structural nature. Focusing of electron beams
showing quadrupolar symmetry by quadrupole fields is already accessible with regard to
the most important problems, on the basis of investigations published in the literature
[72, 244].

88. MAGNETIC FIELDS INDEPENDENT OF z

Before giving the data determining the field, we shall determine an
approximative form of the space-charge term appearing in the equations,
as based on the communication [72].

In the equations of motion 23.11, 23.12 of the beam moving in the
quadrupole field, for simplification we disregard one index of ϱ and both
indexes of Φ and V.

For determination of ϱ_0 (formerly ϱ_{00}) appearing in the equations, we
start from the following.

We consider equations 73.4 and 73.5 and also equation 73.6, which is
derived from these equations, as valid, since in our case, current flows only
in the direction of axis z. ϱ figuring in equation 73.6 can now be identified
with ϱ_0 figuring in equation 9.19, with respect to which it is also true that
this is dependent on coordinate z only.

The beam entering the quadrupole field is chosen as cylindrical. At the
point of entrance

$$x(0) = y(0) = R_0 \qquad\qquad 88.1$$

where R_0 is the radius of the entering beam. Instead of formula 73.11 we
may now write two new formulae. for simplification of our equations (here

the total current of the beam is also introduced by integration of the current density)

$$\varrho_0 = - \frac{I}{\sqrt{2\pi}\sqrt{\eta}\sqrt{\varPhi}} \frac{1}{R_0 x} \tag{88.2}$$

$$\varrho_0 = - \frac{I}{\sqrt{2\pi}\sqrt{\eta}\sqrt{\varPhi}} \frac{1}{R_0 y} \tag{88.3}$$

Therefore, we consider that the space-charge density (constant across the beam) is a function of variable z, via functions x or y. This choice harmonises with the approach since a lower space-charge density pertains to a greater value of x or y. *The fact that the cross section of the beam,* generally approximated to by an ellipse, *is given with the help of $\pi R_0 x$ or $\pi R_0 y$ instead of πxy represents a good approximation due to the small ripple and permits independency of the equations of motion.*
The conditions determining the field are

$$\varPhi = \text{constant} \tag{88.4}$$

$$D = 0 \tag{88.5}$$

$$V = V_0 = \text{constant} \tag{88.6}$$

The components of the induction (with the necessary approximation) are given with the help of equation 88.6, by equations 9.51, 9.52 and 9.53.
The equations of motion are

$$x'' + \left(\frac{\eta V}{(2\eta\varPhi)^{1/2}} - \frac{I}{4\sqrt{2\pi\varepsilon_0}\eta^{1/2}R_0\varPhi^{3/2}} \frac{1}{x} \right) x = 0 \tag{88.7}$$

$$y'' + \left(-\frac{\eta V}{(2\eta\varPhi)^{1/2}} - \frac{I}{4\sqrt{2\pi\varepsilon_0}\eta^{1/2}R_0\varPhi^{3/2}} \frac{1}{y} \right) y = 0 \tag{88.8}$$

Introducing the notation

$$\omega^2 = \frac{\eta V}{(2\eta\varPhi)^{1/2}} \tag{88.9}$$

$$p = \frac{I}{4\sqrt{2\pi\varepsilon_0}\eta^{1/2}R_0\varPhi^{3/2}} \tag{88.10}$$

and the initial conditions

$$x'(0) = x_0' ; \qquad y'(0) = y_0' \tag{88.11}$$

complementary to those given by 88.1, the general solution of the differential equations is

$$x = \left(R_0 - \frac{p}{\omega^2} \right) \cos \omega z + \frac{x_0'}{\omega} \sin \omega z + \frac{p}{\omega^2} \tag{88.12}$$

$$y = \left(R_0 + \frac{p}{\omega^2}\right) \operatorname{ch} \omega x + \frac{y_0'}{\omega} \operatorname{sh} \omega x - \frac{p}{\omega^2} \qquad 88.13$$

It can be seen from the solutions that in the plane x, z the solution is a bounded function in the infinite interval, while in the plane y, z it is unbounded. Focusing is, therefore, not possible by a quadrupole field, which is homogeneous in the given meaning.

If the beams are considered finite sections only, focusing becomes possible. Such finite sections are placed following each other in such manner that the following focusing field is rotated 90° about axis z, with respect to the preceding field. Our problem is to determine the lengths of the finite sections in such a way that the resultant effect of the field should be focusing. One approximative practical realisation of the solution in principle appears in the following paragraph: focusing by periodic field.

89. MAGNETIC FIELDS PERIODIC ALONG z

Based on the statements made in the preceding paragraph, the field may be described by the following data

$$\Phi = \text{constant} \qquad 89.1$$

$$D = 0 \qquad 89.2$$

$$V = \hat{V} \cos \frac{2\pi}{L} z \qquad 89.3$$

With equation 89.3 the approximative expressions of the induction components are (from 9.51, 9.52, 9.53)

$$B_x = -\hat{V}y \cos \frac{2\pi}{L} z \qquad 89.4$$

$$B_y = -\hat{V}x \cos \frac{2\pi}{L} z \qquad 89.5$$

$$B_z = \frac{2\pi \hat{V}}{L} xy \sin \frac{2\pi}{L} z \qquad 89.6$$

The values

$$x(0) = R_0 ; \quad x'(0) = 0 \qquad 89.7$$

$$y(0) = R_0 ; \quad y'(0) = 0 \qquad 89.8$$

are chosen as initial conditions (a cylindrical beam of radius R_0 having a horizontal tangent).

Giving the space-charge term figuring in the equations of motion 23.11 and 23.12 by the expressions 88.2 and 88.3, respectively, our equations of motion are as follows

$$x'' + \left(-\frac{I}{4\sqrt{2}\pi\varepsilon_0\eta^{1/2}R_0\Phi^{3/2}}\frac{1}{x} + \frac{\eta\hat{V}}{(2\eta\Phi)^{1/2}}\cos\frac{2\pi}{L}z \right)x = 0 \qquad 89.9$$

$$y'' + \left(-\frac{I}{4\sqrt{2}\pi\varepsilon_0\eta^{1/2}R_0\Phi^{3/2}}\frac{1}{y} - \frac{\eta\hat{V}}{(2\eta\Phi)^{1/2}}\cos\frac{2\pi}{L}z \right)y = 0 \qquad 89.10$$

With the new variables

$$u = \frac{2\pi}{L}z; \quad X = \frac{1}{R_0}x; \quad Y = \frac{1}{R_0}y \qquad 89.11$$

and the constants

$$A = \frac{\eta VL^2}{4\sqrt{2}\pi^2\eta^{1/2}\Phi^{1/2}} \qquad 89.12$$

$$B = \frac{IL^2}{16\sqrt{2}\pi^3\varepsilon_0\eta^{1/2}R_0^2\Phi^{3/2}} \qquad 89.13$$

the equations of motion 89.9 and 89.10 become

$$X'' + A\cos uX - B = 0 \qquad 89.14$$

$$Y'' - A\cos uY - B = 0 \qquad 89.15$$

Allowing a small ripple, the following approximative formulae are chosen for determination of X and Y

$$X = 1 - \varepsilon_1(1 - \cos u) \qquad 89.16$$

$$Y = 1 + \varepsilon_2(1 - \cos u) \qquad 89.17$$

Both ε_1 and ε_2 are considerably smaller than unity. Now equations 89.16 and 89.17 are substituted into 89.14 and 89.15. Disregarding the coefficient of $\cos 2u$ appearing after the substitution, equations 89.14 and 89.16 yield

$$\varepsilon_1 = \frac{2B}{A} \qquad 89.18$$

$$A = B + (B^2 + 2B)^{1/2} \qquad 89.19$$

and equations 89.15, 89.17 yield

$$\varepsilon_2 = \frac{2B}{A} \qquad 89.20$$

$$A = -B + (B^2 + 2B)^{1/2} \qquad 89.21$$

Equations 89.19 and 89.21 are contradictory unless B is equal to zero. Choosing B very small as an approximation, in both cases A may be approximated by the expression

$$A \simeq (2B)^{1/2} \qquad 89.22$$

Using the approximation 89.22, we obtain

$$\varepsilon_1 = \varepsilon_2 \simeq (2B)^{1/2} \qquad 89.23$$

With equation 89.23, the trajectories are determined by 89.16, 89.17. It is noteworthy that the trajectories are independent of the intensity $\hat{V}$ of the magnetic field and are dependent only on the period. When dimensioning, care must be paid that for the parameters figuring in B, a system of values should be chosen, which satisfies the requirements for ε_1 and ε_2.

The value of intensity $\hat{V}$ is calculated from 89.22. The final result is

$$\hat{V}^2 = \frac{2\sqrt{2\pi}I}{\varepsilon_0 \eta^{3/2} L^2 R_0^2 \Phi^{1/2}} \qquad 89.24$$

Since the value of L was chosen already when determining the form of the trajectory, equation 89.24 gives the value $\hat{V}$ of intensity of the magnetic field.

When dimensioning, the opposite way may also be followed, after choosing $\hat{V}$ the value of L is calculated and thereafter we check whether ε_1 and ε_2 are sufficiently small in comparison with unity.

Example

$\Phi \ = 10\ 000$ V
$I \ = 1$ A
$R_0 = 10^{-3}$ m
$L \ = 9.5 \times 10^{-3}$ m

From 89.23

$\varepsilon_1 = \varepsilon_2 = 0.264$

From 89.24

$\hat{V} = 1.22 \times 10^2$ V s/m

Calculated from equations 89.4, 89.5 and 89.6, the amplitudes of the induction components at a distance R_0 from axis z are

$B_x = 1.22 \times 10^{-1}$ V s/m²;
$B_y = 1.22 \times 10^{-1}$ V s/m²;
$B_z = 3.62 \times 10^{-2}$ V s/m²

90. ELECTRIC AND MAGNETIC FIELDS PERIODIC ALONG z

On the basis of the foregoing (§ 80) this problem is readily dealt with. The characteristics of the field are

$$\Phi = U(1 + \sigma \cos npz) \qquad\qquad 90.1$$

$$D = 0 \qquad\qquad 90.2$$

$$V = \hat{V}(1 - V_0 \cos 2pz) \qquad\qquad 90.3$$

therefore the magnetic field is a superposition of the homogeneous and the periodic fields.

The initial conditions are identical with 89.7 and 89.8. With 88.2 and 88.3, and also 24.29, equations 24.30 and 24.31 (denoting the functions with small letters instead of capitals) become

$$x'' + \left(\frac{3}{16} \frac{\Phi'^2}{\Phi^2} + \frac{\eta V}{(2\eta\Phi)^{1/2}} - \frac{I}{4\sqrt{2\pi\varepsilon_0}\sqrt{\eta}R_0^2 U^{3/2}} \right) x = 0 \qquad\qquad 90.4$$

$$y'' + \left(\frac{3}{16} \frac{\Phi'^2}{\Phi^2} - \frac{\eta V}{(2\eta\Phi)^{1/2}} - \frac{I}{4\sqrt{2\pi\varepsilon_0}\sqrt{\eta}R_0^2 U^{3/2}} \right) y = 0 \qquad\qquad 90.5$$

As in equation 80.8, the space-charge term is considered as constant in equations 90.4 and 90.5. By the method given in § 80, with the omissions there justified, with the new variables

$$u = pz \qquad\qquad 90.6$$

and

$$x = R_0 + R_0 X \quad (X \ll 1) \qquad\qquad 90.7$$

$$y = R_0 + R_0 Y \quad (Y \ll 1) \qquad\qquad 90.8$$

and with the constants

$$\lambda_1 = \frac{3\sigma^2 n^2}{32} + \frac{\eta^{1/2}\hat{V}}{\sqrt{2}p^2 U^{1/2}} \qquad\qquad 90.9$$

$$\lambda_2 = -\frac{\eta^{1/2}\hat{V}V_0}{\sqrt{2}p^2 U^{1/2}} \qquad\qquad 90.10$$

$$\lambda_3 = -\frac{3\sigma^2 n^2}{32} \qquad\qquad 90.11$$

$$\lambda_4 = -\frac{I}{4\sqrt{2\pi\varepsilon_0}\sqrt{\eta}U^{3/2}p^2 R_0^2} \qquad\qquad 90.12$$

and

$$\tau_1 = \frac{3\sigma^2 n^2}{32} - \frac{\eta^{1/2}\hat{V}}{\sqrt{2}p^2 U^{1/2}} \qquad\qquad 90.13$$

$$\tau_2 = \frac{\eta^{1/2} \hat{V} V_0}{\sqrt{2} p^2 U^{1/2}} \qquad\qquad 90.14$$

$$\tau_3 = -\frac{3 \sigma^2 n^2}{32} \qquad\qquad 90.15$$

$$\tau_4 = -\frac{I}{4\sqrt{2} \pi \varepsilon_0 \sqrt{\eta}\, U^{3/2} p^2 R_0^2} \qquad\qquad 90.16$$

equations of structure identical to 80.22 are yielded

$$X'' + (\lambda_1 + \lambda_2 \cos 2u + \lambda_3 \cos nu + \lambda_4)X + \lambda_1 +$$
$$+ \lambda_2 \cos 2u + \lambda_3 \cos nu + \lambda_4 = 0 \qquad\qquad 90.17$$

$$Y'' + (\tau_1 + \tau_2 \cos 2u + \tau_3 \cos nu + \tau_4)Y + \tau_1 +$$
$$+ \tau_2 \cos 2u + \tau_3 \cos nu + \tau_4 = 0 \qquad\qquad 90.18$$

By comparison with the case discussed in § 80 (from equation 80.41) the following equations are derived

$$\frac{3 \sigma^2 n^2}{32} + \frac{\eta^{1/2} \hat{V}}{\sqrt{2} p^2 U^{1/2}} = \frac{I}{4\sqrt{2} \pi \varepsilon_0 \sqrt{\eta}\, U^{3/2} p^2 R_0^2} \qquad\qquad 90.19$$

$$\frac{3 \sigma^2 n^2}{32} - \frac{\eta^{1/2} \hat{V}}{\sqrt{2} p^2 U^{1/2}} = \frac{I}{4\sqrt{2} \pi \varepsilon_0 \sqrt{\eta}\, U^{3/2} p^2 R_0^2} \qquad\qquad 90.20$$

these being the conditions of the parallel flow.

The contradictory equations 90.19 and 90.20 are rendered non-contradictory, by choosing

$$\frac{\eta^{1/2} \hat{V}}{\sqrt{2} p^2 U^{1/2}} = 0 \qquad\qquad 90.21$$

This represents the dimensioning condition (with $p = 2\pi/L$)

$$0 \le \frac{\eta^{1/2} \hat{V} L^2}{4\sqrt{2} \pi^2 U^{1/2}} \le \varepsilon_1 \ll 1 \qquad\qquad 90.22$$

(see formulae 89.12, 89.22, 89.23).

An interesting point of the case discussed is that with the given approximation V_0 appears only in the trajectory equation (λ_2, τ_2).

91. MAGNETIC FIELDS INCREASING WITH z

Taking as an example the simple case discussed in § 82, the characteristic data of the field may be written as

$$\Phi = \text{constant} \qquad\qquad 91.1$$

$$D = 0 \qquad\qquad\qquad\qquad 91.2$$

$$V = V_0 + \hat{V}\left(1 - \cos\frac{2\pi}{L} z\right) \qquad\qquad 91.3$$

The initial conditions are given by equations 89.7 and 89.8. The equations of motion 23.11 and 23.12 are

$$x'' + \left(\frac{\eta(V_0 + \hat{V})}{(2\eta\Phi)^{1/2}} - \frac{\eta\hat{V}}{(2\eta\Phi)^{1/2}}\cos\frac{2\pi}{L} z - \right.$$

$$\left. - \frac{I}{4\sqrt{2\pi}\varepsilon_0\eta^{1/2}R_0\Phi^{3/2}}\frac{1}{x}\right) x = 0 \qquad 91.4$$

$$y'' + \left(-\frac{\eta(V_0 + \hat{V})}{(2\eta\Phi)^{1/2}} + \frac{\eta\hat{V}}{(2\eta\Phi)^{1/2}}\cos\frac{2\pi}{L} z - \right.$$

$$\left. - \frac{I}{4\sqrt{2\pi}\varepsilon_0\eta^{1/2}R_0\Phi^{3/2}}\frac{1}{y}\right) y = 0 \qquad 91.5$$

With the new variables

$$u = \frac{\pi}{L} z; \quad X = \frac{1}{R_0} x; \quad Y = \frac{1}{R_0} y \qquad 91.6$$

and the constants

$$a = \frac{\eta^{1/2}L^2(V_0 + \hat{V})}{\sqrt{2}\pi^2\Phi^{1/2}} \qquad\qquad 91.7$$

$$2q = \frac{\eta^{1/2}L^2\hat{V}}{\sqrt{2}\pi^2\Phi^{1/2}} \qquad\qquad 91.8$$

$$b = \frac{IL^2}{4\sqrt{2\pi^3}\varepsilon_0\eta^{1/2}R_0^2\Phi^{3/2}} \qquad 91.9$$

$$a' = -a \qquad\qquad\qquad 91.10$$

$$2q' = -2q \qquad\qquad\qquad 91.11$$

the equations

$$X'' + (a - 2q\cos 2u)X = b \qquad 91.12$$

$$Y'' + (a' - 2q'\cos 2u)Y = b \qquad 91.13$$

can be derived for determination of the trajectory. *The solution of the equations is given by formula 83.12. Dimensioning is performed according to the pattern given there.*

29*

(I) HOLLOW BEAMS

In connection with the derivation of hollow beams reference should be made to Chapters III, IV and V, where determinations based on various cases are given.

The investigation of hollow beams is justified by the recently developing application, principally in the microwave field, e.g. low-noise tubes.

The methods of magnetic field focusing of hollow beams correspond to those of solid beams. We are interested mainly in the *Brillouin* and periodic focusing. Small changes are observable with respect to solid beams, principally in the implementation. The following discussions are based on the method developed for solid beam focusing. The starting equations used here are the basic equations dealt with earlier.

92. BRILLOUIN FOCUSING IN THE AXIALLY SYMMETRIC CASE

The motion of the electrons is investigated in a field in which the following conditions are valid

$$\Phi = \text{constant}, \qquad 0 \leq z \qquad\qquad 92.1$$

$$B = 0, \qquad\qquad z \leq 0 \qquad\qquad 92.2$$

$$B = \text{constant}, \qquad 0 < z \qquad\qquad 92.3$$

$$A = \frac{1}{2}\, Br \qquad\qquad 92.4$$

$$\frac{\partial \varphi}{\partial r} = 0 \text{ at the position } r = R_1 \qquad\qquad 92.5$$

The conditions with respect to the trajectories are

$$r_1(0) = R_1 ; \qquad\qquad r_2(0) = R_2 \qquad\qquad 92.6$$

$$\dot{r}_1(0) = 0 ; \qquad\qquad \dot{r}_2(0) = 0 \qquad\qquad 92.7$$

$$\dot{\alpha}_1(0) = 0 ; \qquad\qquad \dot{\alpha}_2(0) = 0 \qquad\qquad 92.8$$

We wish to achieve conditions so that

$$\dot{r} = 0 ; \qquad \ddot{r} = 0 \qquad\qquad 92.9$$

are valid for the edge electrons of the beam after the point of entrance.

With consideration of the above conditions, equations 18.10, 18.12 and 18.23 become

$$- r\dot{\alpha}^2 = \eta\, \frac{\partial \varphi}{\partial r} - \eta\dot{\alpha} Br \qquad\qquad 92.10$$

$$\dot{\alpha} = \eta \left(\frac{1}{2}\, B + \frac{C}{r^2} \right) \qquad\qquad 92.11$$

$$\ddot{z} = 0 \qquad\qquad 92.12$$

From equation 92.10 we have

$$\frac{\partial \varphi}{\partial r} = \dot{\alpha} B r - \frac{1}{\eta} r \dot{\alpha}^2 \qquad\qquad 92.13$$

Substituting 92.11 into equation 92.13

$$\frac{\partial \varphi}{\partial r} = \frac{\eta}{4} B^2 r - \eta C^2 \frac{1}{r^3}. \qquad\qquad 92.14$$

From equation 92.14 and with the help of condition 92.5

$$0 = \frac{\eta}{4} B^2 R_1 - \eta C^2 \frac{1}{R_1^3} \qquad\qquad 92.15$$

Expressing C^2 from 92.15

$$C^2 = \frac{1}{4} R_1^4 B^2 \qquad\qquad 92.16$$

We substitute now the constant 92.16 into equations 92.11 and 92.14

$$\dot{\alpha} = \frac{\eta}{2} B \left(1 - \frac{R_1^2}{r^2} \right) \qquad\qquad 92.17$$

$$\frac{\partial \varphi}{\partial r} = \frac{\eta}{4} B^2 \left(1 - \frac{R_1^4}{r^4} \right) r \qquad\qquad 92.18$$

Since the magnetic field satisfying the conditions 92.2 and 92.3 is non-existent in principle, for realisation in practice the following induction distribution must be achieved.

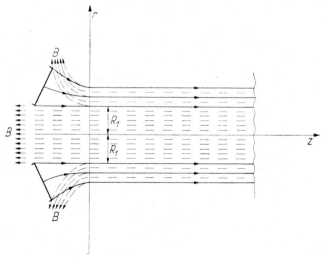

figure VI.7

For every electron leaving the cathode $\dot{\alpha} = 0$ shall be valid. It follows from this that $Br^2 - BR_1^2 = 0$. Therefore, over the entire cathode surface $Br^2 = BR_1^2$, i.e. is constant. The quantity BR_1^2 is proportional to the flux inside a cylindrical surface with radius R_1 (a homogeneous field). This flux or a part of it may not pass through the cathode, since in this case the condition $\dot{\alpha} = 0$ with respect to the entire cathode surface does not hold. Namely, this condition is independent of r only when $B = 0$. Based upon the same motivation the flux or a part of it passing outside a cylindrical surface with radius R_1 may not pass through the cathode. Since magnetic lines of force cannot pass through the cathode, *magnetic shielding of the cathode is essential*. The foregoing is illustrated in figure VI.7.

We now integrate equation 92.18

$$\int_{\varphi_2}^{\varphi} d\varphi = \frac{\eta}{4} B^2 \int_{R_2}^{r} \left(r - \frac{R_1^4}{r^3} \right) dr \qquad 92.19$$

After integration, using the notation

$$\varphi(r = R_1) = \varphi_1 \qquad 92.20$$

and

$$\varphi(r = R_2) = \varphi_2 \qquad 92.21$$

the following is obtained

$$\varphi = \varphi_2 + \frac{\eta}{8} B^2 \left(r^2 - R_2^2 + \frac{R_1^4}{r^2} - \frac{R_1^4}{R_2^2} \right) \qquad 92.22$$

We determine φ_1 from 92.22

$$\varphi_1 = \varphi_2 - \frac{\eta}{8} B^2 R_2^2 \left(1 - \frac{R_1^2}{R_2^2} \right)^2 \qquad 92.23$$

The potential distribution and axis potential of the solid beam, from 92.22, are

$$\varphi(R_1 = 0) = \varphi_2 + \frac{\eta}{8} B^2 (r^2 - R_2^2) \qquad 92.24$$

$$\Phi = \varphi(r = 0; R_1 = 0) = \varphi_2 - \frac{\eta}{8} B^2 R_2^2 \qquad 92.25$$

Since

$$\frac{\partial \varphi}{\partial z} = 0 \qquad 92.26$$

in our case equation 5.11 becomes

$$\frac{\partial^2 \varphi}{\partial r^2} + \frac{1}{r} \frac{\partial \varphi}{\partial r} = - \frac{1}{\varepsilon_0} \varrho \qquad 92.27$$

From 92.22 we now determine the derivatives necessary for 92.27

$$\frac{1}{r}\frac{\partial\varphi}{\partial r} = \frac{\eta}{4}B^2\left(1 - \frac{R_1^4}{r^4}\right) \qquad\qquad 92.28$$

$$\frac{\partial^2\varphi}{\partial r^2} = \frac{\eta}{4}B^2\left(1 + 3\frac{R_1^4}{r^4}\right) \qquad\qquad 92.29$$

With the help of the derivatives 92.28 and 92.29 we obtain from 92.27

$$\varrho = -\frac{\varepsilon_0\eta}{2}B^2\left(1 + \frac{R_1^4}{r^4}\right) \qquad\qquad 92.30$$

In view of the fact that $\dot r = 0$, the energy equation is

$$\dot z^2 = 2\eta\varphi - r^2\dot\alpha^2 \qquad\qquad 92.31$$

Using 92.17 and 92.22 we have

$$\dot z^2 = 2\eta\varphi_1 \qquad\qquad 92.32$$

Only the component of the current density in z direction is taken into consideration

$$j_z = \varrho\dot z = -\frac{\varepsilon_0\eta}{2}B^2\left(1 + \frac{R_1^4}{r^4}\right)(2\eta\varphi_1)^{1/2} \qquad\qquad 92.33$$

The total current flowing in the beam is

$$I = -\int_{R_1}^{R_2} -\frac{\varepsilon_0\eta}{2}B^2\left(1 + \frac{R_4^1}{r^4}\right)(2\eta\varphi_1)^{1/2}\,2\pi\,r\,dr =$$

$$= \frac{\sqrt 2}{2}\pi\varepsilon_0\eta^{3/2}B^2R_2^2\left(1 - \frac{R_1^4}{R_2^4}\right) \qquad\qquad 92.34$$

We now express B^2 from equation 92.34

$$B^2 = \frac{\sqrt 2 I}{\pi\varepsilon_0\eta^{3/2}\varphi_1^{1/2}R_2^2}\frac{R_2^4}{R_2^4 - R_1^4} \qquad\qquad 92.35$$

With knowledge of the beam data (I, φ_1, R_1, R_2) we can calculate the induction required for focusing, from equation 92.35.

Note

(i) Equation 92.35 can be given also as a function of φ_2, if we use equation 92.23.
(ii) Each electron covers the path $z = (2\eta\varphi_1)^{1/2}t$ in the direction of the z axis, in time t.
(iii) According to equation 92.17, the angular velocity of the electrons is a function of r. The electron paths slide upon each other.

(iv) The electron trajectories on a cylinder of radius $r = R_1$ are straight lines parallel with axis z. The electron trajectories on a cylinder of radius $R_1 < r$ are helices.

(v) Solution of equation 92.17 is

$$\alpha = \frac{\eta}{2} B\left(1 - \frac{R_1^2}{r^2}\right) \qquad\qquad 92.36$$

where $R_1 \leq r \leq R_2$, but constant, $r \neq r(t)$.

93. BRILLOUIN FOCUSING IN THE PLANE-SYMMETRIC CASE

The conditions characterising the field are

$$\Phi = \text{constant}, \qquad 0 \leq z \qquad\qquad 93.1$$

$$B = 0, \qquad z \leq 0 \qquad\qquad 93.2$$

$$B = \text{constant}, \qquad 0 \leq z \qquad\qquad 93.3$$

$$A = -By \qquad\qquad 93.4$$

$$\frac{\partial \varphi}{\partial y} = 0 \text{ at the position } y = Y_1 \qquad\qquad 93.5$$

The trajectory conditions are

$$\dot{x}_1(0) = 0 ; \qquad \dot{x}_2(0) = 0 \qquad\qquad 93.6$$

$$y_1(0) = Y_1 ; \qquad y_2(0) = Y_2 \qquad\qquad 93.7$$

$$\dot{y}_1(0) = 0 ; \qquad \dot{y}_2(0) = 0 \qquad\qquad 93.8$$

We shall investigate the case when the conditions

$$\dot{y} = 0 ; \qquad \ddot{y} = 0 \qquad\qquad 93.9$$

are valid for the edge electrons after the entrance.

With the above conditions, equations 19.7, 19.8 and 19.14 become the following

$$\dot{x} = (C - By) \qquad\qquad 93.10$$

$$0 = \eta \frac{\partial \varphi}{\partial y} + \eta B\dot{x} \qquad\qquad 93.11$$

$$\ddot{z} = 0 \qquad\qquad 93.12$$

Substituting 93.10 into 93.11 we have

$$\frac{\partial \varphi}{\partial y} = \eta B^2 y - \eta BC \qquad\qquad 93.13$$

From equation 93.13 and with condition 93.5 we have

$$C = BY_1 \qquad\qquad 93.14$$

We now substitute the constant 93.14 into equations 93.10 and 93.13

$$\dot{x} = \eta B(Y_1 - y) \tag{93.15}$$

$$\frac{\partial \varphi}{\partial y} = \eta B^2 (y - Y_1) \tag{93.16}$$

Here too the cathode must be shielded, according to the justifications given in the axially symmetric case.

We now integrate equation 93.16

$$\int_{\varphi_2}^{\varphi} d\varphi = \eta B^2 \int_{Y_2}^{y} (y - y_1) dy \tag{93.17}$$

With the notations

$$\varphi(y = Y_1) = \varphi_1 \tag{93.18}$$

and

$$\varphi(y = Y_2) = \varphi_2 \tag{93.19}$$

equation

$$\varphi = \varphi_2 + \eta B^2 \left[\frac{1}{2} (y^2 - Y_2^2) + Y_1(y - Y_2) \right] \tag{93.20}$$

is obtained.

φ_1 is determined from 93.20

$$\varphi_1 = \varphi_2 + \frac{\eta B^2}{2} (Y_1 - Y_2)(3Y_1 + Y_2) \tag{93.21}$$

Similarly to the axially symmetric case, the potential distribution and axis potential of the solid beam are obtained from equation 93.20

$$\varphi(Y_1 = 0) = \varphi_2 + \frac{\eta}{2} B^2 (y^2 - Y_2^2) \tag{93.22}$$

$$\Phi = \varphi(y = 0; \ Y_1 = 0) = \varphi_2 - \frac{\eta}{2} B^2 Y_2^2 \tag{93.23}$$

In our case, since

$$\frac{\partial \varphi}{\partial z} = 0 \tag{93.24}$$

equation 7.7 becomes

$$\frac{\partial^2 \varphi}{\partial y^2} = -\frac{1}{\varepsilon_0} \varrho \tag{93.25}$$

The derivatives required for 93.25 are determined from 93.20 and ϱ is expressed

$$\varrho = -\varepsilon_0 \eta B^2 \tag{93.26}$$

In view of the fact that $\dot{y} = 0$, the energy equation is

$$\dot{z}^2 = 2\eta\varphi_1 \qquad\qquad 93.27$$

which, however, is not a very good approximation.

Again only the component of the current density in the z direction is taken into consideration

$$j_z = \varrho\dot{z} = -\varepsilon_0\eta B^2 (2\eta\varphi_1)^{1/2} \qquad\qquad 93.28$$

The current flowing in the beam is

$$I = -\int_{Y_1}^{Y_2} -\varepsilon_0\eta B^2 (2\eta\varphi_1)^{1/2}\, 2W\, dy \qquad\qquad 93.29$$

Calculating the integral 93.29 we obtain

$$I = 2\sqrt{2}\,\varepsilon_0\eta^{3/2} W\varphi_1^{1/2} B^2 (Y_2 - Y_1) \qquad\qquad 93.30$$

Expressing B^2 from equation 93.30

$$B^2 = \frac{I}{2\sqrt{2}\,\varepsilon_0\eta^{3/2} W\varphi_1^{1/2}}\,\frac{1}{Y_2 - Y_1} \qquad\qquad 93.31$$

With knowledge of the beam data (I, φ_1, Y_1, Y_2) the induction necessary for focusing can be calculated from equation 93.31.

Note

(*i*) Equation 93.31 can also be given as a function of φ_2, if equation 93.21 is used.

(*ii*) According to equation 93.15, the x-direction velocity of the electrons is dependent on the height y above (below) the basic plane. The electron trajectories slide upon each other.

(*iii*) The electron trajectories on the plane $y = Y_1$ are straight lines parallel with axis z. The electron trajectories on the planes $Y_1 < y$ are straight lines parallel with the basic plane and deviating from axis z.

(*iv*) Solution of equation 93.15 is

$$x = \eta B(Y_1 - y)t \qquad\qquad 93.32$$

where $Y_1 \leq y \leq Y_2$, but constant: $y \neq y(t)$.

(*v*) The exact equation

$$\dot{z}^2 = 2\eta\varphi - \dot{x}^2 \qquad\qquad 93.33$$

may be used instead of the energy equation 93.27. Substituting equation 93.20, 93.21 and 93.15 into 93.33,

$$\dot{z}^2 = 2\eta[\varphi_1 + 2\eta B^2 Y_1(y - Y_1)] \qquad\qquad 93.34$$

is obtained. Substituting 93.34 and 93.26 into 93.28, the value of

$$I = \frac{2\sqrt{2}\,\varepsilon_0\eta^{1/2} W\varphi_1^{3/2}}{3Y_1}\left[\left(1 + \frac{2\eta B^2 Y_1(Y_2 - Y_1)}{\varphi_1}\right)^{3/2} \pm 1\right] \qquad\qquad 93.35$$

is obtained for the current flowing in the beam. Finally, expressing B^2 from 93.35 we obtain

$$B^2 = \frac{\varphi_1}{2\eta Y_1(Y_2 - Y_1)}\left[\left(\frac{3Y_1 I}{2\sqrt{2}\,\varepsilon_0\eta^{1/2} W\varphi_1^{3/2}} \pm 1\right)^{2/3} - 1\right] \qquad\qquad 93.36$$

(J) OTHER PROBLEMS OF MAGNETIC FOCUSING

94. NEW INTERPRETATION OF THE EQUATIONS OF MOTION
AND THEIR APPLICATION
FOR THE APPROXIMATIVE SOLUTION OF FOCUSING PROBLEMS

We intend to use the new interpretation of the equations of motion chiefly for *approximative* calculation of hollow beams.

All the conditions to be considered in the most general cases of focusing problems are dealt with in full detail in publication [12]. It is undeniable that in the case of hollow beams, first-order (paraxial) equations can very seldom be used for performing the calculations. As it can be seen in Chapter IV of this book, the behavior of hollow beams is to some extent different from that of solid beams.

Nevertheless, practical application of approximative and therefore generally simple formulae and methods is justified. In many cases the calculation formulae are not available, and in these cases the approximative method of calculation provides good service, being better than no method.

The new interpretation of the equations of motion appeared first in paper [73]; this number is related to the References for Chapter I but without application examples.

The basic method of investigation and dimensioning of hollow beams is the solution of the system of coupled differential equations relating to the electron trajectories on the two boundary surfaces. This process is laborious. The reduction of the two coupled equations to one single equation is enabled by recognition of the fact that knowledge of the space-charge term represents knowledge of an arbitrary electron trajectory inside, along the edge, or outside the beam, and in case of a laminar flow the solutions differ only by factors of proportionality. In case of a non-laminar flow this approximation is of lower value.

In the process of the derivation of the general equations of motion of electron beams, a constant, generally denoted by C, is to be introduced. Such a case occurs very seldom in practice, and therefore problems pertaining to the choice of $C = 0$ almost completely satisfy all requirements. In the following, therefore, we shall confine ourselves to motions in either axially symmetric or plane-symmetric fields, pertaining to the case of $C = 0$.

(i) Equations of motion

The equations of motion are given by writing the detailed expressions of the space-charge terms, for the case of the beam in stationary flow; *thus the data of the beam in stationary flow appear in the space-charge term.*

Before writing the paraxial equations of motion, the table of notations used in the axially symmetric case is to be set up

$R_0 = R_0(t)$ and

$R_0 = R_0(z)$ distance of the edge electron of the beam from the axis of rotation;

$r^+ = r^+(t)$ and

$r^+ = r^+(z)$ distance of the electron moving inside the beam, on the edge, or outside the beam, from the axis of rotation;

$\alpha^+ = \alpha^+(t)$ and

$\alpha^+ = \alpha^+(z)$ angular displacement of the electron moving inside the beam, on the edge, or outside the beam;

$z^+ = z^+(t)$ the component to the axis of rotation of the distance of the electron moving inside, on the edge, or outside the beam, from the initial point.

  The corresponding notations for the plane-symmetric case are the following

$$Y_0 = Y_0(t) \quad \text{and} \quad Y_0 = Y_0(z)$$

$$y^+ = y^+(t) \quad \text{and} \quad y^+ = y^+(z)$$

$$x^+ = x^+(t) \quad \text{and} \quad x^+ = x^+(z)$$

$$z^+ = z^+(t)$$

  Now the equations of motion may be written on the basis of Chapter I, substituting equations 73.11 or 74.4.

Axially symmetric case

$$C = \frac{1}{\eta}(r_0^+)^2 \dot{\alpha}_0^+ - \frac{1}{2} B_0 (r_0^+)^2 = 0 \qquad\qquad 94.1$$

The index zero in equation 94.1 represents the initial values.

(a) *Time-dependent equations*

$$\ddot{r}^+ = -\frac{\eta}{2}\left(\Phi'' + \frac{\eta}{2}B^2\right)r^+ + \frac{\sqrt{\eta}I}{2\sqrt{2\pi\varepsilon_0}\sqrt{\Phi}}\frac{r^+}{R_0^2} \qquad\qquad 94.2$$

$$\dot{\alpha}^+ = \frac{\eta}{2}B \qquad\qquad 94.3$$

$$\ddot{z}^+ = \eta\Phi' \qquad\qquad 94.4$$

(b) *Equations of the geometric trajectory*

$$(\alpha^+)' - \frac{\sqrt{\eta}B}{2\sqrt{2}\sqrt{\Phi}} = 0 \qquad\qquad 94.5$$

$$\Phi(r^+)'' + \frac{1}{2}\Phi'(r^+)' + \frac{1}{4}\left(\Phi'' + \frac{\eta}{2}B^2\right)r^+ - $$

$$- \frac{I}{4\sqrt{2\pi\varepsilon_0}\sqrt{\eta}\sqrt{\Phi}}\frac{r^+}{R_0^2} = 0 \qquad\qquad 94.6$$

Plane-symmetric case

$$C = \frac{1}{\eta} \dot{x}_0^+ + B_0 y_0^+ = 0 \qquad\qquad 94.7$$

The index zero in equation 94.7 also represents the initial values.

(a) *Time-dependent equations*

$$\dot{x}^+ = -\eta B y^+ \qquad\qquad 94.8$$

$$\ddot{y}^+ = -\eta(\Phi'' + \eta B^2)y^+ + \frac{\sqrt{\eta} I}{2\sqrt{2}\,\varepsilon_0 W \sqrt{\Phi}} \frac{y^+}{Y_0} \qquad\qquad 94.9$$

$$\ddot{z}^+ = \eta \Phi' + \eta \dot{x}_0^+ B' y^+ \qquad\qquad 94.10$$

(b) *Equations of the geometric trajectory*

$$(x^+)' + \frac{\sqrt{\eta} B}{\sqrt{2}\sqrt{\Phi}} y^+ = 0 \qquad\qquad 94.11$$

$$\Phi(y^+)'' + \frac{1}{2}\Phi'(y^+)' + \frac{1}{2}(\Phi'' + \eta B^2)y^+ -$$

$$- \frac{I}{4\sqrt{2}\,\varepsilon_0 W \sqrt{\eta}\sqrt{\Phi}} \frac{y^+}{Y_0} = 0 \qquad\qquad 94.12$$

Hitherto when calculating beams, and also with the earlier interpretation of equations of motion, the determination of the edge trajectory was considered as basic. The space-charge term ϱ_0 was considered as a function of edge trajectory to be determined, and not as a previously given excitation.

According to the new interpretation the equation of motion determines the trajectory, if Φ (and its derivatives), B and ϱ_0 are known. *No restrictions are necessary regarding the origin of Φ, B and ϱ_0. The term ϱ_0 may be generated as the space-charge of a stationary beam.* In our case we shall follow this method. There exists only one important practical condition. The travelling electron should move in the region $\varrho_0 \neq 0$. This condition is, however, fulfilled since at the space-charge densities occurring in practice, there is no power effect between the individual electrons, *as to the microscopic pattern.* Therefore, when the condition is satisfied, the trajectory of the electron may be placed within the beam producing ϱ_0, or on the edge of or outside the beam. *Therefore, the equation of motion of the new interpretation does include the equation of the earlier interpretation, as a special case,* and with its help the behaviour of the beam may be followed.

(ii) Edge trajectory, inside trajectory

The equation of the edge trajectory is given by substitution of

$$r^+ = R_0 \qquad\qquad 94.13$$

or

$$y^+ = Y_0 \qquad\qquad 94.14$$

Now only equations 94.6, 94.12 are written

$$\Phi R_0'' + \frac{1}{2}\Phi' R_0' + \frac{1}{4}\left(\Phi'' + \frac{\eta}{2}B^2\right)R_0 -$$

$$-\frac{I}{4\sqrt{2}\pi\varepsilon_0\sqrt{\eta}\sqrt{\Phi}}\frac{1}{R_0} = 0 \qquad\qquad 94.15$$

$$\Phi Y_0'' + \frac{1}{2}\Phi' Y_0' + \frac{1}{2}(\Phi'' + \eta B^2)Y_0 -$$

$$-\frac{I}{4\sqrt{2}\varepsilon_0 W\sqrt{\eta}\sqrt{\Phi}} = 0 \qquad\qquad 94.16$$

Equations 94.15 and 94.16 are identical to equations 21.14 and 22.13, $(C = 0)$.

In case of a laminar flow, knowledge of the edge trajectory is equivalent to knowledge of the inside trajectories. Let

$$r^+ = \beta R_0 \qquad\qquad 94.17$$

where $0 \le \beta \le 1$, and constant. Then

$$R_0' = \frac{1}{\beta}(r^+)'; \quad R_0'' = \frac{1}{\beta}(r^+)'' \qquad\qquad 94.18$$

Substituting equations 94.17 and 94.18 into 94.15 and multiplying the resultant equation by β we obtain

$$\Phi(r^+)'' + \frac{1}{2}\Phi'(r^+)' + \frac{1}{4}\left(\Phi'' + \frac{\eta}{2}B^2\right)r^+ -$$

$$-\frac{I}{4\sqrt{2}\pi\varepsilon_0\sqrt{\eta}\sqrt{\Phi}}\frac{\beta^2}{r^+} = 0 \qquad\qquad 94.19$$

Substituting β expressed from equation 94.17 into 94.19 yields 94.6. In case of plane symmetry, this is proved in the same manner.

Again we emphasise the approximative character of the method of calculation based upon the new interpretation of the equations of motion.

(iii) Hollow beam (cylindrical and strip-form)
in periodic magnetic field

We now investigate the motion of electrons in field where the following conditions are in force

$$\Phi = \text{constant} . \qquad\qquad 0 \leq z \qquad\qquad 94.20$$

$$B = 0 , \qquad\qquad z \leq 0 \qquad\qquad 94.21$$

$$B = \hat{B} \cos \frac{2\pi}{L} z , \qquad\qquad 0 < z \qquad\qquad 94.22$$

The conditions relevant to the trajectory are

$$\dot{\alpha}_1(0) = 0 ; \qquad\qquad \dot{\alpha}_2(0) = 0 \qquad\qquad 94.23$$

$$r_1(0) = R_1 = \beta R_2 ; \qquad r_2(0) = R_2 \qquad\qquad 94.24$$

$$r_1'(0) = 0 ; \qquad\qquad r_2'(0) = 0 \qquad\qquad 94.25$$

In the present case the space-charge term (omitting the stars) is

$$\varrho_0 = - \frac{I}{\sqrt{2\pi}\sqrt{\eta}\sqrt{\Phi}} \frac{1}{r_2^2 - r_1^2} \qquad\qquad 94.26$$

Only indicating the space-charge term with equation 94.6 (omitting the star) the following can be given as equations of the two edge trajectories

$$r_1 = \beta r_2 \quad \text{(inner edge trajectory)} \qquad\qquad 94.27$$

$$\Phi r_2'' + \frac{1}{4} \left(\frac{1}{\varepsilon_0} \varrho_0 + \frac{\eta}{2} B^2 \right) r_2 = 0 \qquad\qquad 94.28$$

Using the expression of the induction 94.22, that of the space-charge and also the relation 94.27 in equation 94.28 we obtain

$$\Phi r_2'' + \frac{\eta \hat{B}^2}{8} \cos^2 \left(\frac{2\pi}{L} \right) z r_2 - \frac{I}{4\sqrt{2\pi}\varepsilon_0 \sqrt{\eta}(1 - \beta^2)\sqrt{\Phi}} \frac{1}{r_2} = 0 \qquad\qquad 94.29$$

As regards the structure of equation 94.29, this is identical to equation 78.7 which relates to solid beams. Therefore, no further investigation is necessary. The dimensioning formulae may be written on the basis of § 78

$$\hat{B}^2 = \frac{2\sqrt{2}I}{\pi \varepsilon_0 \eta^{3/2}(1 - \beta^2)R_2^2 \Phi^{1/2}} \qquad\qquad 94.30$$

The induction calculated from equation 94.30 is in harmony with this approach. If the wall thickness of the beam is reduced, i.e. β approaches unity, the induction increases. With constant current I, the space-charge density obviously increases and, therefore, a greater induction is required for the maintenance of the beam

$$L^2 = 32\sqrt{2}\pi^3 \varepsilon_0 \sqrt{\eta} \frac{(1 - \beta^2) R_2^2 \sqrt{\Phi^3}}{I} q \qquad 94.31$$

The period calculated from equation 94.31 also harmonises with the approach. A greater space-charge causes rapid spreading of the beam: consequently, a smaller period is required.

Example

$\Phi = 1000$ V;
$I = 10^{-2}$ A ;
$R_2 = 10^{-3}$ m ;
$\beta = 0.5$;
$q = 6 \times 10^{-2}$

From equations 94.30 and 94.31
$\hat{B} = 240 \times 10^{-4}$ Vs/m^2 ;
$L = 27.2 \times 10^{-3}$ m

The approach is similar in the plane-symmetric case. The most important relations are

$$\varrho_0 = -\frac{I}{2\sqrt{2}W\sqrt{\eta}\sqrt{\Phi}} \frac{1}{y_2 - y_1} \qquad 94.32$$

$$y_1 = \beta y_2 \qquad 94.33$$

$$\Phi y_2'' + \frac{1}{2}\left(\frac{1}{\varepsilon_0}\varrho_0 + \eta B^2\right) y_2 = 0 \qquad 94.34$$

$$\Phi y_2'' + \frac{\eta \hat{B}^2}{2}\cos^2\left(\frac{2\pi}{L}\right) zy_2 - \frac{I}{4\sqrt{2}\varepsilon_0\sqrt{\eta}(1 - \beta)W\sqrt{\Phi}} = 0 \qquad 94.35$$

$$\hat{B}^2 = \frac{I}{\sqrt{2}\varepsilon_0\eta^{3/2}(1 - \beta)Y_2 W\Phi^{1/2}} \qquad 94.36$$

$$L^2 = 32\sqrt{2}\pi^2 \varepsilon_0 \sqrt{\eta} \frac{(1 - \beta)Y_2 W\sqrt{\Phi^3}}{I} q \qquad 94.37$$

Example

$\Phi = 10\ 000$ V;
$I = 1$ A ;
$W = 10^{-3}$ m ;
$Y_2 = 5 \times 10^{-4}$ m ;
$\beta = 0.5$;
$q = 0.11$

From equations 94.36 and 94.37
$\hat{B} = 2080 \times 10^{-4}$ Vs/m^2 ;
$L = 6.72 \times 10^{-3}$ m

Numerous publications are quoted in the literature [99, 100], which give the relations to be used for dimensioning, as results of calculations of greater accuracy. The calculating processes given in these publications are extremely complicated.

95. FOCUSING BY SIMULTANEOUSLY ACTING HOMOGENEOUS AND PERIODIC MAGNETIC FIELDS

According to the investigations described in paper [53] published several years ago, simultaneously acting homogeneous and periodic magnetic fields cause a bigger ripple at the edge of the beam than a purely periodic magnetic field. This is not satisfactory for the operation of tubes, since it reduces the interaction between the wave travelling along the slow-wave structure and the beam.

A recent paper [164] has also investigated the electron trajectories although neglecting the effects of space-charge. Broad stability regions resulting from the application of the field under discussion have been found.

We will see in the following that a nearly parallel flow may also be achieved, and that the stability region calculated with consideration of the space-charge effects is broader than the stability region achieved with focusing with a simple periodic field.

The problem originally investigated for the axially symmetric case will also be discussed with regard to the plane-symmetric case.

(a) The case of axial symmetry

Returning to the notations used in § 78 and replacing equation 78.3 introduced there by

$$B = B_0 + \hat{B} \cos \frac{2\pi}{L} z , \qquad 0 < z \tag{95.1}$$

instead of equation of motion 78.7 we obtain the equation of motion

$$\Phi r'' + \left(\frac{\eta B_0^2}{8} + \frac{\eta B_0 \hat{B}}{4} \cos \frac{2\pi}{L} z + \frac{\eta \hat{B}^2}{8} \cos^2 \frac{2\pi}{L} z - \right.$$
$$\left. - \frac{I}{4\sqrt{2\pi\varepsilon_0}\sqrt{\eta}\sqrt{\Phi}} \frac{1}{R_0^2} \right) r = 0 \tag{95.2}$$

in which we have considered the space-charge term as a constant, striving for a small ripple. With the variables

$$x = \frac{\pi}{L} z \tag{95.3}$$

and

$$r = R_0 + R_0 y \qquad (y \ll 1) \tag{95.4}$$

the new form of equation 95.2 is

$$y'' + \left(\frac{\eta B_0^2 L^2}{8\pi^2 \Phi} + \frac{\eta \hat{B}^2 L^2}{16\pi^2 \Phi} + \frac{\eta B_0 \hat{B} L^2}{4\pi^2 \Phi} \cos 2x + \right.$$
$$\left. + \frac{\eta \hat{B}^2 L^2}{16\pi^2 \Phi} \cos 4x - \frac{IL^2}{4\sqrt{2}\pi^3 \varepsilon_0 \eta^{1/2} R_0^2 \Phi^{3/2}} \right) y +$$
$$+ \frac{\eta B_0^2 L^2}{8\pi^2 \Phi} + \frac{\eta \hat{B}^2 L^2}{16\pi^2 \Phi} + \frac{\eta B_0 \hat{B} L^2}{4\pi^2 \Phi} \cos 2x +$$
$$+ \frac{\eta \hat{B}^2 L^2}{16\pi^2 \Phi} \cos 4x - \frac{IL^2}{4\sqrt{2}\pi^3 \varepsilon_0 \eta^{1/2} R_0^2 \Phi^{3/2}} = 0 \qquad 95.5$$

Let us introduce the notations

$$\lambda_1^* = \frac{\eta B_0^2 L^2}{8\pi^2 \Phi} + \frac{\eta \hat{B}^2 L^2}{16\pi^2 \Phi} \qquad 95.6$$

$$\lambda_2^* = \frac{\eta B_0 \hat{B} L^2}{4\pi^2 \Phi} \qquad 95.7$$

$$\lambda_3^* = \frac{\eta \hat{B}^2 L^2}{16\pi^2 \Phi} \qquad 95.8$$

$$\lambda_4^* = -\frac{IL^2}{4\sqrt{2}\pi^3 \varepsilon_0 \eta^{1/2} R_0^2 \Phi^{3/2}} \qquad 95.9$$

whereupon the new form of the equation of motion is

$$y'' + (\lambda_1^* + \lambda_2^* \cos 2x + \lambda_3^* \cos 4x + \lambda_4^*)y +$$
$$+ \lambda_1^* + \lambda_2^* \cos 2x + \lambda_3^* \cos 4x + \lambda_4^* = 0 \qquad 95.10$$

The structure of equation 95.10 is identical to that of 80.22 ($n = 4$). By substituting $n = 4$ we may use all the forms found there. Thereafter *the minimum ripple condition is given by*

$$\frac{\eta B_0^2 L^2}{8\pi^2 \Phi} + \frac{\eta \hat{B}^2 L^2}{16\pi^2 \Phi} = \frac{IL^2}{4\sqrt{2}\pi^3 \varepsilon_0 \eta^{1/2} R_0^2 \Phi^{3/2}} \qquad 95.11$$

We can see from 95.11 that minimum ripple may be achieved at an arbitrary period.

A generalisation of the design formula 78.20 may be derived from 95.11

$$\hat{B}^2 + 2B_0^2 = \frac{2\sqrt{2}I}{\pi \varepsilon_0 \eta^{3/2} R_0^2 \Phi^{1/2}} \qquad 95.12$$

It may be established from § 80 that the discussed focusing method has broader stability regions than simple focusing by periodic fields.

(b) The case of plane symmetry

Let us return to § 79 and expand equation 79.3 according to 95.1, whereafter we can rewrite equation of motion 79.7 for this case

$$\Phi y'' + \left(\frac{\eta B_0^2}{2} + \eta \hat{B}_0 B \cos \frac{2\pi}{L} z + \frac{\eta \hat{B}^2}{2} \cos^2 \frac{2\pi}{L} z - \right.$$
$$\left. - \frac{I}{4\sqrt{2}\varepsilon_0\sqrt{\eta} W Y_0 \Phi^{1/2}} \right) y = 0 \qquad\qquad 95.13$$

Introducing the variables

$$x = \frac{\pi}{L} z \qquad\qquad 95.14$$

and

$$y = Y_0 + Y_0 v \qquad (v \ll 1) \qquad\qquad 95.15$$

and the abbreviations

$$\tau_1^* = \frac{\eta B_0^2 L^2}{2\pi^2\Phi} + \frac{\eta \hat{B}^2 L^2}{4\pi^2\Phi} \qquad\qquad 95.16$$

$$\tau_2^* = \frac{\eta B_0 \hat{B} L^2}{\pi^2\Phi} \qquad\qquad 95.17$$

$$\tau_3^* = \frac{\eta \hat{B}^2 L^2}{4\pi^2\Phi} \qquad\qquad 95.18$$

$$\tau_4^* = - \frac{I L^2}{4\sqrt{2}\pi^2\varepsilon_0\sqrt{\eta} W Y_0 \Phi^{3/2}} \qquad\qquad 95.19$$

95.13 now becomes

$$v'' + (\tau_1^* + \tau_2^* \cos 2x + \tau_3^* \cos 4x + \tau_4^*)v + \tau_1^* +$$
$$+ \tau_2^* \cos 2x + \tau_3^* \cos 4x + \tau_4^* = 0 \qquad\qquad 95.20$$

Similarly, the structure of equation 95.20 is identical to that of 80.22. The generalised form of the design formula 79.15 is given from the condition of the minimum ripple independent of the period

$$\hat{B}^2 + 2 B_0^2 = \frac{I}{\sqrt{2}\varepsilon_0 \eta^{3/2} W Y_0 \Phi^{1/2}} \qquad\qquad 95.21$$

It is unnecessary to repeat the deductions derived from the case of axial symmetry, since, resulting from the identically structured equations, any of these will also be suitable here.

30*

96. SPECIFIC FOCUSING PROBLEMS
DEALT WITH IN THE LITERATURE

We will first provide some references in connection with the magnetic and electric-magnetic focusing methods discussed in this book and will make some remarks aiming at completing the subject; in this latter case— wherever possible—we will also provide references.

We would call attention, first of all, to part a) of the references. Listed here are the works giving fundamental information for those who desire orientation in focusing problems. These give a survey of developments and will acquaint the reader with the methods of solution. In this context we point out paper [1], which is the lengthiest and the latest in the subject. It critically screens the subject and deals in detail only with the fundamental questions of focusing. The author is an active scholar in space-charge optics, making it all the more unfortunate that this book does not discuss focusing by quadrupole fields which likewise must be listed among the fundamental methods of focusing.

A detailed knowledge of *Mathieu*'s functions is indispensable in discussing the questions of magnetic, and electric-magnetic, focusing; most of the subjects treated necessitate these functions. Consequently, we have listed in the References several books discussing *Mathieu*'s and *Hill*'s functions, and we have also given the title of the most detailed table. A rather small book in Hungarian is already available on *Mathieu*'s functions. From the date (1886) of the communication [5] we learn that *Hill*'s equation is almost one hundred years old.

In connection with further items appearing in the References: the first comprehensive work [13] in this field is today still of geat value; the book [11] is restricted to microwave tubes only; numerous volumes discuss the substance of knowledge covering the field, from aspects of various applications, but only as supplements. Among these fields of application appear the travelling-wave tubes [6], velocity modulated tubes [23], vacuum tubes in general [14], and microwave tubes in general [3, 7, 8]. In connection with later works of reference [Chapter II: 18] is one of the best, the work [15, 16] consisting of two volumes is a large-scale summary, particularly with respect to problems of high-power beams.

The candidature dissertation [12]—by one of the authors of the present work — endeavours to fulfil arbitrary requirements arising in the field of electron optics or space-charge optics insofar as complete solutions of basic problems concerning the most general cases are given. The investigations and results extend to the classical and relativistic cases, the central trajectory may be a space curve, electric and magnetic fields may occur simultaneously, space-charge and current density appear among the excitations, thermal velocity is evaluated, aberrations arising from imaging, chromatic and mass dispersions are calculated, etc.

V. P. Taranenko's book devotes a few pages to the relations between the questions of guns and of focusing; the papers written by *A. M. Strashkevich* are pattern examples for a precise theory discussion method leading to practical applications. The work of *N. S. Zinchenko* contains the most data on beam investigation by measuring.

Part b) of the References is a compilation of the summary appers. The list includes mature summaries both from theoretical and practical aspects. Since the references are listed together with their titles, the contents may be appropriately deduced. Notwithstanding the foregoing, stress is laid on the work [30] which forms an excellent means for information purposes, applications of space-charge flow and focusing, mainly in microwave tubes. This book with its fine illustrations, brief and yet comprehensible demonstrations, and valuable appendices forms a worthy continuation of the well-known *Spangenberg* book in the field of electron tubes of the latest types. The work of *P. A. Lindsay*, dealing with thermal velocities, discusses questions belonging to part j).

Biannual conferences report on the development accomplished in space-charge optics. The conference material, published in books, provide the most reliable orientation in the pace and trends of development. The material of the eight conferences held so far is listed among the references under part c). The designation of conferences has become standardised (MOGA) only since the sixth conference. Evaluation of the references is facilitated by easy identification, hence in the present chapter the related conference series is uniformly denoted by the MOGA acronym (and the corresponding serial number). The diversity of the material embraced by the papers published about the conferences is characterised by the way they even treat questions of a technological nature.

We should add the following observations to the references dealing with fundamental focusing methods, listed under part d).

When focusing electron beams, an exact solution of the focusing problem is seldom achieved and it is usually necessary to accept the approximative solution as given by the first order equations. Apart from a few exceptions, the laminar beam model is employed. As a result of the application requirements, the majority of the beams are high-current beams. Similarly, from the applications stem the requirements which are satisfied in the first place by magnetically focused beams. Electric-magnetic focusing systems are also employed, although to a considerably lesser degree. A great variety of beams may figure, in the first the steady beam types which, dependent upon their size and form, are termed strip, ribbon, and sheet beams. These beam forms are customarily used for the realisation of medium- and high-power density flows, which flows accrue from medium- and high-power density guns. Further solid beam types are the cylindrical and elliptic beams. These beam types are employed with low-power density flows and are generated by means of low-power density guns. The main hollow electron beam types are the hollow strip beam and the tubular beam. Both flow forms, but principally the tubular flow, are used for low- and medium-perveance flows. For the conduction of low-, medium- and high-density electron beams, the magnetic field is generally used, where among the examined characteristics giving the motion of edge electrons, the *Larmor* frequency and the *Larmor* radius also appear. Obviously the most simple form is homogeneous field distribution, and therefore the uniform magnetic field is more generally used. Confined flow forms in the beam placed in a homogeneous field, and then the beam is termed a confined flow beam. In the simplest case the magnetically confined beam stems from a completely immersed cathode (non-shielded cathode). Generation of a completely immersed beam originating from a completely immersed gun is uneconomical. Namely the force available for counterbalancing the space-charge of the beam in a completely immersed flow, originating from the magnetic field, falls within the region of lowest values. Then rotation of the electrons will take place in the neighbourhood of the cyclotron radius or cyclotron frequency, dependent on the value of the space-charge and in compliance with the cyclotron focusing. The immersed beam stemming from the immersed non-shielded gun, also in the case of high currents and the consequent high space-charge forces, can be constrained. In this case an extremely strong magnetic field has to be generated to induce the constrained beam. The constrained flow thus obtained is naturally an immersed flow. In practice a magnetically shielded flow originating from a magnetically shielded gun is of importance. In this case the force given in accordance with *Larmor*'s theorem is produced with the aid of a minimum magnetic field, viz. the space-charge forces arising in the magnetically shielded beam can be maintained in equilibrium with the help of a minimum magnetic field. Even in the case of a permanent magnet excitation, the costs of producing the magnetic field depend upon (and increase together with) the magnitude of the magnetic field, and it is therefore understandable that employment of the shielded flow emitting from the shielded gun is most extensively used. Similarly, forming of the magnetically collimated flow or beam by the same means is the most economical. In addition to shielded beams, partially shielded beams are also employed, which stem from partially shielded cathodes. The degree of shielding of the cathodes is given by the cathode-shielding factor.

Among the innumerable forms of focusing by magnetic field, *Brillouin* focusing is of greater significance. Its practical application, however, represents approximation only, in all cases, since the magnetic induction jump cannot be realised. It may be mentioned that the boundary fields of *Brillouin* focusing are the quasi-*Brillouin* flow and the generalised *Brillouin* flow.

A further focusing method where induction jumps occur in the axis induction is the reversed field focusing. This focusing method and the periodic focusing method are both approximated by section-wise constant and reversed magnetic field focusing where therefore axis induction is a periodic function, a non-sinusoidal periodic field. The decreasing or the increasing magnetic fields are employed for expansion or compression of the beams. Perveance forms an important characteristic of the beam. In use, an increase of the beam perveance is desirable. Increase may be obtained by neutralisation, i.e. nullification of space-charge effects. With nullification, a space-charge of inverse sense is induced in the beam space, where the effect of the inverse sense charges is balanced. Partial space-charge cancellation is also customary.

The most important focusing method is the focusing by the sinusoidal periodic field. With suitable setting of the characteristics of the periodic field, parallel flow may be obtained. The conditions for stability are satisfied by parallel flow. Stability of a beam is dependent on whether the parameters of the beam and the field fall within the stability region. The stability regions and the instability regions follow each other alternately. The first and second passband regions are termed the lower passband regions, and in practice these are more usually employed. The further passband regions are the higher passband regions. Due to various reasons, e.g. non-uniformities in the periodic field, parallel flow does not take place, even in the passband regions. In order to avoid non-parallel flow it is customary to correct the ripple arising. When correcting the ripple it is customary to take into account the percentage ripple in conformity with other fields. Stability of the beam is characterised also by the stiffness value, but within the limits of our present work expounding of beam stiffness does not figure.

Breakup of beam figures principally in the case of hollow beams. Breakup of both the hollow cylindrical beam and the hollow sheet beam can be ascribed to emission unevenness, asymmetry of the fields and initial condition unevenness, due to local space-charge deficiency. It is extremely difficult to prevent this state. Several articles appear in the References investigating this subject. In certain cases the trajectories pertaining to the simple cases deviate considerably from those of more complex cases. An example of the more complex cases is that of trajectories formed by the joint effect of thermal velocity and space-charge. It is obvious that trajectory perturbation greatly hinders calculations. In accordance with the foregoing, trajectory calculations may be performed at most until appearance of the medium velocity motions, since at medium velocity the relativistic effects may still be neglected. Our main task is the calculation of electron beam contours. Hence in the case of complex hollow beams it is necessary to determine the inner electron trajectory, in addition to the outer one of the laminar beam. This task is a problem of initial values, where the initial values are generally prescribed in a given plane, in the input plane. The final values naturally appear automatically in the exit plane. In the case of the plane-symmetric beam, the initial beam height or the beam thickness is given, referred to a defined plane. The same data are valid with regard to the initial beam radius or the beam diameter at some defined plane, in the case of the axially symmetric beam. As a simplifying premise for performing the calculations, acceptance of the uniform space-charge distribution is customary. The uniform charge distribution requirement is well fulfilled in the drift space. Moreover the condition of uniform axial velocity is also fulfilled in the drift region. Non-uniform axial velocity obviously arises where the diameter or thickness of the beam varies. Velocity deviations of a different sense arise from the velocity dispersion occurring at the emission. Direction deviation, known as direction dispersion, occurs on the emitted electrons. From the relations between electron velocity and energy, it follows that energy deviations will arise, therefore energy dispersion must also be taken into account. Later in our calculations, problems of strong focusing were tangentially dealt with, and with these, each of the low-, medium- and high-perveance regimes actually played a part.

The material discussed in Chapter VI deals in effect with the most simple questions of the fundamental cases. The related references may be found in the books listed. In place of a (lengthy) enumeration of these we would rather discuss the specific questions.

The task of binding two different trajectories occurs in nearly every practical case. The trajectories are bound in the vicinity of the cathode by a matching field, elsewhere by bypass fields. Matching fields are developed from transition fields. Some earlier results to be found in the literature are still erroneous [142]; later, however, suitable results were obtained [63]. A further result [129] and criticism thereof [143] facilitated development of this subject-matter, still later a communication relating to turbulent beams was published [176]. A very general relation for analytical expression of the transition field is used [108], and the *Taylor* series approximation is checked by measurements [65]. A fair number of papers have been published treating expressively matching fields. The work [66] deals with matching to a periodic field. Further informations relative to the axially symmetric magnetic field are given in articles [58] and [175]. Due to the great importance of the matching field attaching to periodic field, this subject is further dealt with [125]. In the article [115], simultaneously acting electric and magnetic compressing-matching fields are dealt with, relating to the high current beam and this method can be applied also in the case of low- and medium-current beams. The effect of the transition magnetic field on the beam is investigated with great detail, together with variation of other factors, in the paper [162].

Numerous communications deal also with bypass fields. This type of field is generally necessary for beams focused by a periodic magnetic field, since perturbation of the pure periodic structure is inevitable for the radio frequency field output and input coupling. Communications dealing with the subject [59, 112, 136] and [83, 102, 144] are available in the References.

The references [94, 100, 170, 208] investigate with a view to focusing the effect of electric and magnetic fields acting simultaneously. The articles [53, 164, 165] investigate the problems of focusing by superimposed homogeneous and periodic magnetic fields. Consideration of the space-charge is essential for the various forms of focusing. The force given by the space-charge of a homogeneous, cylindrical beam travelling at constant velocity is calculated in article [155]. Article [98] describes neutralisation of space-charge effects in a convergent electron beam. The publication [158] draws attention to the advantages of periodic focusing over homogeneous focusing. Article [71] gives information on the focusing of low-energy electron beams. Work [54] published the discovery of the cathode image, and beam cross-over in the beam focused by a homogeneous field. Article [154] describes the conception of beam stiffness. Article [174] investigates equivalence of focusing performed in periodic-magnetic and homogeneous-magnetic fields.

Hollow beams are used in a large number of cases, and consequently considerable work has been done in their investigation. The paper [86] is an old publication, which was followed by publication [163] dealing with *Brillouin* focusing of hollow beams, paper [181] takes into account nonsuitable values of entrance conditions also, and investigates the relativistic case, too. Two further communications deal with *Brillouin* focusing of hollow beams [137, 138] and a paper has been published discussing the instability of tubular beams [183]. Further experiments, observations and data concerning the phenomenon of instability are given in the article [79]. The paper [159] treats local space-charge deficiency as an explanation of instability; the same is stated in paper [114] which also gives experiments. Article [84] deals with applications, while article [184] further investigates instability. The hollow beam having a central electrode is described in the work [99]. Article [95] deals with generation of a hollow beam. The publication [76] treats multi-cavity beams and their generation, and the generalisation of *Brillouin* beams. The problem of focusing and stability is investigated in the paper [167]. The generation of multi-cavity beams based on *Harris* flow forms the subject of the paper [77]. The hollow beam is focused with the homogeneous magnetic field, according to the article [122]. Details of further practical applications are given in the publication [96]. Investigation of hollow beams, and setting of the zero value of flux on the cathode forms the subject of the paper [171], from which it also transpires that the required space-charge distribution has not yet been produced. The work [118] gives a detailed explanation of instability, in relation to beams of finite thickness. Ripple of the beam boundary is investigated in the cases of the homogeneous and periodic magnetic fields in the paper [57], and also in periodic fields [99, 100, 167]. A general discussion of hollow beams is found in paper [52], from which earlier specialised cases may be derived. Uniform velocity settings are discussed in the work [128], while the paper [166] compares the stability of solid and hollow beams. An investigation of hollow beam focusing is treated in paper [121], from which it transpires that even in the presence of 20% third harmonics, a current transmission of 92% is possible.

A customary expression in the terminology of this subject is generalised *Brillouin* flow [113, 161, 180], and quasi-*Brillouin* flow [132, 133].

Attention should be devoted to the questions of inhomogeneous amplitude distribution [104, 134, 135, 177], cathode shielding [50, 92], which practically always appears in the case of focusing by periodic magnetic fields. Notably, the first paper discussing periodic focusing [91] was published in 1939. Occasionally, resulting from the difficulties confronting practical application, focusing problems are solved by using pass-bands of a higher order [127].

The publications [93, 110, 132] dealing with non-laminary flow are also included in the bibliography and they deal also with curved line flows [169].

The beam diameter decrease obtained with an increasing magnetic field is a subject matter which has been developing for a comparatively short time. Apart from one single isolated publication accounts of works performed with respect to this subject matter have only been published since 1960. The axis induction in the increasing section of the magnetic field is written in the form of various functions (kz, z^n, z^{-n}, e^{kz}) and the properties of the compressed beam are investigated. Attention is drawn to the work [198] figuring in item e) of the bibliography, in which twenty references are given.

Focusing by means of the reversing magnetic field forms an interesting focusing process. With this method the magnetic field is homogeneous section by section and in the sections following each other the direction of the field changes. From our point of view this method of focusing may be considered as an extreme case of homogeneous magnetic field or periodic magnetic field focusing.

Due to lack of space we are not dealing with the methods of calculating focusing by the reversing magnetic field. This fact, however, does not imply a lower value of the method, as substantiated by the works dealing with further development and applications of the method published in recent times [188, 215]. Neither is it without interest to note that travelling wave tubes employing the reversing magnetic field have even reached the artificial satellites (and other space vehicles) [205].

The articles dealing with this subject matter are listed in item f) of the References.

Literature data dealing with quadrupole focusing [168, 233, 244] are given in item g) of the References, and special mention is made of [235] as the first dealing with the conception, and [236] elaborating the process of calculation. The best known is [72] since this gives consideration to the space-charge effect. An interesting case of focusing performed with the quadrupole field is where the focusing system is built up of magnetic bars [168].

The publications dealing with crossed field focusing [230, 238, 240, 245, 272] also figure within this group. In the present work we are not dealing with this important subject matter which involves numerous unsolved problems.

Literature deals also with other focusing methods: 'meander' (quadrupole) focusing [219, 220], high-frequency field focusing [228], focusing realised by the 'conical' magnetic field [259], focusing by magnetic deflection [265], focusing of the beam rotated by the initial magnetic field [234, 237] and focusing of electrons travelling on trochoidal paths [241]. The publications [222, 269] deal with beam investigation, [227] with visibilising of the beam, and [232] with spreading by the effect of the high-frequency field.

The noise power of the beams can be reduced by employing a strong magnetic field [217, 218, 246]. Beam refrigeration is based on the inverse proportion of noise power to the magnetic induction value, or from another aspect, is inversely proportionate to the cyclotron frequency. The paper [256] investigates the effect of the electron lenses on noise.

Electron beams can be focused also by an RF field [228, 229, 266, 267]. Focusing by radio-frequency fields is in effect focusing by slow-wave or by interdigital circuit, since no additional focusing elements are required. Therefore the slow-wave structure or the slow-wave circuit performs two functions. In the focusing systems the effect of RF field defocusing is also investigated [232, 264].

Important information concerning power flow induced by the beam, and stored energy in the beam, is given in the articles [260, 270, 271].

Paper [253] treats the non-laminar beam, and communications [251, 252] also deal with the non-laminarity topic; the translaminar beam also forms the subject of investigations [231]. The subject matter of laminarity is of significance, since the calculation technique is simple and less laborious. It is to be regretted that the turbulent beam cannot be discussed by paraxial equations. Beams produced by the effect of superimposed periodic and uniform magnetic fields are investigated in paper [221]; another case of superimposed fields is where an additional electric field is coupled to the periodic magnetic field [257]. According to paper [224] correction of the pulsations of magnetic-focused electron beams can be achieved by using local inhomogeneities of a magnetic field.

The axial velocity of electron beams in both unmodulated and modulated cases can be measured with the aid of beam testers [243]; in annular electron beams [261]; and also in the case of quasi-*Brillouin* flow [258]. Aberrations can also be determined with consideration of the space-charge in the axial symmetric case [250, 254], even in relativistic cases [249].

The paper [255] deals with space-charge flow occurring in the magnetic field, which together with numerous others comprise only a focusing based upon a curvilinear central trajectory.

Worthy of interest are papers [263] discussing the prospects for very high-power and high-efficiency RF generators, and energy conversion in electronic devices [242], which in their subject matter even surpass the boundary field.

Finally mention should be made of microwave power measurements employing electron beam techniques [268]. This task can be solved by calibrated means with the greatest difficulty. According to the solution the electron beam passes through a waveguide field, and if the transit moment is correctly chosen, the energy increases. The energy increase is measurable by means of a decelerating field and the full power passing through the waveguide may be calculated from the Poynting vector. The instrument is self-calibrating, and may serve as a standard measurement.

Many high-frequency oscillator types produce outputs of several hundred kilowatts and even megawatts. With outputs of such order the problem of efficiency is of paramount importance. Improvements in efficiency in of oscillators and amplifiers is possible not only by optimum setting of the high-frequency operation, but also by decrease of direct current powers converting into heat. Improvement of efficiency brings about a reduction in the dimensions of the cooling equipment and simplification of the structural solutions. With the help of space-charge optics the properties of a given arrangement can be investigated in the fuction of the voltages applied to the electrodes. These investigations have demonstrated for example that tube efficiency can be greatly improved by reduction of the collector voltage. The beam contour at the end of the generally long beam is a regular shape determined by the focusing system. The final high-potential electrode, the field of the high-potential collector does not give rise to beam perturbations. The potential depression in the decelerating space thus formed causes beam profile change, due mainly to space-charge effects. Methods for protection against space-charge instability caused by depression of the collector potential have been developed extensively, the results obtained are good, and application of the depressed collector voltage is widespread. Further progress has been made in this direction and multisegment collectors have been introduced, with which further efficiency improvement has been attained. As an example, in the case of a two-segment collector, the collector potential pertaining to the depressed collector has become smaller, in comparison with the beam potential. Further collector depression follows this medium-potential electrode, by means of which the low-potential electrode or the low-potential collector is reached. Results of these investigations are given in the works listed in item h).

Within this complex subject matter it is necessary to deal first with secondary emission, problems of collectors divided into several sections, and compensation by magnetic field of the effects of high space-charges due to low velocities. The given publications also include information on the method and means of the investigations [273, 286].

The determination of current density is of considerable importance in the space-charge flow occurring in electron beams, or in more general cases, in a vacuum tube, e.g. the beam tetrode. The final aim is invariably performance improvement. Such improvement may be attained by various methods, but these are all related to current density.

For example, focusing improvement is very important for dense electron beams. The finite current travelling in the electron stream must be conducted to a given point. The current flow must be directed so that the given power distribution appears at the point of utilisation. Since the potential at the point of utilisation is constant, distribution of the power density is proportionate to the current-density distribution. Power measurement is therefore possible via current-density measurement (with current-intensity measurement) along with voltage measurement; this is a constant value only. Similarly to voltage measurement, current measurement-is also a simple task. The majority of the articles referred to later deal with beam tester equipment used for measurement of current densities arising in various electron tubes, describing the method of measurement and the necessary calculations.

With regard to focusing improvement, two aspects must be considered. On the one hand, it is essential that the current density be of a given value at a given point: it must therefore correspond to the focusing strength, or possibly focusing weakness. On the other hand, the total current intensity passing over the cathode surface must be identical to the current intensity passing over the useful surface. Leakage current must be eliminated to the greatest possible extent (leakage current distribution is measured similarly to the distribution of useful current).

Current flow in the beam is generally of *Gauss* distribution. However, distributions divergent from the *Gaussian* curve of current density also exist. In such cases knowledge and measurement of the peak on-axis intensity and density are of great importance. Infinite currents obviously do not occur, but large currents above given limits may arise, and already this represents non-acceptable performance. Measurements are usually performed on the remote beam.

The electric charge distribution (which is obviously a non-uniform charge distribution) follows from the current-density measurement, and therewith the space-charge or space-charge density measurement has taken place, and even the charge measurement; additional calculations are necessary. Although according to the classical theory (see Chapter II) an infinite space-charge appears on the cathode, in reality the space-charge is finite only.

These measurements can be performed with respect to stationary currents and transient currents, also in non-modulated and in modulated beams. The type of beam—circular, ribbon or other beam—presents no obstacle. It is customary to perform the velocity measurement with a retarding field (initial velocity distribution).

The current-density distribution arising as a consequence of different effects is investigated in article [292]; the communication [293] deals with another type of beam investigating equipment; current-density distribution is calculated from a rotary probe measurement, and calculation formulae are presented in communication [294], which are based on measurements performed at 14 points. The article [295] also deals with calculation methods based on measured values, and presents a detailed description of the measuring equipment [296]. The communication [297] investigates current distribution in medium- and high-power klystrons, in both non-modulated and modulated cases. The paper [298] investigates the beam in the thermal velocity case by the pin-hole method also; the communication [299] describes a mechanical scanner for solving the task; the article [300] deals with a scanning slit, and article [301] determines the beam profile. With the widely used method of slit scanning [302] the limiting current density of electron guns of rotational symmetry is investigated in the paper [303]. The current density of the high-power density electron beam may be measured by the threshold method [304], rendering the circular hole or slotted hole—which are difficult to produce—superfluous. Radial current distribution can be measured also by means of X-rays [305]. Space-charge distribution in the electron beam can be determined by photographic methods [306]. Distribution appearing on the grid may be reproduced from the distribution measured on the screen, and the beam diameter also, given from the current-density distribution [307].

The beam forms determined by the calculation methods described are changed to no small degree by the thermal velocities. The articles given in item j) furnish information on the basic principles of the subject matter, form changing of the beams, practical problems and investigation of the beams. The theory has been well elaborated, not only proceeding along the lines of general principle inferences, but also the relevant paraxial equations are published. For the tasks to be performed by computer, descriptions of the most suitable process order, and other data facilitating the work, are available.

In spite of the fact that these problems could not be included within the scope of this work, these form problems of importance, and the effect of thermal velocities is given due consideration in the design and calculation of the latest equipment.

Among the most important applications of electron physics technology is the electron beam technique. This technique has been developed by means of the electron microscope, and now electron beam technology is the only suitable means for investigating certain problems.

The most important factor of this technology is the transformation of the kinetic energy of electrons into thermal energy when impacting the material to be machined or transformed. The course of development demonstrates that these means are in fact electron optical systems, in which the power flow is realised in the form of solid or hollow electron beams, and the design of their electrode system takes place in conformity with the customary methods of electrode design and gun design. Due to the manifold technological applications, various low-, medium- and high-power guns or beams are applied. The resultant low-, medium- and high-voltage or current flows may be greatly varied: toroidal gun and beam, collimated beam and flow, ribbon beam and axially symmetric or cylindrical electron beam, radially or axially injected current (as in other fields, here also the most frequent are the cylindrically symmetric and the axial electron beam; in addition to axial symmetry the combined electric and magnetic fields are similarly general). Among the electrode types, the annular electrode obviously plays a role, likewise the control electrode due to its current controllability, or the control grid, etc. Choice of the electrode potential is determined by the aspects of safe operation and the zero potential is usually the anode potential and not the cathode potential. In beam calculations, calculation of the operating current flow and peak current are among the important items. A further problem is presented by defocusing of the electron beam in concord with other fields, in the domain of the decelerating lens. On occasions, however, it may be worthwhile to determine by experimental means an arrangement of the diverging electron beam confined within certain limits, since the experimental solution is sometimes quicker and less costly than solutions obtained by other means.

In present-day techniques ion physics, in addition to electron physics, belong to the basis. Our primary interest in ion physics follows from our subject matter, and ion beams are employed similarly to electron beams, in order to achieve practical objectives. Focusing and deflection of the ion beam provide an introduction to the ion beam technique, which due to ion technology or ion beam technology have become indispensable, which fact will be illustrated by some examples in the following. The two technological methods mentioned are generally summarised under a common name: electron and ion technology or electron and ion beam technology.

As already stated in the preface of this book, technological application of the electron beam is one of primary importance. Knowledge of examples of the practical applications of the electron technology is readily and comprehensively gained from the subject matter of the various conferences [347, 351, 355, 367]. Even today, the semiconductors and solid materials, or more precisely the circuit components produced from these, and the circuits themselves (including integrated circuits) are of the greatest importance in technology [363, 370], however, due to the exceptional purity obtainable, precision, reproducibility, freedom from rejects, and accuracy, these are attaining increasing success in other fields too [345, 346, 354,365].

Important specialised fields, implements, processes are: electron beam melting [354, 356, 365], ion implantation [366, 369] (in the *initial approximation* these differ in their specific charge from electrons), electron beam welding [348, 349, 376], electron beam machining apparatus [358, 359, 373, 381], electron beam evaporators [357, 374, 377], electron beam cutting and cutting out apparatus [379], electron beam milling apparatus [358, 360], electron beam activation [361, 381], electron beam alloying [345–347, 365], electron beam annealing [345–347, 365], electron beam boring [378], electron beam coating [377], electron beam drying [345–347, 365], electron beam founding [345–347, 365], electron beam heat treatment [352], electron beam mask producing [370, 385], electron beam metallising [345–347, 365], electron beam metallurgy [345–347, 365], electron beam perforation [378], electron beam precision casting [345–347, 365], electron beam purifying [345–347, 365], electron beam refining [345–347, 365], electron beam surface purification [345–347, 365], electron beam zone melting [345–347, 365], electron beam deposition of thin films [377], measurement of thin film sheet resistance [353], resistor fabrication [383–384], inducing of chemical reactions [361], fabrication of small size components, transistors [362, 372], drilling of wire drawing diamonds [364], electron beam etching [371], electron beam brazing [371], fabrication of planar silicon transistors without photoresistant materials [372], visualisation surface charge distribution of semiconductors [375], exposing of materials sensitive to electron beam, for mask making [370], etc. The literary communications deal also with reviews of the physical picture; investigation of heat development [361, 388], penetration of the electron beam into material [380], and they naturally treat the prospective trends of development [389].

The various focusing, deflecting, centering, limiting etc. magnetic fields are indispensable in the operation of microwave tubes, e.g. klystrons and other tubes, e.g. kinescopes. The well-designed magnetic field is a prerequisite of appropriate operation and performance enhancement of tubes, and other equipment. The necessary fields are static magnetic fields, and therefore knowledge of the substance and calculation methods of magnetostatics is necessary. An exact calculation is seldom possible and therefore recourse is made to approximative methods. An approximative solution produced by approximative calculation is used as the predominant characteristics of the axially symmetric magnetic field, for determination of the axis induction distribution or the axis induction function. The magnetic induction calculation resultant from numerical calculation is fully satisfactory for practical purposes, since arbitrary accuracy is obtainable. The numerical solution forms a basis for the calculation of numerous other characteristics of the magnetic field. As an example let us take the calculation of magnetic flux (calculation of flux is indispensable for the knowledge of the total magnetic flux produced by the permanent magnet), or the calculation of the magnetic induction found in a given point for expression of the force of the thin or thick magnetic lenses (these may be cylindrical or axial magnetic lenses; the majority of magnetic lenses are of the thick magnetic cylindrical type), similarly, calculation of magnetic scalar potential pertaining to spatially alternating field, an important step in magnet dimensioning. Various methods for the determination of the magnetic field-strength

distribution are known, and among these is the calculation of the magnetic
vector potential. The plane-symmetric and the homogeneous magnetic
field distribution also figure among the magnetic fields. Generally speaking,
strong magnetic fields belong to planar symmetry. Large magnetic fields
are employed today not only in atom physics, but also in everyday technical
practice. Low and medium magnetic fields are employed in microwave
applications, forming the main part of the present book. Careful attention
must be paid to the magnetic attraction and magnetic repulsion occurring
in strong magnetic fields since these forces may be of an order of several tons.

The first chapter of the book furnishes information on magnetic measurements and magnetometers.

Our book deals principally with details of dimensioning microwave tube
magnet types. The magnet types include the circular, cylindrical, bar, barrel, annular, tubular, toroidal, straight-field, rod, ring-shaped, quadrupole,
and ring magnet forms. In addition to the magnetic material, the keeper
and the yoke of the magnet are of importance, and these actually complete
the magnetic circuit. The pole face forms an indispensable part of the focusing magnet, and the useful magnetic field is formed between these. Among
the magnetic focusing systems, the periodic magnet structure and the
periodic electromagnet emerge on account of their interest and also their
low weight, and their consequent small space requirements. The permanent
magnet focaliser does not require constant current excitation, and therefore
its operation is highly economical. The communication [392] describes a
permanent magnet focusing system and also its dimensioning, and primarily
applications with regard to travelling wave tubes. The article [393] deals
with the optimum design of a periodic magnetic focusing structure. The
tubular magnet of the magnet design is of interest where the multitude of
the factors of theoretical bearing appear in simple form [396]. A classical
case of the permanent magnet focaliser design is the design of the straight-
field permanent magnet [397], operating with graphic design aids. In the
design of the focusing magnet, the leakage flux may not be neglected. The
leakage magnetic flux must be provided by the permanent magnet, and
therefore the distribution of the leakage magnetic flux has to be determined.
The leakage flux distribution is determined by means of the graphic method
dealt with in communication [398]. The tube-type periodic magnetic focusing system forms a newer periodic focusing stack. The communication [401]
deals with this, and provides a mathematical calculation method for the
design of periodic permanent magnet. The design of periodic magnetic
focusing structures has been developed also with respect to the radially
magnetised ring: the design of periodic magnetic structures for medium- and
high-power travelling wave tubes is detailed in article [405]. Periodic permanent magnetic structures are also dealt with in articles [419, 420]. The
barrel magnet may be designed on the basis of article [408]. A focusing
arrangement formed from permanent magnets and its dimensioning are
dealt with in the articles [410, 411]. Further communications [406, 407,
416] dealing with design of the periodic focusing stack; article [403] treating permanent magnets used in microwave tubes, investigation of magnetic
materials [417], temperature dependency of magnetic materials [418],

and the book [415] dealing in general with permanent magnets and their applications. We must emphasise the application of permanent bar magnet for the production of quadrupole fields, and using them, extremely low-weight magnet fittings can be fabricated [168].

In addition to the permanent magnets, coils are of considerable importance, since magnetic fields can also be produced with these. The design of periodic electromagnets or dimensioning of a homogeneous field producing coil is everyday practice, and the solutions are to be found in the respective literature. Attainment of minimum weight is of importance here also [394], in order to minimise the use of copper. Information relating to magnetic field calculations is given in article [395] and measuring of the magnetic field axis is dealt with in the article [414]. A homogeneous field can be produced by placing wafer-type solenoids side by side [402], (the design of wafer-type solenoids is of importance not only with respect to microwave tube applications), the air cored magnet coils are calculated by computer also [404]. The article [409] deals with dimensioning of periodic electromagnets, and details relating to multiturn coils are given in the paper [413]. The design of multiturn coils is one of the most frequently recurring tasks. The paper [422] discusses coils serving travelling wave tube and klystron focusing. The design of focusing coils has attained newer success in the field of weight and space reduction with the introduction of aluminium foil solenoids. The papers [399, 421] deal with the design of aluminium foil solenoids, while the books [400, 412] provide general information on the design of d.c. magnets.

Knowledge of the forces (mechanical fittings) occurring in the high-power focusing coils and of the force distribution (deformation) is necessary. Consequently in coil design work force density calculations may not be omitted. Magnetic force calculations are given in communication [390], with the exact solution of calculations of the force induced by the electromagnet producing the homogeneous field.

The coils produced with superconductors result in power economy, and they are therefore widely used [391]. We make reference to a further book [412], but these two data are not in proportion to the importance of electromagnets on superconductors since these deserve considerably greater interest.

Based upon the information given in the literature it may be stated that many methods for the investigation of focusing problems are available (principles; conclusions; mathematical (quantitative) description of the phenomena; elaboration of processes necessary for employment of computers), *therefore there is no reason, even in the most diverse cases, why satisfactory calculations which solve the requirements of application should not be performed.*

REFERENCES FOR CHAPTER VI

a) *Space-Charge Optics and Related Sciences*

1. (ALYAMOVSKIY, I. V.) Алямовский, И. В.: Электронные пучки и электронные пушки *(Electron Beams and Electron Guns)*. Советское Радио; Москва, 1966.
2. CAMPBELL, R.: Théorie générale de l'équation de Mathieu. Masson et Cie; Paris, 1955.
3. (DZHIGITA, I. S.–SOLOVEVA, E. T.) Джигита, И. С.–Соловьева, Е. Т.: Труды Конференции по электронике СВЧ *(Proceedings of the Microwave Electronics Conference)*. Госэнергоиздат; Москва, 1959.
4. FARKAS, M.: Speciális függvények műszaki-fizikai alkalmazásokkal *(Special Functions, with Technical-Physical Applications)*. Műszaki Könyvkiadó; Budapest, 1964.
5. HILL, G. W.: *Acta Math. Stockholm*, **8** (1886), 1.
6. HUTTER, R. G. E.: Traveling-Wave Tubes. *In: Advances* etc., edited by MARTON, L., **6** (1954), 371.
7. HUTTER, R. G. E.: *Beam and Wave Electronics in Microwave Tubes*. D. Van Nostrand; New York, 1960.
8. KLEEN, W. J.: *Electronics of Microwave Tubes*. Academic Press; New York–London, 1958.
9. MCLACHLAN, N. W.: *Theory and Application of Mathieu Functions*. Clarendon Press; Oxford, 1947.
10. MEIXNER, J.–SCHÄFKE, F. W.: Mathieusche Funktionen und Sphäroidfunktionen. Die Grundlehren der mathematischen Wissenschaften. Band LXXI. Springer; Berlin–Göttingen–Heidelberg, 1954.
11. (MOLOKOVSKIY, S. I.–SUSHKOV, A. D.) Молоковский, С. И.–Сушков, А. Д.: Электронно-оптические системы приборов СВЧ *(Electron Optical Systems of Microwave Appliances)*. Энергия; Москва–Ленинград, 1965.
12. NAGY, GY. A.: A tértöltés elektronoptikája általános alappályán *(Electron Optics of the Space-Charge along the General Central Trajectory)*. Kandidátusi értekezés (Candidature Dissertation); Budapest, 1965.
13. PIERCE J. R.: *Theory and Design of Electron Beams*. D. Van Nostrand; Toronto–New York–London, 1954.
14. ROTHE, H.–KLEEN, W.: Hochvakuum Elektronenröhren. Band I. Akademische Verlagsgesellschaft; Frankfurt am Main, 1955.
15. SEPTIER, A. (Ed.): *Focusing of Charged Particles*, Volume I. Academic Press; New York–London, 1967.
16. SEPTIER, A. (Ed.): *Focusing of Charged Particles*. Volume II. Academic Press; New York–London, 1967.
17. (STRASHKEVICH, A. M.) Страшкевич, А. М.: Электронная оптика электростатических полей, не обладающих осевой симметрией *(Electron Optics of Axially Non-Symmetric Electrostatic Systems)*. Физматгиз; Москва, 1959.
18. (STRASHKEVICH, A. M.) Страшкевич, А. М.: Электронная оптика электростатических систем *(Electron Optics of Electrostatic Systems)*. Энергия; Москва, 1966.
19. STRATTON, J. A.–MORSE, P. M.–CHU, L. J.–HUTNER, R. A.: *Elliptic Cylinder and Spheroidal Wave Functions*. John Wiley and Sons; New York, 1941.
20. STRUTT, M. J. O.: Lamésche, Mathieusche und verwandte Funktionen in Physik und Technik. Springer; Berlin, 1932.
21. TABLES RELATING TO MATHIEU FUNCTIONS. *Characteristic Values, Coefficients and Joining Factors*. Prepared by The Computation Laboratory of the National Applied Mathematics Laboratories, National Bureau of Standards. Columbia University Press; New York, 1951.
22. (TARANENKO, V. P.) Тараненко, В. П.: Электронные пушки *(Electron Guns)*. Техника; Киев, 1964.
23. WARNECKE, R. R.–CHODOROV, M.–GUÉNARD, P. R.–GINZTON, E. L.: Velocity Modulated Tubes. *In: Advances* etc. edited by MARTON, L., **3** (1951), 43.
24. (ZINCHENKO, N. S.) Зинченко, Н. С.: Курс лекций по электронной оптике *(Course in Electron Optics)*. Харьковский Университет; Харьков, 1961.

b) *Summarising Publications*

25. BURKE, P. F. C.–ROGERS, D. C.: Magnetic Focusing of Long Cylindrical Beams. *Onde élect.*, **37** (1957), 174.
26. BURKE, P. F. C.–ROGERS, D. C.: *1st MOGA,** Vol. II, 164.
27. (CHERNOV, Z. S.) Чернов, З. С.: *РИЭ СССР,* **3** (1958), 1227.
28. DOW, W. G.: Nonuniform D–C Electron Flow in Magnetically Focused Cylindrical Beams. *In: Advances* etc., edited by MARTON, L., **10** (1958), 1.
29. (GABOVICH, M. D.) Габович, М. Д.: *Успехи Физ. Наук СССР,* **56** (1955), 215.
30. GEWARTOWSKI, J. W.–WATSON, H. A.: *Principles of Electron Tubes. Including Grid-Controlled Tubes, Microwave Tubes and Gas Tubes.* The Bell Telephone Laboratories Series. D. Van Nostrand; Princeton, New Jersey, 1965.
31. GITTINS, J. F.: *Power Travelling-Wave Tubes.* Applied Physics Guides, General Editor G. SUTTON. The English Universities Press; London, 1965.
32. HECHTEL, J. R.: *Microwave J.,* **3** (1960), 41.
33. HECHTEL, J. R.: *Microwave J.,* **3** (1960), 81.
34. (IGNATENKO, V. P.) Игнатенко, В. П.: *Успехи Физ. Наук СССР,* **73** (1961), 243.
35. (KUKARIN, S. V.) Кукарин, С. В.: Современное состояние в тенденции развития приборов СВЧ по материалам иностранной литературы [*The Present Status and Development Trends of Microwave Appliances (A Survey of Foreign Literature)*]. Советское Радио; Москва, 1962.
36. LINDSAY, P. A.: Velocity Distribution in Electron Streams. *In: Advances* etc., edited by MARTON, L., **13** (1960), 181.
37. MORENO, T.: High-Power Axial-Beam Tubes. *In: Advances* etc., edited by MARTON, L., **14** (1961), 299.
38. SEPTIER, A.: Strong-Focusing Lenses. *In: Advances* etc., edited by MARTON, L., **14** (1961), 85.
39. SÜSSKIND, C.: Electron Guns and Focusing for High-Density Electron Beams. *In: Advances* etc., edited by MARTON, L., **8** (1956), 363.

c) *Microwave Conferences*

1st MOGA, Vol. I:

40. LONGCHAMBON, M.: Sous le haut patronage de: Travaux du Congrès International 'Tubes Hyperfréquences' (TCITH). Paris; 29 mai–2 juin 1956; Tome I. Marcel Bon; Vesoul (Haute-Saône), 1958.

1st MOGA, Vol. II:

41. LONGCHAMBON, M.: Sous le haut patronage de: Travaux du Congrès International 'Tubes Hyperfréquences' (TCITH). Paris; 29 mai–2 juin 1956; Tome II. Marcel Bon; Vesoul (Haute-Saône), 1958.

2nd MOGA

42. International Convention on Microwave Valves, 19th–23rd May, 1958. The Proceedings of the Institution of Electrical Engineers. Volume 105, Part B, Supplement 10–11–12, 1958.

3rd MOGA

43. WOSNIK, J.: Herausgegeben von: Mikrowellenröhren. Vorträge der Internationalen Tagung 'Mikrowellenröhren'. München, 7–11 Juni 1960. Nachrichtentechnische Fachberichte. Band 22, 1961. Friedrich Vieweg und Sohn; Braunschweig, 1961.

4th MOGA

44. Microwaves. Proceedings of the 4th International Congress on Microwave Tubes, Scheveningen, 3–7 September, 1962. Centrex Publishing Company; Eindhoven, 1963.

* See this page, below.

5th MOGA

45. Tubes Pour Hyperfréquences. Travaux du 5ᵉ Congrès International, Paris, 14–18 septembre 1964. Dunod Editeur; Paris, 1965.

6th MOGA

46. Sixth International Conference on Microwave and Optical Generation and Amplification. Cambridge, 12th–16th September, 1966. IEE Conference Publication 27. The Institution of Electrical Engineers; London, 1966.

7th MOGA

47. Seventh International Conference on Microwave and Optical Generation and Amplification. Hamburg, 16th–20th September, 1968. Nachrichtentechnische Fachberichte **35**, VDE Verlag; Berlin, 1968.

8th MOGA

48. Eighth International Conference on Microwave and Optical Generation and Amplification. Amsterdam, 7th–11th September, 1970. Kluwer; Deventer (The Netherlands), 1970.

d) *The More Important Cases of Magnetic Focusing*

49. (ALYAMOVSKIY, I. V.) Алямовский, И. В.: *РИЭ СССР*, **4** (1959), 841
50. (ALYAMOVSKIY, I. V.) Алямовский, И. В.: *РИЭ СССР*, **5** (1960), 827.
51. (ALYAMOVSKIY, I. V.) Алямовский, И. В.: *РИЭ СССР*, **7** (1962), 2037.
52. (ALYAMOVSKIY, I. V.) Алямовский, И. В.: *РИЭ СССР*, **12** (1967), 1227.
53. ANDERSON, J. R.: *Trans. IRE*, **ED–6** (1959), 101.
54. ASHKIN, A.: *J. appl. Phys.*, **28** (1957), 564.
55. ASHKIN, A.: *J. appl. Phys.*, **29** (1958), 1594.
56. (BAKHRAKH, L. E.–KOZEL, I. SH.) Бахрах, Л. Е.-Козель, И. Ш.: *РИЭ СССР,***3** (1958), 819.
57. (BAKHRAKH, L. E.–KOZEL, I. SH.) Бахрах, Л. Е.-Козель, И. Ш.: *РИЭ СССР*, **11** (1966), 1707.
58. BEVC, V.–PALMER, J. L.–SÜSSKIND, C.: *J. Brit. IRE*, **18** (1958), 696.
59. BREWER, G. R.: *J. appl. Phys.*, **25** (1954), 243
60. BREWER, G. R.: *Trans. IRE*, **ED–4** (1957), 134.
61. BREWER, G. R.: *J. appl. Phys.*, **30** (1959), 1022.
62. BRILLOUIN, L.: *Phys. Rev.*, **67** (1945), 260.
63. BRÜCK, L.: *Telefunken Ztg.*, **26** (1953), 85.
64. CAHEN, O.: *Annls. Telecomm.*, **11** (1956), 142.
65. CHANG CHIN-CHUNG: *Acta Electron. Sin.*, **No. 1** (1965), 115.
66. CHANG, K. K. N.: *RCAR*, **16** (1955), 423.
67. CHANG, K. K. N.: *J. appl. Phys.*, **27** (1956), 1527.
68. CHEN, T. S.: *J. Electron.*, **4** (1958), 523.
69. CHODOROW, M.–SÜSSKIND, C.: *Proc. Instn Radio Engrs.*, **46** (1958), 497.
70. CIOFFI, P. P.: *Commun. Electron.*, **3** (1957), 15.
71. CLARKE, W. W. H.–JACOB, L.: *J. appl. Phys.*, **27** (1956), 1519.
72. CLOGSTON, A. M.–HEFFNER, H.: *J. appl. Phys.*, **25** (1954), 436.
73. CONVERT, M. G.: *Annls. Radioélect.*, **4** (1949), 279.
74. CONVERT, M. G.: *Bull. Soc. franç. Electrs.*, **9** (1949), 97.
75. CONVERT, M. G.: *Bull. Soc. franç. Electrs.*, **9** (1949), 550.
76. COOK, E. J.: *J. appl. Phys.*, **30** (1959), 860.
77. COOK, E. J.: *Trans. IRE*, **ED–8** (1961), 140.
78. COURANT, E. D.–SNYDER, H. S.: *Annls. Phys.*, **3** (1958), 1.
79. CUTLER, C. C.: *J. appl. Phys.*, **27** (1956), 1028.
80. CUTLER, C. C.: *Bell tech. Rep.*, **35** (1957), 28.
81. CUTLER, C. C.–QUATE, C. F.: *Phys. Rev.*, **80** (1950), 875.
82. (DANILOV, V. N.) Данилов, В. Н.: *РИЭ СССР*, **11** (1966), 1994.
83. (DANOVICH, I. A.) Данович, И. А.: *Изв. Высш. Учеб. Завед., Сер. Радиофизика*, **9** (1966), 351.

84. DUNN, D. A.: *Trans. IRE*, **ED–4** (1957), 246.
85. DUNN, D. A.–LUEBKE, W. R.: *Trans. IRE*, **ED–4** (1957), 265.
86. FIELD, L. M.: *Proc. Instn Radio Engrs.*, **37** (1949), 34.
87. GILMOUR, A. S.: *Proc. Instn Radio Engrs.*, **49** (1961), 976.
88. (GOLDENBERG, A. L.–PETELIN, M. N.) Гольденберг, А. Л.–Петелин, М. Н.: *РИЭ СССР*, **9** (1964), 1675.
89. HAEFF, A. V.–NERGAARD, L. S.: *Proc. Instn Radio Engrs.*, **28** (1940), 3.
90. HAEFF, A. V.–NERGAARD, L. S.: *Proc. Instn Radio Engrs.*, **28** (1940), 126.
91. HAHN, W. C.–METCALF, G. F.: *Proc. Instn Radio Engrs.*, **27** (1939), 106.
92. HARKER, K. J.: *Trans. IRE*, **ED–2** (1955), 13.
93. HARKER, K. J.: *J. appl. Phys.*, **28** (1957), 645.
94. HARRIS, L. A.: *Proc. Instn Radio Engrs.*, **40** (1952), 700.
95. HARRIS, L. A.: *J. appl. Phys.*, **30** (1959), 826.
96. HARRIS, L. A.: Proc. 3rd Symposium on Electron Beam Techniques, Boston, Massachusetts. Alloyd Electronics Corp., Cambridge, Massachusetts, 1961, 58.
97. HENNE, W.: *Telefunken-Röhre*, **41** (1962), 115.
98. HINES, M. E.: *Proc. Instn Radio Engrs.*, **40** (1952), 61.
99. HIRAMATSU, Y.: Stanford Tech. Rep. 313–1 (1959).
100. HIRAMATSU, Y.–WADE, G.–CRUMLY, C. B.: *Trans. IRE*, **ED–8** (1961), 1.
101. HIRANO, J.: *1st MOGA*,* Vol. I, 209.
102. (IGRITSKIY, A. L.) Игрицкий, А. Л.: *Ж. Тех. Физ. СССР*, **30** (1960), 413.
103. (IGRITSKIY, A. L.) Игрицкий, А. Л.: *РИЭ СССР*, **5** (1960), 255.
104. (IGRITSKIY, A. L.) Игрицкий, А. Л.: *РИЭ СССР*, **5** (1960), 1467.
105. (IGRITSKIY, A. L·) Игрицкий, А. Л.: *РИЭ СССР*, **6** (1961), 137.
106. (IGRITSKIY, A. L.) Игрицкий, А. Л.: *РИЭ СССР*, **6** (1961), 275.
107. (IGRITSKIY, A. L.) Игрицкий, А. Л.: *РИЭ СССР*, **7** (1962), 2043.
108. (IGRITSKIY, A. L.) Игрицкий, А. Л.: *РИЭ СССР*, **8** (1963), 130.
109. JOHNSON, C. C.: *Trans. IRE*, **ED–6** (1959), 409.
110. JOHNSTON, T. W.: *2nd MOGA*,* 907.
111. (KASATKIN, L. V.–DANOVICH, I. A.) Касаткин, Л. В.—Данович, И. А.: *РИЭ СССР*, **10** (1965), 1684.
112. KENMOKU, M.–YASUDA, S.: *2nd MOGA*,* 480.
113. KENT, G.: *Trans. Am. Inst. elect. Engrs.*, **79** (1960), 114.
114. KHYL, R. L.–WEBSTER, H. F.: *Trans. IRE*, **ED–3** (1956), 172.
115. KIKUSHIMA, L.–JOHNSON, C. C.: *Proc. IEEE*, **52** (1964), 82.
116. KIRSTEIN, P. T.: *J. appl. Phys.*, **34** (1963), 3479.
117. KLEEN, W.–PÖSCHL, K.: *Arch. elekt. Übertr.*, **9** (1955), 295.
118. KNAUER, W.: *J. appl. Phys.*, **37** (1966), 602.
119. (KORMILITSIN, V. T.–OVCHAROV, V. T.) Кормилицин, В. Т.–Овчаров, В. Т.: *РИЭ СССР*, **5** (1960), 1112.
120. (KOZEL, I. SH.) Козель, И. Ш.: *In:* (DZHIGITA, I. S.–SOLOVEVA, E. T.) Джигита, И. С.–Соловьева, Е. Т.: Труды Конференции по электронике СВЧ *(Proceedings of the Microwave Electronics Conference)*. Госэнергоиздат; Москва, 1959.
121. KWAN, H. K.–NEWLAND, F. J.–SWAIN, T. E.: *7th MOGA*,** 208.
122. LALLY, P. M.: *Proc. Instn Radio Engrs.*, **49** (1961), 514.
123. LAWSON, J. D.: *Proc. Instn Radio Engrs.*, **42** (1954), 1147.
124. LAWSON, J. D.: *J. Electron.*, **1** (1955), 43.
125. LINN, H. J.: *3rd MOGA*,* 461.
126. LINN, H. J.: *Arch. elekt. Übertr.*, **16** (1962), 381.
127. LINN, H. J.–PÖSCHL, K.–VEITH, W.: *5th MOGA*,** 42.
128. LINN, H. J.–PÖSCHL, K.–VEITH, W.: *7th MOGA*,** 184.
129. MANLEY, B. W.: *J. Electron.*, **2** (1956), 241.
130. MATHIAS, L. E. S.–KING, P. G. R.: *Trans. IRE*, **ED–4** (1957), 280.
131. MENDEL, J. T.–QUATE, C. F.–YOCOM, W. H.: *Proc. IRE*, **42** (1954), 800.
132. MILLER, M. H.: *J. appl. Phys.*, **32** (1961), 1791.
133. MILLER, M. H.: *J. appl. Phys.*, **33** (1962), 2247.
134. MINAKOVIC, B.: *4th MOGA*,* 605.

* See p. 483.
** See p. 484.

135. Minakovic, B.: *Electl. Commun.*, **38** (1963), 415.
136. Mizukaga, Y.–Sawayama, H.: Report of the Microwave Tube Specialists Committee of Japan, Apr. 1957.
137. Molhar, J. P.–Moster, C. R.: *Bell. teleph. Lab. Repts.*, **1** (1951), 2940.
138. Molhar, J. P.–Moster, C. R.: *Bell. teleph. Lab. Repts.*, **1** (1951), 2960.
139. (Molokovskiy, S. I.) Молоковский, С. И.: *Известия ЛЭТИ имени В. И. Ульянова (Ленина)*, (1958), вып. XXXIV.
140. (Molokovskiy, S. I.) Молоковский, С. И.: *РИЭ СССР*, **6** (1961), 1943.
141. Moster, C. R.–Molhar, J. P.: *Some Calculations of the Magnetic Field Requirement for Obtaining Brillouin Flow in Cylindrical Electron Beams*. Report. Bell Telephone Laboratories, 1951.
142. Müller, M.: *Telefunken Zeitung*, **26** (1953), 95.
143. Müller, M.: *J. Electron. Cont.*, **3** (1957), 401.
144. Nagy, Gy. A.: Berechnung von Anpassungs- und Überbrückungsfeldern für Wander-feld- und sonstige Röhren. Proceedings of the Symposium on Electron and Vacuum Physics, Hungary 1962. Akadémiai Kiadó; Budapest, 1963.
145. Nagy, J.: Duté elektronové svazky v periodickém magnetickém poli. Československý Časopis pro Fysiku, Sekce A, **5–6** (1962, Ročnik 12), 447.
146. Nalos, E. J.–Patton, F. K.: *Microwave J.*, **5** (1962), 95.
147. Neal, J. P.: *Trans. IEEE*, **ED–10** (1963), 319.
148. (Ovcharov, V. T.) Овчаров, В. Т.: *ДАН СССР*, **107** (1956), 47.
149. (Ovcharov, V. T.) Овчаров, В. Т.: *РИЭ СССР*, **2** (1957), 696.
150. (Ovcharov, V. T.) Овчаров, В. Т.: *In:* (Dzhigita, I.S.–Soloveva, E. T.) Джигита, И. С.–Соловьева, Е. Т.: Труды Конференции по электронике СВЧ *(Proceedings of the Microwave Electronics Conference)*. Госэнергоиздат; Москва, 1959, 80.
151. (Ovcharov, V. T.) Овчаров, В. Т.: *РИЭ СССР*, **7** (1962), 1367.
152. Palmer, J. L.: *Trans. IRE*, **ED–6** (1959), 262.
153. Palmer, J. L.–Süsskind, C.: *IRE Wescon. Conv. Rec.*, (1957), 130.
154. Palmer, J. L.–Süsskind, C.: *J. Electron Cont.*, **10** (1961), 365.
155. Petrie, D. P. R.: *Electl. Commun.*, **20** (1941), 100.
156. Pierce, J. R.: *Phys. Rev.*, **68** (1945), 229.
157. Pierce, J. R.: *BSTJ*, **30** (1951), 825.
158. Pierce, J. R.: *J. appl. Phys.*, **24** (1953), 1247.
159. Pierce, J. R.: *Trans. IRE*, **ED–3** (1956), 183.
160. (Porev, N. D.) Порев, Н. Д.: *РИЭ СССР*, **6** (1961), 659.
161. Pöschl, K.–Veith, W.: *J. appl. Phys.*, **33** (1962), 1013.
162. Rawls, J. L.: *Int. J. Electron.*, **25** (1968), 165.
163. Samuel, A. L.: *Proc. Instn Radio Engrs.*, **37** (1949), 1252.
164. Seunik, H.: *5th MOGA*,** 39.
165. Seunik, H.: *Trans. IEEE*, **ED–11** (1964), 552.
166. Seunik, H.: *7th MOGA*,** 191.
167. Solymár, L.–Ash, E. A.: *3rd MOGA*,* 448.
168. Stubbins, W. F.: *Rev. Scient. Instrum.*, **26** (1955), 666.
169. Sturrock, P. A.: *J. Electron.*, **7** (1959), 153.
170. Sumi, M.: *1st MOGA*,* Vol. II, 219.
171. Sutherland, A. D.–Countiss, D. E.: Air Force Avionics Lab., Rept. No. AFAL–TR–65–194, Wright–Patterson Air Force Base; Ohio, 1965.
172. (Taranenko, V. P.) Тараненко, В. П.: *Изв. Высш. Учеб. Завед., Сер. Радиотехника*, **3** (1950), 486.
173. Twombly, J. C.–Lauer, J. R.: *4th MOGA*,* 633.
174. Ura, K.–Terada. M.: *Trans. IEEE*, **ED–13** (1966), 930.
175. Veith, W.: *2nd MOGA*,* 932.
176. Vejvddová, J.: *Cesk. Casopis Fys.*, **10** (1960), 480.
177. Villotte, F.: *5th MOGA*,** 45.
178. (Vlasov, A. D.) Власов, А. Д.: *РИЭ СССР*, **5** (1960), 264.
179. (Vlasov, A. D.) Власов, А. Д.: *РИЭ СССР*, **9** (1964), 1234.
180. Walker, L. R.: *J. appl. Phys.*, **26** (1955), 780.

* See p. 483.
** See p. 484.

181. WANG, C. C.: *Proc. Instn Radio Engrs.*, **38** (1950), 135.
182. WATERS, W. E.: Microwave Laboratory Report No. 603, Stanford University, Stanford, California, 1959.
183. WEBSTER, H. F.: *J. appl. Phys.*, **26** (1955), 1386.
184. WEBSTER, H. F.: *J. appl. Phys.*, **28** (1957), 1388.
185. (ZINCHENKO, N. S.–OVCHINNIKOV, I. K.) Зинченко, Н. С.–Овчинников, И. К.: *Изв. Высш. Учеб. Завед., Сер. Радиотехника*, **3** (1960), 69.

e) *Focusing by Increasing Magnetic Field*

186. AMBOSS, K.: *Magnetic Compression of Electron Beams.* Report ECOM–01463–F, Hughes Res. Labs., Malibu, California, 1968.
187. ASH, E. A.: *J. Electron. Cont.*, **15** (1963), 401.
188. BECK, A. H. W.–EDGECOMBE, C. J.–KENYON, N. D.: *6th MOGA.***
189. (BURYANOV, P. D.) Бурянов, П. Д.: *РИЭ СССР*, **11** (1966), 1711.
190. DUNN, D. A.–HOLODAY, R. E.: *J. appl. Phys.*, **32** (1961), 1612.
191. GANDHI, O. P.: *Proc. IEEE*, **53** (1965), 197.
192. GANDHI, O. P.: *Int. J. Electron.*, **20** (1966), 187.
193. GANDHI, O. P.: *Int. J. Electron.*, **23** (1968), 283.
194. GANDHI, O. P.–VAIDYA, N. C.: *Proc. IEEE*, **52** (1964), 1052.
195. GITTINS, J. F.–KING, P. G. R.–LEA-WILSON, C. P.: *SERL Tech. J.*, **5** (1955), 119.
196. KIKUSHIMA, L.–JOHNSON, C. C.: Technical Report NSF–3, University of Utah, Salt Lake City, April 1963.
197. KIKUSHIMA, L.–JOHNSON, C. C.: *Proc. IEEE*, **52** (1964), 82.
198. SEEGER, J. A.: *Trans. IEEE.* **ED–16** (1969), 1.
199. TALBOT, K. I.–JOHNSON, C. C.: *5th MOGA,*** 352.
200. VAIDYA, N. C.: Central Electronics Engineering Research Institute, Pilani, Rajasthan, India, Internal Rept., 1963, 1.
201. VAIDYA, N. C.–GANDHI, O. P.: *5th MOGA.*** 342.
202. VAIDYA, N. C.–GANDHI, O. P.: *Trans. IEEE*, **ED–13** (1966), 453.

f) *Focusing by Reversing Magnetic Field*

203. ANDERSON, N.: *Int. J. Electron.*, **23** (1968), 263.
204. (BAKHRAKH, L. E.–KOZEL, I. A.–MURZIN, V. V.) Бахрах, Л. Е.–Козель, И. А.–Мурзин, В. В.: *РИЭ СССР*, **13** (1968), 1708.
205. BODMER, M. G.–LAICO, J. P.–OLSEN, E. G.–ROSS, A. T.: *BSTJ*, **42** (1963), 1719.
206. BUCK, D. C.: *Trans. IRE*, **ED–4** (1957), 44.
207. BURKE, P. F. C.: *Proc. IEEE*, **51** (1963), 1653.
208. CHANG, K. K. N.: *Proc. Instn Radio Engrs.*, **43** (1955), 62.
209. DUBRAVEC, V.: *7th MOGA,*** 224.
210. KELLY, J.: *J. Electron.*, **14** (1963), 21.
211. MENDEL, J. T.: *Proc. Instn Radio Engrs.*, **43** (1955), 327.
212. MURPHY, B. T.: *2nd MOGA,** 1033.
213. MURPHY, B. T.–KELLY, J.: *3rd MOGA,** 478.
214. NICLAS, K. B.: *Microwave, J.*, **6** (1963), 67.
215. SIEKANOWICZ, W. W.–CASH, J. H.: *5th MOGA,*** 209.
216. WINWOOD, J. M.: *3rd MOGA,*** 485.

g) *Miscellaneous Focusing Methods and Problems*

217. ADLER, R.–WADE, G.: *3rd MOGA,** 409.
218. ADLER, R.–WADE, G.: *J. appl. Phys.*, **31** (1960), 1201.
219. ALFVÉN, H.: *Onde élect.*, **37** (1957), 168.
220. ALFVÉN, H.: *Onde élect.*, **37** (1957), 359.
221. ANDERSON, J. R.: *Trans. IRE*, **ED–6** (1959), 101.

* See p. 483.
** See p. 484.

222. Ashkin, A.: *J. appl. Phys.*, **28** (1957), 564.
223. Ashkin, A.: *J. appl. Phys.*, **29** (1958), 1594.
224. (Bakhrakh, L. E.–Murzin, V. V.–Rozhkov, V. M.) Бахрах, Л. Е.–Мурзин, В. В.–Рожков, В. М.: *РИЭ СССР*, **15** (1970), 571.
225. Bevc, V.–Palmer, J. L.–Süsskind, C.: *J. Brit. IRE*, **18** (1958), 696.
226. Bick, J. H.: *Trans. IEEE*, **ED–12** (1965), 408.
227. Binnie, D. M.–Duane, A.–Miller, D. B.–Neale, W. W.–Newth, J. A.–Potter, D. C.–Walters, J.: *Nuclear Instrum. Meth.*, **31** (1964), 153.
228. Birdsall, C. K.–Rayfield, G. W.: *3rd MOGA*,* 507.
229. Birdsall, C. K.–Rayfield, G. W.: *Proc. Instn Radio Engrs.*, **49** (1961), 819.
230. Bradshaw, J. A.: *Trans. IRE*, **ED–6** (1959), 257.
231. Brewer, G. R.: *J. appl. Phys.*, **30** (1959), 1022.
232. Brewer, G. R.–Anderson, J. R.: *Trans. IRE*, **ED–8** (1961), 528.
233. Burnot, G.–Lafoucriere, J.: *Nucl. Instrum. Meth.*, **32** (1965), 287.
234. Chang, K. K. N.: *Proc. Instn Radio Engrs.*, **45** (1957), 66.
235. Christofilos, N. C.: *Focusing Systems for Ions and Electrons and Application in Magnetic Resonance Particle Accelerators.* Athens, 1950.
236. Courant, E. D.–Livingston, M. S.–Snyder, H. S.: *Phys. Rev.*, **88** (1952), 1190.
237. Crumly, C. B.: *Trans. IRE*, **ED–3** (1956), 62.
238. Davies, D. H.–Sander, K. F.: *J. Electron. Cont.*, **5** (1959), 114.
239. Dorrestein, R.: *Philips Res. Rep.*, **5** (1950), 116.
240. Farago, P. S.: *Proc. R. Soc.*, **66–A** (1962), 1.
241. (Flyagin, V. A.–Pankratova, G. V.) Флягин, В. А.–Панкратова, Г. В.: *РИЭ СССР*, **11** (1966), 731.
242. Gabor, D.: *J. Inst. electr. Engrs.*, (1944).
243. Gilmour, A. S.: Research Report EE 495, Cornell University School of Electrical Engineering, Ithaca, New York, 1961.
244. Glance, B.: *5th MOGA*,** 355.
245. Gupta, K. C.: *Int. J. Electron.*, **18** (1965), 177.
246. Hammer, J. M.–Wen, C. P.: *RCAR*, **25** (1964), 785.
247. Harris, L. A.: *Proc. Instn Radio Engrs.*, **40** (1952), 700.
248. Harris, L. A.: *J. Electron. Cont.*, **8** (1960), 241.
249. Jao Fu-Tyany: *Acta Sci. nat. Univ. pekin.*, **3** (1957), 211.
250. Jo Fu-Den: *Acta Phys. sin.*, **13** (1957), 207.
251. Johnston, T. W.: *2nd MOGA*,* 907.
252. Johnston, T. W.: *J. Electron. Cont.*, **6** (1959), 75.
253. Johnston, T. W.: *J. appl. Phys.*, **30** (1959), 1456.
254. Kanaya, K.–Kawakatsu, H.–Yamazaki, H.: *Brit. J. appl. Phys.*, **16** (1965), 991.
255. Kirstein, P. T.: *J. Electron. Cont.*, **8** (1960), 207.
256. Knechtli, R. C.: *Trans. IRE*, **ED–6** (1958), 84.
257. (Kormilitsin, B. T.) Кормилицин, Б. Т.: *РИЭ СССР*, **11** (1966), 1777.
258. Lindsay, P. A.: *7th MOGA*,** 314.
259. (Loginova, T. F.) Логинова, Т. Ф.: *РИЭ СССР*, **6** (1961), 1540.
260. Louisell, W. H.–Pierce, J. R.: *Proc. Instn Radio Engrs.*, **43** (1955), 425.
261. Nattrass, H. L.–Gers, H. B.: *7th MOGA*,** 235.
262. (Ovcharov, V. T.) Овчаров, В. Т.: *РИЭ СССР*, **4** (1959), 1741.
263. Preist, D.: *6th MOGA*,** 146.
264. Purl, O. T.–Anderson, J. R.: *Proc. Instn Radio Engrs.*, **46** (1958), 441.
265. Sturrock, P. A.: *J. Electron.*, **7** (1959), 162.
266. Sugata, E.–Terada, M.–Ura, K.–Ike-Buchi, Y.: *Proc. Instn Radio Engrs.*, **48** (1960), 1169.
267. Sugata, E.–Terada, M.–Ura, K.: *Proc. Instn Radio Engrs.*, **49** (1961), 820.
268. Thomas, H. A.: *Proc. Instn Radio Engrs.*, **45** (1957), 205.
269. (Troitskiy, Yu. V.) Троицкий, Ю. В.: *Изв. Сибирского Отделения АН СССР*, **1** (1960), 56.
270. Walker, L. R.: *J. appl. Phys.*, **25** (1954), 615.
271. Walker, L. R.: *J. appl. Phys.*, **26** (1955), 1031.
272. Warnecke, R.: *Proc. Instn Radio Engrs.*, **43** (1955), 413.

* See p. 483.
** See p. 484.

h) *Efficiency Improvement by Collector Voltage Reduction*

273. BAKER, A. S.–SIMS, G. D.–STEPHENSON, I. M.: *3rd MOGA*,* 77.
274. BRYANT, M. O.–THOMAS, A.–WELLS, P. W.: *J. Electron. Cont.*, **10** (1962), 49.
275. CHEN, T. S.–WOLKSTEIN, H. J.–McMURROUGH, R. W.: *Trans. IRE*, **ED–10** (1963), 243.
276. DUNN, D. A.–BORGHI, R. P.–MORWOOD, R. C.: *4th MOGA*,* 610.
277. DUNN, D. A.–BORGHI, R. P.–WADA, G.: *Trans. IRE*, **ED–7** (1960), 262.
278. DUNN, D. A.–LUEBKE, W. R.–WADA, G.: *Trans. IRE*, **ED–6** (1959), 294.
279. HANSEN, J. W.–SÜSSKIND, C.: *Trans. IRE*, **ED–7** (1960), 282.
280. KOMPFNER, R.: *Endeavour*, **24** (1965), 106.
281. LAICO, J. P.–McDOWELL, H. L.–MOSTER, C. R.: *BSTJ*, **35** (1956), 1285.
282. MARROW, W. E.–MACK, G. L.–NICHOLS, B. E.–LEONHARD, J.: *Proc. Instn Radio Engrs.*, **44** (1956), 1854.
283. MURATA, S.–KINOSHITA, S.: *3rd MOGA*,* 64.
284. (MURAVEV, V. V.–SHEVCHENKO, V. I.) Муравьев, В. В.–Шевченко, В. И.: *Изв. Высш. Учеб. Завед., Сер. Радиотехника*, **4** (1964), 517.
285. ROWE, J. E.: *4th MOGA*,* 640.
286. SHAW, E. K.–KOOYERS, G. P.: *5th MOGA*,** 325.
287. STERZER, F.: *Trans. IRE*, **ED–5** (1958), 300.
288. (TARANENKO, V. P.–DERENOVSKIY, M. V.) Тараненко, В. П.–Дереновский, М. В.: *Изв. Высш. Учеб. Завед., Сер. Радиотехника*, **4** (1961), 719.
289. WANG, C. C.–VON GUTFELD, R.: *Proc. Instn Radio Engrs.*, **49** (1961), 522.
290. WINKLER, R. H.: Microwave Lab. Rept. No. ML 235, Stanford University, Stanford, California, 1954.
291. WOLKSTEIN, H. J.: *RCAR*, **19** (1958), 259.

i) *Determination of Beam Current Density Distribution*

292. AMBOSS, K.–GALLAGHER, H.: *5th MOGA*,** 364.
293. ARNAUD, M.: *4th MOGA*,* 555.
294. (BABICH, YU. F.–PAVLYUCHENKO, YU. F.) Бабич, Ю. Ф.–Павлюченко, Ю. Ф.: *Изв. Высш. Учеб. Завед., Сер. Радиоэлектроника, СССР*, **11** (1968), 1312.
295. BAS, E. B.: *Optik Berlin*, **12** (1955), 377.
296. BAS, E. B.–CREMOSNIK, G.: *In:* BAKISH, R. (Ed.): *First International Conference on Electron and Ion Beam Science and Technology.* John Wiley and Sons; New York–London–Sydney, 1965.
297. CHODOROW, M.–SHAW, H. J.–WINSLOW, D. K.: *J. appl. Phys.*, **29** (1958), 1525.
298. CUTLER, C. C.–SALOOM, J. A.: *Proc. Instn Radio Engrs.*, **43** (1955), 299.
299. FUJII, T.–SABURI, A.: *2nd MOGA*,* 883.
300. HARKER, K. J.: *J. appl. Phys.*, **28** (1957), 1354.
301. HARRISON, E. R.: *J. appl. Phys.*, **29** (1958), 909.
302. JACOB, L.: *Phil. Mag.*, **28** (1939), 81.
303. MOSS, H.: *J. Electron. Cont.*, **10** (1961), 341.
304. PAHLITZSCH, G.–KUPER, G.: *Ver. d. Ing. Z.*, **111** (1969), 83.
305. THORP, J. S.: *Brit. J. appl. Phys.*, **6** (1955), 366.
306. WALLMARK, J. T.: *J. appl. Phys.*, **24** (1953), 591.
307. WEBER, C.: *Philips tech. Rev.*, **25** (1963/64), 152.

j) *Focusing in the Presence of Thermal Velocities*

308. AMBOSS, K.: *IEEE Trans.*, **ED–11** (1964), 479.
309. AMBOSS, K.: Verification and Use of Herrmann's Optical Theory of Thermal Velocity Effects in Electron Beams in the Low-Perveance Regime. *In:* BAKISH, R. (Ed.): *First International Conference on Electron and Ion Beam Science and Technology.* John Wiley and Sons; New York–London–Sydney, 1965.

* See p. 483.
** See p. 484.

310. AMBOSS, K.–GALLAGHER, H.: *5th MOGA*,** 364.
311. ASHKIN, A.: *J. appl. Phys.*, **29** (1958), 1594.
312. (BAKHRAKH, L. E.) Бахрах, Л. Е.: *РИЭ СССР*, **6** (1961), 656.
313. (BAKHRAKH, L. E.–KOZEL, I. A.–ROZHKOV, V. M.) Бахрах, Л. Е.–Козель, И. А.–Рожков, В. М.: *РИЭ СССР*, 13 (1968), 882.
314. (BAKHRAKH, L. E.–MEDOKS, V. G.) Бахрах, Л. Е.–Медокс, В. Г.: *РИЭ СССР*, **7** (1962), 120.
315. (BAKHRAKH, L. E.–MEDOKS, V. G.) Бахрах, Л. Е.–Медокс, В. Г.: *РИЭ СССР*, **9** (1964), 126.
316. (BAKHRAKH, L. E.–MEDOKS, V. G.) Бахрах, Л. Е.–Медокс, В. Г.: *РИЭ СССР*, 13 (1968), 877.
317. (BAKHRAKH, L. E.–SELIMOV, B. K.) Бахрах, Л. Е.–Селимов, Б. К.: *РИЭ СССР*, **9** (1964), 893.
318. CARROLL, J. E.: *J. Electron.*, **14** (1963), 403.
319. CHISHOLM, T.: *Proc. IEEE*, **57** (1969), 357.
320. CRUMLY, C. B.: Thermal Velocity Effects on Two Dimensional Electron Beams. Stanford Electronics Laboratory Technical Report No. 457–2, Stanford University, Stanford, California, 1958.
321. CUTLER, C. C.–HINES, M. E.: *Proc. Instn Radio Engrs.*, **43** (1955), 307.
322. CUTLER, C. C.–SALOOM, J. A.: *Proc. Instn Radio Engrs.*, **43** (1955), 299.
323. DANIELSON, W. E.–ROSENFELD, J. L.–SALOOM, J. A.: *BSTJ*, **35** (1956), 375.
324. DUNN, D. A.–BORGHI, R. P.–MORWOOD, R. C.: *4th MOGA*,* 610.
325. DUNN, D. A.–HO, I. T.: *AIAA J.* **1** (1963), 2770.
326. HARKER, K. J.: *J. appl. Phys.*, **28** (1957), 645.
327. HERRMANN, G.: *J. appl. Phys.*, **29** (1958), 127.
328. KIRSTEIN, P. T.: *4th MOGA*,* 615.
329. KIRSTEIN, P. T.: *Trans. IRE*, **ED–10** (1963), 69.
330. KIRSTEIN, P. T.: *J. appl. Phys.*, **34** (1963), 3479.
331. KIRSTEIN, P. T.: *J. Electron.*, **17** (1964), 521.
332. KIRSTEIN, P. T.: *5th MOGA*,** 348.
333. MANSELL, J. R.–SMITH, N. W. W.: *5th MOGA*,** 31.
334. PALMER, J. L.: *Effects of Thermal Velocities in Magnetically Focused Electron Beams.* ASD Technical Report 61–125, University of California, Berkeley, California, 1961.
335. PALMER, J. L.–SÜSSKIND, C.: *3rd MOGA*,* 456.
336. PIERCE, J. R.–WALKER, L. R.: *J. appl. Phys.*, **24** (1953), 1328.
337. SZABÓ, A.: *Trans. IRE*, **ED–5** (1958), 183.
338. (TROITSKIY, YU. V.) Троицкий, Ю. В.: *Ж. Тех. Физ. СССР*, **30** (1960), 25.
339. VEJVODOVÁ, J.: *Cesk. Casopis. Fys.*, **7** (1957), 191.
340. VEJVODOVÁ, J.: *J. Brit. IRE*, **21** (1961), 337.
341. WEBER, C.: *Proc. IEEE*, **52** (1964), 996.
342. WEBER, C.: *5th MOGA*,** 47.
343. WEBER, C.: *Philips Res. Rep. Suppl.*, **6** (1967), 1.

k) *Electron and Ion Beam Technology*

344. ANGELLO, S. J.: *IEEE. Trans.*, **ED–17** (1970), 442.
345. BAKISH, R. (ed.): *Introduction to Electron Beam Technology.* John Wiley and Sons; New York–London, 1962.
346. BAKISH, R.–WINKLER, O.: *Vacuum Metallurgy*, Elsevier; Amsterdam, 1971.
347. BAKISH, R. (Ed.): *First International Conference on Electron and Ion Beam Science and Technology. May 3–7, 1964, Toronto, Canada.* John Wiley and Sons; New York–London–Sydney, 1965.
348. BAKISH, R.–WHITE, S. S.: *Handbook of Electron Beam Welding.* John Wiley and Sons; New York–London–Sydney, 1964.
349. BAS, E.–CREMOSNIK, G.: *Vakuum-Tech.*, **8** (1959), 181.
350. BOERSCH, H.–HAMISCH, H.–LOEFLER, K. H.: *Naturwissenschaften*, **46** (1959), 596.

* See p. 483.
** See p. 484.

351. CAHEN, O.–PICQUENDAR, J. E.: Application des techniques électriques et ioniques à la réduction des dimensions des composants semiconducteurs. Colloque International sur la Microélectronique Avancée, Paris, Avril 1970. Editions Chiron, 686.
352. CARTER, G.–COLLIGON, J. S.: *Ion Bombardment of Solids.* Elsevier; New York, 1968.
353. CHESTER, A. N.–KOSICKI, B. B.: *Rev. Scient. Instrum.,* 41 (1970), 1817.
354. FÓTI, E.: Elektrontechnológiák *(Electron Beam Technologies).* Műszaki Könyvkiadó; Budapest, 1965.
355. GLOTIN, P. (Ed.): Proceedings of the International Conference on Applications of Ion Beams to Semiconductor Technology. Ophrys; Grenoble, 1967.
356. GRUBER, H.: *Z. Metallk.,* 52 (1961), 291.
357. HAVENS, O. S.: *J. Scient. Instrum.,* 36 (1959), 95.
358. HOFFMAN, G. R.: *Microelectron. and Reliab.,* 4 (1965), 59.
359. KELLY, J.: *Brit. Commun. Electron.,* 11 (1964), 20.
360. KELLY, J.–KING, H. N. G.: *Microelectron. and Reliab.,* 4 (1965), 85.
361. KING, H. N. G.: *Philips Tech. Rev.,* 28 (1967), 174.
362. LARKIN, M. W.–MATTA, R. K.: *Solid-State Electron.,* 10 (1967), 491.
363. LEWICKI, A.: Einführung in die Mikroelektronik. R. Oldenbourg; München–Wien, 1966.
364. LEWIN, I. H.: *Philips Tech. Rev.,* 28 (1967), 177.
365. MARTON, L.–EL-KARETH, A. B.: *Electron Beam and Laser Beam Technology.* Advances in Electronics and Electron Physics, Supplement 4. Academic Press; London, 1968.
366. MAYER, J. W.–ERIKSSON, L.–DAVIES, J. A.: *Ion Implantation in Semiconductors. Silicon and Germanium.* Academic Press; New York–London, 1970.
367. *Microminiaturization in Automatic Control Equipment and in Digital Computers.* Proceedings of the IFAC/IFIP Symposion, 21st–23rd Oct., 1965, Munich. R. Oldenbourg; München–Wien, 1966.
368. MÖLLENSTEDT, G.–SPEIDEL, R.: *Phys. Bl.,* H4 (1960).
369. NAGY, J.: *Híradástechnika,* 22 (1971), 81.
370. NEWBERRY, S. P.–KLOTZ, T. H.–BUSCHMANN, E. C.: *Integrated Circuit Mask Making by Electron Optical Means.* 1968 NEREM Record, Boston, Massachusetts, 6–8 November 1968, 172.
371. NIXON, W. C.: *Microelectron. and Reliab.,* 3 (1964), 153.
372. O'KEEFFE, T. W.–HARDY, R. W.: *Solid-State Electron.,* 11 (1968), 261.
373. PANZER, S.–SCHLEICH, F.: *Microelectron. and Reliab.,* 4 (1965), 117.
374. RIDDLE, G. C.: Proc. 7th Annual Electron and Laser Beam Symp. 1965.
375. SAITO, H.: *J. appl. Phys. Japan,* 4 (1965), 886.
376. SAYER, L. N.–BURNS, T. E.: *Br. Weld. J.,* 11 (1964), 163.
377. SCHILLER, S.–EFFENBERGER, D.–HEISING, U.–GOEDICKE, K.–SCHNEIDER, S.: *Vakuum-Tech.,* 16 (1967), 205.
378. SCHLUGE, H.: *Elektrowärme, Düsseldorf,* 19 (1961), 217.
379. SCHOLLHAMMER, F. R.: *IEEE. Trans.,* PEP–7 (1963), 16.
380. SCHWARZ, H.: *J. appl. Phys.,* 35 (1964), 2020.
381. SCHOULDERS, K. R.: *Research in Microelectronics Using Electron Beam Activated Machining Techniques.* Off. Tech. Service, US Dept. of Commerce, P.B. 17 1027, 1960 Sept.
382. SIDERIS, G.: *Electronics,* 37 (1964), 82.
383. TE GUDE, H.: *Int. Elektron. Rundsch.,* 19 (1965), 479.
384. TE GUDE, H.: *Int. Elektron. Rundsch.,* 19 (1965), 567.
385. THORNLEY, R. F. M.–HATZAKIS, M.–DHAKA, V. S.: *IEEE Trans.,* ED–17 (1970), 961.
386. ULLERY, L. R.–GARIBOTTI, D. J.: *Semicond. Prod. and Solid State Technol.,* 6 (Dec. 1963), 34.
387. ULLERY, L. R.–GARIBOTTI, D. J.: *Semicond. Prod. and Solid State Technol.,* 7 (Jan. 1964), 25.
388. VINE, J.–EINSTEIN, P. A.: *Proc. Inst. elect. Engrs.,* 111 (1964), 921.
389. VON ARDENNE, M.–SCHILLER, S.–HEISIG, U.: *Technik,* 21 (1966), 257.

l) *Dimensioning of Focusing Magnetic Fields*

390. ATHERTON, D.: *J. appl. Phys.,* 39 (1968), 1411.
391. BOOM, R. W.–LIVINGSTON, R. L.: *Proc. Instn Radio Engrs.,* 50 (1962), 302.
392. BRÜCK, L.: *Vide,* 12 (1957), 327.

393. CHANG, K. K. N.: *RCAR*, **16** (1955), 65.
394. CLARKE, G. M.: *Proc. Instn Radio Engrs.*, **46** (1958), 1652.
395. CLARKE, G. M.–LESS. G. B.: *Proc. Instn Radio Engrs.*, **46** (1958), 914.
396. DE BENNETOT, M.: *Annls. Radioélect.*, **9** (1954), 193.
397. GLASS, M. S.: *Proc. Instn Radio Engrs.*, **45** (1957), 1100.
398. GLASS, M. S.: *Proc. Instn Radio Engrs.*, **46** (1958), 1751.
399. GLASS, R. C.–GOTTFELDT, P.: *Trans. IRE*, **ED–4** (1957), 186.
400. (GORDON, A. V.–SLIVINSKAYA, A. G.) Гордон, А. В.–Сливинская, А. Г.: Электромагниты постоянного тока *(D.C. Electromagnets)*. Госэнергоиздат; Москва, 1960.
401. GURTOVOY, V. I.–RODIONOV, A. D.: *8th MOGA*,** 5–24.
402. GUTMAN, A. S.: *Proc. Instn Radio Engrs.*, **45** (1957), 88.
403. HARROLD, W.–REID, W. R.: *IEEE Trans.*, MAG–4 (1968), 229.
404. HARRY, J. E.: *Proc. Inst. elect. Engrs.*, **117** (1970), 241.
405. HENNE, W.: *Arch. elekt. Übertr.*, **15** (1961), 429.
406. HENNE, W.: *Telefunken-Röhre*, **40** (1961), 73.
407. HENNE, W.: *Elektrotech. Z.*, **82–A** (1961), 819.
408. KLEIN, W.–BRETTING, J.–MAYERHOFER, E.: *4th MOGA*,* 108.
409. MALEY, S. W.–BYRNE, W. J.: *Trans. IRE*, **ED–9** (1962), 188.
410. MEYERER, P.: *Arch. elekt. Übertr.*, **15** (1961), 467.
411. MEYERER, P.: *5th MOGA*,** 206.
412. MONTGOMERY, D. B.: *Solenoid Magnet Design. The Magnetic and Mechanical Aspects of Resistive and Superconducting Systems*. John Wiley and Sons; London, 1969.
413. NICOLL, F. H.: *Trans. IRE*, **ED–4** (1957), 186.
414. NISHIHARA, H.–TERADA, M.: *J. appl. Phys.*, **41** (1970), 3322.
415. PARKER, R. J.–STUDDERS, R. S.: *Permanent Magnets and Applications*. John Wiley and Sons; New York, 1962.
416. SCHINDLER, M. J.: *RCAR*, **21** (1960), 414.
417. SCHRUMPF, D. A.: *IEEE Trans.*, **ED–12** (1965), 217.
418. SCHWABE, E.: *Z. angew. Phys.*, **9** (1957), 183.
419. STERRETT, J. E.–HEFFNER, H.: *Trans. IRE*, **ED–5** (1958), 35.
420. STERZER, F.–SIEKANOWICZ, W. W.: *RCAR*, **18** (1957), 39.
421. WORCESTER, W. G.–WEITZMANN, A. L.–TOWNLEY, R. J.: *Trans. IRE*, **ED–3** (1965), 70.
422. ZACK, A.: *Electronics*, **34** (1961), 66.

* See p. 483.
** See p. 484.

INDEX